2020

The ARRL HANDBOOK FOR RADIO COMMUNICATIONS

NINETY-SEVENTH EDITION

Volume 1: Introduction and Fundamental Theory — Ch. 1-4

Volume 2: Practical Design and Principles Part 1 — Ch. 5-11

▶ **Volume 3:** Practical Design and Principles Part 2 — Ch. 12-18

Volume 4: Antenna Systems and Radio Propagation — Ch. 19-21

Volume 5: Equipment Construction and Station Accessories — Ch. 22-24

Volume 6: Test Equipment, Troubleshooting, RFI, and Index — Ch. 25-28

Editor
H. Ward Silver, NØAX

Contributing Editors
Steven R. Ford, WB8IMY
Mark J. Wilson, K1RO

Editorial Assistant
Maty Weinberg, KB1EIB

Technical Consultants
Bob Allison, WB1GCM
Edward F. Hare, Jr., W1RFI
Zachary H.J. Lau, W1VT

Cover Design
Sue Fagan, KB1OKW
Bob Inderbitzen, NQ1R

Production
Michelle Bloom, WB1ENT
Jodi Morin, KA1JPA
David F. Pingree, N1NAS

Additional Contributors to the 2020 Edition
John Brooks, N9ZL
Jim Brown, K9YC
Glen Brown, W6GJB
Ralph Crumrine, NØKC

Don Daso, K4ZA
Joel Hallas, W1ZR
Bill Koch, W2RMA
Rick Lindquist, WW1ME
Glenn Loake, GØGBI
Helmut Berka, DL2MAJ
Oliver Micic, DG7XO
Carl Luetzelschwab, K9LA
Phil Salas, AD5X
Rob Sherwood, NCØB
Cory Sickles, WA3UVV
George Steber, WB9LVI
Jim Tonne, W4ENE
Paul Wade, W1GHZ

Published by:
ARRL The national association for AMATEUR RADIO®
225 Main Street, Newington, CT 06111-1400 USA
www.arrl.org

Copyright © 2019 by
The American Radio Relay League, Inc.

Copyright secured under the Pan-American Convention

International Copyright secured

All rights reserved. No part of this work may be reproduced in any form except by written permission of the publisher. All rights of translation are reserved.

Printed in the USA

Quedan reservados todos los derechos

ISBN: 978-1-62595-107-6 Softcover
ISBN: 978-1-62595-113-7 Six-Volume Set

Kindle eBook Editions
   ISBN: 978-1-62595-091-8 — Volume 1
   ISBN: 978-1-62595-092-5 — Volume 2
   ISBN: 978-1-62595-093-2 — Volume 3
   ISBN: 978-1-62595-094-9 — Volume 4
   ISBN: 978-1-62595-095-6 — Volume 5
   ISBN: 978-1-62595-096-3 — Volume 6

Ninety-Seventh Edition

About the cover:
The collection of components comprises the HF Packer miniHFPA2 amplifier kit. Although the kit is not featured in this 2020 edition of the ARRL Handbook, its components represent the spirit of project design and craftsmanship that has been part of Amateur Radio from the beginning.

Contents

A more detailed Table of Contents is included at the beginning of each chapter.

VOLUME 1

INTRODUCTION AND FUNDAMENTAL THEORY

1 What is Amateur (Ham) Radio?
1.1 Do-It-Yourself Wireless
1.2 Joining the Ham Radio Community
1.3 Your Ham Radio Station
1.4 Getting on the Air
1.5 Your Ham Radio "Lifestyle"
1.6 Public Service
1.7 Ham Radio in the Classroom
1.8 Resources
1.9 Glossary

2 Electrical Fundamentals
2.1 Introduction to Electricity
2.2 Resistance and Conductance
2.3 Basic Circuit Principles
2.4 Power and Energy
2.5 Circuit Control Components
2.6 Capacitance and Capacitors
2.7 Inductance and Inductors
2.8 Semiconductor Devices
2.9 References and Bibliography

3 Radio Fundamentals
3.1 AC Waveforms
3.2 Measuring AC Voltage, Current and Power
3.3 Effective Radiated Power
3.4 AC in Capacitors and Inductors
3.5 Working with Reactance
3.6 Impedance
3.7 Quality Factor (Q) of Components
3.8 Resonant Circuits
3.9 Analog Signal Processing
3.10 Electromagnetic Waves
3.11 References and Bibliography

4 Circuits and Components
4.1 Practical Resistors
4.2 Practical Capacitors
4.3 Practical Inductors
4.4 Transformers
4.5 Practical Semiconductors
4.6 Amplifiers
4.7 Operational Amplifiers
4.8 Miscellaneous Analog ICs
4.9 Analog-Digital Interfacing
4.10 Analog Device and Circuits Glossary
4.11 Heat Management
4.12 References and Bibliography

VOLUME 2

PRACTICAL DESIGN AND PRINCIPLES — PART 1

5 **RF Techniques**
5.1 Introduction
5.2 Lumped-Element versus Distributed Characteristics
5.3 Effects of Parasitic (Stray) Characteristics
5.4 Semiconductor Circuits at RF
5.5 Ferrite Materials
5.6 Impedance Matching Networks
5.7 RF Transformers
5.8 Noise
5.9 Two-Port Networks
5.10 RF Design Techniques Glossary
5.11 References and Bibliography

6 **Computer-Aided Circuit Design**
6.1 Circuit Simulation Overview
6.2 Simulation Basics
6.3 Limitations of Simulation at RF
6.4 Electromagnetic Analysis of RF Circuits
6.5 References and Bibliography

7 **Power Sources**
7.1 Power Processing
7.2 AC-AC Power Conversion
7.3 Power Transformers
7.4 AC-DC Power Conversion
7.5 Voltage Multipliers
7.6 Current Multipliers
7.7 Rectifier Types
7.8 Power Filtering
7.9 Power Supply Regulation
7.10 "Crowbar" Protective Circuits
7.11 DC-DC Switchmode Power Conversion
7.12 High-Voltage Techniques
7.13 Batteries
7.14 Glossary of Power Source Terms
7.15 References and Bibliography
7.16 Power Supply Projects

8 **DSP and SDR Fundamentals**
8.1 Introduction to DSP
8.2 Introduction to SDR
8.3 Analog-Digital Conversion
8.4 Data Converters for SDR and DSP
8.5 Digital Signal Processors
8.6 Digital (Discrete-time) Signals
8.7 The Fourier Transform
8.8 Glossary of DSP and SDR Terms
8.9 References and Bibliography

9 **Oscillators and Synthesizers**
9.1 How Oscillators Work
9.2 LC Variable Frequency Oscillator (VFO) Circuits
9.3 Building an Oscillator
9.4 Crystal Oscillators
9.5 Oscillators at UHF and Above
9.6 Frequency Synthesizers
9.7 Phase Noise
9.8 Glossary of Oscillator and Synthesizer Terms
9.9 References and Bibliography

10 **Analog and Digital Filtering**
10.1 Introduction
10.2 Filter Basics
10.3 Passive LC Filters
10.4 Active Audio Filters
10.5 Digital Filters
10.6 Quartz Crystal Filters
10.7 SAW Filters
10.8 Transmission Line VHF/UHF/Microwave Filters
10.9 Helical Resonators
10.11 Filter Projects
10.12 Glossary of Filter Terms
10.13 References and Bibliography

11 **Modulation**
11.1 Introduction
11.2 Amplitude Modulation (AM)
11.3 Angle Modulation
11.4 FSK and PSK
11.5 Quadrature Modulation
11.6 Analytic Signals and Modulation
11.7 Image Modulation
11.8 Spread Spectrum Modulation
11.9 Pulse Modulation
11.10 Modulation Bandwidth and Impairments
11.11 Glossary of Modulation Terms
11.12 References and Further Reading

VOLUME 3

PRACTICAL DESIGN AND PRINCIPLES — PART 2

12 Receiving
12.1 Characterizing Receivers
12.2 Heterodyne Receivers
12.3 SDR Receivers
12.4 Mixing and Mixers
12.5 Demodulation and Detection
12.6 Automatic Gain Control (AGC)
12.7 Noise Management
12.8 References and Bibliography

13 Transmitting
13.1 Characterizing Transmitters
13.2 Transmitter Architecture
13.3 Modulators
13.4 Transmitting CW
13.5 Transmitting AM and SSB
13.6 Transmitting Angle Modulation
13.7 Effects of Transmitted Noise
13.8 Microphones and Speech Processing
13.9 Voice Operation
13.10 Transmitter Power Stages
13.11 References and Bibliography

14 Transceiver Design Topics
14.1 Signal Chains in SDR Transceivers
14.2 User Interfaces
14.3 Configuration and Control Interfaces
14.4 SDR Design Tools

15 Digital Protocols and Modes
15.1 Digital "Modes"
15.2 Unstructured Digital Modes
15.3 Fuzzy Modes
15.4 Structured Digital Modes
15.5 Networking Modes
15.6 Digital Mode Table
15.7 Glossary of Digital Protocol and Mode Terms
15.8 References and Bibliography

16 Amateur Radio Data Platforms
16.1 Platform Overview
16.2 Sensors
16.3 Navigation Data and Telemetry
16.4 Payloads
16.5 High Altitude Balloon Platforms
16.6 Unmanned Aerial Vehicles (UAVs)
16.7 Rockets
16.8 Robotics
16.9 Fixed Stations
16.10 References and Bibliography

17 RF Power Amplifiers
17.1 High Power, Who Needs It?
17.2 Types of Power Amplifiers
17.3 Vacuum Tube Basics
17.4 Tank Circuits
17.5 Transmitting Tube Ratings
17.6 Sources of Operating Voltages
17.7 Tube Amplifier Cooling
17.8 Vacuum Tube Amplifier Stabilization
17.9 MOSFET Design for RF Amplifiers
17.10 Solid-State RF Amplifiers
17.11 Solid State Amplifier Projects
17.12 Tube Amplifier Projects
17.13 References and Bibliography

18 Repeaters
18.1 A Brief History
18.2 Repeater Overview
18.3 FM Voice Repeaters
18.4 D-STAR Repeater Systems
18.5 System Fusion Repeater Systems
18.6 Digital Mobile Radio (DMR)
18.7 Other Digital Voice Repeater Technologies
18.8 Glossary of FM and Repeater Terminology
18.9 References and Bibliography

VOLUME 4

ANTENNA SYSTEMS AND RADIO PROPAGATION

19 Propagation of Radio Signals
19.1 Fundamentals of Radio Waves
19.2 Sky-Wave Propagation and the Sun
19.3 MUF Predictions
19.4 Propagation in the Troposphere
19.5 VHF/UHF Mobile Propagation
19.6 Propagation for Space Communications
19.7 Noise and Propagation
19.8 Propagation Below the AM Broadcast Band
19.9 Glossary of Radio Propagation Terms
19.10 References and Bibliography

20 Transmission Lines
20.1 Transmission Line Basics
20.2 Choosing a Transmission Line
20.3 The Transmission Line as Impedance Transformer
20.4 Matching Impedances in the Antenna System
20.5 Baluns and Transmission-Line Transformers
20.6 PC Transmission Lines
20.7 Waveguides
20.8 Glossary of Transmission Line Terms
20.9 References and Bibliography

21 Antennas
21.1 Antenna Basics
21.2 Dipoles and the Half-Wave Antenna
21.3 Vertical (Ground-Plane) Antennas
21.4 T and Inverted-L Antennas
21.5 Slopers and Vertical Dipoles
21.6 Yagi Antennas
21.7 Quad and Loop Antennas
21.8 HF Mobile Antennas
21.9 VHF/UHF Mobile Antennas
21.10 VHF/UHF Antennas
21.11 VHF/UHF Beams
21.12 Radio Direction Finding Antennas
21.13 Rotators
21.13 Glossary
21.14 References and Bibliography

VOLUME 5

EQUIPMENT CONSTRUCTION AND STATION ACCESSORIES

22 Component Data and References
22.1 Component Data
22.2 Resistors
22.3 Capacitors
22.4 Inductors
22.5 Transformers
22.6 Semiconductors
22.7 Tubes, Wire, Materials, Attenuators, Miscellaneous
22.8 Computer Connectors
22.9 RF Connectors and Transmission Lines
22.10 Reference Tables

23 Construction Techniques
23.1 Electronic Shop Safety
23.2 Tools and Their Use
23.3 Soldering Tools and Techniques
23.4 Surface Mount Technology (SMT)
23.5 Constructing Electronic Circuits
23.6 CAD for PCB Design
23.7 Microwave Construction
23.8 Mechanical Fabrication

24 Assembling a Station
24.1 Fixed Stations
24.2 Mobile Installations
24.3 Portable Installations
24.4 Remote Stations

VOLUME 6

TEST EQUIPMENT, TROUBLESHOOTING, RFI, AND INDEX

25 Test Equipment and Measurements
25.1 Introduction
25.2 DC Measurements
25.3 AC Measurements
25.4 RF Measurements
25.5 Receiver Measurements
25.6 Transmitter Measurements
25.7 Antenna System Measurements
25.8 Miscellaneous Measurements
25.9 Construction Projects
25.10 References and Further Reading
25.11 Glossary of Test Equipment and Measurement Terms

26 Troubleshooting and Maintenance
26.1 Test Equipment
26.2 Components
26.3 Getting Started
26.4 Inside the Equipment
26.5 Testing at the Circuit Level
26.6 After the Repairs
26.7 Professional Repairs
26.8 Typical Symptoms and Faults
26.9 Radio Troubleshooting Hints
26.10 Antenna Systems
26.11 Repair and Restoration of Vintage Equipment
26.12 References and Bibliography

27 RF Interference
27.1 Managing Radio Frequency Interference
27.2 FCC Rules and Regulations
27.3 Elements of RFI
27.4 Identifying the Type of RFI Source
27.5 Locating Sources of RFI
27.6 Power-Line Noise
27.7 Elements of RFI Control
27.8 Troubleshooting RFI
27.9 Automotive RFI
27.10 RFI Projects
27.11 Glossary of RFI Terms
27.12 References and Bibliography

28 Safety
28.1 Electrical Safety
28.2 Antenna and Tower Safety
28.3 RF Safety

Advertiser's Index
Index
Project Index
Author's Index

DOWNLOADABLE CONTENT AND TOOLS

Space Communications
Digital Communications
Image Communications
Digital Basics
Station Accessories and Projects
2020 HF Transceiver Survey
Radio Mathematics

Contents

12.1 Characterizing Receivers
    12.1.1 Receiver Sensitivity and Noise
    12.1.2 Noise Figure of Cascaded Stages
    12.1.3 Receiver Selectivity
    12.1.4 Receiver Dynamic Range

12.2 Heterodyne Receivers
    12.2.1 The Direct Conversion Receiver
    12.2.2 Superheterodyne Receivers
    12.2.3 Superheterodyne Bandwidth
    12.2.4 Superheterodyne FM Receivers
    12.2.5 Superheterodyne Image Rejection
    12.2.6 Preselectors
    12.2.7 Superhet Design for Dynamic Range

12.3 SDR Receivers
    12.3.1 Digitizing at IF
    12.3.2 Direct RF Digitizing
    12.3.3 Sample-Rate Down-Conversion
    12.3.4 Decimation and Dynamic Range
    12.3.5 Phase Noise in Sampled Systems

12.4 Mixing and Mixers
    12.4.1 Mixers and Distortion
    12.4.2 Switching Mixers
    12.4.3 The Diode Double-Balanced Mixer (DBM)
    12.4.4 Active Mixers
    12.4.5 The Tayloe Mixer
    12.4.6 The NE602/SA602/SA612 Gilbert Cell Mixer

12.5 Demodulation and Detection
    12.5.1 Envelope Detection and Full-Carrier AM
    12.5.2 Detecting AM Signals
    12.5.3 Demodulating SSB Signals
    12.5.4 Demodulating FM and PM

12.6 Automatic Gain Control (AGC)
    12.6.1 Audio-Derived AGC
    12.6.2 AGC Circuits

12.7 Noise Management
    12.7.1 The Noise Limiter
    12.7.2 The Noise Blanker
    12.7.3 Operating Noise Limiters and Blankers
    12.7.4 Noise Canceling
    12.7.5 Diversity Reception
    12.7.6 DSP Noise Reduction
    12.7.7 DSP Notch Filtering

12.8 References and Bibliography

Chapter 12 — Downloadable Supplemental Content

Supplemental Files

- "Amateur Radio Equipment Development — An Historical Perspective" by Joel Hallas, W1ZR
- Selected "SDR: Simplified" columns in *QEX* since 2009 by Ray Mack, W5IFS
- Selected "Hands-On SDR:" columns in *QEX* since 2014 by Scotty Cowling, WA2DFI
- "Noise Power Ratio (NPR) Testing on HF Receivers" by Adam Farson, VA7OJ/AB7OJ
- Receiver projects from previous editions of the *ARRL Handbook*.
- VHF and UHF Receivers and UHF and Microwave Techniques sections from previous editions of the *ARRL Handbook*.
- "A Tunable RF Preamplifier Using a Variable Capacitance Diode" by George Steber, WB9LVI
- "Universal MMIC Preamp" by Paul Wade, W1GHZ

Chapter 12

Receiving

Receivers have traditionally been at the forefront of Amateur Radio technology and certainly are today, even as the long-reigning analog superheterodyne architecture is being overtaken by the digital software defined radio. While commercial designs and devices abound, receiving in the crowded amateur bands is still a demanding application with strong signals immediately adjacent to signals at the noise floor, a variety of natural and man-made interferences to reject, and modes ranging from manually sent Morse to the latest experimental modulations. Like the equipment in use today, expect this chapter to change from edition to edition as technology marches on.

In order to address these challenges, this chapter focuses on the functions of receiving and how they are implemented, whether by analog or digital technologies. Metrics of receiver performance are discussed, recognizing that digital receivers behave differently than their established analog counterparts, requiring new measurement definitions and techniques. Receiver home-brew projects from past editions have been collected into a set of projects in the downloadable supplemental information accompanying this book,

This chapter's material has been adapted and updated from or provided by a number of authors. A great deal of the receiver material was originally written by Joel Hallas, W1ZR, and the sections on mixers by Dave Newkirk, W9VES, and Rick Karlquist, N6RK. Some sections on SDR functions were adapted from "SDR: Simplified" columns in *QEX* magazine by Ray Mack, W5IFS. Material on SDR receivers, architecture, and noise reduction was contributed by Steve Hicks, N5AC, and Doug Grant, K1DG. Jim Brown, K9YC provided material on active noise canceling and diversity reception. Bob Allison, WB1GCM, ARRL Lab Staff Engineer, also contributed material on receiver testing. Additional material was taken from Chapters 10 and 11 in *Experimental Methods in RF Design* by Hayward, Campbell, and Larkin. The reader interested in the professional perspective and depth of detail is referred to the comprehensive *Communications Receivers — Principles and Design*, 4th Edition by Rohde, Whitaker, and Zahnd.

As in previous editions, W1ZR's downloadable supplement on receiver and transmitter development, "Amateur Radio Equipment Development — An Historical Perspective," provides valuable insight as to how transceiver design progressed. As we prepare for the coming generations of SDR products, understanding the evolution of our equipment remains as important as ever.

Coverage of VHF/UHF/microwave receivers from previous editions is included in the downloadable supplemental material. Coverage of this topic will be revised and updated in future editions of the *ARRL Handbook*.

The major subsystems of a radio receiving system are the antenna, the receiver and the information processor. The antenna's task is to provide a transition from an electromagnetic wave in space to an electrical signal that can be conducted on wires. The receiver has the job of retrieving the information content from a particular signal coming from the antenna and presenting it in a useful format to the processor for use.

The processor typically is an operator, but can also be an automated system. When you consider that most "processors" require signals in the range of volts (to drive an operator's speaker or headphones, or even the input of an A/D converter), and the particular signal of interest arrives from the antenna at a level of mere microvolts, the basic function of the receiver is to amplify the desired signal by a factor of a million. It must do this, while in the presence of signals many orders of magnitude greater and of completely different characteristics, without distortion of the desired signal or loss of the information it carries.

12.1 Characterizing Receivers

As we discuss receivers we will need to characterize their performance, and often their performance limitations, using certain key parameters. The most commonly encountered are as described in the following sections. These are often the key performance parameters, but in many cases there are others that are important to specify, as well. Examples are audio output power, power consumption, size, weight, control capabilities and so forth.

The ARRL Lab has developed an extensive set of standardized tests that it performs on transceivers in support of *QST* Product Reviews. These tests are described in the test procedure document referenced in the **Test Equipment and Measurements** chapter and in the book *Amateur Radio Transceiver Performance Testing* by ARRL Lab Staff Engineer, Bob Allison WB1GCM.

12.1.1 Receiver Sensitivity and Noise

Sensitivity is a measure of how weak a signal the receiver can extract information from. This generally is expressed at a particular signal-to-noise ratio (SNR) since noise is generally the limiting factor. A typical specification might be: "Sensitivity: 1 µV for 10 dB SNR with 3 kHz bandwidth." The bandwidth is stated because the amount (or power) of the noise, the denominator of the SNR fraction, increases directly with bandwidth. Generally the noise parameter refers to the noise generated within the receiver, often less than the noise that arrives with the signal from the antenna. (See the **RF Techniques** chapter for a more complete discussion of noise and noise sources.)

The sensitivity of a receiver is a measure of the lowest power input signal that can be received with a specified signal-to-noise ratio. In the early days of radio, this was a very important parameter and designers tried to achieve the maximum practical sensitivity. In recent years, device and design technology have improved to the point that other parameters may be of higher importance, particularly in the HF region and below. Sensitivity remains an issue for receiving systems at VHF and above, particular with respect to noise.

Noise level is as important as signal level in determining sensitivity. This section builds on the discussion of noise in the **RF Techniques** chapter. The most important noise parameters affecting receiver sensitivity are *noise bandwidth*, *noise figure*, *noise factor*, and *noise temperature*.

Since received noise power is directly proportional to receiver bandwidth, any specification of sensitivity must be made for a particular noise bandwidth. For DSP receivers with extremely steep filter skirts, receiver bandwidth is approximately the same as the filter or operating bandwidth. For other filter types, noise bandwidth is somewhat larger than the filter's 6 dB response bandwidth.

The relationship of noise bandwidth to noise power is one of the reasons that narrow bandwidth modes, such as CW, have a significant signal-to-noise advantage over modes with wider bandwidth, such as voice, assuming the receiver bandwidth is the minimum necessary to receive the signal. For example, compared to a 2400-Hz SSB filter bandwidth, a CW signal received in a 200 Hz bandwidth will have a 2400/200 = 12 = 10.8 dB advantage in received noise power. That is the same difference as an increase in transmitter from 100 to 1200 W.

SOURCES OF NOISE

Any electrical component will generate a certain amount of noise due to random electron motion. Any gain stages after the internal noise source will amplify the noise along with the signal. Thus a receiver with no signal input source will have a certain amount of noise generated and amplified within the receiver itself.

Upon connecting an antenna to a receiver, there will be introduction of any noise external to the receiver that is on the received frequency. The usual sources and their properties are described below. **Table 12.1** presents typical levels of external noise in a 10 kHz bandwidth present in the environment from different sources.

Atmospheric noise. This is noise generated within our atmosphere due to natural phenomena. The principal cause is lightning which sends wideband signals great distances. All points on the Earth receive this noise, but it is much stronger in some regions than others depending on the amount of local lightning activity. This source is usually the strongest noise source in the LF range and may dominate well into the HF region, depending on the other noises in the region. The level of atmospheric noise tends to drop off by around 50 dB every time the frequency is increased by a factor of 10. This source usually drops in importance by the top of the HF range (30 MHz).

Man-made noise. This source acts in a similar manner to atmospheric noise, although it is more dependent on local activity rather than geography and weather. The sources tend to be sparks from rotating and other kinds of electrical machinery as well as gasoline engine ignition systems and some types of lighting. In recent years, noise from computing and network equipment, switch-mode power supplies, and appliances has increased significantly in urban and suburban environments. All things being equal, this source, on average, drops off by about 20 dB every time the frequency is increased by a factor of ten. The slower decrease at higher frequencies is due to the sparks having faster rise times than lightning. The effect tends to be comparable to atmospheric noise in the broadcast band, less at lower frequencies and a bit more at HF.

Galactic Noise. This is noise generated by the radiation from heavenly bodies outside our atmosphere. Of course, while this is noise to communicators, it is the desired signal for radio-astronomers. This noise source is a major factor at VHF and UHF and is quite dependent on exactly where you point an antenna (antennas for those ranges tend to be small and are often pointable). It also happens that the Earth turns and sometimes moves an antenna into a position where it inadvertently is aimed at a noisy area of the galaxy. If the Sun, not surprisingly the strongest signal in our solar system, appears behind a communications satellite, communications is generally disrupted until the Sun is out of the antenna's receiving pattern. Galactic noise occurs on HF, as well: Noise from the planet Jupiter can be heard on the 15 meter band under quiet conditions, for example.

Thermal Noise. Unlike the previous noise sources, this one comes from our equipment. All atomic structures have electrons that move within their structures. This motion results in very small currents that generate small amounts of wideband signals. While each particle's radiation is small, the cumulative effect of all particles becomes significant as the previous sources roll off with increasing frequency. The reason that this effect is called *thermal* noise is because the electron motion increases with the particle's temperature. In fact the noise strength is directly proportional to the temperature, if measured in terms of absolute zero (0 K). For example, if we increase the temperature from 270 to 280 K, that represents an increase in noise power of 10/270 = 0.037, or about 0.16 dB. Some extremely sensitive microwave receivers use cryogenically-cooled front-end amplifiers to provide large reductions in thermal noise.

Oscillator Phase Noise. As noted in the **Oscillators and Synthesizers** chapter, real oscillators will have phase-noise sidebands that extend out on either side of the nominal carrier frequency at low amplitudes. Any such noise will be transferred to the received signal and through *reciprocal mixing* create noise products from signals on adjacent channels through the mixer. A good receiver will be designed to have phase noise that is well below the level of other internally generated noise.

NOISE POWER AND SENSITIVITY

There are a number of related measures that can be used to specify the amount of noise that is generated within a receiver. If that noise approaches, or is within perhaps 10 dB of the amount of external noise received, then it must be carefully considered and becomes a major design parameter. If the internally generated noise is less than perhaps 10 dB below that expected from the environ-

Table 12.1
Typical Noise Levels (Into the Receiver) and Their Source, by Frequency

Frequency Range	Dominant Noise Sources	Typical Level (μV/m)*
LF 30 to 300 kHz	atmospheric	150
MF 300 to 3000 kHz	atmospheric/man-made	70
Low HF 3 to 10 MHz	man-made/atmospheric	20
High HF 10 to 30 MHz	man-made/thermal	10
VHF 30 to 300 MHz	thermal/galactic	0.3
UHF 300 to 3000 MHz	galactic/ thermal	0.2

*The level assumes a 10 kHz bandwidth. Data from *Reference Data for Engineers*, 4th Ed, p 273, Figure 1.

ment, efforts to minimize internal noise are generally not beneficial and can, in some cases, be counterproductive.

While the total noise in a receiving system is, as discussed, proportional to bandwidth, the noise generating elements are generally not. Thus it is useful to be able to specify the internal noise of a system in a way that is independent of bandwidth. It is important to note that even though such a specification is useful, the actual noise is still directly proportional to bandwidth and any bandwidth beyond that needed to receive signal information will result in reduced SNR.

To evaluate the effect of noise power on sensitivity, refer to the discussion of noise in the **RF Techniques** chapter. The discussion hinges on the value of N_i, the equivalent noise power in watts at the input of a perfect receiver that would result in the same noise output. Ni is generally expressed in dBm$_i$:

$$dBm_i = -198.6 + (10 \times \log_{10} B) + (10 \times \log_{10} T_E)$$

where B is the system bandwidth in Hz and T_E is the equivalent noise temperature expressed in K.

If input noise (N_i) is greater than the noise generated internally by the receiver, the receiver's sensitivity is limited by the external noise. This is usually the case for HF receivers where atmospheric and man-made noise are much stronger than the receiver's internal noise floor. If N_i is within, perhaps, 10 dB greater than the receiver's internal noise, then the effect of the receiver's internal circuits on overall system sensitivity must be taken into account. At VHF and above, noise generated by the system components begins to exceed input noise.

12.1.2 Noise Figure of Cascaded Stages

Often we are faced with the requirement of determining the noise figure of a system of multiple stages. In general adding an amplification stage between the antenna and the rest of the system will reduce the equivalent noise figure of the system by the amount of gain of the stage but adds in the noise of the added stage directly. The formula for determining the resultant noise factor is:

$$F = F_1 + \frac{F_2 - 1}{G_1}$$

where
F_1 is the noise factor of the stage closest to the input,
F_2 is the noise factor of the balance of the system, and
G_1 is the gain of the stage closest to the input.

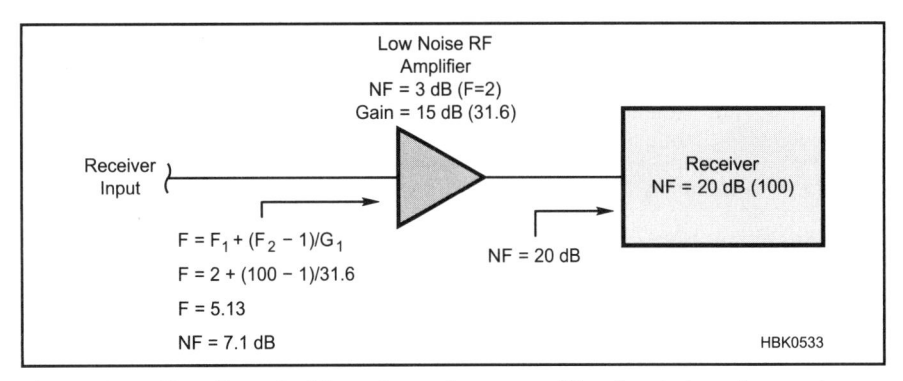

Figure 12.1 — The effect of adding a low-noise preamplifier ahead of a noisy receiver system.

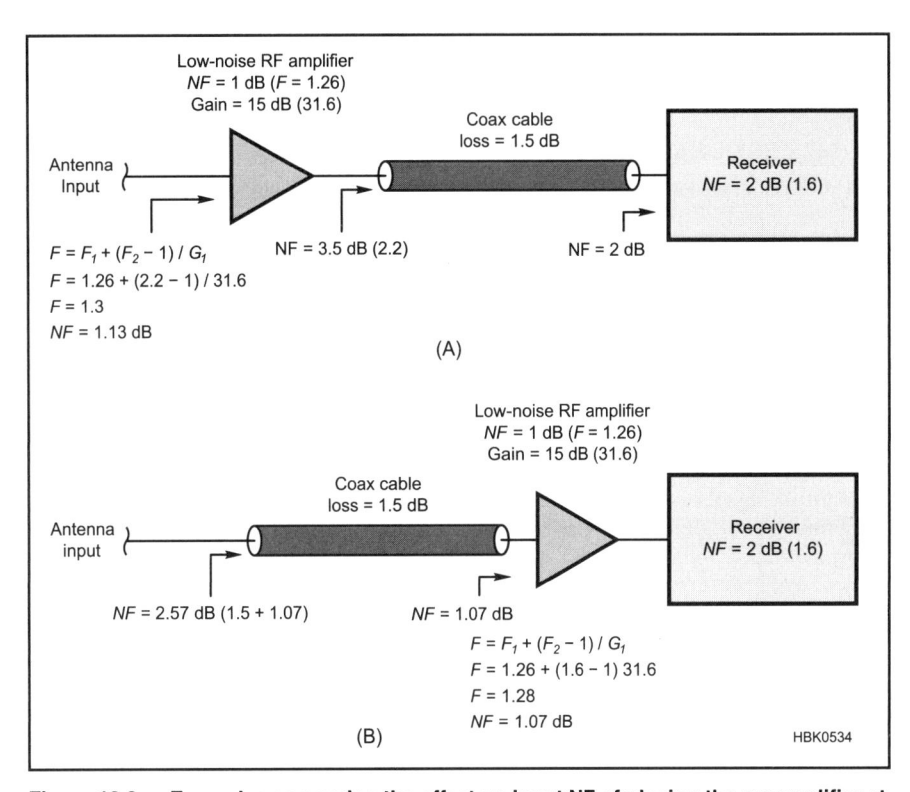

Figure 12.2 — Examples comparing the effect on input NF of placing the preamplifier at different places in the antenna system. At (A), the preamplifier is ahead of the coax cable loss, resulting in an input NF of 1.13 dB. At (B), the coax loss before the preamp results in an input NF of 2.57 dB, a reduction in sensitivity.

Noise figure (NF) is equal to log(F).

Many elements of a receiving system exhibit loss rather than gain. Since they reduce the desired signal, while not changing the noise of following stages, they increase the noise figure at their input by an amount equal to the loss. This is the reason that a VHF *preamplifier* or *low noise preamplifier (LNA)* is mounted at the antenna, ahead of a noisy receiver as shown in **Figure 12.1**. As shown in the figure for fairly typical values, while the addition of a low noise preamplifier does reduce the system's noise figure, as can be observed, the amplifier gain and noise figure of the rest of the receiver can make a big difference.

As an example of the difference, if the coax between the antenna and radio has a loss of 1 dB, and the preamp has a noise figure of 1 dB, the resulting noise figure with the preamp at the radio will be 2 dB, while if at the antenna, the noise added by the coax will be reduced by the gain of the preamp, resulting in a significant improvement in received SNR at VHF and above. **Figure 12.2** shows a typical example.

To determine the system noise factor of multiple cascaded stages:

$$F = F_1 + \frac{F_2 - 1}{G_1} + \frac{F_3 - 1}{G_1 G_2} \ldots + \frac{F_N - 1}{G_1 G_2 \ldots G_{N-1}}$$

Receiving 12.3

Noise Measurement Terminology

There are many ways to measure and specify noise, each with its unique name and abbreviation. Most amateurs are familiar with SNR (signal-to-noise ratio) at least in a general sense, but fewer are aware of the need to specify bandwidth and possibly temperature. Communications professionals and receiver designers use a variety of names and methods to specify noise performance. Many of these are explained in Walt Kester's excellent tutorial "Understand SINAD, ENOB, SNR, THD, THD+N, and SFDR so You Don't Get Lost in the Noise Floor" published by Analog Devices as MT-003. See the References section for the complete URL for this document.

---

where F_N and G_N are the noise factor and gain of the Nth stage. This equation can be extended from the antenna input to the last linear stage, stopping at the point of detection or analog-to-digital conversion, whichever occurs first.

EFFECT OF INPUT NOISE

A receiver designer needs to know how strong the signals are to establish the range of signals the receiver will be required to handle. One may compare the equivalent noise power (N_i) with the expected external noise to determine whether the overall receiver SNR will be determined by external or internal noise. A reasonable design objective is the have the internal noise be less than perhaps 10 to 20 dB below the expected noise. As noted above, this is related closely to the frequency of signals we want to receive. Any additional sensitivity will not provide a noticeable benefit to SNR, and may result in reduced dynamic range, as will be discussed in the next section.

For frequencies at which external noise sources are strongest, the noise power (and signal power) will also be a function of the antenna design. In such cases, the signal-to-noise ratio can be improved by using an antenna that picks up more signal and less noise, such as with a directional antenna that can reject noise from directions other than that of the signal. Some antennas improve SNR simply by rejecting noise, such as the Beverage antenna. Signals from a Beverage antenna are usually much weaker than from a conventional antenna but their ability to reject noise from undesired directions creates a net improvement in the SNR at the receiver output.

MINIMUM DETECTABLE (DISCERNABLE) SIGNAL (MDS)

Also referred to as the *noise floor* of a receiver, the MDS is the strength of the smallest input signal that produces a specified increase in the output noise power of a receiver. MDS depends on the required SNR (SNR_{MIN} in dB), the system bandwidth (B in Hz), the temperature of the receiver (T_E), and the receiver noise figure (NF). (Measurement of MDS is discussed in the **Test Equipment and Measurements** chapter.)

An ideal receiver at room temperature with a bandwidth of 1 Hz has a theoretical MDS of –174 dBm. This is often referred to as the "1 Hz noise floor."

As bandwidth, noise figure, and temperature increase, so does MDS as follows:

MDS (in dBm) = –174 + 10 log (B) + NF + SNR_{MIN} + 10 log (T_E/290)

For example, if a receiver at room temperature has a bandwidth of 1 kHz and a noise figure of 2.5 dB, for an SNR_{MIN} of 3 dB:

MDS = –174 + 30 + 2.5 + 3 + 0
    = –138.5 dBm

If the receiver's equivalent temperature then increases to 300 K, the MDS also increases to:

MDS = –174 + 30 + 2.5 + 3 + 0.15
    = –138.35 dBm

Many commercial radios achieve an MDS of –135 to –140 dBm in a 500 Hz bandwidth — which is quite good — but at HF the external noise is much higher, making the lower MDS specification somewhat irrelevant. As frequency increases through the higher HF bands and into VHF, MDS becomes more important.

12.1.3 Receiver Selectivity

Selectivity — Selectivity is just the bandwidth discussed above. This is important because to a first estimate it identifies the receiver's ability to separate stations. With a perfect "brick wall" filter in an ideal receiver, stations within the bandwidth will be heard, while those outside it won't be detected. The selectivity thus describes how closely spaced adjacent channels can be. With a perfect 3 kHz bandwidth selectivity, and signals restricted to a 3 kHz bandwidth at the transmitter, a different station can be assigned every 3 kHz across the spectrum. In a less than ideal situation, it is usually necessary to include a *guard band* between channels.

How Phase Noise Affects a Receiver
By Steve Hicks, N5AC

Today's receivers are generally built from one of two primary technologies: mixing or sampling. Some receivers will have components of both. In either case, an oscillator sets the frequency of the mixing or the sampling rate. Let's take a look at how phase noise from an oscillator can affect performance of our receiver, looking first at mixing.

Figure 12.A1 has a block diagram of a typical mixer circuit. The oscillator used with a mixer is called a local oscillator (LO) and the mixing process is also known as heterodyning. Let's assume for the moment that our radio designer selected an off-the-shelf synthesizer IC to use as a local oscillator. The phase noise chart in **Figure 12.A2** represents the phase noise provided by the manufacturer of the synthesizer integrated circuit. Assuming that the phase noise in our design matches the manufacturer's data, we can use the phase noise plot to determine how phase noise will affect our receiver. Phase noise will generally change as the oscillator frequency is moved and, in the case of a synthesizer can also change with the parameters used to lock to a reference signal (An overview of PLL operation can be found in the **Oscillators and Synthesizers** chapter and in a number of good references — for example: www.ti.com/lit/an/swra029/swra029.pdf and in www.analog.com/media/en/training-seminars/tutorials/MT-086.pdf). For now, let's assume this plot was taken at 14 MHz and this is where our receiver will operate.

The two numbers we will use in our example are at an offset of 2 kHz and 10 kHz. Reading the plot, we see that the 2 kHz phase noise is –93 dBc/Hz and the 10 kHz phase noise is –96 dBc/Hz. The measurement units of dBc/Hz indicates the noise that would be present in a 1 Hz bandwidth receiver, the number of dB below the

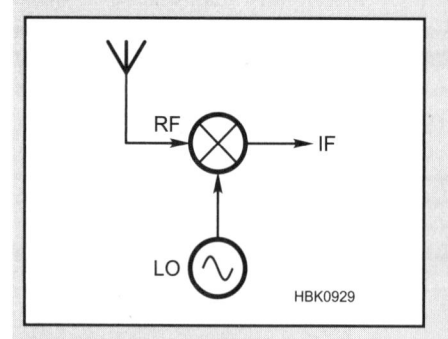

Figure 12.A1 — Typical mixer block diagram.

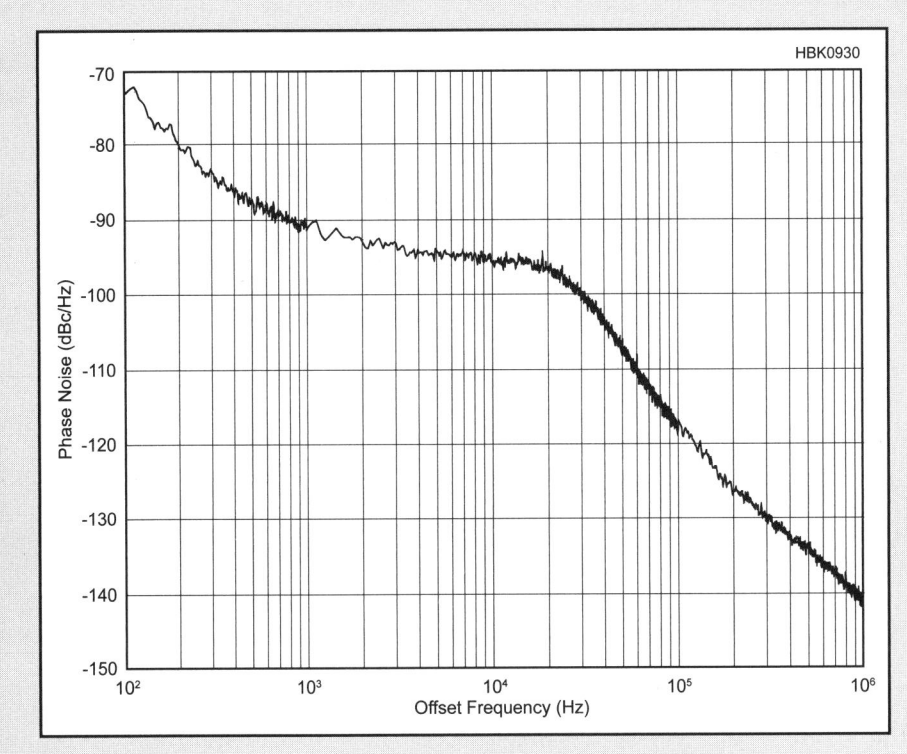

Figure 12.A2 — Plot of phase noise versus frequency separation from the carrier.

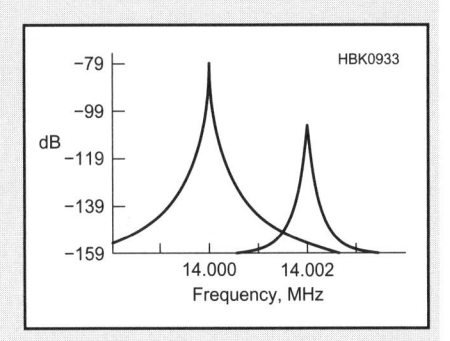

Figure 12.A3 — Spectrum showing adjacent CW signals and the phase noise from each.

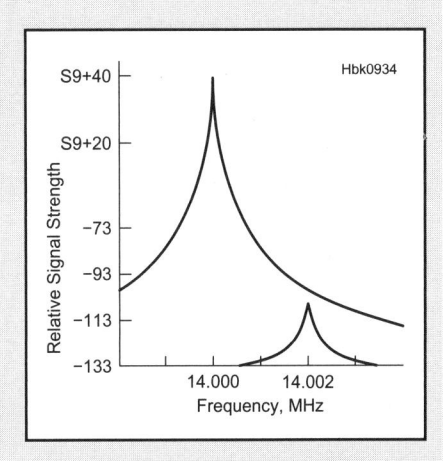

Figure 12.A4 — Same spectrum as Figure 12.A3 but with the left-hand signal replaced with one that is much stronger.

carrier. For example, –93 dBc/Hz indicates that the noise floor would be 93 dB below a carrier signal measured using a 1 Hz bandwidth receiver. To convert this to a 100 Hz bandwidth we might use in a CW filter we must add 10 log (100 Hz/1 Hz) or 20 dB to our phase noise numbers. So at a 2 kHz offset from our carrier, we have –93 dBc + 20 dB = –73 dBc and at 10 kHz, –96 dBc + 20 dB = –76 dBc. In a mixer, this noise will be added to all signals present in the receiver.

Looking at **Figure 12.A3**, we show a strong S8 CW signal at 14.000 MHz. S8 corresponds to –79 dBm as shown in the graph. Two kilohertz away is the signal we are trying to receive, an S3 (–109 dBm) CW signal using a 100 Hz CW filter. Using our phase noise calculation, the S8 signal at –79 dBm would have phase noise at a 2 kHz offset of –79 dBm – 73 dB = –152 dBm. This is well below our atmospheric noise floor and will not interfere with our ability to listen to the signal at 14.002 MHz.

Figure 12.A4 shows a signal in the same location that is S9+40 dB or –33 dBm. Using the same math, at 14.002 MHz we will experience phase noise of –33 dBm – 73 dB = –106 dBm. Since the signal we are trying to receive is S3 (–109 dBm), our noise floor in 100 Hz is 3 dB above this level, causing us interference while trying to copy the signal. The amount of actual interference received also depends on the required signal-to-noise ratio required to successfully copy a signal.

Although it varies by type of oscillator, phase noise generally decreases the further we are from the carrier, meaning that weak signals that are closer to strong signals are more likely to be interfered with than weak signals farther away from a strong carrier. Stations operating in a rural area with modest antennas and no strong neighbors are much less likely to suffer from the effects of phase noise than are multi-multi contest stations with large antennas and local transmitters in the same band. Field Day is another situation where many are familiar with the effects of phase noise. If you've ever operated the sideband station at your local Field Day and heard the noise floor modulated to the sound of the CW station next to you (or vice versa), you've experienced the effects of interference from phase noise.

The effects of phase noise will also vary by mode. A CW signal may be copied with a SNR in the –10 to –20 dB range while a sideband signal may require an SNR of >+10 dB. Since sideband signals require a larger filter, we must also run our calculations with this larger filter, recognizing that more noise will be present. Both the additional noise and the larger SNR required to copy a sideband signal make it more susceptible to phase noise interference than a CW transmission.

Division is Good

In most local oscillators for superheterodyne receivers, the phase noise of the oscillator will benefit from division. This means that the more the oscillator is reduced in frequency through division, the better the resulting phase noise of the oscillator. Typically, we will see a 6 dB improvement in phase noise with each division by two of the original oscillator frequency. So a radio that might have good oscillator performance on 20 meters could lose 11 dB or more performance when operating on 6 meters. The superheterodyne receiver designer can take advantage of this by using a good oscillator design and dividing down the oscillator as much as possible, thereby achieving better phase noise.

Receiving 12.5

Table 12.2
Typical Communications Bandwidths for Various Operating Modes

Mode	Bandwidth (kHz)
FM Voice	15
AM Broadcast	10
AM Voice	4-6.6
SSB Voice	1.8-3
Digital Voice	1.0-1.2
RTTY (170-850 Hz shift)	0.3-1.5
CW	0.1-0.5

Note that the word *channel* is used here in its generic form, meaning the amount of spectrum occupied by a signal, and not defining a fixed frequency such as an AM broadcast channel. A CW channel is about 300 Hz wide, a SSB channel about 2.5-3 kHz wide, and so forth. "Adjacent channel" refers to spectrum immediately higher or lower in frequency. **Table 12.2** shows the bandwidth required for such a "channel" in various services and modes.

Selectivity under linear operating conditions is determined by the receiver's filters. In analog heterodyne designs, the filters are typically crystal filters with a fixed bandwidth. Clever frequency shifting schemes (Passband Tuning or IF Shift, for example) create a continuously adjustable filter by shifting two fixed passbands relative to each other. DSP is also used in both hybrid and direct-sampling SDR designs to provide performance unavailable to filters using discrete components. Both types of filters are discussed in the **Analog and Digital Filtering** chapter.

12.1.4 Receiver Dynamic Range

In the case of all real receivers, there is a range of signals that a receiver can respond to linearly without distortion. This is referred to as *dynamic range* and, as will be discussed in more detail, can be established based on a number of different criteria. In the most general sense, dynamic range can be defined as the ratio of the strongest to the weakest signal that a system, in this case our receiver, can respond to linearly. This range typically extends from the receiver's noise floor to a level at which some intermediate stage or stages overload in some way.

Table 12.1 gives us an idea of how small a signal we might want to receive. The designer must create a receiver that will handle signals from below the noise floor to as strong as the closest nearby transmitter can generate. Most receivers have a specified (or sometimes not) highest input power that can be tolerated, representing the other end of the spectrum. Usually the maximum power specified is the power at which the receiver will not be damaged, while a somewhat lower power level is generally the highest that the receiver can operate at without overload and the accompanying degradation of quality of reception of the desired signal.

The type and severity of the overload is often part of the specification. A straightforward example might be a 130 dB dynamic range. The nature of the distortion will determine the observed phenomenon. If the weakest and strongest signals are both on the same channel, for example, we would not expect to be able to process the weaker of the two. However, the more interesting case would be with the strong signal in an adjacent channel. In an ideal receiver, we would never notice that the adjacent signal was there. In a real receiver with a finite dynamic range or non-ideal selectivity, there will be some level of adjacent channel signal or signals that will interfere with reception of the weaker on-channel signal.

Dynamic range is also affected by preamplifiers in the receiver front-end circuitry. (Passive resistive attenuators have less effect on dynamic range as they typically remain linear over a very wide range of signals.) Turning on a preamplifier may worsen various types of dynamic range performance if the preamplifier's dynamic range is less than that of the rest of the receiver. Conversely, in some SDR receivers having the preamp on may improve performance. Dynamic range specifications and measurements must include whether a preamp is on or off.

It is important to note that the behavior of a heterodyne receiver and an SDR receiver are quite different with respect to dynamic range. The notion of an "intercept point" discussed below is based on the assumption of intermodulation products increasing in a certain way that is characteristic of analog circuitry. This assumption is not valid for direct-sampling SDR equipment. An SDR's input ADC is basically linear up to the point where the instantaneous sum of all signals present at the receiver input exceeds the full-scale range of the input ADC. (See the **DSP and SDR Fundamentals** chapter.) Beyond that point, the receiver will generate spurious products based on its software and how that specific ADC responds. Hybrid analog/digital receivers that apply DSP at IF or audio frequencies behave more like traditional analog receivers.

ON-CHANNEL DYNAMIC RANGE

The signal you wish to listen to can range from the strongest to the weakest, sometimes changing rapidly with conditions, or in a situation with multiple stations such as a net. While a slow change in signal level can be handled with manual gain controls, rapid changes require automatic systems to avoid overload and operator discomfort.

This is a problem that has been long solved with automatic gain control (AGC) systems. These systems are described in a later section of the chapter, but it is worth pointing out that the measurement and gain control points need to be applied carefully to the most appropriate portions of the receiver to maintain optimum performance. If all control is applied to early stages, the SNR for strong stations may suffer, while if applied in later stages, overload of early stages may occur in the presence of strong stations. Thus, gain control has to be designed into the receiver distributed from the input to the detector.

The next two sections illustrate a frequent limitation of receiver performance — dynamic range between the reception of a weak signal in the presence of one or more strong signals outside of the channel.

BLOCKING GAIN COMPRESSION

A very strong signal outside the channel bandwidth can cause a number of problems that limit receiver performance. *Blocking gain compression* (or "blocking") occurs when strong signals overload the receiver's high gain amplifiers and reduce its ability to amplify weak signals. (Note that the term "blocking" is often used outside Amateur Radio when referring to reciprocal mixing of oscillator noise with strong local signals.)

While listening to a weak signal, all stages operate at maximum gain. If the weak signal were at a level of S0, a strong signal could be at S9 + 60 dB. Using the standard of S9 representing a 50 µV input signal, and each S unit reflecting a change of 6 dB, the receiver's front-end stages would be receiving a 0.1 µV signal and a 50,000 µV into the front end at the same time. A perfectly linear receiver would amplify each signal equally until the undesired signal is eliminated at the operating bandwidth setting stage. However, in practical receivers, after a few stages of full gain amplification, the stronger signal causes amplifier clipping, which reduces the gain available to the strong signal. This is seen as a gradual reduction in gain as the input signal amplitude increases. Gain reduction also reduces the amplitude of the weaker signal which is perceived to fade as the strong signal increases in amplitude. Eventually, the weaker signal is no longer receivable and is said to have been "blocked", thus the name for the effect.

The ratio in dB between the strongest signal that a receiver can amplify linearly, with no more than 1 dB of gain reduction, and the receiver's noise floor in a specified bandwidth is called the receiver's *blocking dynamic range* or *BDR* or the *compression-free dynamic range* or *CFDR*. In an analog superhet, BDR is established by the linear regions of the IF amplifiers and mixers. If the receiver

Nonlinear Signal Combinations

Although a mixer is often thought of as nonlinear, it is neither necessary nor desirable for a mixer to be nonlinear. An ideal mixer is one that linearly multiplies the LO voltage by the signal voltage, creating two products at the sum and difference frequencies and only those two products. From the signal's perspective, it is a perfectly linear but time-varying device. Ideally a mixer should be as linear as possible.

If a signal is applied to a nonlinear device, however, the output will not be just a copy of the input, but can be described as the following infinite series of output signal products:

$$V_{OUT} = K_0 + K_1 \times V_{IN} + K_2 \times V_{IN}^2 + K_3 \times V_{IN}^3 + \ldots + K_N \times V_{IN}^N$$

What happens if the input V_{IN} consists of two sinusoids at F_1 and F_2, or $A \times [\sin(2\pi F_1) \times t]$ and $B \times [\sin(2\pi F_2) \times t]$? Begin by simplifying the notation to use angular frequency in radians/second ($2\pi F = \omega$). Thus V_{IN} becomes $A\sin\omega_1 t$ and $B\sin\omega_2 t$ and equation A becomes:

$$V_{OUT} = K_0 + K_1 \times (A\sin\omega_1 t + B\sin\omega_2 t) + K_2 \times (A\sin\omega_1 t + B\sin\omega_2 t)^2 + K_3 \times (A\sin\omega_1 t + B\sin\omega_2 t)^3 + \ldots + K_N \times (A\sin\omega_1 t + B\sin\omega_2 t)^N$$

The zero-order term, K_0, represents a dc component and the first-order term, $K_1 \times (A\sin\omega_1 t + B\sin\omega_2 t)$, is just a constant times the input signals. The second-order term is the most interesting for our purposes. Performing the squaring operation, we end up with:

Second order term = $[K_2 A^2 \sin^2\omega_1 t + 2K_2 AB(\sin\omega_1 t \times \sin\omega_2 t) + K_2 B^2 \sin^2\omega_2 t]$

Using the trigonometric identity (see the **Radio Mathematics** supplement):

$$\sin á \sin â = 1/2 \{\cos(á - â) - \cos(á + â)\}$$

the product term becomes:

$$K_2 AB \times [\cos(\omega_1 - \omega_2)t - \cos(\omega_1 + \omega_2)t]$$

These products are at the sum and difference frequency of the input signals! The signals, originally sinusoids are now cosinusoids, signifying a phase shift. These signals, however, are just two of the many products created by the nonlinear action of the circuit, represented by the higher-order terms in the original series.

In the output of a mixer or amplifier, those unwanted signals create noise and interference and must be minimized or filtered out. This nonlinear process is responsible for the distortion and intermodulation products generated by amplifiers operated nonlinearly in receivers and transmitters.

---

employs DSP, the range of the analog-to-digital converter usually establishes the receiver's BDR. The spacing of the signals must also be specified so that any internal filtering is accounted for. Typical signal spacing is 2, 5, 20, and 100 kHz.

A related term is "near-far interference" which is used primarily in the commercial environment to refer to a strong signal causing a receiver to reduce its gain and along with it the strength of weak received signals.

INTERMODULATION DYNAMIC RANGE

Blocking dynamic range is the straightforward response of a receiver to a single strong interfering signal outside the operating passband. In amateur operation, we often have more than one interferer. While such signals contribute to the blocking gain compression in the same manner as a single signal described above, multiple signals also result in a potentially more serious problem resulting from *intermodulation (IM) products*. As noted previously, analog heterodyne and SDR receivers behave quite differently with respect to intermodulation.

If we look again at the equation for two sinusoids in the sidebar on Nonlinear Signal Combinations, we note that there are an infinite number of higher order terms. In general, the coefficients of these terms are progressively lower in amplitude, but they are still greater than zero. Of primary interest is third-order term, $K_3 \times V_{IN}^3$, when considering V_{IN} as the sum of two interfering signals (f_1 and f_2) near our desired signal (f_0) and within the first IF passband, but outside the operating bandwidth.

$$V_{OUT} = K_3 \times [A\sin(f_1)t + B\sin(f_2)t]^3$$
$$= K_3 \times \{A^3\sin^3(f_1)t + 3A^2B[\sin^2(f_1)t \times \sin(f_2)t] + 3AB^2[\sin(f_1)t \times \sin^2(f_2)t] + B^3\sin^3(f_2)t\}$$

The cubic terms (the first and last terms) result in products at three times the frequency and can be ignored in this discussion. Using trigonometric identities to reduce the remaining $\sin^2$ terms and the subsequent $\cos()\sin()$ products reveal individual intermodulation (IM) products, recognizing that the signals have cross-modulated each other due to the nonlinear action of the circuit. (Math handbooks such as the *CRC Standard Mathematical Tables and Formulae* have all the necessary trigonometry information.)

IM products have frequencies that are linear combinations of the input signal frequencies, written as $n(f_1) \pm m(f_2)$, where n and m are integer values. The entire group of products that result from intermodulation are broadly referred to as *intermodulation distortion* or IMD. The ratio in dB between the amplitude of the interfering signals, f_1 and f_2, and the resulting IM products is called the *intermodulation ratio*.

If *all* of the higher-order terms in the original equation are considered, n and m can take on any integer value. If the sum of n and m is odd, (2 and 1, or 3 and 2, or 3 and 4, etc.) the result is products that have frequencies near our desired signal, for example, $2(f_1) - 1(f_2)$. Those are called *odd-order* products. Odd-order products have frequencies close enough to those of the original signals that they can cause interference to the desired signal. If the sum of n and m is three, those are *third-order IM products* or *third-order IMD*. For fifth-order IMD, the sum of n and m is five, and so forth. The higher the order of the IM products, the smaller their amplitude, so our main concern is with third-order IMD.

If the two interfering signals have frequencies of $f_0 + \Delta$, and $f_0 + 2\Delta$, where Δ is some offset frequency, we have for the third-order term:

$$V_{OUT} = K_3 \times [A \sin(f_0 + \Delta)t + B \sin(f_0 + 2\Delta)t]^3$$

A good example would be interfering signals with offsets of 2 kHz and 2 × 2 kHz or 4 kHz from the desired frequency, a common situation on the amateur bands.

Discarding the cubic terms and applying

the necessary trigonometric identities shows that a product can be produced from this combination of interfering frequencies that has a frequency of exactly f_0 — the same frequency as the desired signal! (The higher-order terms of the sidebar's equation for sinusoid signals can also produce products at f_0, but their amplitude is usually well below those of the third-order products.)

Thus we have two interfering signals that are not within our operating bandwidth so we don't hear either by themselves. Yet they combine in a nonlinear circuit and produce a signal exactly on top of our desired signal. If the interfering signals are within the passband of our first IF and are strong enough the IM product will be heard.

As the strength of the interfering signals increases, so does that of the resulting intermodulation products. For every dB of increase in the interfering signals, the third-order IM products increase by approximately 3 dB. Fifth-order IM increases by 5 dB for every dB increase in the interfering signals, and so forth. Our primary concern, however, is with the third-order products because they are the strongest and cause the most interference.

Third-order IMD dynamic range (3IMD_DR) is the difference between a receiver's MDS and the input level of two interfering signals that create an IMD product on the same frequency and as strong as a desired signal. (The complete test is described in the **Test Measurements and Instruments** chapter and in the book by Allison.) The test is performed with the interfering signals at different spacings (usually 2, 5, and 20 kHz) and with the desired signal at several different levels. The ARRL uses a signal at the MDS, at S5 (–97 dBm) and 0 dBm. For *QST* Product Reports, the test is performed on the 3.5, 14, and 50 MHz bands. All of these conditions must be specified and no single number characterizes 3IMD_DR performance entirely.

This dynamic range is particularly important to the contest and DX community since they often need to copy very weak signals with very strong signals on an adjacent channel or just a few kHz away. Combined with reciprocal mixing, band noise, and spurious emissions from transmitters, third-order IMD products can make for very difficult reception. Note that SDR receivers do not specify this dynamic range because their circuitry does not behave the same as analog superheterodyne receivers as discussed the sections below.

INTERCEPT POINT

Intercept point describes the IMD performance of an individual stage or a complete receiver. For example, in an analog heterodyne receiver, third-order IM products increase at the rate of 3 dB for every 1-dB increase in the level of each of the interfering input signals (ideally, but not always exactly true). As the input levels increase, the distortion products seen at the output on a spectrum analyzer could catch up to, and equal, the level of the two desired signals if the receiver did not begin to exhibit blocking as discussed earlier. Remember that SDR equipment will behave differently.

The input level at which this occurs is the *input intercept point*. **Figure 12.3** shows the concept graphically, and also derives from the geometry an equation that relates signal level, distortion and intercept point. The intercept point of the most interest in receiver evaluation is that for third-order IM products and is called the *third-order intercept point* or *IP_3*. A similar process is used to get a second-order intercept point for second-order IMD. A higher IP_3 means that third-order IM products will be weaker for specific input signal strengths and the operator will experience less interference from IM products from strong adjacent signals.

From the geometry of the figure
$$\frac{I-D}{I-S} = 3$$

Solve for I to get
I = S + 0.5 (S/D)
where S/D is signal to distortion ratio in dB,
S is in dBm and I is in dBm.

For second-order intermodulation,
I = S + (S/D)

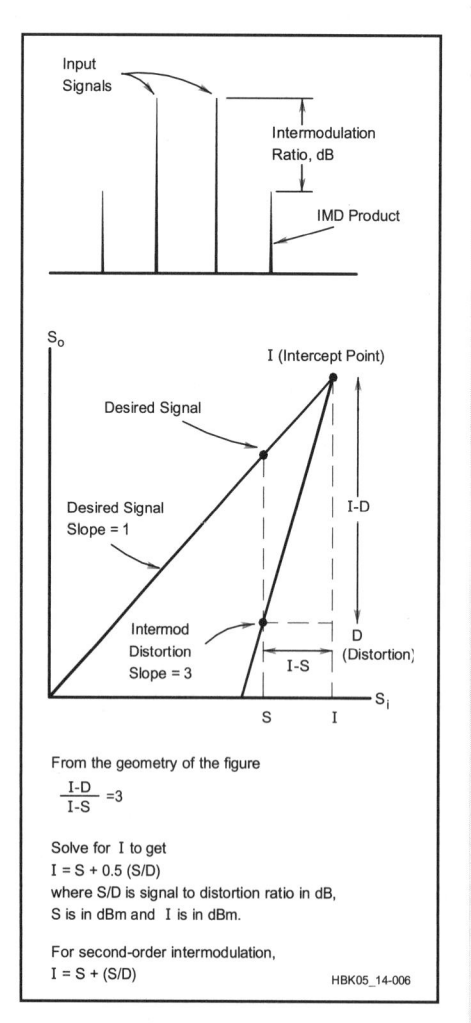

Figure 12.3 — Graphical representation of the third-order intercept concept.

Testing and Calculating Intermodulation Distortion in Receivers

Second and third-order IMD can be measured using the setup of **Figure 12.B1**. The outputs of two signal generators are combined in a 3-dB hybrid coupler. Such couplers are available from various companies, and can be homemade. The 3-dB coupler should have low loss and should itself produce negligible IMD. The signal generators are adjusted to provide a known signal level at the output of the 3-dB coupler, say, –20 dBm for each of the two signals. This combined signal is then fed through a calibrated variable attenuator to the device under test. The shielding of the cables used in this system is important: At least 90 dB of isolation should exist between the high-level signal at the input of the attenuator and the low-level signal delivered to the receiver.

The measurement procedure is simple: adjust the variable attenuator to produce a signal of known level at the frequency of the expected IMD product ($f_1 \pm f_2$ for second-order, $2f_1 - f_2$ or $2f_2 - f_1$ for third-order IMD).

To do this, of course, you have to figure out what equivalent input signal level at the receiver's operating frequency corresponds to the level of the IMD product you are seeing. There are several ways of doing this. One way — the way used by the ARRL Lab in their receiver tests — uses the minimum discernible signal. This is defined as the signal level that produces a 3-dB increase in the receiver audio output power. That is, you measure the receiver output level with no input signal, then insert a signal at the operating frequency and adjust the level of this input signal until the output power is 3 dB greater than the no-signal power. Then, when doing the IMD measurement, you adjust the attenuator of Figure 12.B1 to cause a 3-dB increase in receiver output. The level of the IMD product is then the same as the MDS level you measured.

There are several things I dislike about doing the measurement this way. The problem is that you have to measure noise power. This can be difficult. First, you need an RMS voltmeter or audio power meter to do it at all. Second, the measurement varies with time (it's noise!), making it difficult to nail down a number. And third, there is the question of the audio response of the receiver; its noise output may not be flat across the output spectrum. So I prefer to measure, instead of MDS, a higher reference level. I use the receiver's S meter as a reference. I first determine the input signal level it takes to get an S1 reading. Then, in the IMD measurement, I adjust the attenuator to again give an S1 reading. The level of the IMD product signal is now equal to the level I measured at S1. Note that this technique gives a different IMD level value than the MDS technique. That's OK, though. What we are trying to determine is the *difference* between the level of the signals applied to the receiver input and the level of the IMD product. Our calculations will give the same result whether we measure the IMD product at the MDS level, the S1 level or some other level.

An easy way to make the reference measurement is with the setup of Figure 12.B1. You'll have to switch in a lot of attenuation (make sure you have an attenuator with enough range), but doing it this way keeps all of the possible variations in the measurement fairly constant. And this way, the difference between the reference level and the input level needed to produce the desired IMD product signal level is simply the difference in attenuator settings between the reference and IMD measurements.

Calculating Intercept Points

Once we know the levels of the signals applied to the receiver input and the level of the IMD product, we can easily calculate the intercept point using the following equation:

$$IP_n = \frac{n \times P_A - P_{IM_n}}{n - 1} \quad (A)$$

Here, n is the order, P_A is the receiver input power (of one of the input signals), P_{IMn} is the power of the IMD product signal, and IP_n is the nth-order intercept point. All powers should be in dBm. For second and third-order IMD, equation A results in the equations:

$$IP_2 = \frac{2 \times P_A - P_{IM_2}}{2 - 1} \quad (B)$$

$$IP_3 = \frac{3 \times P_A - P_{IM_3}}{3 - 1} \quad (C)$$

You can measure higher-order intercept points, too.

Example Measurements

To get a feel for this process, it's useful to consider some actual measured values.

The first example is a Rohde & Schwarz model EK085 receiver with digital preselection. For measuring second-order IMD, signals at 6.00 and 8.01 MHz, at –20 dBm each, were applied at the input of the attenuator. The difference in attenuator settings between the reference measurement and the level needed to produce the desired IMD product signal level was found to be 125 dB. The calculation of the second-order IP is then:

$$IP_2 = \frac{2(-20 \text{ dBm}) - (-20 \text{ dBm} - 125 \text{ dB})}{2 - 1}$$

$$= -40 \text{ dBm} + 20 \text{ dBm} + 125 \text{ dB} = +105 \text{ dB}$$

For IP_3, we set the signal generators for 0 dBm at the attenuator input, using frequencies of 14.00 and 14.01 MHz. The difference in attenuator settings between the reference and IMD measurements was 80 dB, so:

$$IP_3 = \frac{3(0 \text{ dBm}) - (0 \text{ dBm} - 80 \text{ dB})}{3 - 1}$$

$$= \frac{0 \text{ dBm} + 80 \text{ dB}}{2} = +40 \text{ dBm}$$

We also measured the IP_3 of a Yaesu FT-1000D at the same frequencies, using attenuator-input levels of –10 dBm. A difference in attenuator readings of 80 dB resulted in the calculation:

$$IP_3 = \frac{3(-10 \text{ dBm}) - (-10 \text{ dBm} - 80 \text{ dB})}{3 - 1}$$

$$= \frac{-30 \text{ dBm} + 10 \text{ dBm} + 80 \text{ dB}}{2}$$

$$= \frac{-20 \text{ dBm} + 80 \text{ dB}}{2}$$

$$= +30 \text{ dBm}$$

Synthesizer Requirements

To be able to make use of high third-order intercept points at these close-in spacings requires a low-noise LO synthesizer. You can estimate the required noise performance of the synthesizer for a given IP_3 value. First, calculate the value of receiver input power that would cause the IMD product to just come out of the noise floor, by solving equation A for P_A, then take the difference between the calculated value of P_A and the noise floor to find the dynamic range. Doing so gives the equation:

$$ID_3 = \frac{2}{3}(IP_3 + P_{min}) \quad (D)$$

where ID_3 is the third-order IMD dynamic range in dB and P_{min} is the noise floor in dBm. Knowing the receiver bandwidth, BW (2400 Hz in this case) and noise figure, NF (8 dB) allows us to calculate the noise floor, P_{min}:

$$P_{min} = -174 \text{ dBm} + 10 \log(BW) + NF$$

$$= -174 \text{ dBm} + 10 \log(2400) + 8$$

$$= -132 \text{ dBm}$$

The synthesizer noise should not exceed the noise floor when an input signal is present that just causes an IMD product signal at the noise floor level. This will be accomplished if the synthesizer noise is less than:

ID + 10 log (BW) = 114.7 dB + 10 log (2400) = 148.5 dBc/Hz

in the passband of the receiver. Such synthesizers hardly exist.
— Dr Ulrich L. Rohde, N1UL

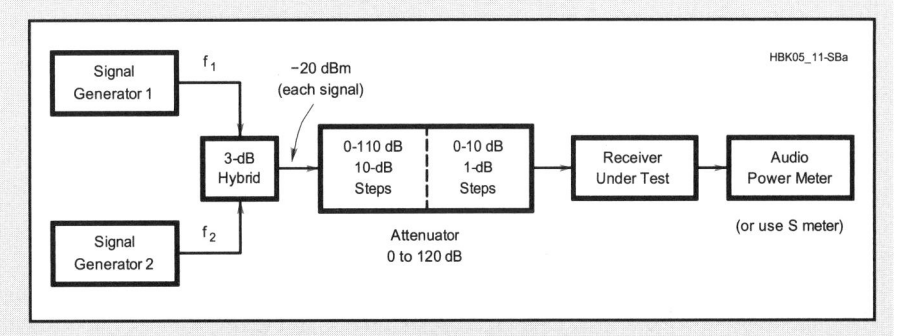

Figure 12.B1 — Test setup for measurement of IMD performance. Both signal generators should be types such as HP 608, HP 8640, or Rohde & Schwarz SMDU, with phase noise performance of –140 dBc/Hz or better at 20 kHz from the signal frequency.

These formulas are very useful in designing radio systems and circuits. If the input intercept point (dBm) and the gain of the stage (dB) are added the result is an output intercept point (dBm). Receivers are specified by input intercept point, referring distortion back to the receive antenna input. Intercept point is a major performance limitation of receivers used in high density contest or DX operations. Keep in mind that we have been discussing this as an effect of two signals, one that is Δ away from our operating frequency and another at twice Δ. In real life, we may be trying to copy a weak signal at f_0, and have other signals at $f_0 \pm 500$, 750, 1000, 1250…5000 Hz. There will be many combinations that produce products at or near our weak signal's frequency.

Note that the products don't need to end up exactly on top of the desired signal to cause a problem; they just need to be within the operating bandwidth. So far we have been talking about steady carriers, such as would be encountered during CW operation with interference from nearby CW stations. SSB or other wider bandwidth modes with spectrum distributed across a few kHz will have signal components that go in and out of a relationship that results in on-channel interference from IMD. This manifests itself as a time-varying synthetic noise floor, composed of all the resulting products across the channel. The difference in this low level "noise" can be dramatic between different receivers, especially when added to phase noise received from other stations and reciprocal mixing inside the receiver!

SPURIOUS-FREE DYNAMIC RANGE (SFDR)

IM products increase with the amplitude of the interfering signals that cause them and at some point become detectable above the receiver's noise floor. The ratio of the strength of the interfering signals to the noise floor, in dB, is the receiver's *spurious-free dynamic range* or *SFDR*. This is the range of signal strengths over which the receiver does not produce any detectable spurious products. SFDR can be specified for a specific order of IM products; for example, SFDR3 is the SFDR measured for third-order IM products only. The bandwidth for which the receiver's noise floor is measured must also be specified, since smaller bandwidths will result in a lower noise floor.

INTERFERENCE FREE SIGNAL STRENGTH (IFSS)

To address the behavior of SDR receivers for which the IP_3 specification is irrelevant new performance metrics have been proposed. One such measurement is the *interference-free signal strength* or *IFSS*. This measures the largest input signal for which no interference products are produced above the receiver noise floor. The noise floor is specified using the Rec. ITU P.372.7 band-noise levels. IFSS is similar to SFDR but does not specify a type of intermodulation products.

As a consequence of using the ITU band-noise levels noise levels (see the **RF Techniques** chapter), the IFSS for a given receiver can be much higher on the lower HF bands, where external band noise is high and will mask any interfering products. On the upper HF and VHF bands where band noise is lower, the IFSS can also be lower. Similarly, there can be a difference between the rural, suburban, and urban environments. As such, IFSS measurements ignore distortion products below the noise floor.

IFSS measurements on current receivers show a great deal of variation in the performance over a wide range of signal levels. The best performers show a smooth increase in the distortion product level beginning at the input signal level where the interference products are equal to the noise floor. These radios exhibit predictable performance over a wide range of inputs. Other models show large swings in distortion product levels, even decreasing with increased input over some ranges of signal levels. This indicates a need for better understanding of SDR behavior and design. Nevertheless, IFSS is a useful tool in assessing SDR performance.

RECIPROCAL MIXING DYNAMIC RANGE (RMDR)

All oscillators produce some phase noise. When the oscillator is used to control a receiver or transmitter, the noise is transferred to signals, causing extra noise in the receiver passband and in the transmitter output signal. In an analog heterodyne receiver, the noise is transferred to the signals in the mixing process from the local oscillator(s). While all of the LOs contribute some noise, in practice the first mixer is the dominant source. In an SDR receiver, phase noise is transferred primarily from the sampling clock for the input ADC and the DDS signal sources in the receiver. Some noise is contributed by jitter in the digitizing ADC, as well.

RMDR is measured by increasing a test input signal until the noise in the receive channel increases by a specified amount, usually 3 dB. The difference between the input signal level and the receiver's noise floor (MDS) is the RMDR.

The raised background noise will mask weak signals, in effect raising the receiver's noise floor when a nearby strong signal is present to transfer the oscillator noise. For example, if a receiver's noise floor or MDS is –127 dBm and an input signal of –37 dBm causes the 3 dB increase in noise, the receiver's RMDR = –37 – (–127) = 90 dB.

Since oscillator noise is lower farther from the oscillator frequency, the transferred noise will have a similar profile. (The discussion of phase noise in the **Oscillators and Synthesizers** chapter shows the noise profile of typical oscillators.) This requires RMDR to be measured with the strong signal a specified distance from the receiver channel in which noise is being measured. Typical separations are 2, 5, and 20 kHz.

RMDR tends to be the most limiting dynamic range at the close signal spacing of 2 and 5 kHz. Since close-spaced signals are typical of the most demanding receiver environments for contesting and DXing, this is an important measurement to compare when purchasing a transceiver.

NOISE POWER RATIO (NPR)

Another test method applicable to both SDR and heterodyne receivers, *noise power ratio* tests were originally developed for multiplexed telephone systems. These early system combined many individual channels on one transmission system, cable or radio. Nonlinearities in the system would generate distortion products and interfere with the channels. To simulate the effect of many active channels, wideband noise was transmitted with one channel removed by a narrow notch filter. (See **Figure 12.4**)

The noise simulated the presence of complex speech waveforms in the other channels. Any distortion products from the noise would appear as a raised noise floor in the notched channel. As the noise amplitude was raised, the in-channel noise would rise, as well.

This is a close analogue to a busy band with multiple channels of communication. Nonlinearities in the receiver generate distortion products in the monitored channel. The ratio of the out-of-channel to in-channel noise is the noise power ratio. The more linear the receiver, the more noise power can be injected for a given amount of increase in the in-channel noise. (NPR is explained in the March/April 2015 *QEX* article, "Noise Power Ratio (NPR) Testing on HF Receivers" by Adam Farson, VA7OJ, and in the Analog Devices tutorial MT-005, "Noise Power Ratio (NPR)" — see the References section.

TYPICAL PERFORMANCE

As we would expect, the blocking and IMD dynamic range (IMD DR) performance of a heterodyne receiver will depend on a combination of the early stage filtering, the linearity of the mixers and amplifiers, and the dynamic range of any ADC used for DSP at the IF or audio stages.

Product reviews of receivers and the receiver sections of transceivers published in *QST* now provide the measured dynamic range in the presence of interfering signals with spacings of 2, 5 and 20 kHz. (Details of the test procedures used are given in the **Test**

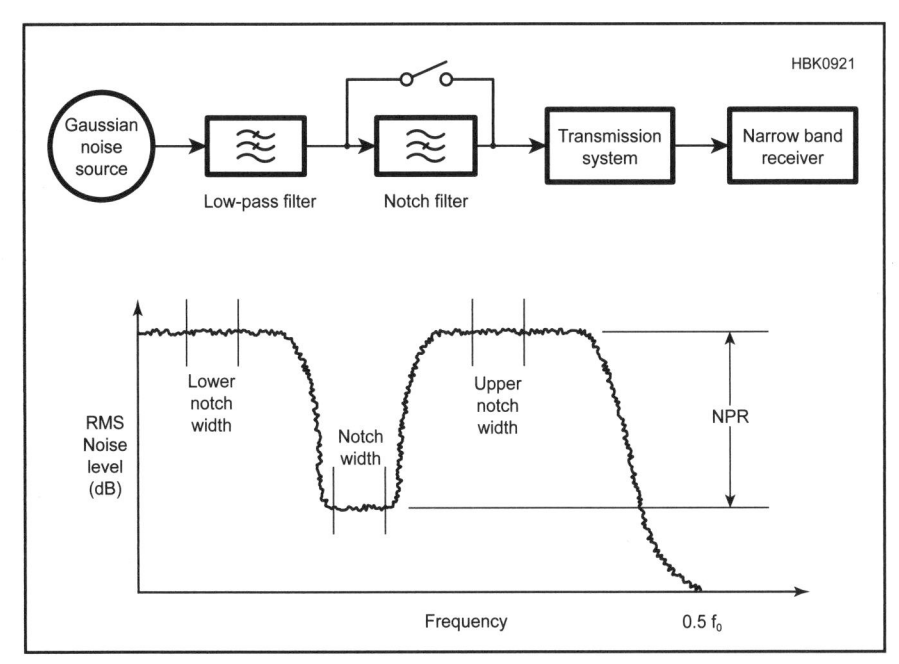

Figure 12.4 — Noise power measurement test set and typical spectrum (after Analog Devices MT-005, see References).

would have to have a combined power equal to S9 +27 dB, or each at S9 +24 dB. This is not unusual on today's amateur bands. On the other hand, if we had an IMD dynamic range of 102 dB, the interfering signals would have to be S9 +66 dB, much less likely. How much dynamic range you need depends in large measure on the kind of operating you do, how much gain your receiving antennas have and the closeness of the nearest station that operates on the same bands as you. Given that transmitters generate both phase noise and IMD products of their own, the dynamic range of most receivers on the market today is quite adequate for even the most demanding situations. Receivers may have other performance issues to consider such as filter design, AGC reaction, audio distortion, and so forth.

Keep in mind also that it is often difficult to tell whether or not you are hearing internal receiver-generated IMD — it just sounds like there are many more signals than are really present. A good test to assess the source of interference is first switch off any preamplifiers and noise-blankers or noise-reduction systems that affect the receiver's linearity. Observe the level of the interference (if it's still there) and then switch in some attenuation at the front-end of the receiver. If the level of the interference goes down by *more* than the level of attenuation (estimate 6 dB per S unit), then the interference is being generated (or at least aggravated) by nonlinearity inside the receiver. Continue to increase attenuation until the interference either goes away or goes down at the same rate as the attenuation is increased. You might be surprised at how much better the band "sounds" when your receiver is operating in its linear region!

Equipment and Measurements chapter and in the book by Allison.) At 20 kHz spacing, the interfering signal is usually outside of the roofing filter bandwidth of any of the above architectures. Spacing of 2 and 5 kHz represents likely conditions on a crowded band.

A look at recent top-performing receiver measurements indicates that receivers have IMD (or distortion-product) dynamic range with 2 kHz spacing results in the following ranges:
• Direct-sampling SDR: 80 to 108 dB
• Upconverting with VHF IF: 80 to 105 dB
• Downconverting with HF IF: 75 to 110 dB
• Hybrid superhet/DSP architecture: Omni VII, 82 dB (2007); Icom IC-PRO3, 75 dB (2009)

(Note that SDR distortion products are not necessarily IMD. Receiver block diagrams are provided in the following sections. Data is taken from ARRL Lab tests and the long-term test program conducted by Rob Sherwood, NCØB, at **www.sherweng.com/table.html**.)

Let's take an example of what this would mean. If we are listening to a signal at S3, for signals to generate a third-order IMD product at the same level in a receiver with a dynamic range of 60 dB, the $f_0 + \Delta$ and $f_0 + 2\Delta$ signals

12.2 Heterodyne Receivers

The *heterodyne* receiver combines the input signal with a signal from a *local oscillator* (LO) in a mixer as discussed previously to generate the sum and difference frequencies as shown in **Figure 12.5**. The receiver may be designed so the output signal is anything from dc (a so-called *direct conversion* receiver) to any frequency above or below either of the two frequencies. The major benefit is that most of the gain, bandwidth setting and processing are performed at a single frequency, simplifying the design dramatically.

By changing the frequency of the LO, the operator shifts a signal at the input frequency the output, along with all its modulated infor-

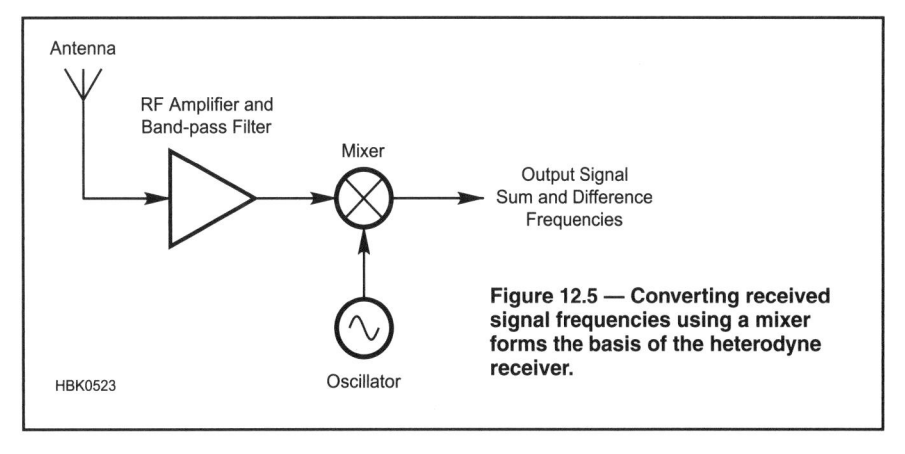

Figure 12.5 — Converting received signal frequencies using a mixer forms the basis of the heterodyne receiver.

Receiving   12.11

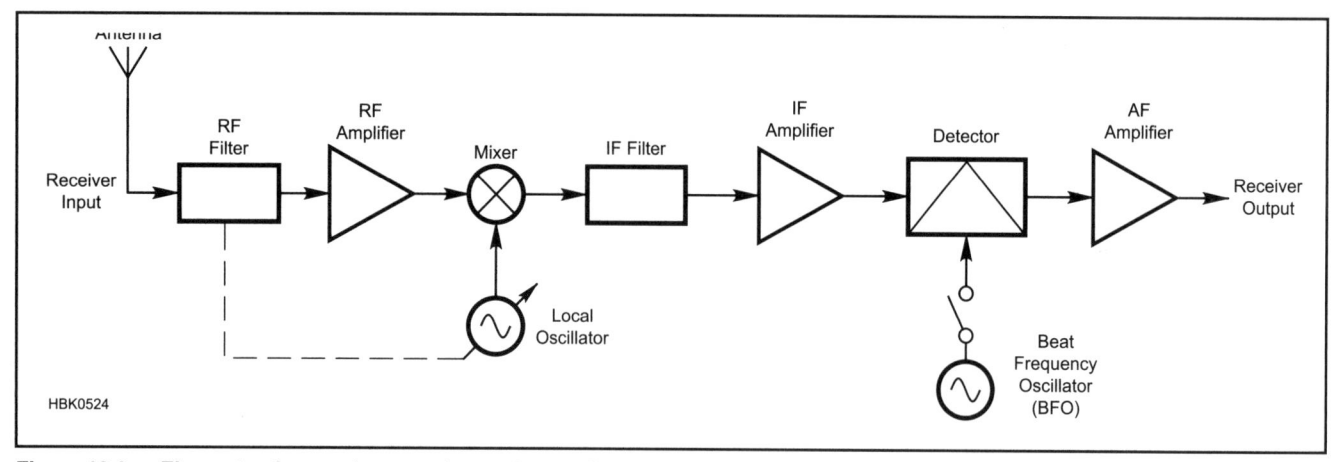

Figure 12.6 — Elements of an analog superheterodyne radio receiver.

mation. In most receivers the mixer output frequency is designed to be an RF signal, either the sum or difference — the other being filtered out at this point. This output frequency is called an *intermediate frequency* or *IF*. The IF amplifier system can be designed to provide the selectivity and other desired characteristics centered at a single fixed frequency.

When more than one frequency conversion process is used, the receiver becomes a *superheterodyne* or *superhet*. A block diagram of a typical superhet receiver is shown in **Figure 12.6**. In traditional form, the RF filter is used to limit the input frequency range to those frequencies that include only the desired sum or difference but not the other — the so-called *image* frequency. The dotted line represents the fact that in receivers with a wide tuning range, such as a simple AM broadcast receiver that tunes from 500 to 1700 kHz, a more than 3:1 range, the input RF amplifier and filter is often tracked along with the local oscillator. The IF filter is used to establish selectivity — the operating bandwidth required by the information. Circuits from the antenna input through and including the mixer (the first mixer if more than one mixing stage is used) are generally referred to as the receiver's *front-end*.

For reception of suppressed carrier single-sideband voice (SSB) or on-off or frequency-shift keyed (FSK) signals, a second *beat frequency oscillator* or *BFO* is employed to provide an audible voice, an audio tone or tones at the output for operator or FSK processing. This is the same as a heterodyne mixer with an output centered at dc, although the IF filter is usually designed to remove one of the output products.

Recent superhet receivers convert the incoming signal to digital form at one of the intermediate frequencies. DSP techniques are then used to control operating bandwidth and demodulate the input signal. See the **DSP and SDR Fundamentals** chapter for more information on these techniques.

12.2.1 The Direct Conversion Receiver

The heterodyne process can occur at a number of different points in the receiver. The simplest form of heterodyne receiver is called a *direct conversion* or *DC* receiver because it performs the translation directly from the signal frequency to the audio output. It is, in effect, just the BFO and detector of the general superhet shown in Figure 12.6. In this case, the detector is often preceded by an RF amplifier with a typical complete receiver shown in **Figure 12.7**. Such a receiver can be very simple to construct, yet can be quite effective — especially for the ultra-compact low-power consumer-oriented portable station known as the mobile telephone! In fact, given the direct conversion receiver's use in the mobile telephone, it is the most widely used of all receivers.

The basic function of a mixer is to multiply two sinusoidal signals and generate two new signals with frequencies that are the sum and difference of the two original signals. This function can be performed by a linear multiplier, a switch that turns one input signal on and off at the frequency of the other input signal, or a nonlinear circuit such as a diode. (The output of a nonlinear circuit is made up of an infinite series of products, all different combinations of the two input signals, as described in the sidebar on Nonlinear Signal Combinations.) Much more information about the theory, operation and application of mixers may be found in this chapter's section on them.

Figure 12.8 shows the progression of the spectrum of an on-off keyed CW signal through such a receiver based on the relationships described above. (This example is based on the "Rock-Bending Receiver for 7 MHz" which is included in the online projects.) In 12.8C, we include an undesired image signal on the other side of the local oscillator that also shows up in the output of the receiver. Note each of the desired and undesired responses that occur as outputs of the mixer.

Some mixers are designed to be *balanced* in order to cancel one of the input signals at the output while a *double-balanced* mixer

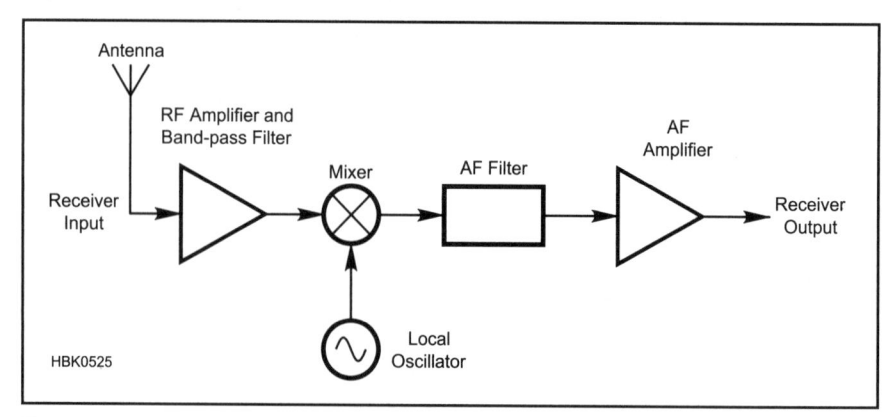

Figure 12.7 — Block diagram of a direct conversion receiver.

12.12   Chapter 12

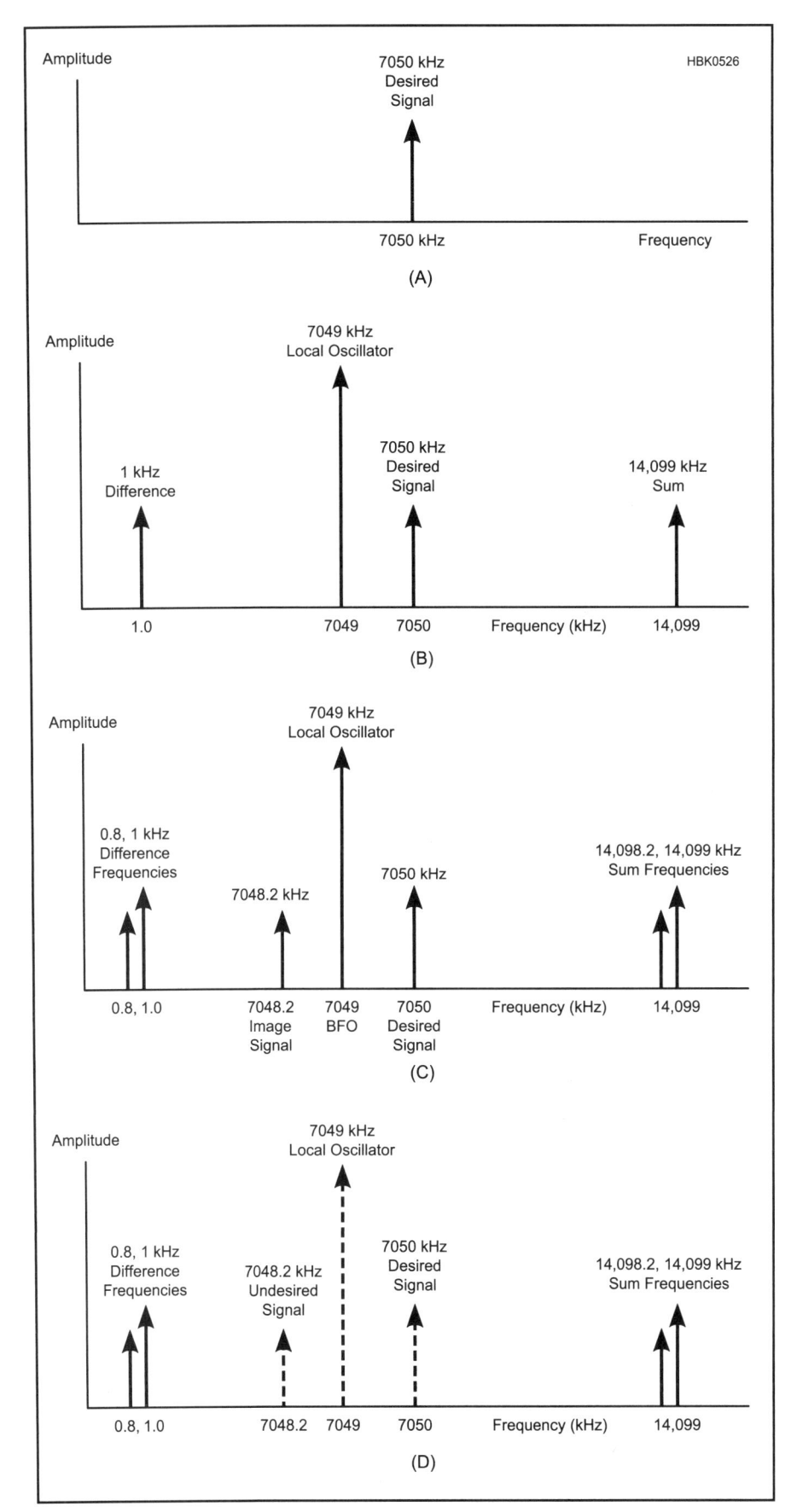

Figure 12.8 — Frequency relationships in a direct conversion receiver. At (A), the desired receive signal from antenna, a 7050 kHz on-off keyed carrier. At (B), the internal local oscillator (LO) and receive frequency relationships. At (C), the frequency relationships of mixer/detector products (not to scale). At (D), the sum and difference outputs from a double balanced mixer (not to scale). Note the mixer inputs that are balanced out so that they cancel in the output (dashed lines).

cancels both. A double-balanced mixer simplifies the output filtering job as shown in Figure 12.8D.

Products generated by nonlinearities in the mixing process (see the previous sidebar on Nonlinear Signal Combinations) are heard as intermodulation distortion signals that we will discuss later. Note that the nonlinearities also allow mixing with unwanted signals near multiples of local oscillator frequency. These signals, such as those from TV or FM broadcast stations, must be eliminated in the filtering before the mixer since their audio output will be right in the desired passband on the output of the mixer.

12.2.2 Superheterodyne Receivers

In many instances, it is not possible to achieve all the receiver design goals with a single-conversion receiver and multiple conversion steps are used, creating the superheterodyne architecture. Traditionally, the first conversion is tasked with removing the RF image signals, while the second generates the IF signal where the signal is amplified and filtered.

The superheterodyne concept was introduced by Major Edwin Armstrong, a US Army artillery officer, just as WW I was coming to a close. He is the same Armstrong who invented frequency modulation (FM) some years later and who held many radio patents between WW I and WW II.

In a superhet, a local oscillator and mixer are used to translate the received signal to an intermediate frequency rather than directly to audio. This provides an opportunity for additional amplification and processing. Then a second mixer is used as in the DC receiver to detect the IF signal, translating it to audio. The configuration was shown previously in Figure 12.6.

An example will illustrate how this works. Let's pick a common IF frequency used in a simple AM broadcast radio, 455 kHz. If we want to listen to a 600 kHz broadcast station, the RF stage would be set to amplify the 600 kHz signal and the LO should be set to 600 + 455 kHz or 1055 kHz. The 600 kHz signal, along with any audio information it contains, is translated to the IF frequency and is amplified and then detected.

Note that we could have also set the local oscillator to 600 – 455 kHz or 145 kHz. By setting it to the sum, we reduce the relative range that the oscillator must tune. To cover the 500 to 1700 kHz with the difference, our LO would have to cover from 45 to 1245, a 28:1 range. Using the sum requires LO coverage from 955 to 2155 kHz, a range of about 2.5:1 — much easier to implement.

Note that to detect standard AM signals, the receiver's second oscillator, the beat frequency oscillator (BFO), is turned off since the AM station provides its own carrier signal over the air. Receivers designed only for standard AM reception generally don't have a BFO at all.

It's not clear yet that we've gained anything by doing this; so let's look at another example. If we decide to change from listening to the station at 600 kHz and want to listen to another station at, say, 1560 kHz, we can tune the single dial of our superhet to 1560 kHz. The RF stage is tuned to 1560 kHz, the LO is set to 1560 + 455 or 2010 kHz, and now the desired station is translated to our 455 kHz IF where the bulk of our amplification can take place. Note also that with the superheterodyne configuration, selectivity (the ability to separate stations) occurs primarily in the intermediate-frequency (IF) stages and is thus the same no matter what frequencies we choose to listen to. This simplifies the design of each stage considerably.

12.2.3 Superheterodyne Bandwidth

Now we will discuss the bandwidth requirements of different operating modes and how that affects superhet design. One advantage of a superhet is that the operating bandwidth can be established by the IF stages, and further limited by the audio system. It is thus independent of the RF frequency to

Table 12.3
Typical Communications Bandwidths for Various Operating Modes

Mode	Bandwidth (kHz)
FM Voice	15
AM Broadcast	10
AM Voice	4-6.6
SSB Voice	1.8-3
Digital Voice	1.0-1.2
RTTY (170-850 Hz shift)	0.3-1.5
CW	0.1-0.5

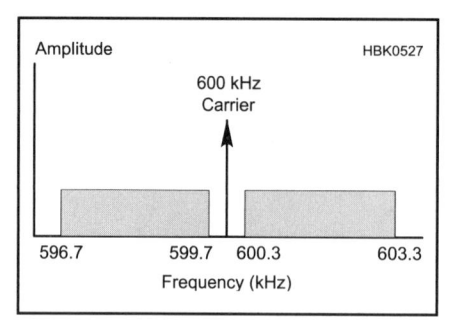

Figure 12.9 — Spectrum of sidebands of an AM voice signal with a carrier frequency of 600 kHz.

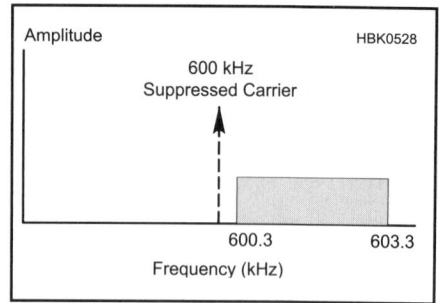

Figure 12.10 — Spectrum of single sideband AM voice signal with the suppressed carrier frequency of 600 kHz.

which the receiver is tuned. It should not be surprising that the detailed design of a superhet receiver is dependent on the nature of the signal being received. We will briefly discuss the most commonly received modulation types and the bandwidth implications of each below. The typical operating modes expected to be encountered by an HF communications receiver are tabulated in **Table 12.3**. (Each modulation type is discussed in more detail in the **Modulation** or **Digital Protocols and Modes** chapters.) The same concerns for receiver bandwidth apply to SDR receivers although the filters are implemented using DSP techniques.

AMPLITUDE MODULATION AM)

As shown in Figure 12.8, multiplying (in other words, modulating) a carrier with a single tone results in the tone being translated to frequencies of the sum and difference of the two. Thus, if a transmitter were to multiply a 600 Hz tone and a 600 kHz carrier signal, we would generate additional new frequencies at 599.4 and 600.6 kHz. If instead we were to modulate the 600 kHz carrier signal with a band of frequencies corresponding to human speech of 300 to 3300 Hz (the usual range of communication quality voice signals), we would have a pair of information-carrying sidebands extending from 596.7 to 603.3 kHz, as shown in **Figure 12.9**.

Note that the total bandwidth of this AM voice signal is twice the highest modulation signal frequency, or 6600 Hz. If we choose to transmit speech and limited-range music, we might allow modulating frequencies up to 5000 Hz, resulting in a bandwidth of 10,000 Hz or 10 kHz. This is the standard channel spacing that commercial AM broadcasters use in the US. (9 kHz is used in Europe) In actual use, transmitters on adjacent channels are generally geographically separated, so broadcasters can extend some energy into the next channels for improved fidelity. We would refer to this as a *narrow-bandwidth* mode.

What does this say about the bandwidth needed for our receiver? If we want to receive the full information content transmitted by a US AM broadcast station, then we need to set the bandwidth to at least 10 kHz. What if our receiver has a narrower bandwidth? Well, we will lose the higher frequency components of the transmitted signal — perhaps ending up with a radio suitable for voice but not very good at reproducing music.

On the other hand, what is the impact of having too wide a bandwidth in our receiver? In that case, we will be able to receive the full transmitted spectrum but we will also receive some of the adjacent channel information. This will sound like interference and reduce the quality of what we are receiving. If there are no adjacent channel stations, we will get any additional noise from the additional bandwidth and minimal additional information. The general rule is that the received bandwidth should be matched to the bandwidth of the signal we are trying to receive to maximize SNR and minimize interference.

As the receiver bandwidth is reduced, intelligibility suffers, although the SNR is improved. With the carrier centered in the receiver bandwidth, most voices are difficult to understand at bandwidths less than around 4 kHz. In cases of heavy interference, full carrier AM can be received as if it were SSB, as described below, with the carrier inserted at the receiver, and the receiver tuned to whichever sideband has the least interference.

SINGLE-SIDEBAND (SSB)

A single-sideband signal is contains just one of the AM signal's sideband and no carrier, as shown in **Figure 12.10**. To receive the SSB signal, the receiver uses a BFO (beat frequency oscillator) in the receiver to provide a substitute carrier. The BFO oscillator signal is multiplied with the sideband in order to provide demodulated audio output. The implications in the receiver are that the bandwidth can be slightly less than half that required for double sideband AM (DSB). The tradeoff is that the BFO signal must be at exactly the right frequency. If the frequency is improperly set, the frequency of the demodulated audio will be offset from the original signal. The effect is quite audible even for small frequency errors of a few tens of Hz. (The *QST* article "About SSB" by the editor illustrates this effect, including a video on tuning in an SSB signal — see the References section.)

This results in a requirement for a much more stable receiver design with a much finer tuning system — a more expensive proposition than the DC receiver. An alternate is to transmit a reduced level carrier and have the receiver lock on to the weak carrier, usually called a *pilot* carrier. Note that the pilot carrier need not be of sufficient amplitude to demodulate the signal, just enough to allow a BFO to lock to it. These alternatives are effective, but tend to make SSB receivers expensive, complex and most appropriate for the case in where a small number of receivers are listening to a single transmitter, as is the case of two-way amateur communication.

Note that the bandwidth required to effectively demodulate an SSB signal is actually less than half that required for the AM signal because the range centered on the AM carrier need not be received. Thus the communications-quality range of 300 to 3300 Hz can be received in a bandwidth of 3000 not 3300 Hz. Early SSB receivers typically used a bandwidth of around 3 kHz, but with the heavy interference frequently found in the amateur bands, it is more common for amateurs to use bandwidths of 1.8 to 2.4 kHz with the corresponding loss of some of the higher- and lower-frequency speech sounds.

RADIOTELEGRAPHY (CW)

We have described radiotelegraphy as being transmitted by "on-off keying of a carrier." You might think that since a carrier takes up just a single frequency, the receive bandwidth needed should be almost zero. This is only true if the carrier is never turned on and off. In the case of CW, it will be turned on and off quite rapidly. The rise and fall of the carrier results in sidebands extending on either side of the carrier, and they must be received in order to reconstruct the signal in the receiver.

A rule of thumb is to consider the rise and fall time as about 10% of the pulse width and the bandwidth as the reciprocal of the quickest of rise or fall time. This results in a bandwidth requirement of about 50 to 200 Hz for the usual CW transmission rates. Another way to visualize this is with the bandwidth being set by a high-Q tuned circuit. Such a circuit will continue to "ring" after the input pulse is gone. Thus, too narrow a bandwidth will actually "fill in" between the code elements and act like a "no bandwidth" full period carrier and this is exactly what is heard if a very narrow crystal filter is used when receiving CW.

DIGITAL MODULATION

(This is a short overview to establish receiver requirements for the digital modes. See the **Modulation** and **Digital Protocols and Modes** chapters and the **Digital Communications** chapter in the *Handbook* downloadable supplemental information for more in-depth treatment.)

The Baudot code (used for teletype communications) and ASCII code — two popular digital communications codes used by amateurs — are constructed with sequences of elements or bits. The state of each bit — ON or OFF — is represented by a signal at one of two distinct frequencies: one designated *mark* and one designated *space*. This is referred to as *frequency shift keying* (FSK). The transmitter frequency shifts back and forth with each character's individual elements.

Amateur operators typically use a 170 Hz separation between the mark and space frequencies for the most popular FSK mode, radioteletype or RTTY, depending on the data rate and local convention, although 850 Hz is sometimes used. The minimum bandwidth required to recover the data is approximately twice the spacing between the tones. Note that the tones can be generated by directly shifting the carrier frequency (*direct FSK*), or by using a pair of 170 Hz spaced audio tones applied to the audio input of an SSB transmitter (*audio FSK* or *AFSK*). Direct FSK and AFSK are indistinguishable to a receiver.

Note that if the standard audio tones of 2125 Hz (mark) and 2295 Hz (space) are used, they fall within the bandwidth of a voice channel and thus a voice transmitter and receiver can be employed without any additional processing needed outside the radio equipment.

If the receiver can shift its BFO frequency appropriately, the two tones can be received through a filter designed for CW reception with a bandwidth of about 300 Hz or wider. Some receivers provide such a narrow filter with the center frequency shifted midway between the tones (2210 Hz) to avoid the need for retuning. The most advanced receivers provide a separate filter for mark and space frequencies, thus maximizing interference rejection and signal-to-noise ratio (SNR). Using a pair of tones for FSK or AFSK results in a maximum data rate of about 1200 bit/s over a high-quality voice channel.

Phase shift keying (PSK) can also be used to transmit bit sequences, requiring good frequency stability to maintain the required time synchronization to detect shifts in phase. If the channel has a high SNR, as is often the case at VHF and higher, telephone network data-modem techniques such as Bell 102 and Bell 202 can be used. (FCC §97.307(f) specifies a maximum transmitted symbol rate for each band.)

At HF, the signal is subjected to phase and amplitude distortion as it travels. Noise is also substantially higher on the HF bands. Under these conditions, modulation and demodulation techniques designed for "wireline" connections become unusable at bit rates of more than a few hundred baud. As a result, amateurs have begun adopting and developing state of the art digital modulation techniques. These include the use of multiple carriers (MFSK, Clover, PACTOR III, etc.), multiple amplitudes and phase shifts (QAM and QPSK techniques), and advanced error detection and correction methods to achieve a net data throughput as high as 3600 bits per second (bps) over a voice-bandwidth channel. Newly developed coding methods for digital voice using QPSK modulation result in a signal bandwidth of less than 1200 Hz. (See **freedv.org** for more information.) Spread-spectrum techniques are also being adopted on the amateur UHF bands, but are beyond the scope of this discussion.

The bandwidth required for data communications can be as low as 100 Hz for PSK31 to 1 kHz or more for the faster speeds of PACTOR III and Clover. Beyond having sufficient bandwidth for the data signal, the primary requirements for receivers used for data communications are linear amplitude and phase response over the bandwidth of the data signal to avoid distorting these critical signal characteristics. The receiver must also have excellent frequency stability to avoid drift and frequency resolution to enable the receiver filters to be set on frequency.

FREQUENCY MODULATION (FM)

Another popular voice mode is *frequency modulation* or *FM*. FM can be found in a number of variations depending on purpose. In Amateur Radio and commercial mobile communication use on the shortwave bands, it is universally *narrow band FM* or *NBFM*. In NBFM, the frequency deviation is limited to around the maximum modulating frequency, typically 3 kHz. The bandwidth requirements at the receiver can be approximated by Carson's Rule of BW = 2 × (D + M), where D is the deviation and M is the maximum modulating frequency. Thus 3 kHz deviation and a maximum voice frequency of 3 kHz results in a bandwidth of 12 kHz, not far beyond the requirements for broadcast AM. (Additional signal components extend beyond this bandwidth, but are not required for voice communications.)

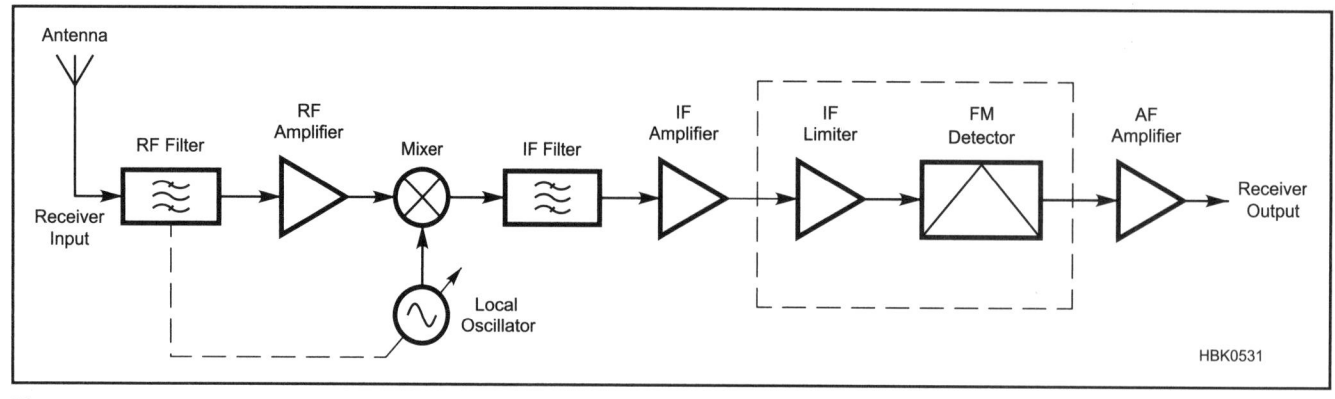

Figure 12.11 — Block diagram of an FM superheterodyne receiver. Changes from an AM/SSB receiver are enclosed by the dashed line.

In contrast, broadcast or *wideband FM* or *WBFM* occupies a channel width of 150 kHz. Originally, this provided for a higher modulation index, even with 15 kHz audio that resulted in an improved SNR. However, with multiple channel stereo and sub-channels all in the same allocated bandwidth the deviation is around the maximum transmitted signal bandwidth.

In the US, FCC amateur rules limit wideband FM use to frequencies above 29 MHz. Some, but not all, HF communication receivers provide for FM reception. For proper FM reception, two changes are required in the receiver architecture as shown within the dashed line in **Figure 12.11**. The fundamental change is that the detector must recover information from the frequency variations of the input signal. The most common such detector is called a *discriminator*. The discriminator does not require a BFO, so that is turned off, or eliminated in a dedicated FM receiver. Since amplitude variations convey no information in FM, they are generally eliminated by a *limiter*. The limiter is a high-gain IF amplifier stage that clips the positive and negative peaks of signals above a certain threshold. Since most noise of natural origins is amplitude modulated, the limiting process also strips away noise from the signal.

12.2.4 Superheterodyne FM Receivers

Narrow-band frequency modulation (NBFM) is the most common mode used on VHF and UHF. **Figure 12.12** is a block diagram of an FM receiver for the VHF/UHF amateur bands. Many FM transmitters are actually phase-modulated (PM) but aside from frequency response of the transmitted audio, the two types of signals can be received with the same equipment. This section's references to FM include PM signals unless noted otherwise.

FRONT END

A low-noise front end is desirable because of the decreasing atmospheric noise level at these frequencies and also because portable gear often uses short rod antennas at ground level. Nonetheless, the possibilities for gain compression and harmonic IMD, multi-tone IMD and cross modulation are also substantial. Therefore dynamic range is an important design consideration, especially if large, high-gain antennas are used. FM limiting should not occur until after the crystal filter. Because of the high occupancy of the VHF/UHF spectrum by powerful broadcast transmitters and nearby two-way radio services, front-end preselection is desirable, so that a low noise figure can be achieved economically within the amateur band. (See the section on Preselectors elsewhere in this chapter.)

DOWN-CONVERSION

Down-conversion to the final IF can occur in one or two stages. Favorite IFs are in the 5 to 10 MHz region (10.7 MHz is common), but at the higher frequencies rejection of the image 10 to 20 MHz away can be difficult,

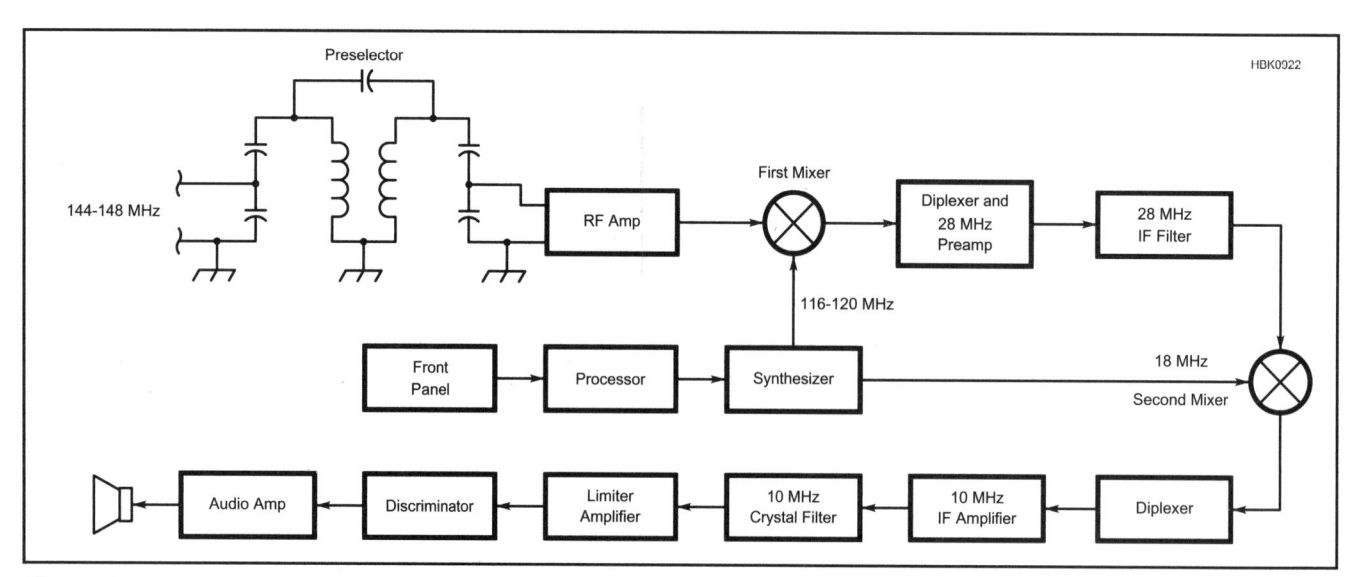

Figure 12.12 — Block diagram of a typical VHF FM receiver using dual down-conversion.

requiring considerable preselection as discussed in the sections below on IF selection and image rejection. At the higher frequencies an intermediate IF in the 30 to 50 MHz region is a better choice. Figure 12.12 shows dual down-conversion.

IF FILTERS

The customary peak frequency deviation in amateur FM on frequencies above 29 MHz is about 5 kHz and the audio speech band extends to 3 kHz. This defines a maximum modulation index (defined as the deviation ratio) of 5/3 = 1.67. An inspection of the Bessel functions that describe the resulting FM signal shows that this condition confines most of the 300 to 3000 Hz speech information sidebands within a 15 kHz or so bandwidth. Using filters of this bandwidth, channel separations of 20 or 25 kHz are achievable.

Many amateur FM transceivers are channelized in steps that can vary from 1 to 25 kHz. For low distortion of the audio output (after FM detection), this filter should have good phase linearity across the bandwidth. This would seem to preclude filters with very steep descent outside the passband, which tend to have very nonlinear phase near the band edges. But since the amount of energy in the higher speech frequencies is naturally less, the actual distortion due to this effect may be acceptable for speech purposes. The normal practice is to apply pre-emphasis to the higher speech frequencies at the transmitter and de-emphasis compensates at the receiver.

LIMITING AND DEMODULATION

After the filter, hard limiting of the IF is needed to remove any amplitude modulation components. In a high-quality receiver, special attention is given to any nonlinear phase shift that might result from the limiter circuit design. This is especially important in data receivers in which phase response must be controlled. In amateur receivers for speech it may be less important. Also, the *ratio detector* largely eliminates the need for a limiter stage, although the limiter approach is probably still preferred. FM demodulation is described in the section on Demodulation and Detection.

FM PERFORMANCE FOR WEAK SIGNALS

The noise bandwidth of the IF filter is not much greater than twice the audio bandwidth of the speech modulation, less than it would be in wideband FM. Therefore such things as capture effect, the threshold effect and the noise quieting effect so familiar to wideband FM are still operational, but somewhat less so, in FM. For FM receivers, sensitivity is specified in terms of a SINAD (see the **Test Equipment and Measurements** chapter) ratio of 12 dB. Typical values are –110 to –125 dBm, depending on the low-noise RF pre-amplification that often can be selected or deselected (in strong signal environments).

EFFECT OF LO PHASE NOISE

In an FM receiver, LO phase noise is superimposed on phase modulation, and therefore creates frequency modulation of the desired signal. This reduces the ultimate signal-to-noise ratio within the passband. This effect is called *incidental FM (IFM)*. The power density of IFM (W/Hz) is proportional to the phase noise power density (W/Hz) multiplied by the square of the modulating frequency (the familiar parabolic effect in FM). If the receiver uses high-frequency de-emphasis at the audio output (–6 dB per octave from 300 to 3000 Hz, a common practice), the IFM level at higher audio frequencies can be reduced. Ordinarily, as the signal increases the noise would be "quieted" (that is, "captured") in an FM receiver, but in this case the signal and the phase noise riding "piggy back" on the signal increase in the same proportion as described in this and the **Oscillators and Synthesizers** chapter's discussion of reciprocal mixing. IFM is not a significant problem in modern FM radios, but phase noise can become a concern for adjacent-channel interference.

As the signal becomes large the signal-to-noise ratio therefore approaches some final value. A similar ultimate SNR effect occurs in SSB receivers. On the other hand, a perfect AM receiver tends to suppress LO phase noise. (See the reference entry for Sabin.)

FM RECEIVER ICs

A wide variety of special ICs for communications-bandwidth FM receivers are available. Many of these were designed for "cordless" or mobile telephone applications and are widely used. One is an RF amplifier chip (NE/SA5204A) for 50 Ω input to 50 Ω output with 20 dB of gain. The second chip (NE/SA602A) is a front-end device with an RF amplifier, mixer and LO. The third is an IF amplifier, limiter and quadrature FM detector (NE/SA604A) that also has a very useful RSSI (logarithmic Received Signal Strength Indicator) output and also a "mute" function. The fourth is the LM386, a widely used audio-amplifier chip. Another FM receiver chip, complete in one package, is the MC3371P.

The MC13135 features double conversion and two IF amplifier frequencies. This allows more gain on a single chip with less of the cross coupling that can degrade stability. This desirable feature of multiple down-conversion was mentioned previously in this chapter.

Design details and specific parts values can be learned from a careful study of the data sheets and application notes provided by the IC vendors. Amateur designers should learn how to use these data sheets and other information such as application notes available online from the manufacturers.

12.2.5 Superheterodyne Image Rejection

Now that we have established the range of bandwidths that our receiver will need to pass, we are in a position to discuss the selection of the IF frequency at which those bandwidths will be established.

In addition, selection of the first and any following IF frequencies is important in receiving weak signals on bands where strong signals are present. If the desired signal is near the noise, a signal at an image frequency could easily be 100 dB stronger, and thus to avoid interference, an image rejection of 110 dB would be needed. While some receivers meet that target, the receiver sections of most current amateur transceivers are in the 70 to 100 dB range.

IF IMAGE RESPONSE

As noted earlier, a superhet with a single local oscillator or LO and specified IF can receive two frequencies, selected by the tuning of the RF stage. For example, using a receiver with an IF of 455 kHz to listen to a desired signal at 7000 kHz can use an LO of 7455 kHz. However, the receiver will also receive a signal at 455 kHz above the LO frequency, or 7910 kHz. This undesired signal frequency, located at twice the IF frequency from the desired signal, is called an *image*.

Images will be separated from the desired frequency by twice the IF and the filter ahead of the associated mixer must reduce the image signal by the amount of the required *image rejection*. For a given IF, this gets more difficult as the received frequency is increased. For example, with a 455 kHz single conversion system tuned to 1 MHz, the image will be at 1.91 MHz, almost a 2:1 frequency ratio and relatively easy to reject with a filter. The same receiver tuned to 30 MHz, would have an image at 30.91 MHz, a much more difficult filtering problem

While an image that falls on an occupied channel is obviously a problem — it's rarely desirable to receive two signals at the same time — problems occur even if the image frequency is clear of signals. This is because the atmospheric noise in the image bandwidth is added to the noise of the desired channel, as well as any internally-generated noise in the RF amplifier stage. If the image response is at the same level as the desired signal response, there will be a 3 dB reduction in SNR.

REDUCING IMAGES BY INCREASING IF

An obvious solution to the RF image response is to raise the IF frequency high enough so that signals at twice the IF frequency from the desired signal are sufficiently attenuated by filters ahead of the mixer. This can easily be done with IF stages operating at 5 to 10% of the highest receiving frequency (1.5 to 3 MHz for a receiver that covers the 3-30 MHz HF band). The concept is used at higher frequencies as well. The FM broad-cast band (150 kHz wide channels over 87.9 to 108 MHz in the US) is generally received on superhet receivers with an IF of 10.7 MHz, which places all image frequencies outside the FM band, eliminating interference from other FM stations.

The use of higher-frequency tuned circuits for IF selectivity works well for the 150 kHz wide FM broadcast channels, but not so well for the relatively narrow channels encountered on HF or lower, or even for many V/UHF narrowband services. Fortunately, there are three solutions that were commonly used to resolve this problem.

The first, *double conversion*, converted the desired signal to a relatively high IF followed by a second conversion to a lower IF to set the selectivity. This was a popular technique in the 1950s. Improvements on the double conversion technique led to *triple conversion* with a very low, highly selective third IF. The *Collins system* of moving a single-range VFO to the second mixer and using switchable crystal oscillators for the first mixer also became popular. The *pre-mixed* arrangement, a third approach to double conversion was a combination of the two, used a single variable oscillator range, as with the Collins, but mixes the VFO and LO before applying them to the first mixer – outside of the signal path.

These methods are obsolete for current receivers but are commonly encountered in vintage equipment. They are discussed in previous editions of the *Handbook*.

HIGH-FREQUENCY CRYSTAL LATTICE FILTERS

Commercial quartz-crystal filters with bandwidths appropriate for CW and SSB became available in the 1970s with center frequencies into the 10 MHz range. This allowed a single-conversion receiver (see Figure 12.2) with an IF in the HF range to provide both high image rejection and needed channel selectivity. This single-conversion architecture remains popular among designers of portable and low-power equipment. Crystal filter design is discussed in the **Analog and Digital Filtering** chapter along with downloadable supplemental information.

As an example **Figure 12.13** shows the IF section of a single-conversion superhet using simple filters centered 1500 kHz. While the filters shown are actually buildable by amateurs at low cost, multiple-section filters with much better performance can be purchased or constructed. Other IF frequencies can be used, depending on crystal or filter availability.

The circuit shown demonstrates the concepts involved and can be reproduced at low cost. Remaining receiver functional blocks such as the AGC circuitry, detectors and BFO, and audio amplifiers and filters can be found elsewhere in the book.

DSP IF FILTERS

Digital signal processing provides a level of filter performance not practical with other technologies. (See the **Analog and Digital Filtering** chapter) While much better than most low frequency IF LC bandwidth filters, the very good crystal or mechanical bandwidth filters in amateur gear are not very close to the rectangular shaped frequency response of an ideal filter, but rather have skirts with a 6 to 60 dB response of perhaps 1.4 to 1. That means if we select an SSB filter with a nominal (6 dB) bandwidth of 2400 Hz, the width at 60 dB down will typically be 2400 × 1.4 or 3360 Hz. Thus a signal in the next channel that is 60 dB stronger than the signal we are trying to copy (as often happens) will have energy just as strong as our desired signal.

DSP filtering approaches the ideal response. **Figure 12.14** shows the ARRL Lab measured response of a DSP bandwidth filter with a 6 dB bandwidth of 2400 Hz. Note how rapidly the skirts drop to the noise level. In addition, while analog filtering generally requires a separate filter assembly for each desired bandwidth, DSP filtering is adjustable — often in steps as narrow as 50 Hz — in both bandwidth and center frequency. In addition to bandwidth filtering, the same DSP can often provide digital noise reduction and digital notch filtering to remove interference from fixed frequency carriers.

UP-CONVERSION AND DOWN-CONVERSION

Current crystal filter technology allows *down-conversion* HF receivers to use an IF in the 4-10 MHz range. With a 10 MHz IF and an LO above the signal frequency, a

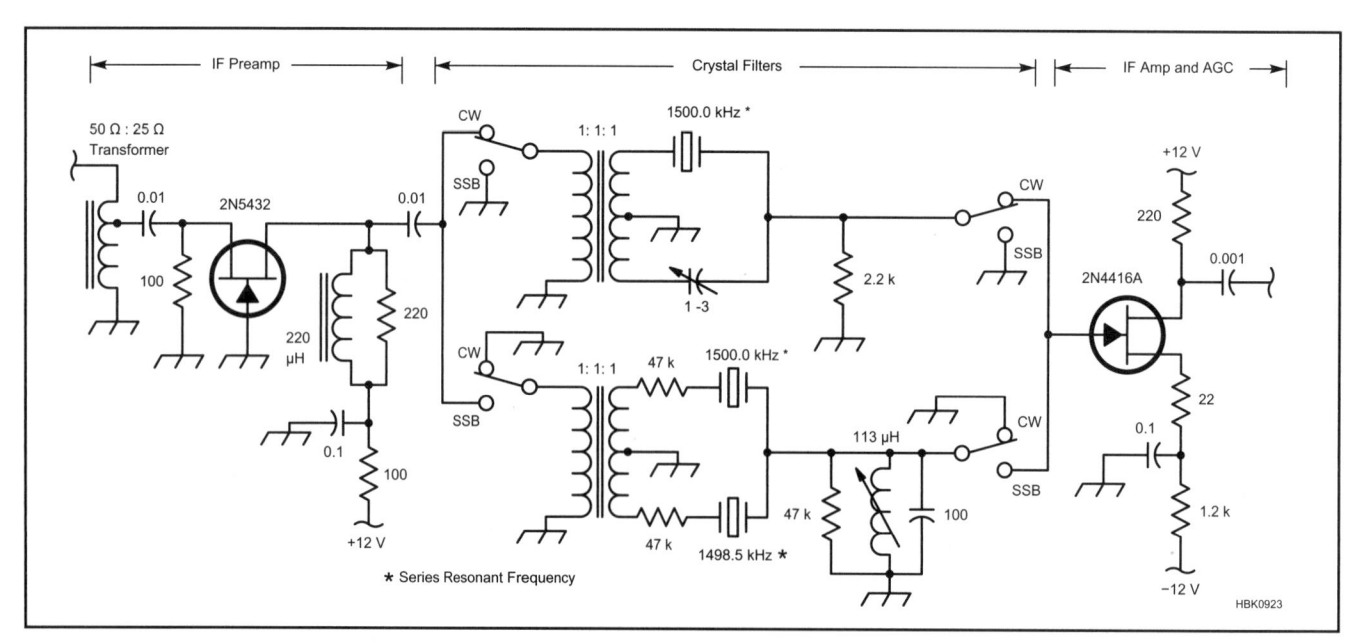

Figure 12.13 — The IF section of a superhet using crystal filters to establish receiver bandwidth.

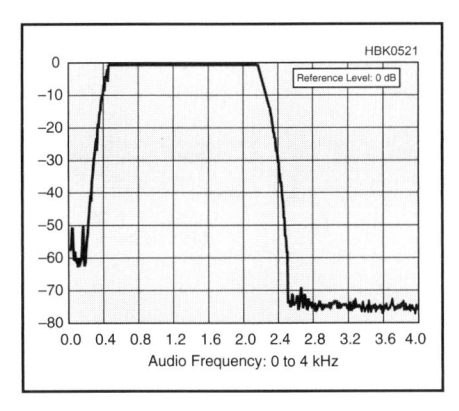

Figure 12.14 — ARRL Lab measured response of an aftermarket 2400 Hz DSP bandpass filter.

30 MHz signal would have an image at 50 MHz. This makes image-rejection filtering relatively straightforward, although many receiver IF frequencies tend to be at the lower end of the above range. Still, as will be discussed in the next section, they have other advantages.

Many current HF receivers (or receiver sections of transceivers) have elected to employ an *up-conversion* architecture. They typically have an IF in the VHF range, perhaps 60 to 70 MHz, making HF image rejection easy. A 30 MHz signal with a 60 MHz IF will have an image at 150 MHz. Not only is it five times the signal frequency, but signals in this range (other than perhaps the occasional taxicab) tend to be weaker than some undesired HF signals. Receivers with this architecture have image responses at the upper end of the above range, often with the image rejected by a relatively simple low-pass filter with a cut off at the top of the receiver range.

Another advantage of this architecture is that the local oscillator can cover a wide continuous range, making it convenient for a general coverage receiver. For example, with a 60 MHz IF, a receiver designed for LF through HF would need an LO covering 60.03 to 90 MHz, a 1.5 to 1 range, easily provided by a number of synthesizer technologies, as described in the **Oscillators and Synthesizers** chapter. The article "A High Performance 45 MHz IF Amplifier" by Colin Horrabin, G3SBI, has been included in the downloadable supplemental information as an example of circuits suitable for up-conversion receivers.

The typical up-converting receiver uses multiple conversions to move signals to frequencies at which operating bandwidth can be established. While crystal filters in the VHF range used by receivers with upconverting IFs have become available with bandwidths as narrow as around 3 kHz, they do not yet achieve the shape factor of similar bandwidth filters at MF and HF. Thus, these are commonly used as *roofing filters*, discussed in the next section, prior to a conversion to one or more lower IF frequencies at which the operating bandwidth is established. **Figure 12.15** is a block diagram of a typical upconverting receiver using DSP for setting the operating bandwidth.

THE IMAGE-REJECTING MIXER

Another technique for reduction of image response in receivers is not as commonly encountered in HF receivers as the preceding designs, but it deserves mention because it has some very significant applications. The *image-rejecting* mixer requires phase-shift networks, as shown in **Figure 12.16**. Frequency F_1 represents the input frequency while F_2 is that of the local oscillator. Note that the two 90° phase shifts are applied at different frequencies. The phase shift network following Mixer 1 is at a fixed center frequency corresponding to the IF, while the phase shift network at F_2 must provide the required phase shift as the local oscillator tunes across the band.

If the local oscillator is required to tune over a limited fractional frequency range, this is a very feasible approach. On the other hand, maintaining a 90° phase shift over a wide range can be tricky. The good news is that this approach provides image reduction that is independent of, and in addition to, any other mechanisms such as filters that are employed toward that end.

Additionally, with the ability of DSP components to operate at higher and higher frequencies, the necessary operations seen in Figure 12.16 can be performed in software which does not depend on precision hardware design to maintain nearly exact phase relationships.

The image-rejecting mixing process has several attractive features:

• It is the only way to provide "single signal" reception with a direct conversion receiver, effectively reducing the audio image. This can make the DC receiver a very good performer, although the added complexity is not always warranted in typical amateur DC applications.

• This option is frequently found in microwave receivers in which sufficiently selective RF filtering can be difficult to obtain. Since

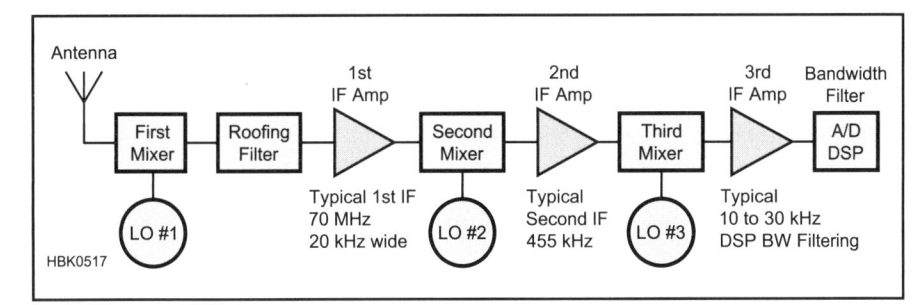

Figure 12.15 — Block diagram of a typical upconverting receiver using DSP for the 3rd IF filter which sets operating bandwidth. Hybrid heterodyne/SDR receivers applying DSP filters at IF frequencies are common.

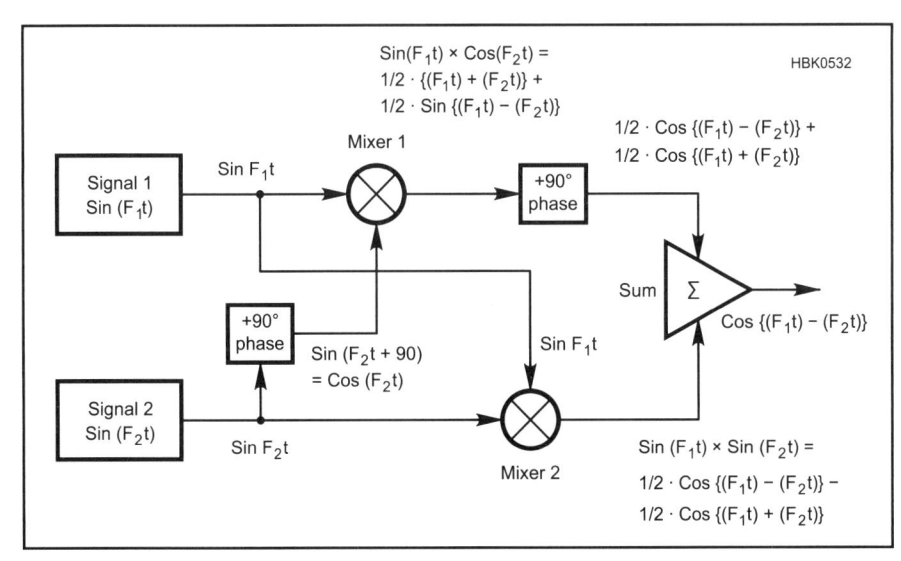

Figure 12.16 — Image rejecting mixer, block diagram, and signal relationships.

they often operate on fixed frequencies, maintaining the required phase shift can be straightforward.

• It is found in advanced receivers that are trying to achieve optimum performance. Even with a high first IF frequency, additional image rejection can be provided.

• In transmitters, the same system is called the *phasing method* of SSB generation. The same blocks run "backwards" — one of the phase shift networks can be applied to the speech band and used to cancel one sideband. This is discussed in the **Transmitting** chapter.

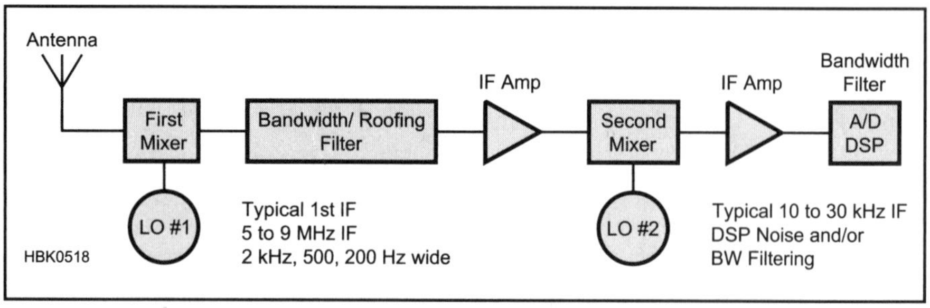

Figure 12.17 — Block diagram of a down-converting amateur band receiver with "roofing" and operating bandwidth filters to improve performance in the presence of strong in-band signals.

12.2.6 Preselectors

Placing a filter at the receiver's antenna input, called a *preselector*, is a technique that improves both image rejection and overload from out-of-band signals. You can see such a filter at the front-end of several of the receiver block diagrams in this chapter. Preselection to avoid overload is often required with the inexpensive USB "dongle" style SDR receivers that are designed for DTV reception and not for strong-signal performance.

There are three types of preselectors:

• Manually-tuned — a tuned circuit or tuned input transformer that is adjusted by the operator for maximum signal level. The tuned circuit usually has several ranges that are selected by the receiver band switch. These were once common, especially on general-coverage receivers. Preselectors were also very popular in European equipment where extremely strong signals from high-power shortwave broadcast (SWBC) stations often caused receiver overload unless attenuated with a filter.

• Switched band-pass — a bank of band-pass filters selected by the band switch or under control of the receiver's controlling microprocessor. Most of the top-performing receivers feature switched band-pass preselectors that do not require manual adjustment.

• Tracking — a continuously-variable tuned circuit or band-pass filter that is controlled by software to have peak response at the frequency of operation. This feature is relatively expensive to implement so it is only available on high-end receivers.

The downloadable supplemental content includes a pair of preselector designs. The manual general-coverage preselector from *Ham Radio* magazine is by George Hirshfield, W5OZF, covers from 0.5 to 30 MHz with a tuning capacitor augmented by fixed capacitors and tapped inductors. A software-controlled switched band-pass preselector covering 1.8 to 30 MHz from *QEX* is included as a project. Designed by Juan Onate, MØWWA and Xavier de Fortuny, the preselector includes a number of auxiliary features (input protection, attenuators, LNA, and so on) and is controlled by a PIC microcontroller. All software is available from the ARRL as described in the article.

12.2.7 Superhet Design for Dynamic Range

In the past, the receivers with the best close-in third order intermodulation distortion and maximum blocking dynamic range were amateur-band-only receivers, such as the primary receiver in the TEN-TEC Orion and Omni series, and the receivers in the Elecraft K2 and K3. A look at a typical block diagram, as shown in **Figure 12.17**, makes it easy to see why. The problems resulting from strong unwanted signals near a desired one are minimized if the unwanted signals are kept out of the places in the receiver where they can be amplified even more and cause the nonlinear effects that we try to avoid.

Note that in Figure 12.17, the only place where the desired and undesired signals all coexist is before the first mixer. If the first mixer and any RF preamp stages have sufficient strong-signal handling capability, the undesired signals will be eliminated in the filter immediately behind the first mixer. This HF crystal filter is generally switchable to support desired bandwidths as narrow as 200 Hz. The later amplifier, mixer and DSP circuits only have to deal with the signal we want. For additional discussion of these issues, see "International Radio Roofing Filters for the Yaesu FT-1000 MP Series Transceivers," by Joel Hallas, W1ZR, in *QST* Product Review for February 2005.

Now look at a typical modern general-coverage receiver as shown previously in Figure 12.15. In this arrangement, a single digital synthesizer, perhaps covering from 70 to 100 MHz, shifts the incoming signal(s) to a VHF IF, often near 70 MHz. A roofing filter at 70 MHz follows the first mixer. This arrangement offers simplified local oscillator (LO) design and the possibility of excellent image rejection. Unfortunately, crystal filter technology has only recently been able to produce narrow filters for 70 MHz, and so far they have much wider skirts than the crystal filters used in Figure 12.17. As technology is rapidly shifting to SDR designs, the current models are likely exhibiting the peak performance level for upconverting receivers.

Many receivers and transceivers set the roofing filter bandwidth wider than any operating bandwidth and use DSP filtering much later in the signal chain to set the final operating bandwidth. For a receiver that will receive FM and AM, as well as SSB and CW, that usually means a roofing filter with a bandwidth of around 20 kHz. With this arrangement, all signals in that 20 kHz bandwidth pass all the way through IF amplifiers and mixers and into the A/D converter before we attempt to eliminate them using DSP filters. By that time they have had an opportunity to generate intermodulation products and cause the blocking and IMD problems that we are trying to eliminate. However, top of the line heterodyne radios feature both general coverage at HF and VHF roofing filters, such as the Icom IC-7851 and Yaesu FTdx9000 transceivers. (See the Transceiver Survey by W1ZR in the *Handbook's* downloadable supplemental material for more information on the latest models.)

A hybrid architecture was implemented in the TEN-TEC Omni VII transceiver that effectively combines the two technologies. The first IF has a 20 kHz wide roofing filter at 70 MHz, followed by selectable steep skirted 455 kHz Collins mechanical filters at the second IF and then DSP filters at the third IF. This transceiver is no longer in production but offered excellent performance at the time of its introduction.

Careful attention to gain distribution among the stages between the filters maintains desired sensitivity, but not so high that the undesired products have a chance to become a serious problem. With bandwidths of 20, 6 and 2.5 kHz supplied, and 500 and 300 Hz as accessories, the undesired close-in signals are eliminated before they have an opportunity to cause serious trouble in the DSP stages that follow.

Another variation is found in the Kenwood TS-590S and SG models which switch between down-conversion on the more crowded "contest bands" (160, 80, 40, 20 and 15 meters) and up-conversion on the remaining bands. In effect, this trades sensitivity for dynamic range.

12.3 SDR Receivers

The SDR was introduced in the **DSP and SDR Fundamentals** chapter. Repeated here are the sections of that chapter describing SDR architecture and performance issues. This section presents and compares several block-diagram-level concepts for software-defined radio. For the basic elements of SDR and DSP, see the chapter referenced above.

12.3.1 Digitizing at IF

The first generation of radios to make use of DSP techniques at RF performed the analog-digital conversion on an IF signal. **Figure 12.18** shows such a design. In such a receiver, placing the A/D converter after a crystal IF filter improves the blocking dynamic range (BDR) for interfering signals that fall outside the crystal filter bandwidth. As shown, the down-conversion to I/Q format still uses lower-speed A/D converters, but often the signal is actually at a low IF, say, 15 kHz or so. This allows an SSB-bandwidth signal to be contained within the 20 kHz bandwidth of a typical audio codec and avoids errors due to dc offsets in the signal path. With careful design, a receiver with such an architecture can achieve 140 dB or more of BDR (if there are no other limiting factors such as LO phase noise). The third-order dynamic range is similar to that achieved with a conventional analog architecture since the circuitry up to the crystal filter, including amplifiers and mixer(s) is the same.

Another advantage of the IF-based approach compared to directly sampling the RF frequency is that the ADC does not have to run at such a high sample rate. In fact, because the crystal filter acts as a high-performance, narrow-bandwidth anti-aliasing filter, *undersampling* is possible if the A/D converter has sufficient sampling bandwidth (ADCs intended for audio applications generally do not). With bandwidths of a few kHz or less, sample rates in the tens of kHz can be used even though the center frequency of the IF signal is much higher, so long as the ADC's sample-and-hold circuit has sufficient bandwidth.

12.3.2 Direct RF Digitizing

The ultimate SDR architecture is to convert between the analog and digital domains right at the frequency to be transmitted or received, or convert a wide range of frequencies and do all filtering in the digital domain. The receive path of such a design is shown in **Figure 12.19**. In this receiver, the only remaining analog components in the signal chain are a wide-band anti-aliasing filter and an amplifier to improve the noise figure of the ADC if necessary. A preselector stage may be used to prevent overload from strong signals far from the selected frequency or frequency band. The local oscillator, mixer, IF filters, AGC, demodulators and other circuitry are all replaced by digital hardware and software. The digital/software implementations of these functions are perfectly stable with time, temperature, and need no adjustments.

It has only been recently that low-cost high-speed ADCs have become available with specifications good enough to allow reasonable performance in an RF-sampling communications receiver. Today it is possible

Sampling Rates

Digital audio equipment, that is audio equipment that uses digital sampling at some point in the device, has been around since the 1970s. There are two primary fundamental sampling rates that are used in all digital audio equipment: 44.1 ksps and 48 ksps. From these two rates, all other rates are derived by using factors of these two numbers. In amateur radio, the latter number, 48 kHz, is most often used and is why all our signal chains typically operate at a multiple or sub-multiple of these numbers. The most common processing speeds are 24 ksps, 36 ksps, 48 ksps, 96 ksps and 192 ksps. 48 ksps is by far the most common, but it varies by the manufacturer and radio design.

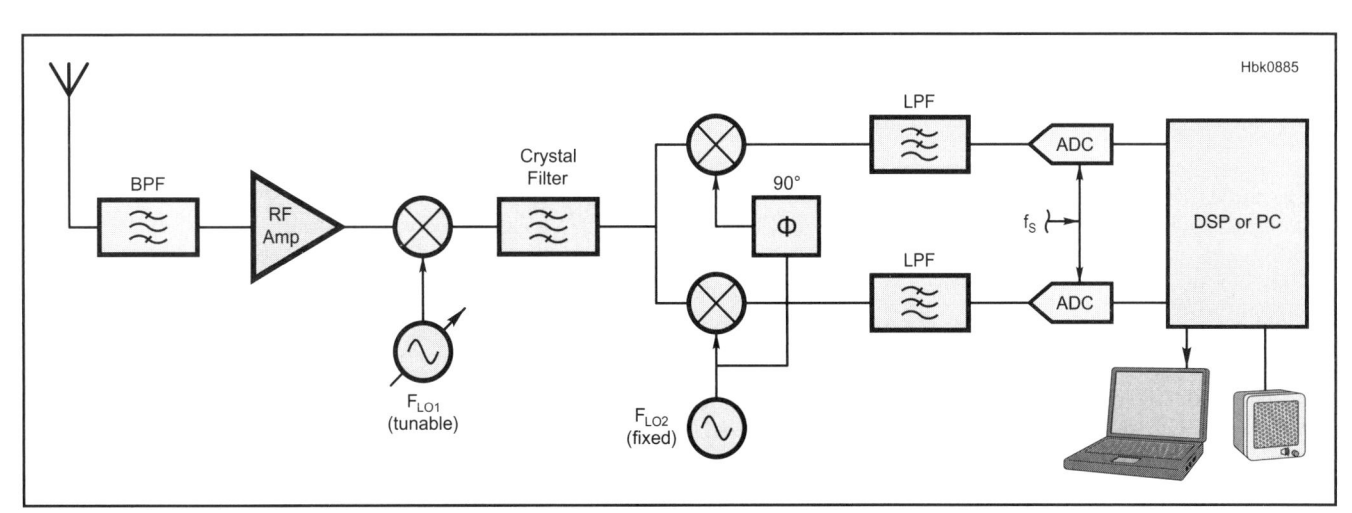

Figure 12.18 — Hybrid superhet/DSP SDR receiver architecture.

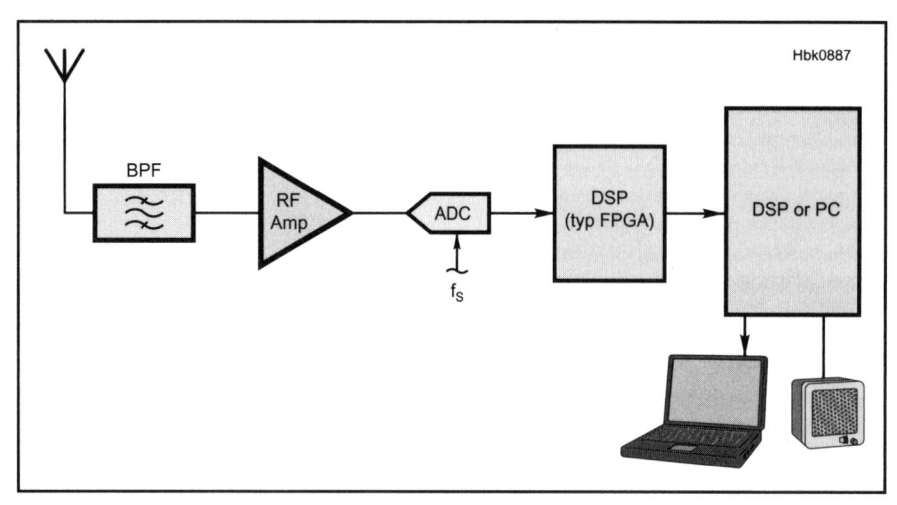

Figure 12.19 — Direct RF-sampling DSP SDR receiver architecture.

to achieve blocking dynamic range of 130 dB. That is not quite as good as the best analog or hybrid radios, but with every new generation of A/D converter that becomes available for use in SDR, the performance gap becomes narrower.

It is worth noting here that while huge BDR numbers can be measured in the laboratory, the performance achieved in a real-world environment with a receiver connected to an antenna is quite different. Often local noise sources raise the noise floor such that the receiver's full BDR cannot be utilized and other specifications become more important. In many of these specifications (dynamic range for close-spaced signals, etc.), RF-sampling SDRs can provide performance comparable or superior to conventional all-analog and IF-sampling receivers.

Third-order dynamic range (3IMD_DR) is not a meaningful specification for this type of radio because it is based on the behavior of analog circuits. In addition, calculation of IP_3 assumes that distortion products increase 3 dB for each 1 dB increase in signal level, which is not always true for an ADC. The level of the distortion products in an ADC tends to be more-or-less independent of signal level until the signal peak exceeds the ADC's full scale input, at which point the distortion increases dramatically. It is important to read the data sheet carefully and note the test conditions for the distortion measurements.

There are definite advantages to sampling at RF. For one thing, it saves a lot of analog circuitry. Even though a high-speed ADC is more expensive than an audio converter, the radio may be end up being cheaper to build because of the reduced component count and fewer adjustments. Performance is improved in some areas. For example, image rejection is no longer a worry, as long as the anti-aliasing filter is doing its job. (As well as any preselector filters that may be present.) The dynamic range of an SDR theoretically does not depend on signal spacing — close-in dynamic range is often better than with a conventional architecture that uses a wide IF filter. With no crystal filters in the signal chain, the entire system has a completely linear phase response, which can improve the quality of both analog and digital signals after demodulation.

The biggest challenge with RF sampling is what to do with the torrent of high-speed data coming out of the receiver's ADC. To cover 0-54 MHz without aliasing requires a sample rate of at least 120 or 130 MHz, and commercial products typically operate the ADC at sample rates well over 200 MHz. That is much faster than a typical microprocessor or programmable DSP can handle. The local oscillator, mixer, and decimator or interpolator must be implemented in digital hardware so that the DSP can send and receive data at a more-reasonable sample rate. *Digital downconverters* (DDC) perform those functions and output a lower-sample-rate digital I/Q signal to the DSP. Stand-alone DDC ICs were available in the past, but the function is now usually integrated with the A/D converter. It is also possible to implement a DDC in a *field-programmable gate array* or FPGA. (See the "Hands-On SDR" *QEX* columns provided in the downloadable supplemental information.) *Digital upconverters* (DUC) do the same conversion in reverse for the transmitter and are available integrated with the D/A converter or can be implemented in an FPGA. Some commercial integrated DDC/DAC products even include the capability to encode several digital modulation formats such as GMSK, QPSK and π/4 DQPSK. In an attempt to simplify the interface to the digital domain, many high-speed converters now use a standardized serial interface specification called JESD204B, capable of handling up to 12 Gb/s. Code to implement this interface on the digital FPGA is readily available.

Some designers have been successful in repurposing a graphics processor (GPU) for this purpose, and some GPU manufacturers now offer FFT libraries to assist in the design process.

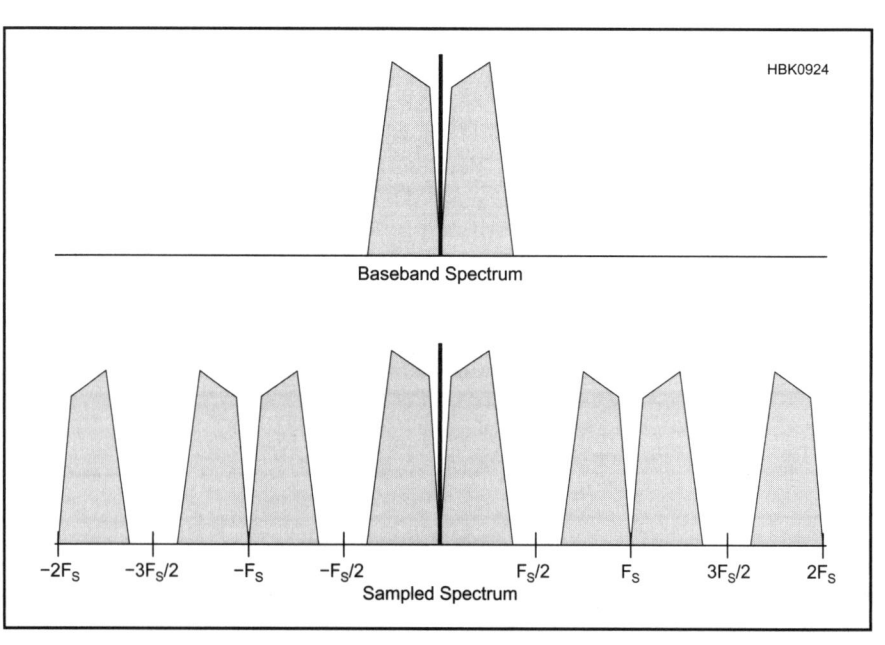

Figure 12.20 — The baseband spectrum of an analog signal before sampling is given at A, showing both positive and negative frequencies. Part B shows the spectrum of the baseband signal after it is sampled by an ideal sampling waveform. Note that there is an upper and lower sideband version of the baseband for each harmonic of the sampling frequency, just as if it were a double sideband suppressed carrier signal.)

12.3.3 Sample-Rate Down-Conversion

SDR receivers generally do not use analog mixers to convert RF frequencies to an IF or to baseband. Down-conversion is achieved by the process of *decimation* as described in the **DSP and SDR Fundamentals** chapter. It describes how the frequency of a sampled signal can be divided by N by removing every Nth sample from the digital signal data. This actually creates an alias of the original signal as if it had been sampled at a rate lower than the Nyquist rate. As shown in **Figure 12.20**, this process creates a replica of the original signal or original spectrum at harmonics of the sampling rate. One of the replica spectra can then be selected with a filter and operated on just as if it had been processed by an analog mixer.

This is one example *multirate signal processing* which is not nearly as complicated as it sounds. The topic we are interested in now is sample-rate down conversion (decimation). (*Sample-rate up conversion* is another multirate signal processing technique that performs frequency multiplication in much the same way as down-conversion performs frequency division.)

If we want to receive directly at the 40 meter band for instance, we would need to sample above 14.6 MHz in order to satisfy the Nyquist criterion. We do not need a sample rate that fast to actually manipulate the information on receive, though, since the bandwidth of the widest signal will be on the order of 7 kHz or less. Even if we want to look at the entire band and generate a spectrum display, we only need about 650 kHz for the sample rate since the band is only 300 kHz wide. Any higher sample rate on receive is a waste of processor resources.

There are two main reasons why we would want to match the sample rate closely to our intended bandwidth. The first reason to lower the sample rate is that the transition band and ripple of our filters are dependent on the ratio of the filter length (the number of taps) to the sample rate. The second reason is to allow more CPU cycles for processing each sample.

An AM radio is a good example for sample rate conversion. Let's say we want to receive an band of signals through a tuned-circuit input filter with a bandwidth of 80 kHz centered at 590 kHz. If we undersample the input at a rate of 100 kHz, we create a range of signals centered at 90 kHz so that the energy is all within the range of dc to 125 kHz. This is *low-pass filter decimating*. (See the *QEX SDR: Simplified* column for July/August 2009 for a more complete discussion of this process.)

The first step in the decimation process is to filter the input signal so that there is no energy above one fourth the sample frequency. A DSP low-pass filter with cutoff at one fourth of the sample frequency has a very easy set of coefficients and can be implemented with a small number of taps. We sampled our AM radio at 500 kHz, so we need 125 kHz cutoff for the low pass filter. We now have a signal that has no energy above 125 kHz and is sampled at 500 kHz. We can throw away every other sample at this point to create a signal that is sampled at 250 kHz, with energy up to 125 kHz. The Nyquist criterion is satisfied with this new signal. **Figure 12.21** shows the spectrum of the process.

The signal at 90 kHz is only about 40 kHz wide (70 kHz to 110 kHz), so it would be nice if we could drop the sample frequency even further. It turns out that our signal will fit into the band from dc to 62.5 kHz if it were translated down in frequency. That would only require a 125 kHz sample rate. This is *integer band-pass decimating*. If we throw

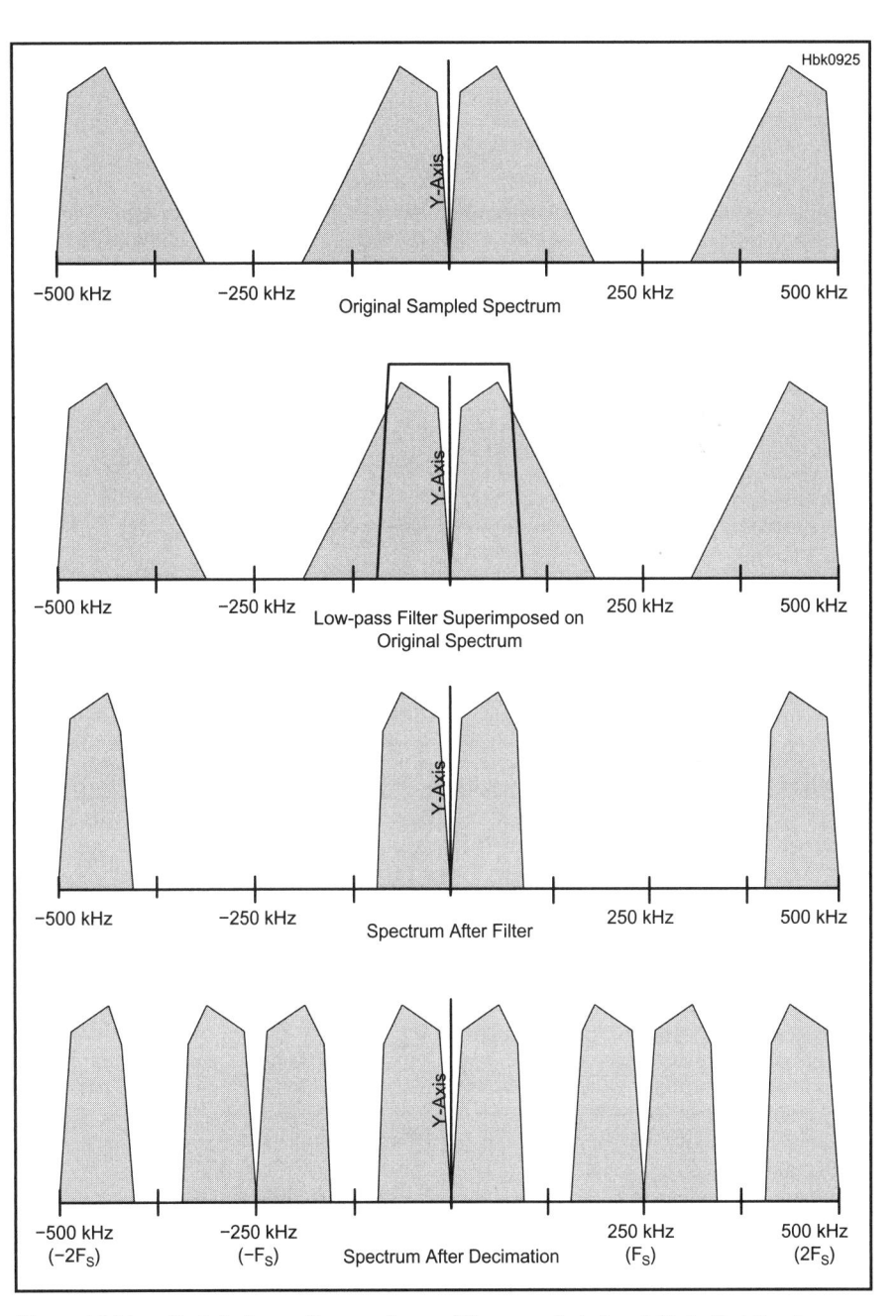

Figure 12.21 — Part A shows the spectrum of the sampled signal. Note that the frequency only extends from −500 kHz to +500 kHz since that is the extent that the math will manage. Part B shows the digital low-pass filter response superimposed on the sampled spectrum. The spectrum of the filtered signal, which is still sampled at 500 kHz, is shown at C. Part D shows the spectrum of the resulting sampled waveform after decimation by 2 (every other sample discarded). This is the spectrum of the signal when it is sampled at 250 kHz.)

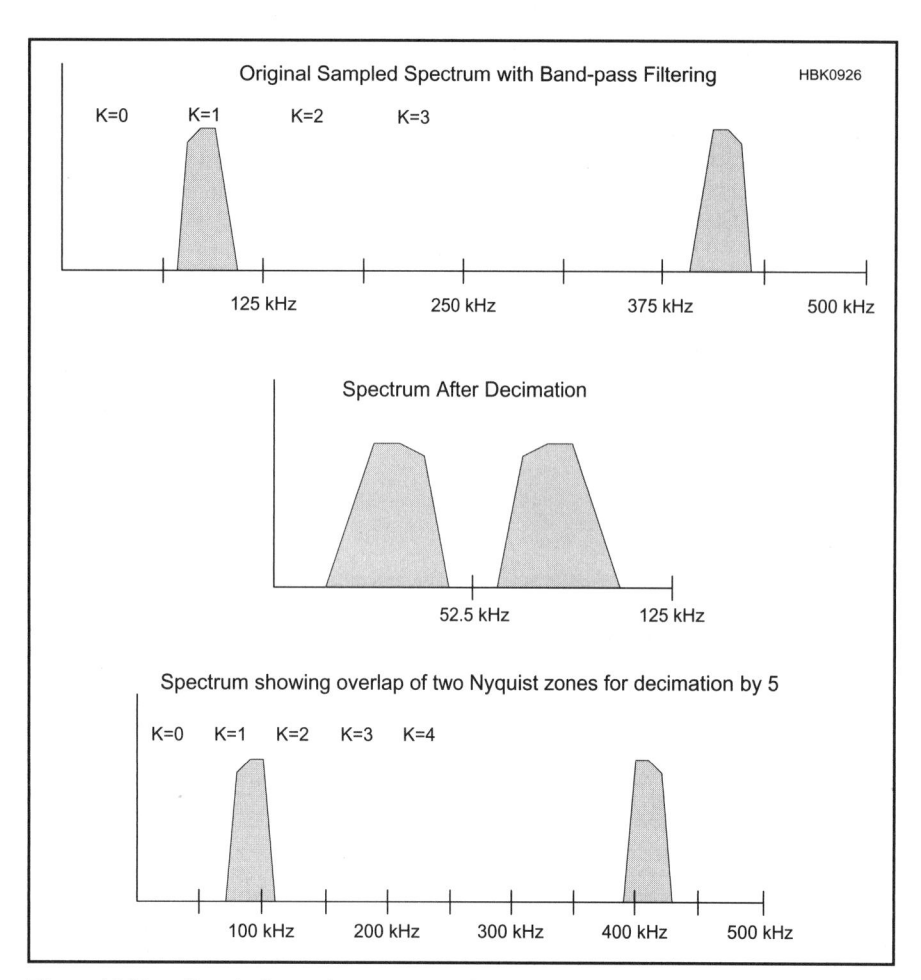

Figure 12.22 — Part A shows the spectrum of a 90 kHz signal that was band-pass filtered and then sampled at 500 kHz (only one-half of the spectrum is shown for clarity). The resulting spectrum when the signal is decimated by 4 (3 of every 4 samples discarded) is shown in Part B. Notice that this causes the signal to be aliased and the signal in the first Nyquist zone (k =0) has its frequencies inverted just as a lower sideband signal is inverted. The signal is now sampled at 125 kHz. The initial sampled signal, showing the Nyquist zones that would occur if a decimation by 5 were attempted, is shown at C. Note that input energy exists in both the second and third Nyquist zones.

away every 3 samples of the original data, we can accomplish both frequency translation and sample rate reduction. The energy now spans from 15 kHz to 55 kHz. The signal spectrum is also inverted. In a superhet AM radio, you would need to band-pass filtered the signal before sampling. It is possible to do the band pass filtering digitally with a small number of taps, and then do the decimation.

We succeeded in reducing the sample rate by a factor of 4. We cannot further reduce the sample rate using straight decimation. Each integer sample rate reduction requires that the band limited data fit completely within one of the Nyquist regions for the new sample rates. The next integer sample rate would reduce the sample rate by 5. The new sample rate would be 100 kHz. The data is contained in both the k = 1 (50 kHz to 100 kHz) and k = 2 (100 kHz to 150 kHz) Nyquist bands. **Figure 12.22** shows the overlap. The overlap into the third Nyquist zone prevents further rate reduction. The requirement that all of the energy fits into one Nyquist zone limits the usefulness of this technique.

Integer sample rate reduction is a very useful tool because the filters are easily realized in hardware such as a field programmable gate array (FPGA) or other dedicated hardware.

12.3.4 Decimation and Dynamic Range

When we talk about dynamic range, we are discussing the range of largest to smallest signals that can represented simultaneously. What does dynamic range buy us? Having a high dynamic range allows us to represent or hear weak signals in the presence of large signals. With a lower dynamic range, our receiver may overload in the presence of a large signal or we may be forced to shift what dynamic range we have to accommodate the large signals. For example, if we only had 80 dB of dynamic range in our receiver with the weakest signal possible of –120 dBm and the largest of –40 dBm, this means the strongest signal we can hear is S9+33 dB (–50 dBm). If an S9+50 dB (–23 dBm) signal is present in our receiver, we would overload.

To allow the reception of large and small signal, receivers can implement automatic gain control (AGC) in the RF section. The AGC will add attenuation to the receiver, shifting the available dynamic range up. For example, it the AGC adds 20 dB of attenuation, we can now hear signals from –100 dBm to –20 dBm. Note that we have just reduced the sensitivity of our receiver by 20 dB and if we were trying to listen to a weak CW signal with a power of –110 dBm, we will now be unable to hear it. RF AGC is necessary in some receivers where the instantaneous dynamic range is not sufficient to handle both very strong and very weak signals simultaneously. This should not be confused with audio-derived AGC which is discussed in the section on AGC below.

A common question about direct sampling receivers centers around available dynamic range. We are taught that for each bit in an ADC, we can have 6 dB of dynamic range. Often, someone will attempt to look at wideband sampled converter (ADC), multiply the bits by 6 dB and state that this is the available dynamic range for narrowband operation. As it turns out, this is an incorrect if not uncommon error. In a wideband sampled system where the receiver outputs are narrowband, we use a process called decimation to reduce the bandwidth for our narrowband receiver and increase dynamic range. How does this work?

Decimation is a two-step process: we first apply a digital filter to the samples and then we discard a portion of the samples. In decimation by two, we apply a filter to cut the RF bandwidth in half and then we discard one half of the samples. In doing so, the digital filter combines multiple samples to produce the output sample stream and in this combination, we pick up additional bits of resolution in the output samples. This increase in dynamic range is called *processing gain*. Specifically, in decimation by two we typically pickup about ½-bit of resolution for each decimation by two. Imagining for a moment a sampled system with 16-bits of resolution at 196.608 Msps, if we decimate down to 48 ksps, this represents twelve decimate-by-two operations. This means that we pick up about six bits per sample, increasing our dynamic range by about 36 dB. As a practical matter, the dynamic range of an ADC depends not only on the number of samples in the output, but also the level of the spurs. ADC manufacturers consider any level below the spurs to be tarnished by the spurs and therefore not included in the specified dynamic range. As a first order approximation for the dynamic range that can be achieved, we can take the dynamic range specified by the ADC manufacturer and add the processing gain that we've computed.

Finally, in Amateur Radio we generally talk about dynamic range in terms of a 500 Hz bandwidth. So for the purposes of dynamic range in the amateur world, we don't use the entire 48 ksps bandwidth, we look just at the 500 Hz bandwidth as if we had a 500 Hz filter. To determine the total processing gain we would achieve through decimation and filtering, we use can use the formula $3\log_2$(sampling rate/final bandwidth) to get an approximation of the processing gain from our original sampling rate to a 500 Hz bandwidth receiver. Using a logarithmic identity, it may be easier to compute on a calculator as $3\log_{10}$(sampling rate/final bandwidth)/$\log_{10}(2)$.

12.3.5 Phase Noise in Sampled Systems

Just like with mixers, analog to digital converters that sample signals and produce a digital output are also susceptible to phase noise. Many of today's older transceivers use superheterodyne receivers which use mixers and terminate in an ADC operating at baseband. For receiver systems where the ADC is operating in the tens to hundreds of ksps, phase noise introduced by the ADC is rarely an issue. Since good phase noise is easily achievable in this frequency range, most designers ensure that phase noise will not impact the design in the ADC. It's much more likely in such a radio that the LO feeding the mixers nearer the antenna would be at fault. With today's technology, the high we go in oscillator frequency, the more difficult it is to design a low phase noise oscillator.

In an RF sampled system where the ADC is placed either right on the antenna or just behind an amplifier and/or preselectors, we will be sampling at a significantly higher frequency. Because of the Nyquist sampling theorem, if we want to design an HF through 6 meter receiver, we must sample at least 2x the highest frequency, 54 MHz. This means we will be sampling above 108 MHz, with 122.88 MHz being a common frequency because it divides evenly down to standard audio sampling rates (see the sidebar on sampling rates). In these systems, the local oscillator may be called a clock oscillator and phase noise may be referred to as jitter. While phase noise and jitter are roughly interchangeable, jitter benefits the digital designer's view of the world and discusses a time-domain effect while phase noise benefits the RF designer and discusses a frequency domain effect. Most ADCs that will be used for RF will specify both. In case you're wondering, there is no absolute conversion from jitter directly to phase noise, but there are estimates that make assumptions about the characteristics of the oscillator.

Unlike the superheterodyne system, phase noise in a direct sampling receiver is imparted on the signal during the sampling process at the sampling frequency. What does this mean? While a superheterodyne system may rely on the division of the clock to produce an excellent phase noise signal on the band of interest, signals in a direct sampling system inherit the phase noise of the ADC clock at the sampling frequency. So if our phase noise is –110 dBc/Hz at 10 kHz for a 122.88 MHz clock, this is the phase noise we will have on all sampled frequencies. This makes clock (or LO) selection for the direct sampling receiver all the more important. We must ensure that the oscillator's phase noise characteristics will not be an issue at any frequency of interest.

More detailed discussions about the effects of phase noise in direct-sampled receivers can be found in Analog Devices application notes AN-741 and AN-756. (See the reference section.)

12.4 Mixing and Mixers

This section examines mixers which are used for frequency shifting or conversion in heterodyne receivers and transmitters. Mixers are often used as modulators and demodulators because they translate information to an RF signal and back again. These translation processes can be thought of as forms of frequency translation or frequency shifting — the function traditionally ascribed to mixers. We'll therefore begin our investigation by examining what a mixer is (and isn't), and what a mixer does.

MULTIPLYING VERSUS ADDING

Mixer is the term for a circuit that shifts one signal's frequency up or down by combining it with another signal. The word *mixer* is also the name of a device used to blend multiple audio inputs together for recording, broadcast or sound reinforcement. A radio mixer makes new frequencies from its input signals and an audio mixer does not. In their most basic, ideal forms, both devices have two inputs and one output.

The audio mixer is a *combiner* that simply *adds* the instantaneous voltages of the two signals together to produce the output at each point in time (**Figure 12.23**). The radio mixer, on the other hand, *multiplies* the instantaneous voltages of the two signals together to produce its output signal from instant to instant (**Figure 12.24**). Comparing the output spectra of the combiner and mixer, we see that the combiner's output contains only the frequencies of the two inputs, and nothing else, while the mixer's output contains *new* frequencies. The process is called *heterodyning* as used in the heterodyne receivers described in the preceding sections. The sidebar, "Mixer Math: Mixing as Multiplication," describes this process mathematically. Use of the word "mixer" in this book should be assumed to mean the radio mixer.

The key principle of a radio mixer is that in mixing multiple signal voltages together, *it adds and subtracts their frequencies to produce new frequencies*. (In the field of signal processing, this process, *multiplication in the time domain,* is recognized as equivalent to the process of *convolution in the frequency domain*. Those interested in this alternative approach to describing the generation of new frequencies through mixing can find more information about it in the many textbooks available on this subject.)

The difference between the mixer we've been describing and any mixer, modulator or demodulator that you'll ever use is that it's ideal. We put in two signals and got just two signals out. *Real* mixers, modulators and demodulators, on the other hand, also produce *distortion* products that make their output spectra "dirtier" or "less clean," as well as putting out some energy at input-signal frequencies and their harmonics. Much of the art and science of making good use of multiplication in mixing, modulation and demodulation goes into minimizing these unwanted multiplication products (or their effects) and making multipliers perform frequency translation as efficiently as possible.

12.4.1 Mixers and Distortion

This radio-amateur-oriented discussion of mixers, modulators and demodulators will begin with a look at their common underlying mechanism before discussing practical mixer, modulator and demodulator circuits. This will make it easier to understand the

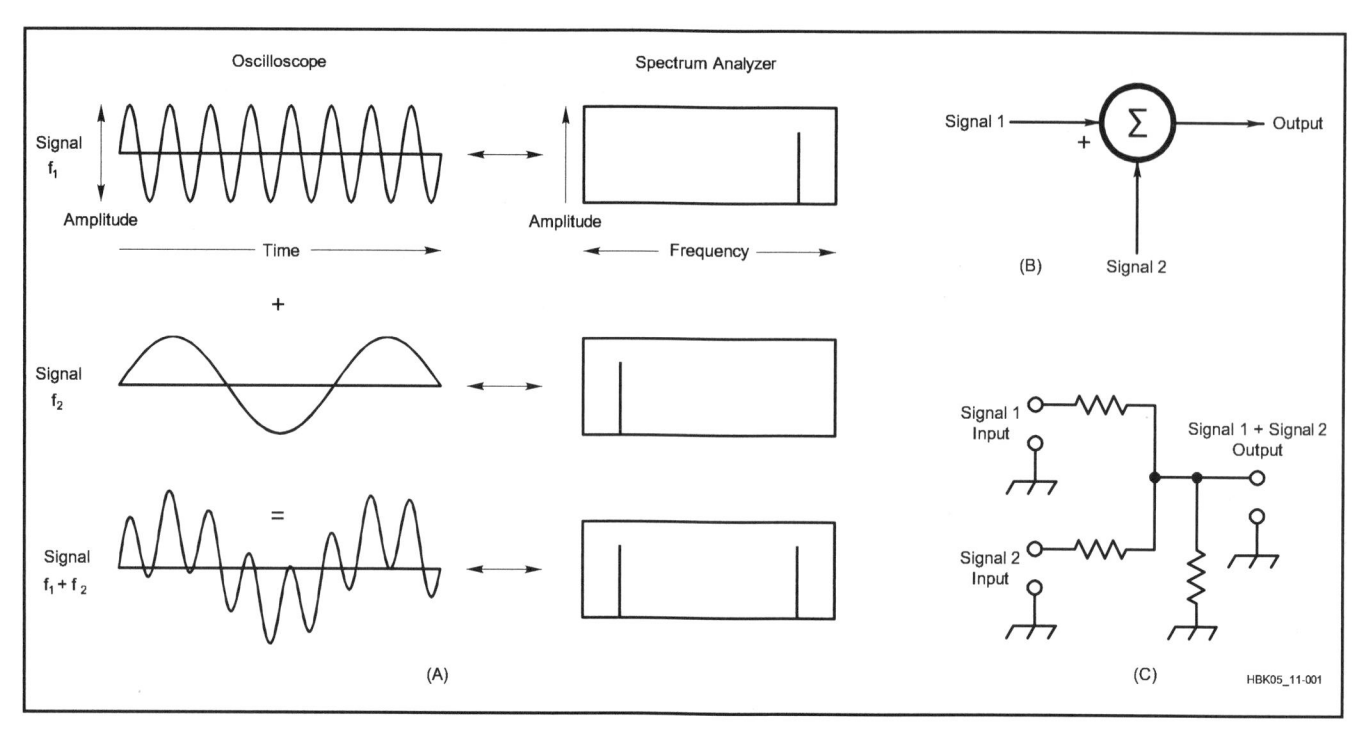

Figure 12.23 — *Adding or summing* two sine waves of different frequencies (f_1 and f_2) combines their amplitudes without affecting their frequencies. Viewed with an *oscilloscope* (a real-time graph of amplitude versus time), adding two signals appears as a simple superimposition of one signal on the other. Viewed with a spectrum analyzer (a real-time graph of signal amplitude versus frequency), adding two signals just sums their spectra. The signals merely coexist on a single cable or wire. All frequencies that go into the adder come out of the adder, and no new signals are generated. Drawing B, a block diagram of a summing circuit, emphasizes the stage's mathematical operation rather than showing circuit components. Drawing C shows a simple summing circuit, such as might be used to combine signals from two microphones. In audio work, a circuit like this is often called a mixer — but it does not perform the same function as an RF mixer.

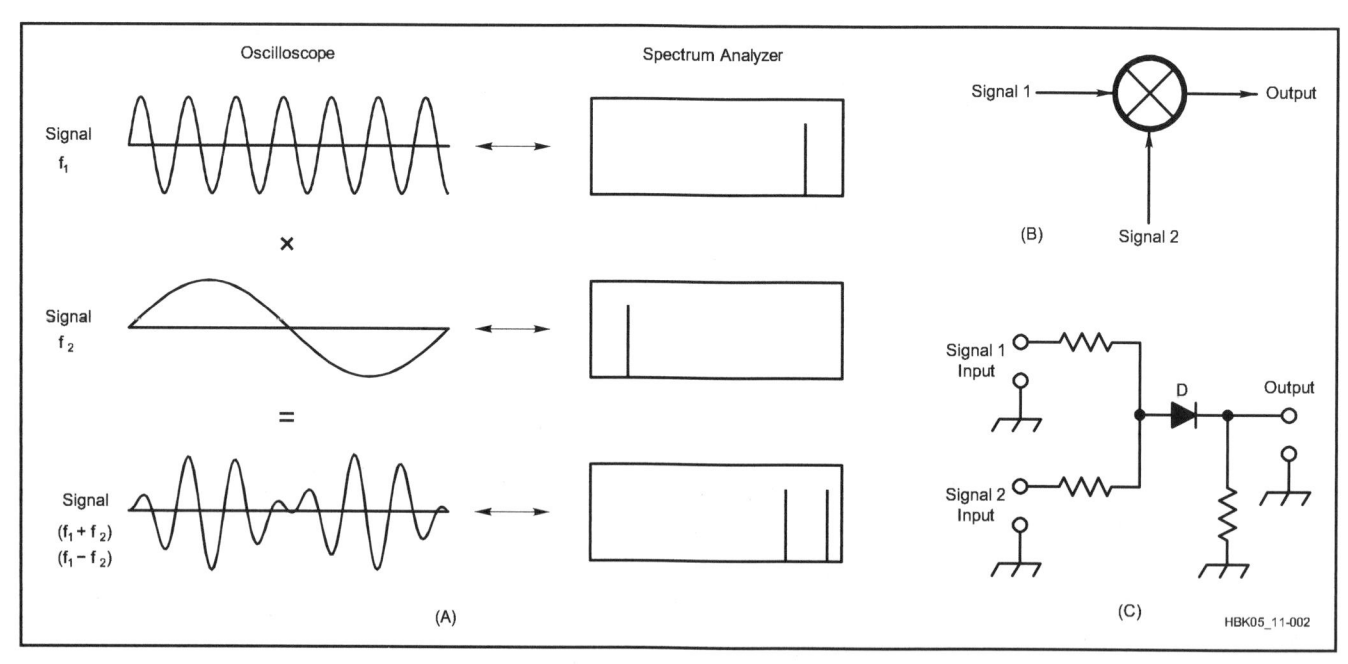

Figure 12.24 — *Multiplying* two sine waves of different frequencies produces a new output spectrum. Viewed with an oscilloscope, the result of multiplying two signals is a composite wave that seems to have little in common with its components. A spectrum-analyzer view of the same wave reveals why: The original signals disappear entirely and are replaced by two new signals — at the *sum* and *difference* of the original signals' frequencies. Drawing B diagrams a multiplier, known in radio work as a mixer. The circled X emphasizes the stage's mathematical operation. (The circled X is only one of several symbols you may see used to represent mixers in block diagrams, as Figure 12.25 explains.) Drawing C shows a very simple multiplier circuit. The diode, D, does the mixing. Because this circuit does other mathematical functions and adds them to the sum and difference products, its output is more complex than $f_1 + f_2$ and $f_1 - f_2$, but these can be extracted from the output by filtering.

Mixer Math: Mixing as Multiplication

Since a mixer works by means of multiplication, a bit of math can show us how they work. To begin with, we need to represent the two signals we'll mix, A and B, mathematically. Signal A's instantaneous amplitude equals

$$A_a \sin 2\pi f_a t$$

in which A is peak amplitude, f is frequency, and t is time. Likewise, B's instantaneous amplitude equals

$$A_b = A \sin(2\pi f_b t)$$

Since our goal is to show that multiplying two signals generates sum and difference frequencies, we can simplify these signal definitions by assuming that the peak amplitude of each is 1. The equation for Signal A then becomes

$$a(t) = A \sin(2\pi f_a t)$$

and the equation for Signal B becomes

$$b(t) = B \sin(2\pi f_b t)$$

Each of these equations represents a sine wave and includes a subscript letter to help us keep track of where the signals go.

Merely combining Signal A and Signal B by letting them travel on the same wire develops nothing new:

$$a(t) + b(t) = A \sin(2\pi f_a t) + B \sin(2\pi f_b t)$$

As simple as that equation may seem, we include it to highlight the fact that multiplying two signals is a quite different story. From trigonometry, we know that multiplying the sines of two variables can be expanded according to the relationship

$$\sin x \sin y = \frac{1}{2}[\cos(x-y) - \cos(x+y)]$$

Conveniently, Signals A and B are both sinusoidal, so we can use equation 6 to determine what happens when we multiply Signal A by Signal B. In our case, $x = 2\pi f_a t$ and $y = 2\pi f_b t$, so plugging them into equation 6 gives us

$$a(t) \times b(t) = \frac{AB}{2}\cos\left(2\pi\left[f_a - f_b\right]t\right) - \frac{AB}{2}\cos\left(2\pi\left[f_a + f_b\right]t\right)$$

Now we see two momentous results: a sine wave at the frequency *difference* between Signal A and Signal B $2\pi(f_a - f_b)t$, and a sine wave at the frequency *sum* of Signal A and Signal B $2\pi(f_a + f_b)t$. (The products are cosine waves, but since equivalent sine and cosine waves differ only by a phase shift of 90°, both are called *sine waves* by convention.)

This is the basic process by which we translate information into radio form and translate it back again. If we want to transmit a 1-kHz audio tone by radio, we can feed it into one of our mixer's inputs and feed an RF signal — say, 5995 kHz — into the mixer's other input. The result is two radio signals: one at 5994 kHz (5995 − 1) and another at 5996 kHz (5995 + 1). We have performed modulation.

Converting these two radio signals back to audio is just as straightforward. All we do is feed them into one input of another mixer, and feed a 5995-kHz signal into the mixer's other input. Result: a 1-kHz tone. We have performed demodulation.

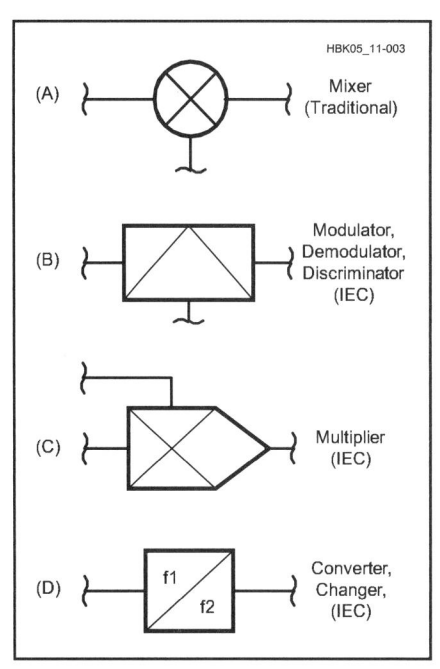

Figure 12.25 — The traditional symbol for a mixer is a circled X (A) although current standards allocate this symbol to a lamp. Current practice is to use one of the three IEC symbols shown at B, C, or D. For the frequency converter or changer symbol at D, a third connection can be included for the local oscillator. (IEC stands for *International Electrotechnical Commission* and the symbols are published in the IEEE 315A standard.)

functions of those circuits. **Figure 12.25** shows the block symbol for a traditional mixer along with several IEC symbols for other functions mixers may perform.

NONLINEAR DISTORTION

The mechanism underlying multiplication, mixing, modulation and demodulation is a pretty straightforward thing: Any circuit structure that *nonlinearly distorts* ac waveforms acts as a multiplier to some degree.

The phrase *nonlinear distortion* sounds redundant, but isn't. Distortion, an externally imposed change in a waveform, can be linear; that is, it can occur independently of signal amplitude. Consider a radio receiver front-end filter that passes only signals between 6 and 8 MHz. It does this by *linearly distorting* the single complex waveform corresponding to the wide RF spectrum present at the radio's antenna terminals, reducing the amplitudes of frequency components below 6 MHz and above 8 MHz relative to those between 6 and 8 MHz. (Considering multiple signals on a wire as one complex waveform is just as valid, and sometimes handier, than considering them as separate signals. In this case, it's a bit easier to think of distortion as something that happens to a waveform rather than something that happens to separate signals relative to each other. It would be just as valid — and certainly more in keeping with the consensus view — to say merely that the filter attenuates signals at frequencies below 6 MHz and above 8 MHz.) The filter's output waveform certainly differs from its input waveform; the waveform has been distorted. But because this distortion occurs independently of signal level or polarity, the distortion is linear. No new frequency components are created; only the amplitude relationships among the wave's existing frequency components are altered. This is *amplitude* or *frequency* distortion, and all filters do it or they wouldn't be filters.

Phase or *delay distortion*, also linear, causes a complex signal's various component frequencies to be delayed by different amounts of time, depending on their frequency but independently of their amplitude. No new frequency components occur, and amplitude relationships among existing frequency components are not altered. Phase distortion occurs to some degree in all real filters.

The waveform of a non-sinusoidal signal can be changed by passing it through a circuit that has only linear distortion, but only *non-*

linear distortion can change the waveform of a simple sine wave. It can also produce an output signal whose output waveform changes as a function of the input amplitude, something not possible with linear distortion. Nonlinear circuits often distort excessively with overly strong signals, but the distortion can be a complex function of the input level.

Nonlinear distortion may take the form of *harmonic distortion*, in which integer multiples of input frequencies occur, or intermodulation distortion (IMD), in which different components multiply to make new ones, as described in previous sections.

Any departure from absolute linearity results in some form of nonlinear distortion, and this distortion can work for us or against us. Any amplifier, including a so-called linear amplifier, distorts nonlinearly to some degree; any device or circuit that distorts nonlinearly can work as a mixer, modulator, demodulator or frequency multiplier. An amplifier optimized for linear operation will nonetheless mix, but inefficiently; an amplifier biased for nonlinear amplification may be practically linear over a given tiny portion of its input-signal range. The trick is to use careful design and component selection to maximize nonlinear distortion when we want it (as in a mixer), and minimize it when we don't. Once we've decided to maximize nonlinear distortion, the trick is to minimize the distortion products we don't want, and maximize the products we want.

MINIMIZING UNWANTED DISTORTION PRODUCTS

Ideally, a mixer multiplies the signal at one of its inputs by the signal at its other input, but does not multiply a signal at the same input by itself, or multiple signals at the same input by themselves or by each other. (Multiplying a signal by itself — squaring it — generates harmonic distortion [specifically, *second-harmonic* distortion] by adding the signal's frequency to itself. Simultaneously squaring two or more signals generates simultaneous harmonic and intermodulation distortion.)

Consider what happens when a mixer must handle signals at two different frequencies (f_1 and f_2) applied to its first input, and a signal at a third frequency (f_3) applied to its other input. Ideally, a mixer multiplies f_1 by f_3 and f_2 by f_3, but does not multiply f_1 and f_2 by each other. This produces output at the sum and difference of f_1 and f_3, and the sum and difference of f_2 and f_3, but *not* the sum and difference of f_1 and f_2. **Figure 12.26** shows that feeding two signals into one input of a mixer results in the same output as if f_1 and f_2 are each first mixed with f_3 in two separate mixers, and the outputs of these mixers are combined. This shows that a mixer, even though constructed with nonlinearly

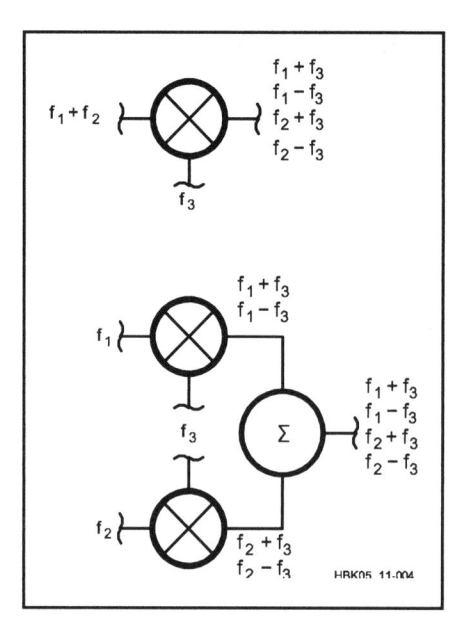

Figure 12.26 — Feeding two signals into one input of a mixer results in the same output as if f_1 and f_2 are each first mixed with f_3 in two separate mixers, and the outputs of these mixers are combined.

distorting components, actually behaves as a *linear frequency shifter*. Traditionally, we refer to this process as mixing and to its outputs as *mixing products*, but we may also call it *frequency conversion*, referring to a device or circuit that does it as a *converter*, and to its outputs as *conversion products*. If a mixer produces an output frequency that is higher than the input frequency, it is called an up-converter; if the output frequency is lower than the input, a down-converter.

Real mixers, however, at best act only as reasonably linear frequency shifters, generating some unwanted IMD products — spurious signals, or *spurs* — as they go. Receivers are especially sensitive to unwanted mixer IMD because the signal-level range over which they must operate without generating unwanted IMD is often 90 dB or more, and includes infinitesimally weak signals. In a receiver, IMD products so weak that you'd never notice them in a transmitted signal can easily obliterate weak signals. This is why receiver designers apply so much effort to achieving "high dynamic range."

The degree to which a given mixer, modulator or demodulator circuit produces unwanted IMD is often the reason why we use it, or don't use it, instead of another circuit that does its wanted-IMD job as well or even better.

MISCELLANEOUS MIXING PRODUCTS

In addition to desired sum-and-difference products and unwanted IMD products, real mixers also put out some energy at their input frequencies. Some mixer implementations may *suppress* these outputs — that is, reduce one or both of their input signals by a factor of 100 to 1,000,000, or 20 to 60 dB. This is good because it helps keep input signals at the desired mixer-output sum or difference frequency from showing up at the IF terminal — an effect reflected in a receiver's *IF rejection* specification. Some mixer types, especially those used in the vacuum-tube era, suppress their input-signal outputs very little or not at all.

Input-signal suppression is part of an overall picture called *port-to-port isolation*. Mixer input and output connections are traditionally called *ports*. By tradition, the port to which we apply the shifting signal is the *local-oscillator (LO)* port. By convention, the signal or signals to be frequency-shifted are applied to the *RF (radio frequency)* port, and the frequency-shifted (product) signal or signals emerge at the *IF (intermediate frequency)* port. This illustrates the function of a mixer in a heterodyne receiver: Since it is often impractical to achieve the desired gain and filtering at the incoming signal's frequency (at RF), a mixer is used to translate the incoming RF signal to an intermediate frequency (the IF), where gain and filtering can be applied. The IF maybe be either lower or higher than the incoming RF signal. In a transmitter, the modulated signal may be created at an IF, and then translated in frequency by a mixer to the operating frequency.

A mixer may be used in an SDR to convert a range of signals into the range the SDR can process. This is very common when using SDR equipment designed for VHF and higher frequencies to receive HF signals. In that case an up-converting mixer is required.

Some mixers are *bilateral*; that is, their RF and IF ports can be interchanged, depending on the application. Diode-based mixers are usually bilateral. Many mixers are not bilateral (*unilateral*); the popular SA602/612 Gilbert cell IC mixer is an example of this.

It's generally a good idea to keep a mixer's input signals from appearing at its output port because they represent energy that we'd rather not pass to subsequent circuitry. It therefore follows that it's usually a good idea to keep a mixer's LO-port energy from appearing at its RF port, or its RF-port energy from making it through to the IF port. But there are some notable exceptions.

12.4.2 Switching Mixers

Depending on the application, mixers may vary from the extremely simple to the complex. For example, a simple half-wave rectifier (a signal diode, such as a 1N34 [germanium] or a 1N914 [silicon]) can do the job. This is an example of a *switching mixer*, in which mixing occurs as one signal

— in this case, the carrier, which in effect turns the diode on and off as its polarity reverses — interrupts the transmission of another (in demodulation of full-carrier AM, the sidebands).

A switch can be thought of as an amplifier toggled between two gain states, off and on, by a control signal. It turns out that a binary amplifier is not necessary; any device that can be gain-varied in accordance with the amplitude of a control signal can serve as a mixer.

Most modern radio mixers act more like fast analog switches than analog multipliers. In using a mixer as a fast switching device, we apply a square wave to its LO input with a square wave rather than a sine wave, and feed sine waves, audio, or other complex signals to the mixer's RF input. The RF port serves as the mixer's "linear" input, and therefore must preferably exhibit low intermodulation and harmonic distortion. Feeding a ±1-V square wave into the LO input alternately multiplies the linear input by +1 or –1. Multiplying the RF-port signal by +1 just transfers it to the output with no change. Multiplying the RF-port signal by –1 does the same thing, except that the signal inverts (flips 180° in phase). The LO port need not exhibit low intermodulation and harmonic distortion; all it has to do is preserve the fast rise and fall times of the switching signal.

REVERSING-SWITCH MIXERS

We can multiply a signal by a square wave without using an analog multiplier at all. All we need is a pair of balun transformers and four diodes (**Figure 12.27A**).

With no LO energy applied to the circuit, none of its diodes conduct. RF-port energy (1) can't make it to the LO port because there's no direct connection between the secondaries of T1 and T2, and (2) doesn't produce IF output because T2's secondary balance results in energy cancellation at its center tap, and because no complete IF-energy circuit exists through T2's secondary with both of its ends disconnected from ground.

Applying a square wave to the LO port biases the diodes so that, 50% of the time, D1 and D2 are on and D3 and D4 are reverse-biased off. This unbalances T2's secondary by leaving its upper wire floating and connecting its lower wire to ground through T1's secondary and center tap. With T2's secondary unbalanced, RF-port energy emerges from the IF port.

The other 50% of the time, D3 and D4 are on and D1 and D2 are reverse-biased off. This unbalances T2's secondary by leaving its lower wire floating, and connects its upper wire to ground through T1's secondary and center tap. With T2's secondary unbalanced, RF-port energy again emerges from the IF port — shifted 180° relative to the first case

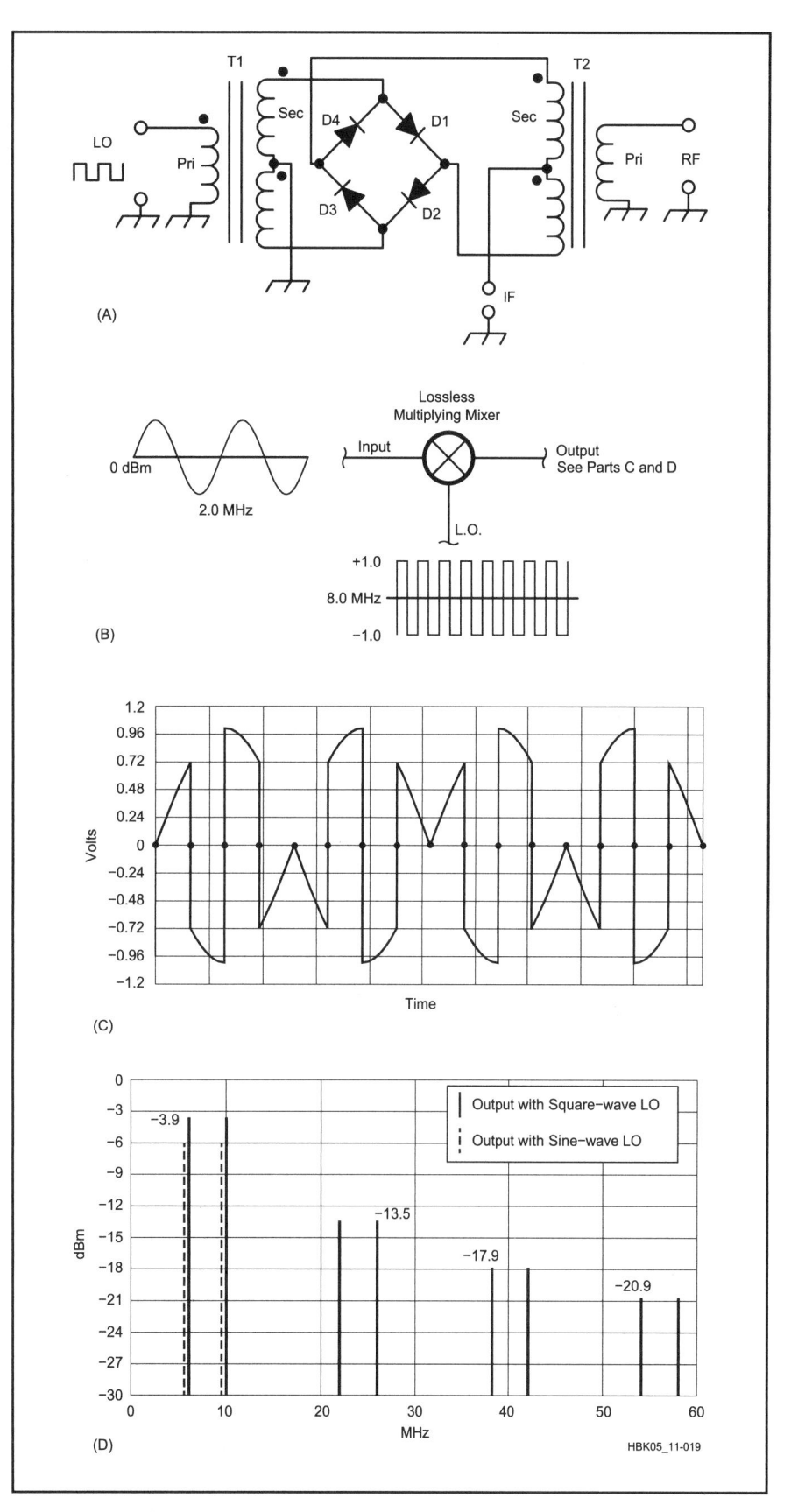

Figure 12.27 — Part A shows a general-purpose diode *reversing-switch* mixer. This mixer uses a square-wave LO and a sine-wave input signal. The text describes its action. Part B is an ideal *multiplier* mixer. The square-wave LO and a sine-wave input signal produce the output waveform shown in part C. The solid lines of part D show the output spectrum with the square-wave LO. The dashed lines show the output spectrum with a sine-wave LO.

because T2's active secondary wires are now, in effect, transposed relative to its primary.

A reversing switch mixer's output spectrum is the same as the output spectrum of a multiplier fed with a square wave. This can be analyzed by thinking of the square wave in terms of its Fourier series equivalent, which consists of the sum of sine waves at the square wave frequency and all of its odd harmonics. The amplitude of the equivalent series' fundamental sine wave is $4/\pi$ times (2.1 dB greater than) the amplitude of the square wave. The amplitude of each harmonic is inversely proportional to its harmonic number, so the third harmonic is only ⅓ as strong as the fundamental (9.5 dB below the fundamental), the 5th harmonic is only ⅕ as strong (14 dB below the fundamental) and so on. The input signal mixes with each harmonic separately from the others, as if each harmonic were driving its own separate mixer, just as we illustrated with two sine waves in Figure 12.26. Normally, the harmonic outputs are so widely removed from the desired output frequency that they are easily filtered out, so a reversing-switch mixer is just as good as a sine-wave-driven analog multiplier for most practical purposes, and usually better — for radio purposes — in terms of dynamic range and noise.

An additional difference between multiplier and switching mixers is that the signal flow in a switching mixer is reversible (that is, bilateral). It really only has one dedicated input (the LO input). The other terminals can be thought of as I/O (input/output) ports, since either one can be the input as long as the other is the output.

CONVERSION LOSS IN SWITCHING MIXERS

Figure 12.27B shows a perfect *multiplier* mixer. That is, the output is the product of the input signal and the LO. The LO is a perfect square wave. Its peak amplitude is ±1.0 V and its frequency is 8 MHz. Figure 12.27C shows the output waveform (the product of two inputs) for an input signal whose value is 0 dBm and whose frequency is 2 MHz. Notice that for each transition of the square-wave LO, the sine-wave output waveform polarity reverses. There are 16 transitions during the interval shown, at each zero-crossing point of the output waveform. Figure 12.27D shows the mixer output spectrum. The principle components are at 6 MHz and 10 MHz, which are the sum and difference of the signal and LO frequencies. The amplitude of each of these is –3.9 dBm. Numerous other pairs of output frequencies occur that are also spaced 4 MHz apart and centered at 24 MHz, 40 MHz and 56 MHz and higher odd harmonics of 8 MHz. The ones shown are at –13.5 dBm, –17.9 dBm and –20.9 dBm. Because the mixer is lossless, the sum of all of the outputs must be exactly equal to the value of the input signal. As explained previously, this output spectrum can also be understood in terms of each of the odd-harmonic components of the square-wave LO operating independently.

If the mixer switched without losses, such as in Figure 12.27A, with diodes that are perfect switches, the results would be mathematically identical to the above example. The diodes would commutate the input signal exactly as shown in Figure 12.27C.

Now consider the perfect multiplier mixer of Figure 12.27B with an LO that is a perfect sine wave with a peak amplitude of ±1.0 V. In this case the dashed lines of Figure 12.27D show that only two output frequencies are present, at 6 MHz and 10 MHz (see also Figure 12.24). Each component now has a –6 dBm level. The product of the 0 dBm sine-wave input at one frequency and the ±1.0V sine-wave LO at another frequency (see equation 6 in this chapter) is the –3 dBm total output.

These examples illustrate the difference between the square-wave LO and the sine-wave LO, for a perfect multiplier. For the same peak value of both LO waves, the square-wave LO delivers 2.1 dB more output at 6 MHz and 10 MHz than the sine-wave LO. An actual diode mixer such as Figure 12.27A behaves more like a switching mixer. Its sine-wave LO waveform is considerably flattened by interaction between the diodes and the LO generator, so that it looks somewhat like a square wave. The diodes have nonlinearities, junction voltages, capacitances, resistances and imperfect parameter matching. (See the **RF Techniques** chapter.) Also, "re-mixing" of a diode mixer's output with the LO and the input is a complicated possibility. The practical end result is that diode double-balanced mixers have a conversion loss, from input to each of the two major output frequencies, in the neighborhood of 5 to 6 dB. (Conversion loss is discussed in a later section.)

12.4.3 The Diode Double-Balanced Mixer (DBM)

The diode *double-balanced mixer* (DBM) is standard in many commercial, military and amateur applications because of its excellent balance and high dynamic range. DBMs can serve as mixers (including image-reject types), modulators (including single- and double-sideband, phase, biphase, and quadrature-phase types) and demodulators, limiters, attenuators, switches, phase detectors and frequency doublers. In some of these applications, they work in conjunction with power dividers, combiners and hybrids.

THE BASIC DBM

We have already seen the basic diode DBM circuit (Figure 12.27A). In its simplest form, a DBM contains two or more unbalanced-to-balanced transformers and a Schottky-diode ring consisting of $4 \times n$ diodes, where n is the number of diodes in each leg of the ring. Each leg commonly consists of up to four diodes.

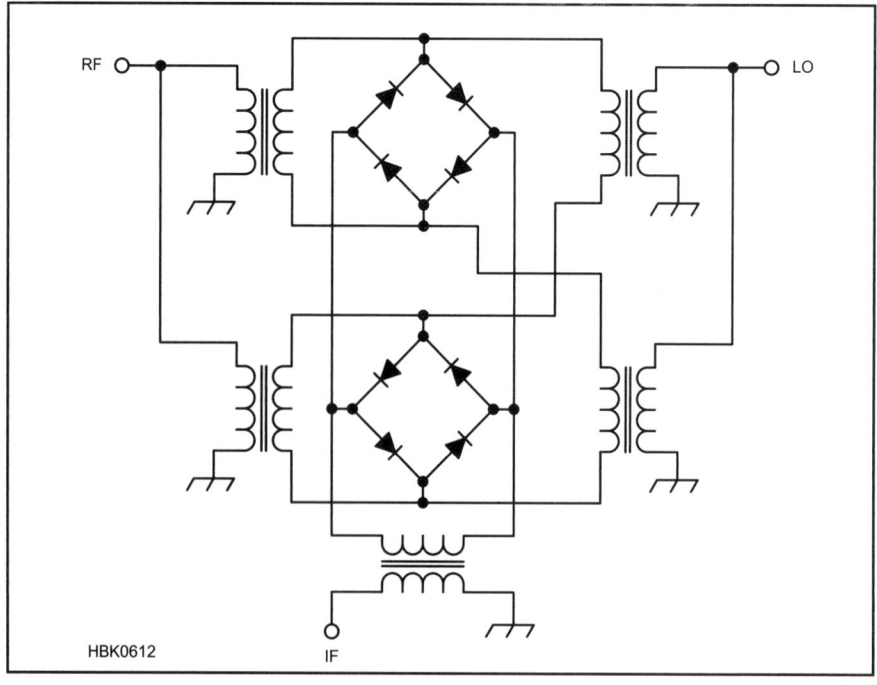

Figure 12.28 — The triple-balanced mixer uses a pair of diode rings and adds an additional balancing transformer to the IF port.

As we've seen, the degree to which a mixer is *balanced* depends on whether either, neither or both of its input signals (RF and LO) emerge from the IF port along with mixing products. An unbalanced mixer suppresses neither its RF nor its LO; both are present at its IF port. A single-balanced mixer suppresses its RF or LO, but not both. A double-balanced mixer suppresses its RF *and* LO inputs. Diode and transformer uniformity in the Figure 12.27 circuit results in equal LO potentials at the center taps of T1 and T2. The LO potential at T1's secondary center tap is zero (ground); therefore, the LO potential at the IF port is zero.

Balance in T2's secondary likewise results in an RF null at the IF port. The RF potential between the IF port and ground is therefore zero — except when the DBM's switching diodes operate!

The Figure 12.27 circuit normally also affords high RF-IF isolation because its balanced diode switching precludes direct connections between T1 and T2. A diode DBM can be used as a current-controlled switch or attenuator by applying dc to its IF port, albeit with some distortion. This causes opposing diodes (D2 and D4, for instance) to conduct to a degree that depends on the current magnitude, connecting T1 to T2.

TRIPLE-BALANCED MIXERS

The triple-balanced mixer shown in **Figure 12.28** (sometimes called a "double double-balanced mixer") is an extension of the single-diode-ring mixer. The diode rings are fed by power-splitting baluns at the RF and LO ports. An additional balun is added at the IF output. The circuit's primary advantage is that the IF output signal is balanced and isolated from the RF and LO ports over a large bandwidth — commercial mixer IF ranges of 0.5 to 10 GHz are typical.

It has higher signal-handling capability and dynamic range (a 1-dB compression point within 3 to 4 dB below LO signal levels) and lower intermodulation levels (by 10 dB or more) than a single-ring mixer. The triple-balanced mixer is used when a very wide IF range is required.

Adding the balancing transformer in the IF output path increases IF-to-LO and IF-to-RF isolation. This makes the conversion process much less sensitive to IF impedance mismatches. Since the IF port is isolated from the RF and LO ports, the three frequency ranges (RF, LO and IF) can overlap. A disadvantage of IF transformer coupling is that a dc (or low-frequency) IF output is not available, so the triple-balanced mixer cannot be used for direct-conversion receivers.

DIODE DBM COMPONENTS

Commercially manufactured diode DBMs generally consist of a supporting base, a diode ring, two or more ferrite-core transformers commonly wound with two or three twisted-pair wires, encapsulating material, an enclosure.

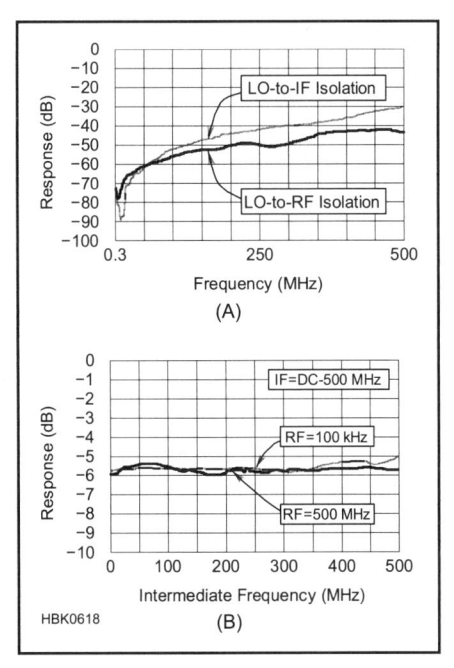

Figure 12.29 — The port-to-port isolation of a diode DBM depends on how well its diodes match and how well its transformers are balanced. (A) shows LO-IF and LO-RF isolation versus frequency and (B) shows conversion loss for a typical diode DBM, the Synergy Microwave CLP-403 mixer. In (B), LO driver level is +7 dBm.

Diodes

Hot-carrier (Schottky) diodes are the devices of choice for diode-DBM rings because of their low ON resistance, although ham-built DBMs for non-critical MF/HF use commonly use switching diodes like the 1N914 or 1N4148. The forward voltage drop, V_f, across each diode in the ring determines the mixer's optimum local-oscillator drive level. Depending on the forward voltage drop of each of its diodes and the number of diodes in each ring leg, a diode DBM will often be specified by the optimum LO drive level in dBm (typical values are 0, 3, 7, 10, 13, 17, 23 or 27). As a rule of thumb, the LO signal must be 20 dB stronger than the RF and IF signals for proper operation. This ensures that the LO signal, rather than the RF or IF signals, switches the mixer's diodes on and off — a critical factor in minimizing IMD and maximizing dynamic range.

Transformers

From the DBM schematic shown in Figure 12.27, it's clear that the LO and RF transformers are unbalanced on the input side and balanced on the diode side. The diode ends of the balanced ports are 180° out of phase throughout the frequency range of interest. This property causes signal cancellations that result in higher port-to-port isolation. **Figure 12.29A** plots LO-RF and LO-IF isolation versus frequency for Synergy Microwave's CLP-403 DBM, which is specified for +7 dBm LO drive level. Isolations on the order of 70 dB occur at the lower end of the band as a direct result of the balance among the four diode-ring legs and the RF phasing of the balanced ports.

As we learned in our discussion of generic switching mixers, transformer efficiency plays an important role in determining a mixer's conversion loss and drive-level requirement. Core loss, copper loss and impedance mismatch all contribute to transformer losses. Ferrite in toroidal, bead, balun (multi-hole) or rod form can serve as DBM transformer cores. Radio amateurs commonly use Fair-Rite Mix 43 ferrite ($\mu = 950$) in HF and VHF applications.

RF transformers combine lumped and distributed capacitance and inductance. The interwinding capacitance and characteristic impedance of a transformer's twisted wires sets the transformer's high-frequency response. The core's μ and size, and the number of winding turns, determine the transformer's lower frequency limit. Covering a specific frequency range requires a compromise in the number of turns used with a given core. Increasing a transformer's core size and number of turns improves its low-frequency response. Cores may be stacked to meet low-frequency performance specs.

Inexpensive mixers operating up to 2 GHz most commonly use twisted trifilar (three-wire) windings made of a wire size between #36 and #32. The number of twists per unit length of wire determines a winding's characteristic impedance. Twisted wires are analogous to transmission lines. The transmission-line effect predominates at the higher end of a transformer's frequency range.

PRACTICAL DIODE DBMS

Important DBM specifications include conversion loss and amplitude flatness across the required IF bandwidth; variation of conversion loss with input frequency; variation of conversion loss with LO drive, 1-dB compression point; LO-RF, LO-IF and RF-IF isolation; intermodulation products; noise figure (usually within 1 dB of conversion loss); port SWR; and dc offset, which is directly related to isolation among the RF, LO and IF ports. Most of these parameters also apply to other mixer types.

Conversion Loss of Diode DBMs

Figure 12.29B shows conversion loss versus intermediate frequency in a typical DBM. The curves show conversion loss for two fixed

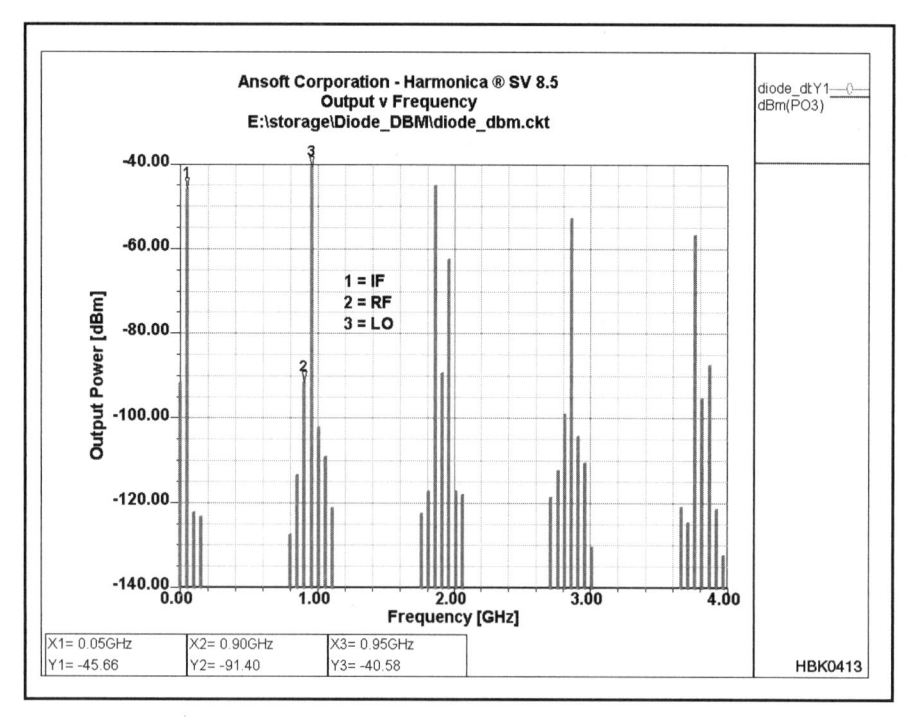

Figure 12.30 — Simulated diode-DBM output spectrum with four LO harmonics evaluated. Note that the desired output products (the highest two products, RF − LO and RF + LO) emerge at a level 5 to 6 dB below the mixer's RF input (−40 dBm). This indicates a mixer conversion loss of 5 to 6 dB. (*Serenade SV8.5* simulation.)

RF-port signals, one at 100 kHz and the another at 500 MHz, while varying the LO frequency from 100 kHz to 500 MHz.

Figure 12.30 graphs a diode DBM's simulated output spectrum. Note that the RF input (900 MHz) is −40 dBm and the desired IF output (51 MHz, the frequency difference between the RF and LO signals) is −46 dBm, implying a conversion loss of 6 dB. Very nearly the same value (5 dB) applies to the sum of both signals (RF + LO). We minimize a diode DBM's conversion loss, noise figure and intermodulation by keeping its LO drive high enough to switch its diodes on fully and rapidly. Increasing a mixer's LO level beyond that sufficient to turn its switching devices all the way on merely makes them dissipate more LO power without further improving performance.

Insufficient LO drive results in increased noise figure and conversion loss. IMD also increases because RF-port signals have a greater chance to control the mixer diodes when the LO level is too low.

APPLYING DIODE DBMS

At first glance, applying a diode DBM is easy: We feed the signal(s) we want to frequency-shift (at or below the maximum level called for in the mixer's specifications, such as −10 dBm for the Mini-Circuits SBL-1 and TUF-3, and Synergy Microwave S-1, popular 7 dBm LO power parts) to the DBM's RF port, feed the frequency-shifting signal (at the proper level) to the LO port, and extract the sum and difference products from the mixer's IF port.

There's more to it than that, however, because diode DBMs (along with most other modern mixer types) are *termination-sensitive*. That is, their ports — particularly their IF (output) ports — must be resistively terminated with the proper impedance (commonly 50 Ω, resistive). A wideband, resistive output termination is particularly critical if a mixer is to achieve its maximum dynamic range in receiving applications. Such a load can be achieved by:

• Terminating the mixer in a 50-Ω resistor or attenuator pad (a technique usually avoided in receiving applications because it directly degrades system noise figure);

• Terminating the mixer with a low-noise, high-dynamic-range *post-mixer amplifier* designed to exhibit a wideband resistive input impedance; or

• Terminating the mixer in a *diplexer*, a frequency-sensitive signal splitter that appears as a two-terminal resistive load at its input while resistively dissipating unwanted outputs and passing desired outputs through to subsequent circuitry.

Termination-insensitive mixers are available, but this label can be misleading. Some termination-insensitive mixers are nothing more than a termination-sensitive mixer packaged with an integral post-mixer amplifier. True termination-insensitive mixers are less common and considerably more elaborate. Amateur builders will more likely use one of the many excellent termination-sensitive mixers available in connection with a diplexer, post-mixer amplifier or both.

Figure 12.31 shows one diplexer implementation. In this approach, L1 and C1 form a series-tuned circuit, resonant at the desired IF, that presents low impedance between the diplexer's input and output terminals at the IF. The high-impedance parallel-tuned circuit formed by L2 and C2 also resonates at the desired IF, keeping desired energy out of the diplexer's 50-Ω load resistor, R1.

The preceding example is called a *bandpass diplexer*. **Figure 12.32** shows another type: a *high-pass/low-pass diplexer* in which each inductor and capacitor has a reactance of 70.7 Ω at the 3-dB cutoff frequency. It can be used after a "difference" mixer (a mixer in which the IF is the difference between the signal frequency and LO) if the desired IF and its image frequency are far enough apart so that the image power is "dumped" into the network's 51-Ω resistor. (For a "summing" mixer — a mixer in which the IF is the sum of the desired signal and LO — interchange the 50-Ω idler load resistor and the diplexer's "50-Ω Amplifier" connection.)

Figure 12.33 shows a BJT post-mixer amplifier design made popular by Wes Hayward, W7ZOI, and John Lawson, K5IRK. RF feedback (via the 1-kΩ resistor) and emitter degeneration (the ac-coupled 5.6-Ω emitter resistor) work together to keep the stage's input impedance near 50 Ω and uniformly resistive across a wide bandwidth. Performance comparable to the Figure 10.28 circuit can be obtained at MF and HF by using paralleled 2N3904s as shown in **Figure 12.34**.

Phase Detection with a DBM

As we saw in our exploration of quadrature detection, applying two signals of equal frequency to a DBM's LO and RF ports produces an IF-port dc output proportional to the cosine of the signals' phase difference (**Figure 12.35**). This assumes that the DBM has a dc-coupled IF port, of course. If it doesn't — and some DBMs don't — phase-detector operation is out. Any dc output offset introduces error into this process, so critical phase-detection applications use low-offset DBMs optimized for this service.

12.4.4 Active Mixers

We've covered diode DBMs in depth because their ease of use in homebrew projects, high performance, and suitability for direct connection into 50-Ω systems makes them attractive to amateur builders. The abundant availability of high-quality manufac-

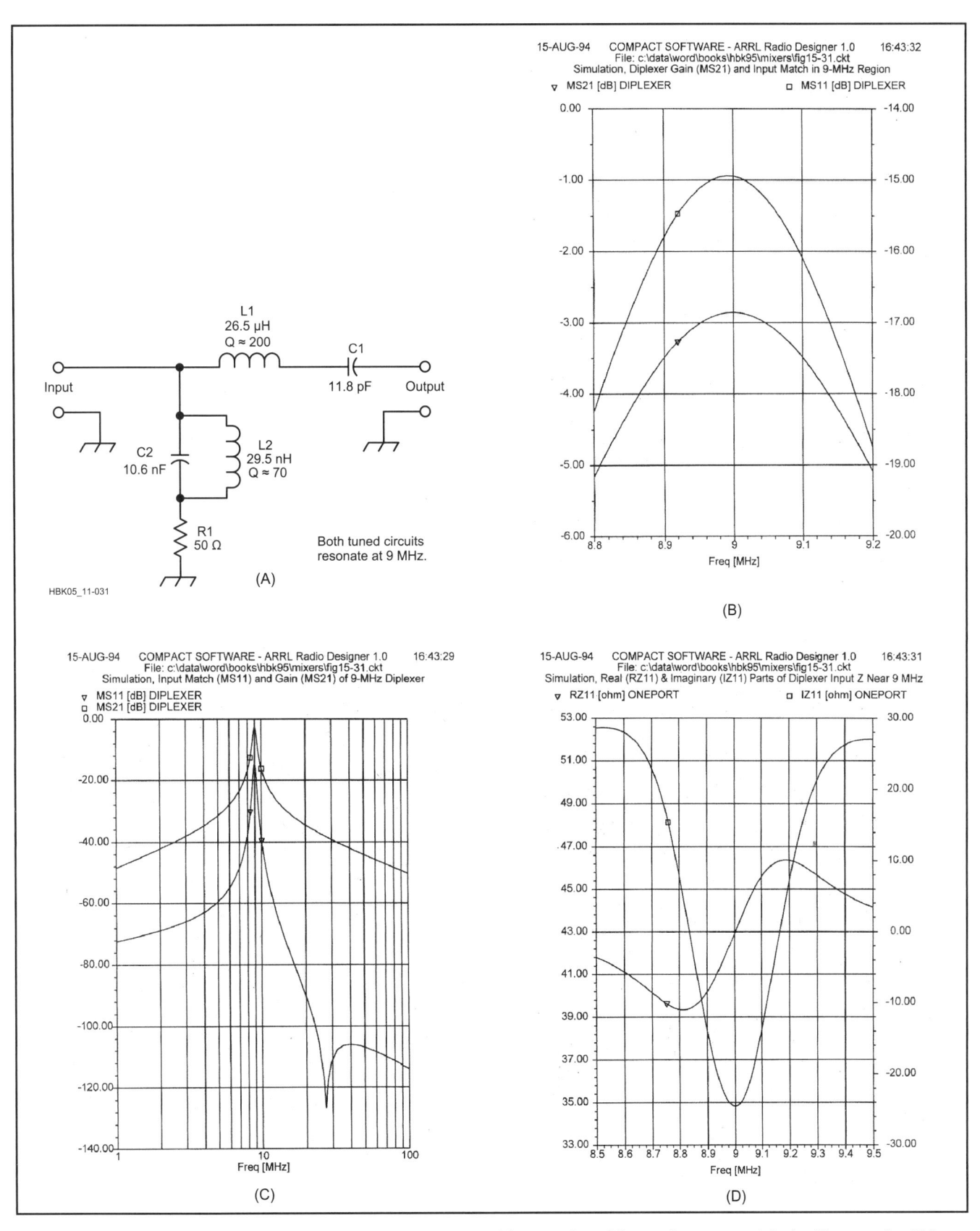

Figure 12.31 — A diplexer resistively terminates energy at unwanted frequencies while passing energy at desired frequencies. This band-pass diplexer (A) uses a series-tuned circuit as a selective pass element, while a high-C parallel-tuned circuit keeps the network's terminating resistor R1 from dissipating desired-frequency energy. Computer simulation of the diplexer's response with *ARRL Radio Designer 1.0* characterizes the diplexer's insertion loss and good input match from 8.8 to 9.2 MHz (B) and from 1 to 100 MHz (C); and the real and imaginary components of the diplexer's input impedance from 8.8 to 9.2 MHz with a 50-Ω load at the diplexer's output terminal (D). The high-C, low-L nature of the L2-C2 circuit requires that C2 be minimally inductive; a 10,000-pF chip capacitor is recommended. This diplexer was described by Rohde and Bucher in *Communications Receivers: Principles and Design*, 3rd Edition.

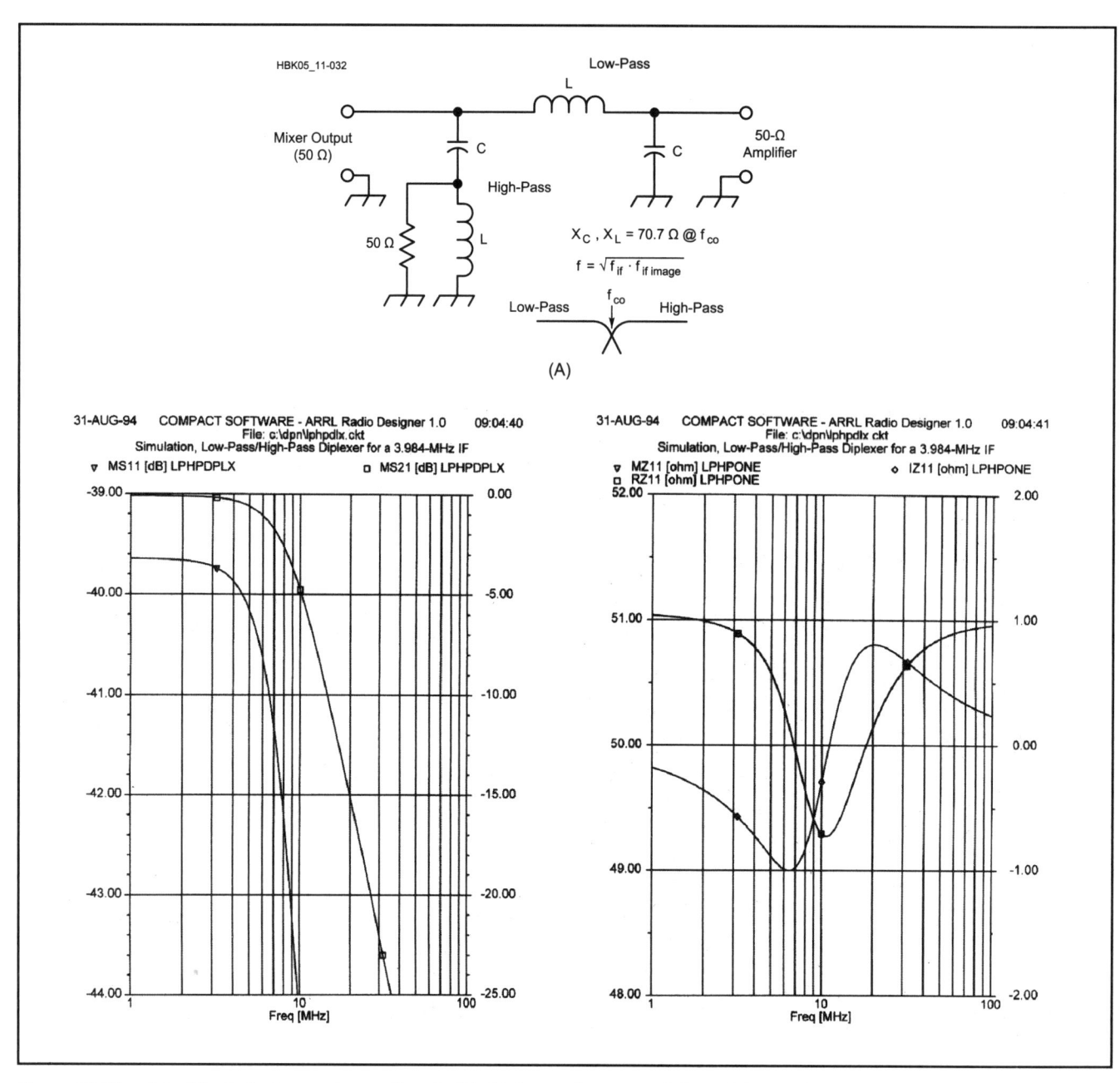

Figure 12.32 — All of the inductors and capacitors in this high-pass/low-pass diplexer (A) exhibit a reactance of 70.7 Ω at its tuned circuits' 3-dB cutoff frequency (the geometric mean of the IF and IF image). B and C show *ARRL Radio Designer* simulations of this circuit configured for use in a receiver that converts 7 MHz to 3.984 MHz using a 10.984-MHz LO. The IF image is at 17.984 MHz, giving a 3-dB cutoff frequency of 8.465 MHz. The inductor values used in the simulation were therefore 1.33 μH (Q = 200 at 25.2 MHz); the capacitors, 265 pF (Q = 1000). This drawing shows idler load and "50-Ω Amplifier" connections suitable for a receiver in which the IF image falls at a frequency *above* the desired IF. For applications in which the IF image falls below the desired IF, interchange the 50-Ω idler load resistor and the diplexer's "50-Ω Amplifier" connection so the idler load terminates the diplexer low-pass filter and the 50-Ω amplifier terminates the high-pass filter.

tured diode mixers at reasonable prices makes them excellent candidates for home construction projects. Although diode DBMs are common in telecommunications as a whole, their conversion loss and relatively high LO power requirement have usually driven the manufacturers of high-performance MF/HF Amateur Radio receivers and transceivers to other solutions. Those solutions have generally involved single- or double-balanced FET mixers — MOSFETs in the late 1970s and early 1980s, JFETs from the early 1980s to date. A comprehensive paper that explores the differences between various forms of active mixers, "Performance Capabilities of Active Mixers," by Ulrich Rohde, N1UL, is included in the downloadable supplemental information accompanying this *Handbook*.

Many of the JFET designs are variations of a single-balanced mixer circuit introduced to *QST* readers in 1970. **Figure 12.36** shows the circuit as it was presented by William Sabin in "The Solid-State Receiver," *QST*, July 1970. Two 2N4416 JFETs operate in a common-source configuration, with push-pull RF input and parallel LO drive. **Figure 12.37** shows a similar circuit as implemented in the ICOM IC-765 transceiver. In this version, the JFETs (2SK125s) operate in common-gate, with the LO applied across a 220-Ω

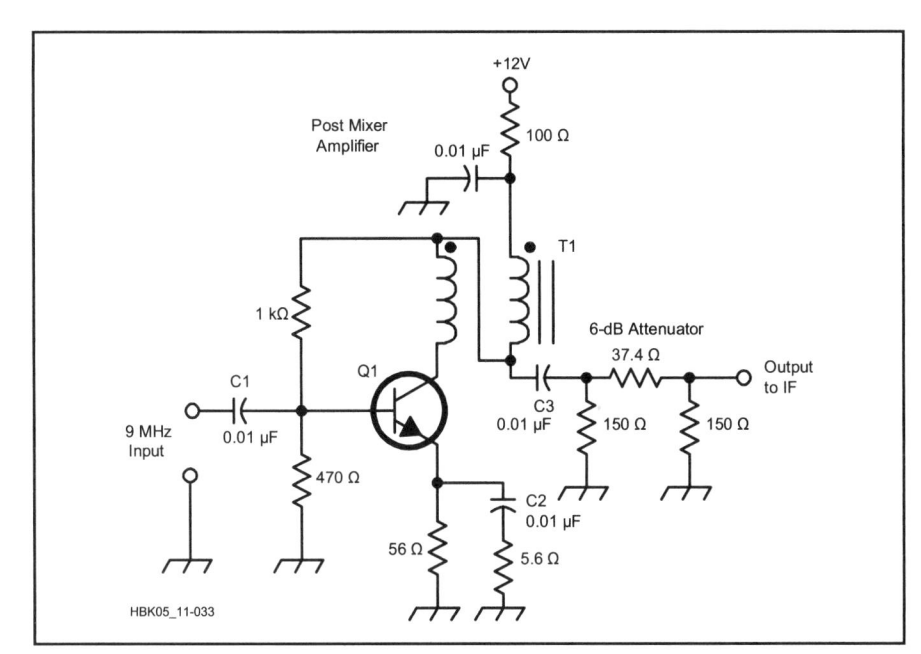

Figure 12.33 — The post-mixer amplifier from Hayward and Lawson's "Progressive Communications Receiver" (November 1981 QST). This amplifier's gain, including the 6-dB loss of the attenuator pad, is about 16 dB; its noise figure, 4 to 5 dB; its output intercept, 30 dBm. The 6-dB attenuator is essential if a crystal filter follows the amplifier; the pad isolates the amplifier from the filter's highly reactive input impedance. This circuit's input match to 50 Ω below 4 MHz can be improved by replacing 0.01-µF capacitors C1, C2 and C3 with low-inductance 0.1-µF units (chip capacitors are preferable). Q1 is a TO-39 CATV-type bipolar transistor, f_T = 1 GHz or greater (2N3866, 2N5109, 2SC1252, 2SC1365 or MRF586 suitable.) Use a small heat sink on this transistor. T1 is a broadband ferrite transformer, ≈42 µH per winding: 10 bifilar turns of #28 enameled wire on an FT 37-43 core.

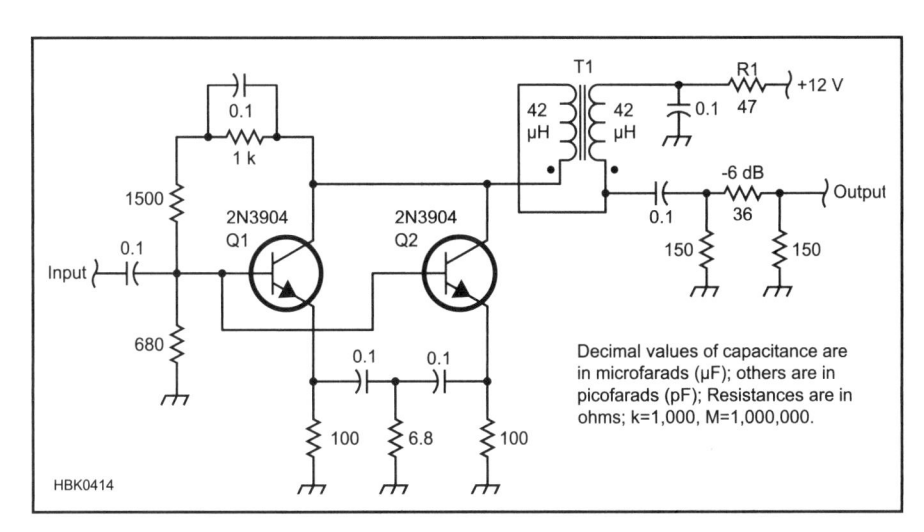

Figure 12.34 — At MF and HF, paralleled 2N3904 BJTs can provide performance comparable to that of the Figure 12.33 circuit with sufficient attention paid to device standing current, here set at »30 mA for the pair. The value of decoupling resistor R1 is critical in that small changes in its value cause a relatively large change in the 2N3904s' bias point. This circuit is part of the "EZ-90 Receiver," described by Hayward, Campbell and Larkin in *Experimental Methods in RF Design*.

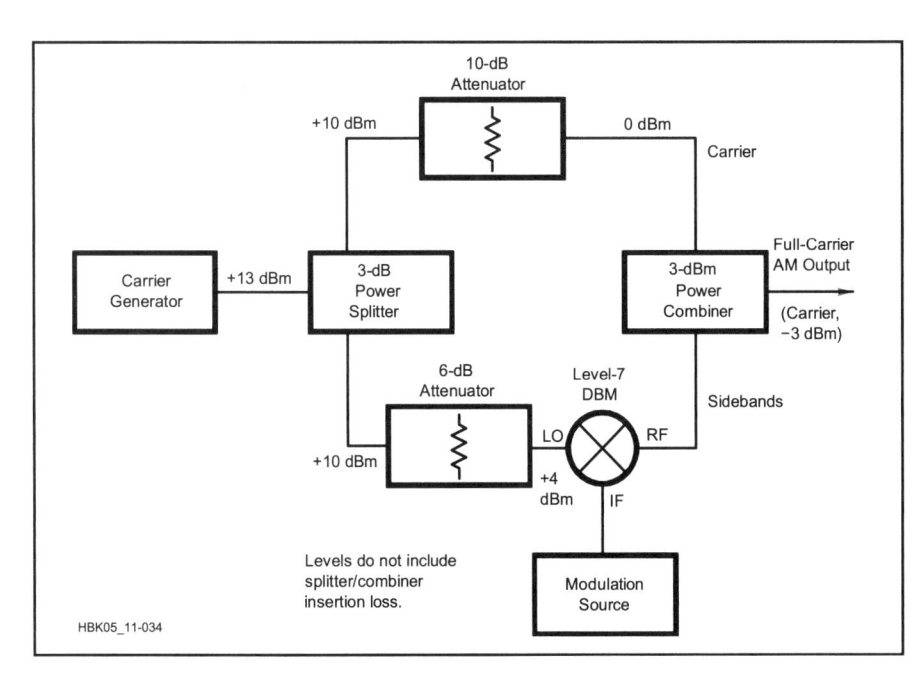

Figure 12.35 — Generating full-carrier AM with a diode DBM. A practical modulator using this technique is described in *Experimental Methods in RF Design*.

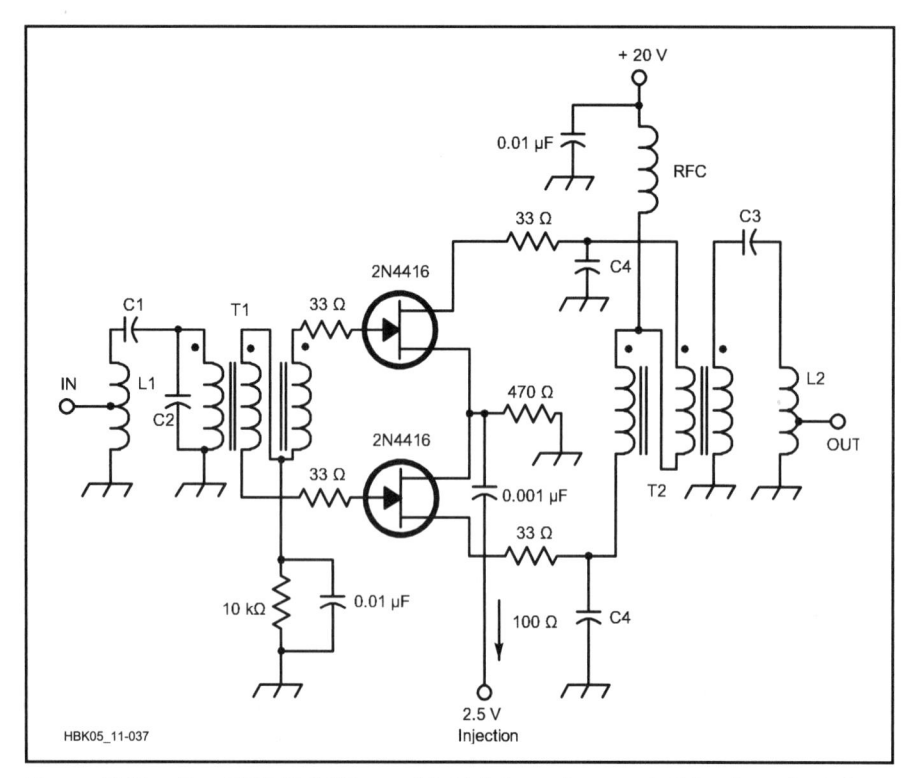

Figure 12.36 — Two 2N4416 JFETs provide high dynamic range in this mixer circuit from Sabin, *QST*, July 1970. L1, C1 and C2 form the input tuned circuit; L2, C3 and C4 tune the mixer output to the IF. The trifilar input and output transformers are broadband transmission-line types.

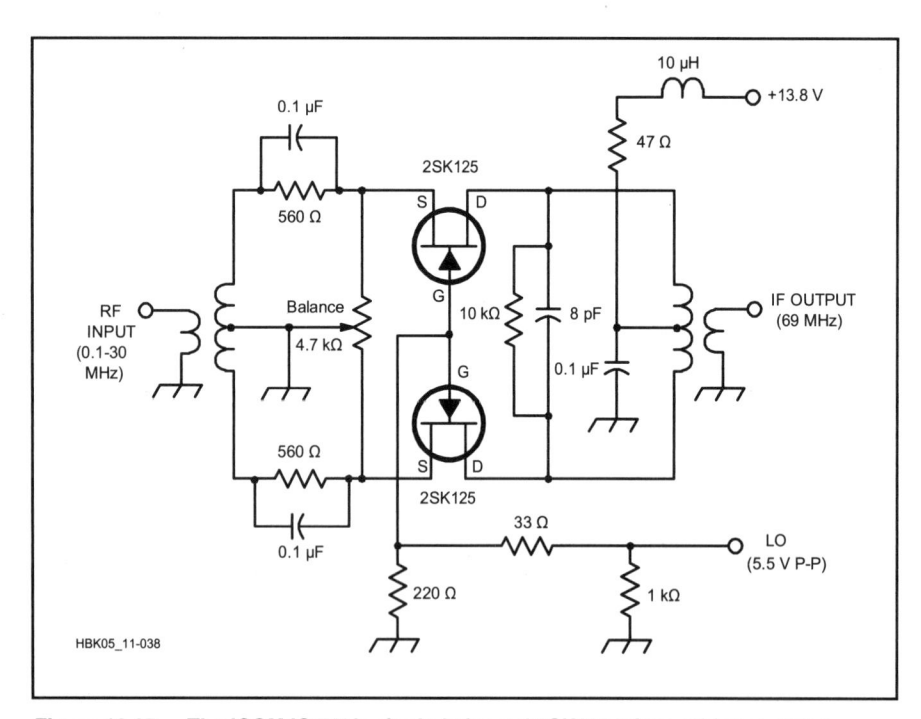

Figure 12.37 — The ICOM IC-765's single-balanced 2SK125 mixer achieves a high dynamic range (per *QST* Product Review, an IP$_3$ of 10.5 dBm at 14 MHz with preamp off). The first receive mixer in many commercial Amateur Radio transceiver designs of the 1980s and 1990s used a pair of 2SK125s or similar JFETs in much this way.

resistor between the gates and ground.

Current state of the art for active mixers in the HF through GHz range replaces discrete device designs with integrated designs such as the Analog Devices AD8342 (www.analog.com). Using an IC greatly improves matching of the active devices, improving circuit balance. The AD8342 has a conversion gain of 3.7 dB, a noise figure of 12.2 dB, and an input IP$_3$ of 22.7 dBm. The device operates with a single-voltage power supply and is well-suited to interface with digital hardware,

Testing Mixer Performance

In order to make proper tests on mixers using signal generators, a hybrid coupler with at least 40 dB of isolation between the two input ports and an attenuator are required. The test set-up provided by DeMaw and Collins in *QST*, January 1981, shown in **Figure 12.C1** is ideal for this.* Two signal generators operating near 14 MHz are combined in the hybrid coupler, then isolated from the mixer under test (MUT) by a variable attenuator. The LO is supplied by a VFO covering 5.0-5.5 MHz and applied to the MUT through another variable attenuator. The output is isolated with another attenuator, amplified and applied to a spectrum analyzer for analysis.

Attenuation should be sufficient to provide isolation (minimum of 6 to 10 dB required) and to result in signal levels to the mixer under test (MUT) appropriate for the required testing and as suitable for the particular mixer device.

The 2N5109 amplifier shown may not be sufficient for extremely high intercept point tests as this stage may no longer be transparent (operate linearly) at high signal levels. For stability tests, it is recommended to have a reactive network at the output of the mixer for the sole purpose of checking whether the mixer can become unstable.

The two 14 MHz oscillators must have extremely low harmonic content and very low noise sidebands. A convenient oscillator circuit is provided in **Figure 12.C2**, based on a 1975 *Electronic Design* article.** — *Dr Ulrich L. Rohde, N1UL*

*DeMaw, W1FB, and Collins, ADØW, "Modern Receiver Mixers for High Dynamic Range," QST, Jan 1981, p 19.
**U. Rohde, "Crystal Oscillator Provides Low Noise," *Electronic Design*, Oct 11, 1975.

such as for SDR applications. Reference circuits for applications at HF and VHF/UHF are provided in the device's datasheet.

12.4.5 The Tayloe Mixer

[The following description of the Tayloe Product Detector (a.k.a. — the Tayloe Mixer) is adapted from the July 2002 QEX article, "Software-Defined Radio For the Masses, Part 1" by Gerald Youngblood AC5OG, now K5SDR. — Ed.]

The beauty of the Tayloe detector (see reference listings for Tayloe) is found in both its design elegance and its exceptional performance. In its simplest form, you can build a complete quadrature downconverter with only three or four ICs (less the local oscillator) at a cost of less than $10.

Figure 12.38 illustrates a single-balanced version of the Tayloe detector. It can be visualized as a four-position rotary switch revolving at a rate equal to the carrier frequency. The 50-Ω antenna impedance is connected to the rotor and each of the four switch positions is connected to a *sampling capacitor*. Since the switch rotor is turning at exactly the RF carrier frequency, each capacitor will track the carrier's amplitude for exactly one-quarter of the cycle and will then hold its value for the remainder of the cycle. The rotating switch will therefore sample the signal at 0°, 90°, 180° and 270°, respectively.

As shown in **Figure 12.39**, the 50-Ω impedance of the antenna and the sampling capacitors form an R-C low-pass filter during the period when each respective switch is turned on. Therefore, each sample represents the integral or average voltage of the signal during its respective one-quarter cycle. When the switch is off, each sampling capacitor will hold its value until the next revolution. If the RF carrier and the rotating frequency were exactly in phase, the output of each capacitor will be a dc level equal to the average value of the sample.

If we differentially sum outputs of the 0° and 180° sampling capacitors with an op amp (see Figure 12.38), the output would be a dc voltage equal to two times the value of the individually sampled values when the switch rotation frequency equals the carrier frequency. Imagine, 6 dB of noise-free gain! The same would be true for the 90° and 270° capacitors as well. The 0°/180° summation forms the *I* channel and the 90°/270° summation forms the *Q* channel of a quadrature downconversion. (See the **Modulation** chapter for more information on I/Q modulation.)

As we shift the frequency of the carrier away from the sampling frequency, the values of the inverting phases will no longer be dc levels. The output frequency will vary according to the "beat" or difference frequency between the carrier and the switch-rotation frequency to provide an accurate representation of all the signal components converted to baseband.

Figure 12.40 is the schematic for a simple, single-balanced Tayloe detector. It consists of a PI5V331, 1:4 FET demultiplexer (an analog switch) that switches the signal to each of the four sampling capacitors. The 74AC74 dual flip-flop is connected as a divide-by-four Johnson counter to provide the two-phase clock to the demultiplexer chip. The outputs of the sampling capacitors are differentially summed through the two LT1115 ultra-low-noise op amps to form the *I* and *Q* outputs, respectively.

Note that the impedance of the antenna forms the input resistance for the op-amp gain as shown in the equation for gain below. This impedance may vary significantly with the actual antenna. In a practical receiver, a buffer amplifier should be used to stabilize and control the impedance presented to the mixer.

Since the duty cycle of each switch is 25%, the effective resistance in the RC network is

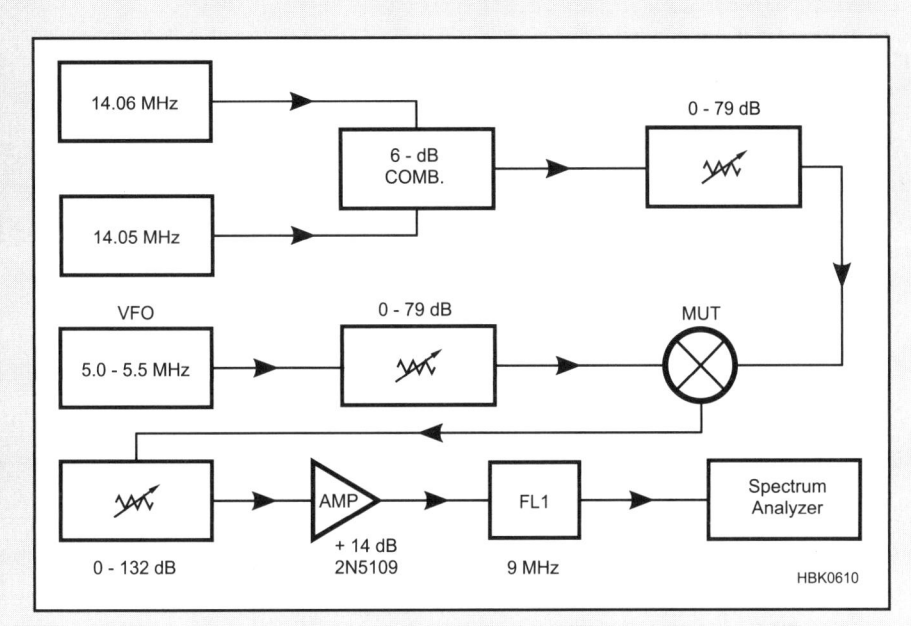

Figure 12.C1 — The equipment setup for measuring mixer performance at HF.

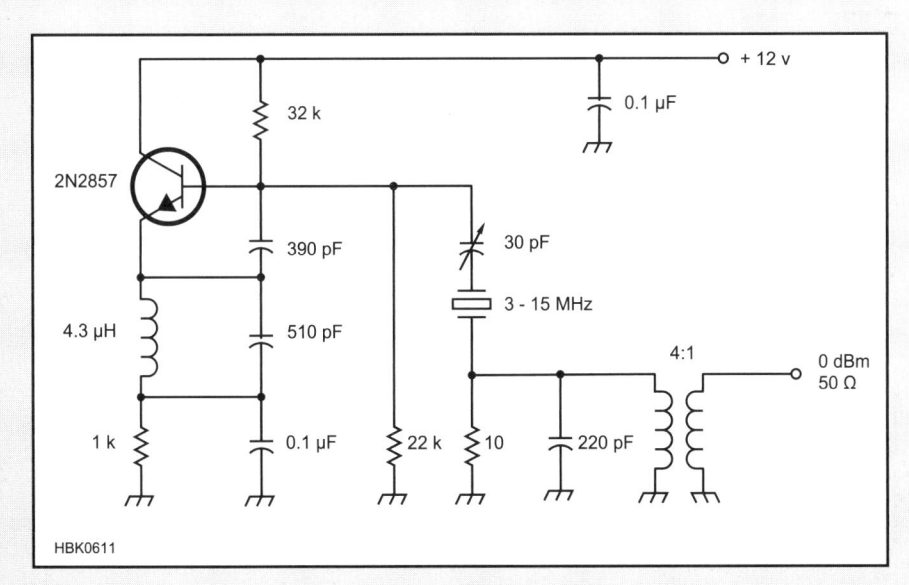

Figure 12.C2 — A low-noise VXO circuit for driving the LO port of the mixer under test in Figure 12.C1.

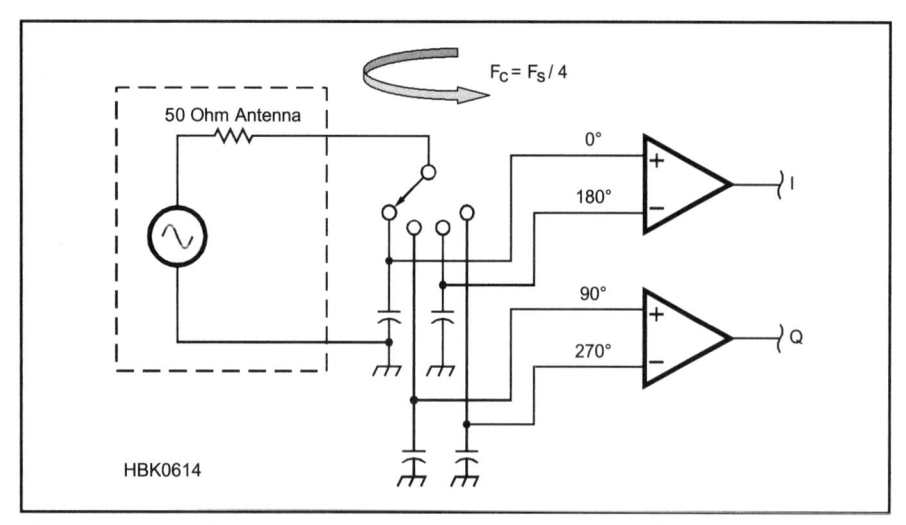

Figure 12.38 — Tayloe detector: The switch rotates at the carrier frequency so that each capacitor samples the signal once each revolution. The 0° and 180° capacitors differentially sum to provide the in-phase (I) signal and the 90° and 270° capacitors sum to provide the quadrature (Q) signal.

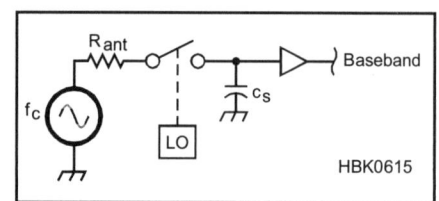

Figure 12.39 — Track-and-hold sampling circuit: Each of the four sampling capacitors in the Tayloe detector form an RC track-and-hold circuit. When the switch is on, the capacitor will charge to the average value of the carrier during its respective one-quarter cycle. During the remaining three-quarters cycle, it will hold its charge. The local-oscillator frequency is equal to the carrier frequency so that the output will be at baseband.

Figure 12.40 — Single-balanced Tayloe detector.

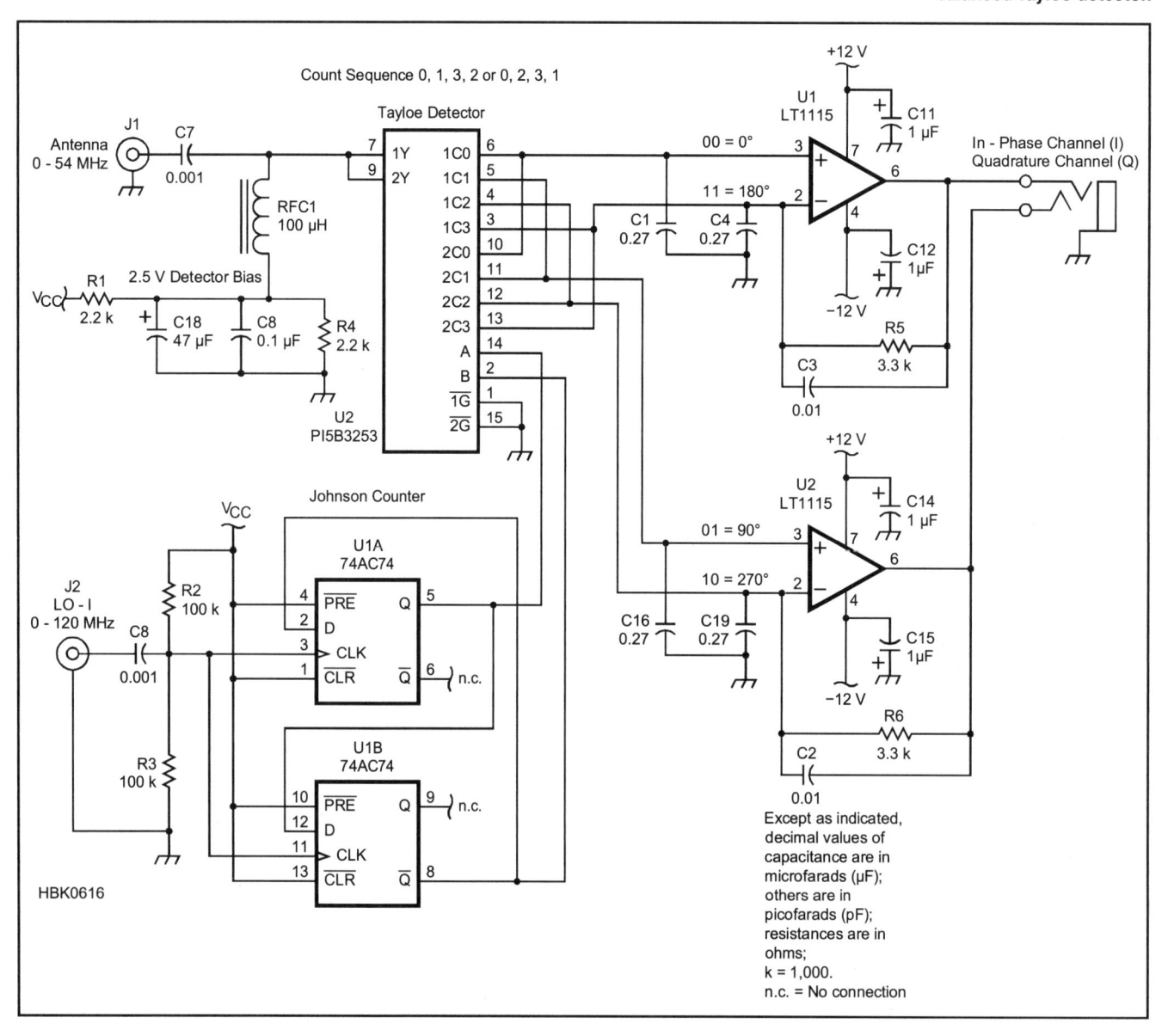

Except as indicated, decimal values of capacitance are in microfarads (µF); others are in picofarads (pF); resistances are in ohms; k = 1,000. n.c. = No connection

12.38   Chapter 12

the antenna impedance multiplied by four in the op-amp gain formula:

$$G = \frac{R_f}{4 R_{ant}}$$

For example, with a feedback resistance, R_f, of 3.3 kΩ and antenna impedance, R_{ant}, of 50 Ω, the resulting gain of the input stage is:

$$G = \frac{3300}{4 \times 50} = 16.5$$

The Tayloe detector may also be analyzed as a *digital commutating filter* (see reference by Kossor). This means that it operates as a very-high-Q tracking filter, where the following equation determines the bandwidth:

$$BW_{det} = \frac{1}{\pi\, n\, R_{ant}\, C_s}$$

where n is the number of sampling capacitors, R_{ant} is the antenna impedance and C_s is the value of the individual sampling capacitors. Q_{det} of the filter is:

$$Q_{det} = \frac{f_c}{BW_{det}}$$

where f_c is the center frequency and BW_{det} is the bandwidth of the filter.

By example, if we assume the sampling capacitor to be 0.27 μF and the antenna impedance to be 50 Ω, then BW and Q at an operating frequency of 14.001 MHz are computed as follows:

$$BW_{det} = \frac{1}{\pi \times 4 \times 50 \times (2.7 \times 10^{-7})} = 5895\ \text{Hz}$$

$$Q_{det} = \frac{14.001 \times 10^{-6}}{5895} = 2375$$

The real payoff in the Tayloe detector is its performance. It has been stated that the *ideal* commutating mixer has a minimum conversion loss (which determines noise figure — see the **RF Techniques** chapter) of 3.9 dB. Typical high-level diode mixers have a conversion loss of 6-7 dB and noise figures 1 dB higher than the loss. The Tayloe detector has less than 1 dB of conversion loss, remarkably. How can this be? The reason is that it is not really a mixer but a sampling detector in the form of a quadrature track-and-hold circuit. This means that the design adheres to discrete-time sampling theory, which, while similar to mixing, has its own unique characteristics. Because a track and hold actually holds the signal value between samples, the signal output never goes to zero. (See the **DSP and SDR Fundamentals** chapter for more on sampling theory.)

This is where aliasing can actually be used to our benefit. Since each switch and capacitor in the Tayloe detector actually samples

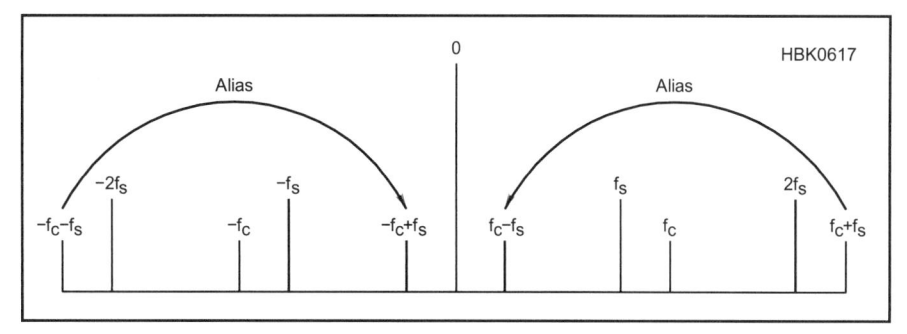

Figure 12.41 — Alias summing on Tayloe detector output: Since the Tayloe detector samples the signal, the sum frequency ($f_c + f_s$) and its image ($-f_c - f_s$) are located at the first alias frequency. The alias signals sum with the baseband signals to eliminate the mixing product loss associated with traditional mixers. In a typical mixer, the sum frequency energy is lost through filtering thereby increasing the noise figure of the device.

the RF signal once each cycle, it will respond to alias frequencies as well as those within the Nyquist frequency range. In a traditional direct-conversion receiver, the local-oscillator frequency is set to the carrier frequency so that the difference frequency, or IF, is at 0 Hz and the sum frequency is at two times the carrier frequency. We normally remove the sum frequency through low-pass filtering, resulting in conversion loss and a corresponding increase in noise figure. In the Tayloe detector, the sum frequency resides at the first alias frequency as shown in **Figure 12.41**. Remember that an alias is a real signal and will appear in the output as if it were a baseband signal. Therefore, the alias adds to the baseband signal for a theoretically lossless detector. In real life, there is a slight loss, usually less than 1 dB, due to the resistance of the switch and aperture loss due to imperfect switching times.

12.4.6 The NE602/SA602/SA612 Gilbert Cell Mixer

Introduced as the Philips NE602 in the mid-1980s, the NXP SA602/SA612 mixer-oscillator IC has become greatly popular with amateur experimenters for receive mixers, transmit mixers and balanced modulators. The SA602/612's mixer is a *Gilbert cell* multiplier. **Figure 12.42** shows its equivalent

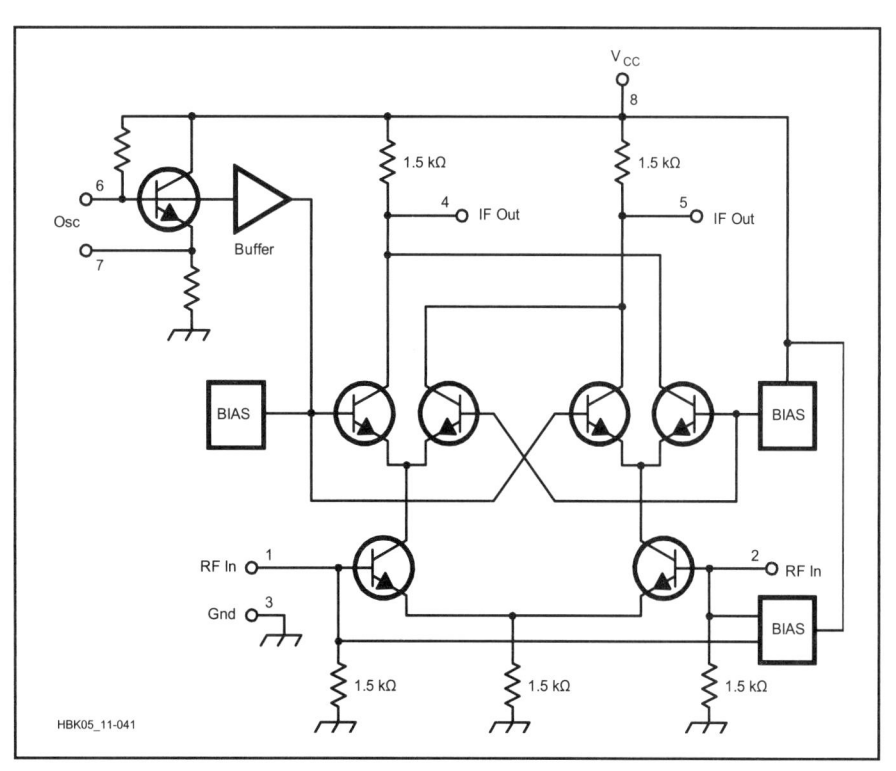

Figure 12.42 — The SA602/612's equivalent circuit reveals its Gilbert-cell origins.

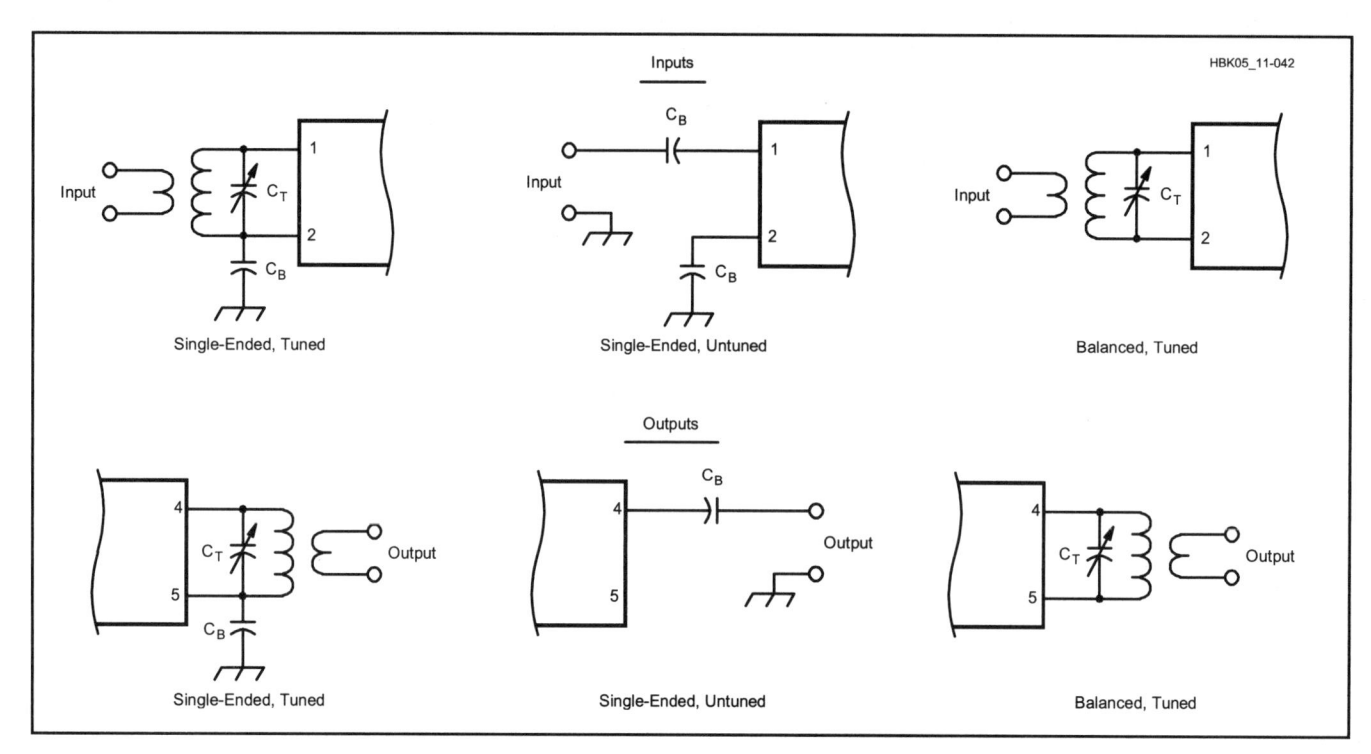

Figure 12.43 — The SA602/612's inputs and outputs can be single- or double-ended (balanced). The balanced configurations minimize second-order IMD and harmonic distortion, and unwanted envelope detection in direct-conversion service. C_T tunes its inductor to resonance; C_B is a bypass or dc-blocking capacitor. The arrangements pictured don't show all the possible input/output configurations; for instance, a center-tapped broadband transformer can be used to achieve a balanced, untuned input or output.

circuit. A Gilbert cell consists of two differential transistor pairs whose bias current is controlled by one of the input signals. The other signal drives the differential pairs' bases, but only after being "predistorted" in a diode circuit. (This circuit distorts the signal equally and oppositely to the inherent distortion of the differential pair.) The resulting output signal is an accurate multiplication of the input voltages.

SA602/612A VARIANTS

The SA602/612 began life as the NE602/SA602. SA-prefixed 602/612 parts are specified for use over a wider temperature range than their NE-prefixed equivalents. Parts without the A suffix have a slightly lower IP_3 specification than their A counterparts. The pinout-identical NE612A and SA612A cost less than their 602 equivalents as a result of wider tolerances. All variants of this popular part should work satisfactorily in most "NE602" experimenter projects. The same mixer/oscillator topology, modified for slightly higher dynamic range at the expense of somewhat less mixer gain, is also available in the mixer/oscillator/FM IF chips NE/SA605 (input IP_3 typically −10 dBm) and NE/SA615 (input IP_3 typically −13 dBm).

SA602/612 USAGE NOTES

The SA602/612's typical current drain is 2.4 mA; its supply voltage range is 4.5 to 8.0 V. Its inputs (RF) and outputs (IF) can be single- or double-ended (balanced) according to design requirements (**Figure 12.43**). The equivalent ac impedance of each input is approximately 1.5 kΩ in parallel with 3 pF; each output's resistance is 1.5 kΩ. **Figure 12.44** shows the use of an NPN transistor at

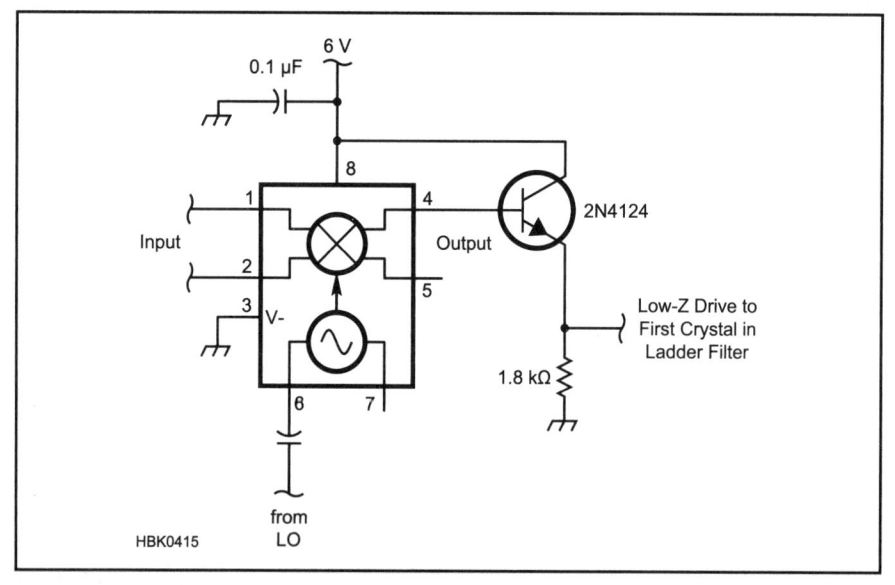

Figure 12.44 — An NPN transistor at the output of an SA602/612 mixer provides power gain and low-impedance drive for a 4.914-MHz crystal filter. A low-reactance coupling capacitor can be added between the emitter and the circuitry it drives if dc blocking is necessary. [Circuit from the Elecraft KX1 transceiver courtesy of Wayne Burdick, N6KR]

the SA602/612 output to obtain low-impedance drive for a crystal filter; **Figure 12.45** shows how AGC can be applied to an SA602/612.

The SA602/612 mixer can typically handle signals up to 500 MHz. At 45 MHz, its noise figure is typically 5.0 dB; its typical con-

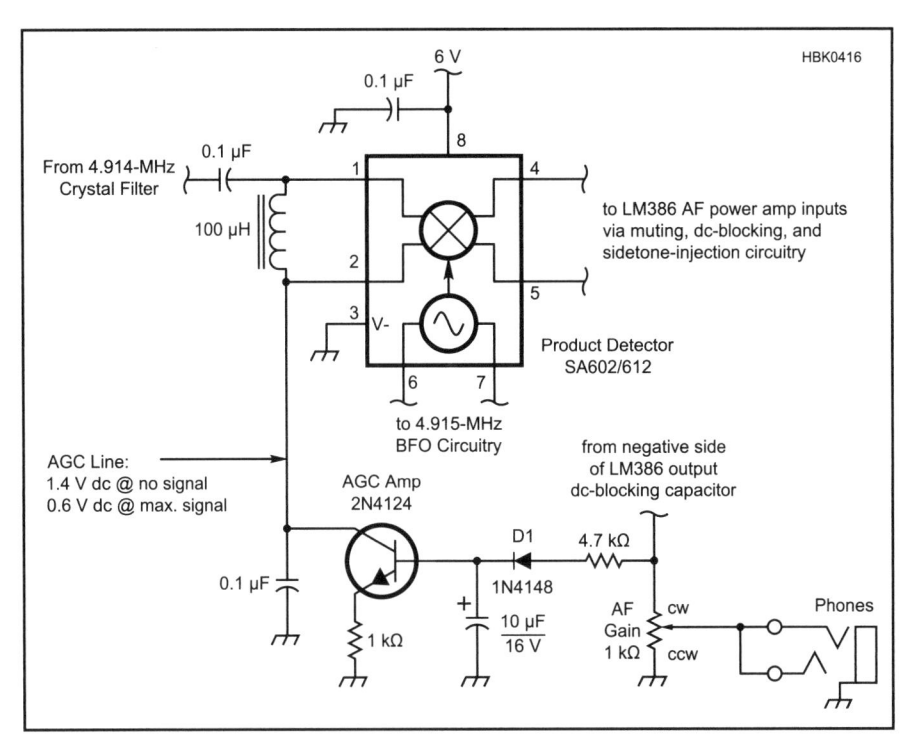

Figure 12.45 — SA602/612 product detector AGC from the Elecraft KX1 transceiver. Designed by Wayne Burdick, N6KR, this circuit first appeared in the Wilderness Radio SST transceiver with an LED used at D1 for simultaneous signal indication and rectification. The selectivity provided by the crystal filter preceding the detector works to mitigate the effects of increasing detector distortion with gain reduction. [Circuit courtesy of Wayne Burdick, N6KR, and Bob Dyer, K6KK]

version gain, 18 dB. Note that in contrast to the diode-based mixers described earlier, which have conversion *loss*, most Gilbert-cell mixers have conversion *gain*. Considering the SA602/612's low current drain, its input IP_3 (measured at 45 MHz with 60-kHz spacing) is usefully good at −15 dBm. Factoring in the mixer's conversion gain results in an equivalent output IP_3 of about 3 dBm.

The SA602/612's on-board oscillator can operate up to 200 MHz in LC and crystal-controlled configurations (**Figure 12.46** shows three possibilities). Alternatively, energy from an external LO can be applied to the chip's pin 6 via a dc blocking capacitor. At least 200 mV P-P of external LO drive is required for proper mixer operation.

The SA602/612 was intended to be used as the second mixer in double-conversion FM cellular radios, in which the first IF is typically 45 MHz, and the second IF is typically 455 kHz. Such a receiver's second mixer can be relatively weak in terms of dynamic range because of the adjacent-signal protection afforded by the high selectivity of the first-IF filter preceding it. When used as a first mixer, the SA602/612 can provide a two-tone third-order dynamic range between 80 and 90 dB, but this figure is greatly diminished if a preamplifier is used ahead of the SA602/612 to improve the system's noise figure.

When the SA602/612 is used as a second mixer, the sum of the gains preceding it should not exceed about 10 dB. An SA602/612 can serve as low-distortion (THD <1%) product detector if overload is avoided through the use of AGC and appropriate attenuation between the '602/612 and the IF strip that drives it.

The SA602/612 is generally not a good choice for VHF and higher-frequency mixers because of its input noise and diminishing IMD performance at high frequencies. There are applications, however, where 6-dB noise figure and 60- to 70-dB dynamic range performance is adequate. If your target specifications exceed these numbers, you should consider other mixers at VHF and up.

Figure 12.47 shows the schematic of a complete 7-MHz direct-conversion receiver based on the SA602/612 and the widely used LM386 AF power amplifier IC. Such simple product-detector-based receivers sometimes suffer from incidental envelope detection, which causes audio from strong, full-carrier-AM shortwave or medium-wave broadcast stations to be audible regardless of where the receiver LO is tuned. RF attenuation and/or band-limiting the receiver input with a double- or triple-tuned-circuit filter can usually reduce this effect to inaudibility.

Receiving   12.41

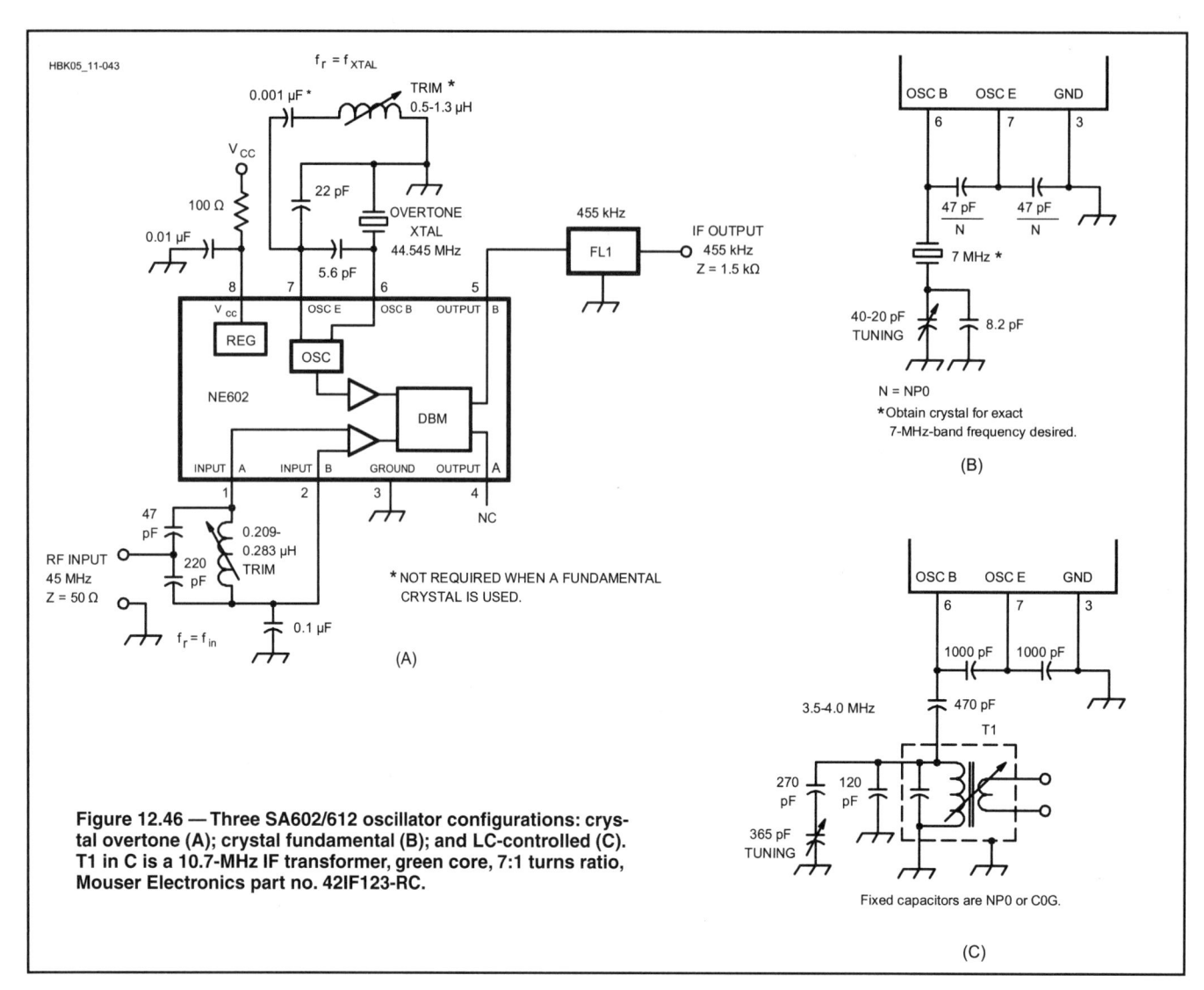

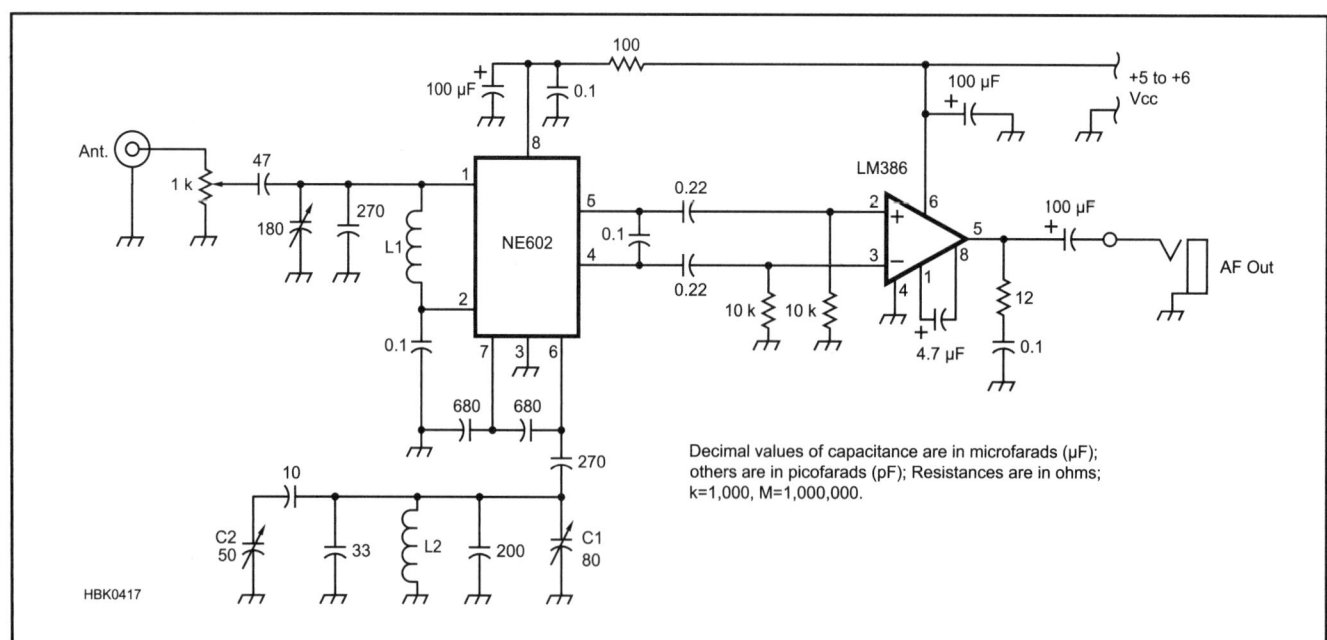

Figure 12.46 — Three SA602/612 oscillator configurations: crystal overtone (A); crystal fundamental (B); and LC-controlled (C). T1 in C is a 10.7-MHz IF transformer, green core, 7:1 turns ratio, Mouser Electronics part no. 42IF123-RC.

Figure 12.47 — A 7-MHz direct-conversion receiver based on the NE602/SA602/612. Equipped with a stage or two of audio filtering and a means of muting during transmit periods, such a receiver is entirely sufficient for basic Amateur Radio communication at MF and HF. L1 and L2 are 1.2 µH. This receiver is described in greater detail in *Experimental Methods in RF Design*.

12.42   Chapter 12

12.5 Demodulation and Detection

Translating information from radio form back into its original form — demodulation — is also traditionally called *detection*. If the information signal we want to detect consists merely of a baseband signal frequency-shifted into the radio realm, almost any low-distortion frequency-shifter that works according to the sidebar "Mixer Math: Mixing as Multiplication" can do the job acceptably well.

Sometimes we recover a radio signal's information by shifting the signal back to its original form with no intermediate frequency shifts. This is direct conversion. More commonly, we first convert a received signal to an intermediate frequency so we can amplify, filter and level-control it prior to detection. This is superheterodyne reception.

Whatever the receiver type, however, the received signal ultimately makes its way to one last mixer or demodulator (analog or digital) that completes the final translation of information back into audio, video, or into a signal form suitable for device control or computer processing.

In a heterodyne receiver's last translation, the incoming signal is converted back to recovered-information form by mixing it with one last RF signal. In heterodyne or *product detection*, that final frequency-shifting signal comes from a BFO. The incoming-signal energy goes into one mixer input port, BFO energy goes into the other, and audio (or whatever form the desired information takes) results.

In SDR receivers, the process may involve the digital equivalent of the analog process or some other mathematical process may be used.

12.5.1 Envelope Detection and Full-Carrier AM

If the incoming signal is full-carrier AM and we don't need to hear the carrier as a tone, we can modify this process somewhat, if we want. We can use the carrier itself to provide the heterodyning energy in a process called *envelope detection*.

A full-carrier AM signal's *modulation envelope* corresponds to the shape of the modulating wave. If we can derive from the

Figure 12.48 — Radio's simplest demodulator, the diode rectifier (A), demodulates an AM signal by acting as a switch that multiplies the carrier and sidebands to produce frequency sums and differences, two of which sum into a replica of the original modulation (B). Modern receivers often use an emitter follower to provide low-impedance drive for their diode detectors (C).

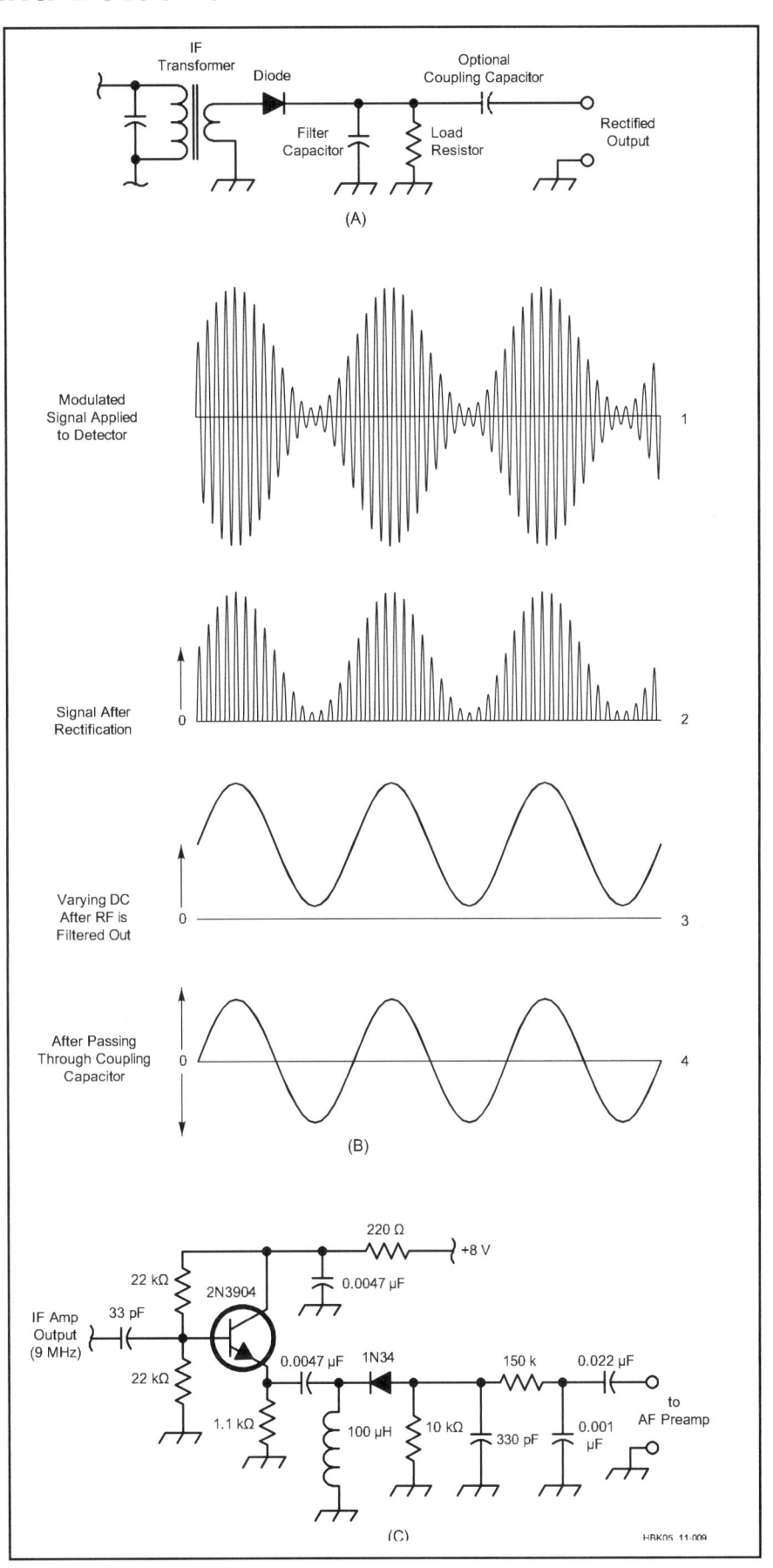

Receiving 12.43

modulated signal a voltage that varies according to the modulation envelope, we will have successfully recovered the information present in the sidebands. This process is called *envelope detection*, and we can achieve it by doing nothing more complicated than half-wave-rectifying the modulated signal with a diode (**Figure 12.48**).

That a diode demodulates an AM signal by allowing its carrier to multiply with its sidebands may jar those long accustomed to seeing diode detection ascribed merely to "rectification." But a diode is certainly nonlinear. It passes current in only one direction, and its output voltage is (within limits) proportional to the square of its input voltage. These nonlinearities allow it to multiply.

Exploring this mathematically is tedious with full-carrier AM because the process squares three summed components (carrier, lower sideband and upper sideband). Rather than fill the better part of a page with algebra, we'll instead characterize the outcome verbally: In "just rectifying" a DSB, full-carrier AM signal, a diode detector produces

• Direct current (the result of rectifying the carrier);
• A second harmonic of the carrier;
• A second harmonic of the lower sideband;
• A second harmonic of the upper sideband;
• Two difference-frequency outputs (upper sideband minus carrier, carrier minus lower sideband), each of which is equivalent to the modulating wave-form's frequency, and both of which sum to produce the recovered information signal; and
• A second harmonic of the modulating waveform (the frequency difference between the two sidebands).

Three of these products are RF signals. Low-pass filtering, sometimes little more than a simple RC network, can remove the RF products from the detector output. A capacitor in series with the detector output line can block the carrier-derived dc component. That done, only two signals remain: the recovered modulation and, at a lower level, its second harmonic — in other words, second-harmonic distortion of the desired information signal.

12.5.2 Detecting AM Signals

Note that the shape of the envelope of the modulated RF signal matches the shape of the modulating signal. (This is only true for full AM including the carrier and both sidebands. The envelope of a single-sideband SSB signal is not an accurate reproduction of the modulating signal which is why it cannot be recovered by an envelope detector.) That suggests a possible demodulation method. A diode detector puts out a signal

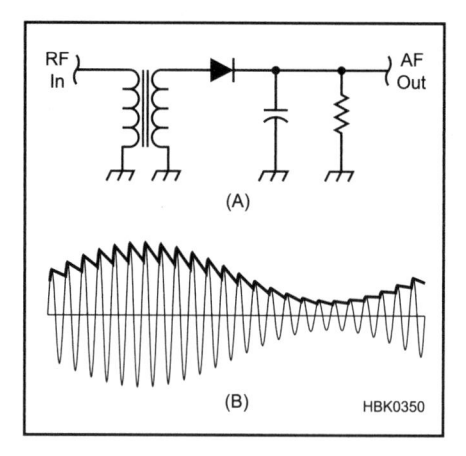

Figure 12.49 — A simple diode-type AM detector, also known as an *envelope detector* (A). The demodulated output waveform has the same shape as the envelope of the RF signal (B). In (B) the thin line is the RF signal modulated with a sine wave and the darker line is the demodulated audio frequency with some residual RF ripple.

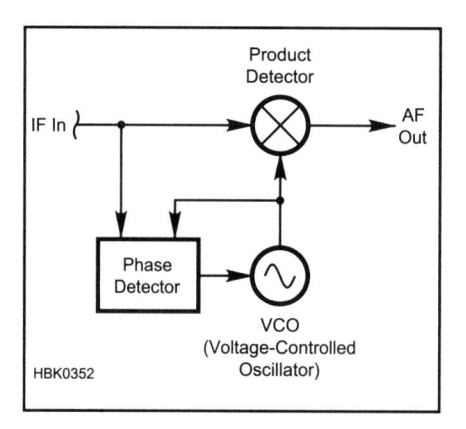

Figure 12.50 — Block diagram of a synchronous detector. The voltage-controlled oscillator (VCO) is part of a phase-locked loop that locks the oscillator to the carrier frequency of the incoming AM or DSBRC signal.

proportional to the envelope of the RF signal, recovering the original modulation. See **Figure 12.49**. The capacitor should be large enough that it filters out most of the RF ripple but not so large that it attenuates the higher audio frequencies.

One problem with AM is that if the amplitude of the carrier becomes attenuated for any reason, then the modulation is distorted, especially the negative-going portion near the 100%-modulation (zero power) point. This can happen due to a propagation phenomenon called *selective fading*. It occurs when the signal arrives simultaneously at the receive antenna via two or more paths, such as ground wave and sky wave. If the difference in the distance of the two paths is an odd number of half-wavelengths, then the two signals are out of phase. If the amplitudes are nearly the same, they cancel and a deep fade results. Since wavelength depends on frequency, the fading is frequency-selective. On the lower-frequency amateur bands it is possible for an AM carrier to be faded while the two sidebands are still audible.

A solution is to regenerate the carrier in the receiver. Since the carrier itself carries no information about the modulation, it is not necessary for demodulation. The transmitted signal may be a standard full-carrier AM signal or the carrier may be suppressed, resulting in double sideband, suppressed carrier (DSB-SC). An AM detector that regenerates the carrier from the signal is known as a *synchronous detector*. Often the regenerated carrier oscillator is part of a phase-locked loop (PLL) that locks onto the incoming carrier. See **Figure 12.50**. Synchronous detectors not only reduce the effects of selective fading but also are usually more linear than diode detectors so they have less distortion. Some commercial short-wave broadcasts include a reduced, but not suppressed, carrier (DSB-RC) to allow operation with PLL-type synchronous detectors.

Since the advent of single sideband in the 1960s, full-carrier double-sideband AM has become less popular in Amateur Radio. It does retain several advantages however. We have already mentioned the simplicity of the circuitry. Another advantage is that, because of the presence of the carrier, the automatic gain control system in the receiver remains engaged at all times, ensuring a constant audio level. Unlike with SSB, there is no rush of noise during every pause in speech. Also tuning is less critical than with SSB. There is no "Donald Duck" sound if the receiver is slightly mistuned. Finally, the audio quality of an AM signal is usually better than that of SSB because of the lack of a crystal filter in the transmit path and the wider filter in the receiver.

SDR AM SQUARE-LAW DETECTOR

(*This section is taken from the Jul/Aug 2009 QEX column SDR: Simplified by W5IFS.*) We need to convert the full-carrier double sideband signal into the baseband information. One of the classic AM demodulation methods is a *square-law detector*. Very few devices have a true square law response over a large range of signals. The JFET comes close, but has limited range. With DSP we can implement a square law detector with range that is limited only by the size of the data that the DSP can handle. If we use 16-bit data for the input, our multiplier must have a 32-bit result. This is a very simple and fast operation for the DSP.

The square-law response to a DSB-AM signal with a carrier, sin(y), and two sidebands, cos(x-y) and cos(x+y) is as follows:

$V_{out} = (1\sin(y) + \frac{1}{2}\cos(x-y) - \frac{1}{2}\cos(x+y))^2$

Applying trig identities and working through the math:

$V_{out} = \sin(y)^2 + \sin(y)\cos(x-y) - \sin(y)\cos(x+y) + \frac{1}{4}\cos(x+y)^2 + \frac{1}{4}\cos(x-y)^2$

$V_{out} = \frac{3}{4} - \frac{1}{2}\sin(2y) + \frac{1}{2}\sin(x) + \frac{1}{2}\sin(2y-x) - \frac{1}{2}\sin(-x) - \frac{1}{2}\sin(2y+x) + \frac{1}{8}\cos(2y+2x) + \frac{1}{8}\cos(2y-2x)$

Finally:

$V_{out} = \frac{3}{4} + 1\sin(x) - \frac{1}{2}\sin(2y) + \frac{1}{2}\sin(2y-x) - \frac{1}{2}\sin(2y+x) + \frac{1}{8}\cos(2y+2x) + \frac{1}{8}\cos(2y-2x)$

(This result will have 32 bits, but our filter math should only be 16 bits. We can divide the result by 65536 to get the signal back into range for further operations. In software, this just means we throw away the bottom 16 bits of data before we store the result.)

The signal we want is sin(x), but we have a significant dc component (¾) and a whole bunch of unwanted signals at or close to twice the carrier frequency, 2y. The only real problem is the dc component, since it is really close to the desired audio signal. We need to use a band-pass filter to remove the dc and the RF components. Since all but the dc are far removed from the desired audio, we can use a relatively simple band-pass filter.

12.5.3 Demodulating SSB Signals

A complete discussion of the three main techniques used to receive and demodulate SSB signals — filter, phasing, and Weaver — can be found in the **Modulation** chapter. Examples of practical circuits that implement these methods are included in the receiver projects provided in the downloadable supplemental information.

HETERODYNE RECEIVERS

As with an AM synchronous detector, the carrier is regenerated in a superheterodyne receiver but since only one sideband is present, the synchronous detector's phase-locked loop (described above) is not possible. Instead, the detector uses a free-running *beat-frequency oscillator* (BFO). The detector itself is called a *product detector* because its output is the mathematical product of the BFO and the SSB signal. The BFO must be tuned to the same frequency as the suppressed carrier to prevent distortion of the recovered audio. That is done by carefully tuning the local oscillator (the main tuning dial) such that after conversion to the intermediate frequency, the suppressed carrier aligns with the BFO frequency. Demodulation of SSB signals in an analog heterodyne receiver must be done using a product detector or equivalent technique. Envelope detection will not work because the waveform does not have the shape of the modulating waveform.

SDR RECEIVERS

SDR receivers use I/Q quadrature demodulator architecture for SSB and many other modes. This technique is discussed in the **Modulation** chapter. A block diagram of an SDR demodulator for SSB is shown in **Figure 12.51**. This particular system shows the phasing method of SSB generation in reverse. The excellent tutorial, "Understanding the 'Phasing Method' of Single Sideband Demodulation" by Rick Lyons (www.dsprelated.com/showarticle/176.php) explains the technique in detail. The filter method and the Weaver method can also be implemented with an I/Q architecture although this is not the usual method used by designers.

A quadrature I/Q demodulator generates the I_1 and Q_1 signals which are low-pass filtered to remove high-frequency components, then down-converted using decimation. The I and Q channels are band-pass filtered, with a Hilbert transformer applied to the Q channel as described in the **DSP and SDR Fundamentals** chapter. The resulting streams are then combined so that the Q channel is subtracted from the I channel. This leaves the USB signal, which is converted to analog audio, and low-pass filtered.

If a LSB signal is being received, change the summing symbol immediately preceding the DAC so as to add the I and Q channels together. This produces the LSB signal which is then converted to audio and filtered as before. In practice, both the LSB and USB signals are available at any time and the digital audio stream can be routed to the DAC and low-pass filter under software control.

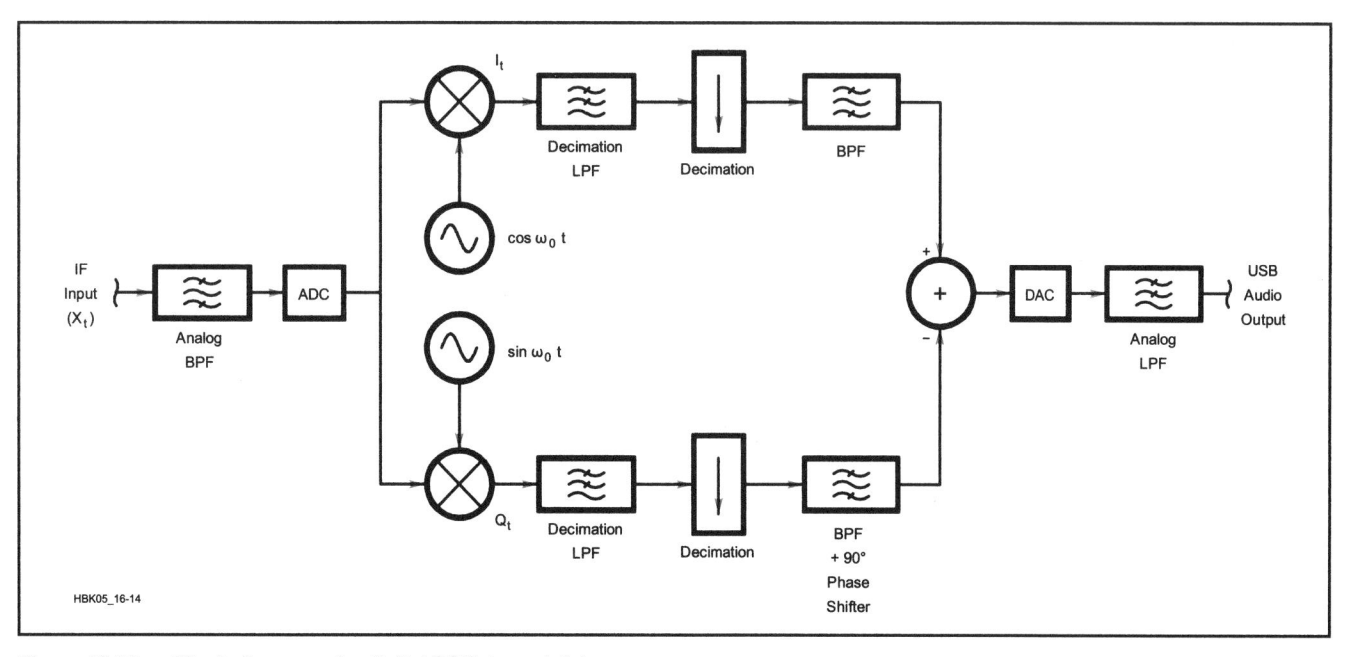

Figure 12.51 — Block diagram of a digital SSB demodulator.

Figure 12.52 — Frequency-sweeping a constant-amplitude signal and passing it through a low-pass filter results in an output signal that varies in amplitude with frequency. This is the principle behind the angle-demodulation process called *frequency discrimination*.

12.5.4 Demodulating FM and PM

ANALOG DEMODULATORS

Although angle modulation does generate an infinite number of sidebands, demodulating angle modulation requires little more than turning it into AM and then envelope- or product-detecting it! But this is what happens in many of our FM receivers and transceivers, and we can get a handle on this process by realizing that a form of angle-modulation-to-AM conversion is created from linear distortion of the modulation by amplitude-linear circuitry. This happens to angle-modulated signals in any linear circuit that doesn't have an amplitude-versus-frequency response that's utterly flat out to infinity.

Think of what happens, for example, when we sweep a constant-amplitude signal up in frequency — say, from 1 kHz to 8 kHz — and pass it through a 6-dB-per-octave filter (**Figure 12.52**). The filter's rolloff causes the output signal's amplitude to decrease as frequency increases. Now imagine that we linearly sweep our constant-amplitude signal *back and forth* between 1 kHz and 8 kHz at a constant rate of 3 kHz per second. The filter's output *amplitude* now varies cyclically over time as the input signal's *frequency* varies cyclically over time. Right before our eyes, a frequency change turns into an amplitude change. The process of converting angle modulation to amplitude modulation has begun.

This is what happens whenever an angle-modulated signal passes through circuitry with an amplitude-versus-frequency response that isn't flat out to infinity. As the signal deviates across the frequency-response curves of whatever circuitry passes it, its

Figure 12.53 — A *discriminator* (A) converts an angle-modulated signal's deviation into an amplitude variation (B) and envelope-detects the resulting AM signal. For undistorted demodulation, the discriminator's amplitude-versus-frequency characteristic must be linear across the input signal's deviation. A *crystal discriminator* uses a crystal as part of its frequency-selective circuitry. The *ratio detector* at (C) operates similarly but has an improved rejection of amplitude modulated noise.

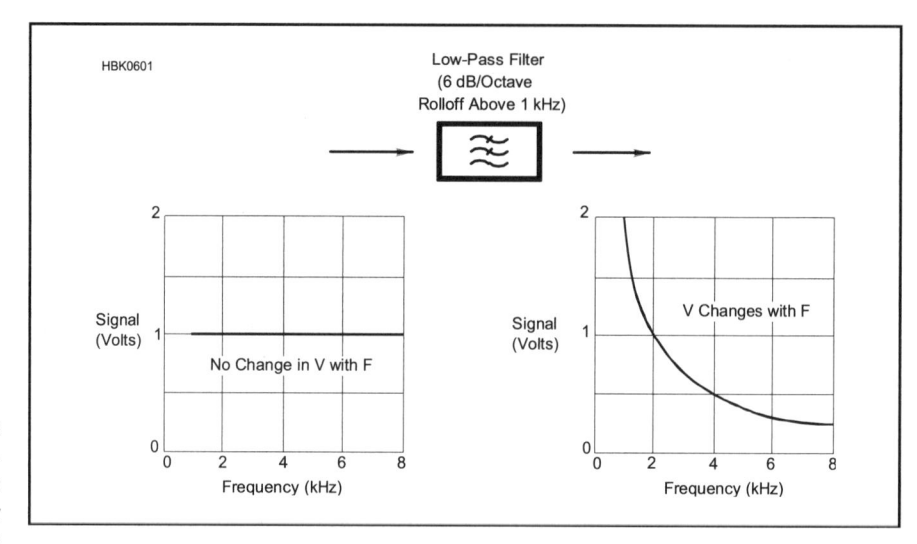

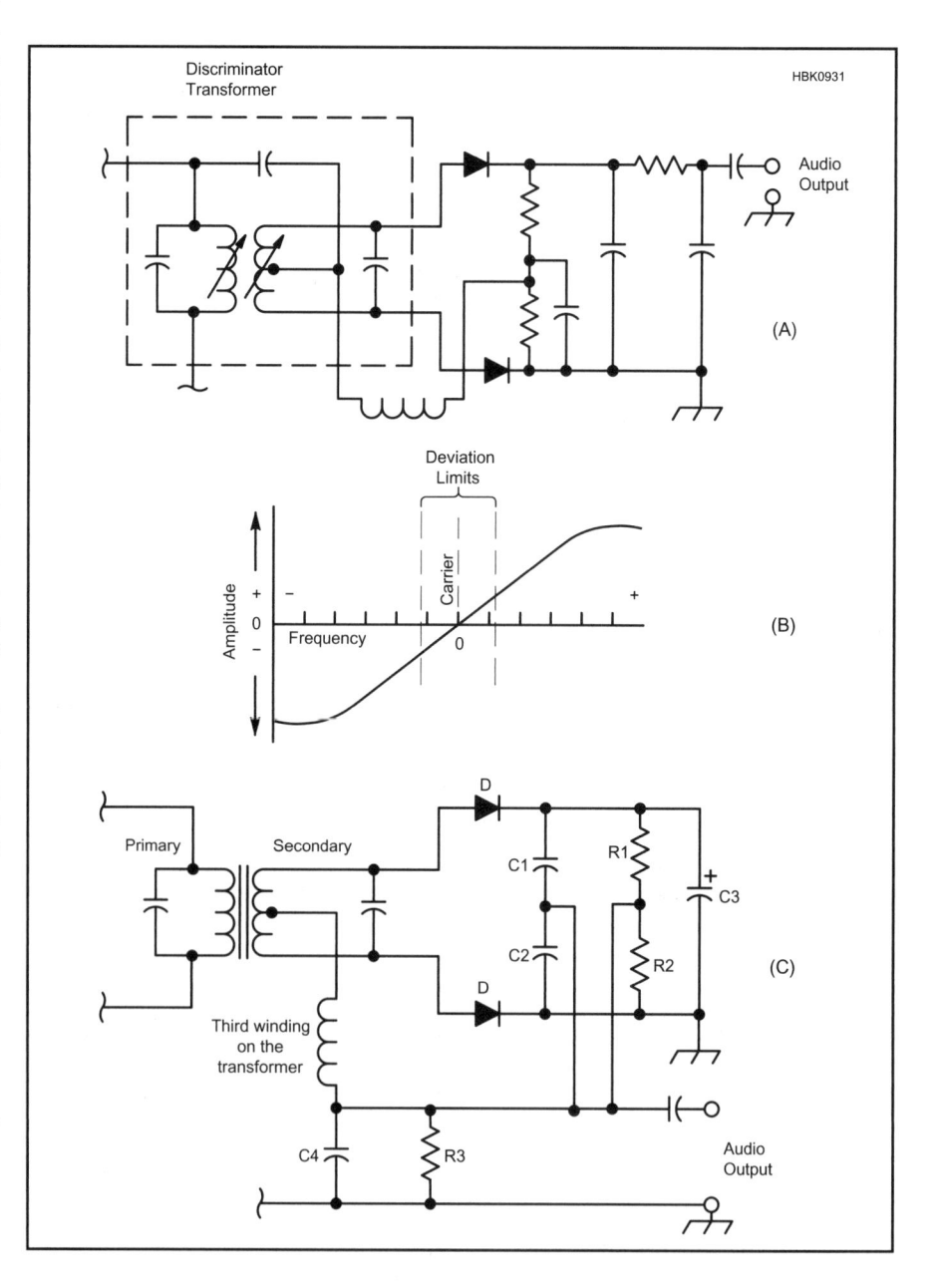

angle modulation is, to some degree, converted to AM — a form of crosstalk between the two modulation types, if we wish to look at it that way. (Variations in system phase linearity also cause distortion and FM-to-AM conversion, because the sidebands do not have the proper phase relationship with respect to each other and with respect to the carrier.)

All we need to do to put this effect to practical use is develop a circuit that does this frequency-to-amplitude conversion linearly across the frequency span of the modulated signal's deviation. Then we envelope-demodulate the resulting AM, and we have achieved angle demodulation.

Figure 12.53 shows such a circuit — a Foster-Seeley *discriminator* — and the sort of amplitude-versus-frequency response we expect from it. (**www.radio-electronics.com/info/rf-technology-design/fm-reception/foster-seeley-fm-detector-discriminator.php**) It's actually possible to use an AM receiver to recover understandable audio from a narrow angle-modulated signal by "off-tuning" the signal so its deviation rides up and down on one side of the receiver's IF selectivity curve. This *slope detection* process served as an early, suboptimal form of frequency discrimination in receivers not designed for FM It is always worth trying as a last-resort-class means of receiving narrowband FM with an AM receiver.

The ratio detector in Figure 12.53C is a variation on the discriminator which is better at rejecting AM noise mixed with the FM signal. (**www.radio-electronics.com/info/rf-technology-design/fm-reception/ratio-fm-detector-discriminator.php**) Note that the diodes are in series in this circuit. A similar phase shift occurs in the third transformer winding as the signal moves away from the frequency of the tuned transformer winding. This causes an imbalance in the transformer secondary and current flows in the third winding. That signal is then filtered by C_4 and R_3 before being passed to the audio stages of the receiver.

QUADRATURE DETECTORS

It's also possible to demodulate an angle-modulated signal merely by multiplying it with a time-delayed copy of itself in a double-balanced mixer as shown in **Figure 12.54**; the sidebar, "Mixer Math: Quadrature Demodulation," explains the process numerically.

An ideal quadrature detector puts out 0 V dc when no modulation is present (with the carrier at f_c). The output of a real quadrature detector may include a small *dc offset* that requires compensation. If we need the detector's response all the way down to dc, we've got it; if not, we can put a suitable blocking capacitor in the output line for ac-only coupling.

Quadrature detection is more common than frequency discrimination in current receivers because it doesn't require a special discriminator transformer or resonator, and because the necessary balanced-detector circuitry can easily be implemented in IC structures along with limiters and other receiver circuitry. The NXP Semiconductor SA604A FM IF IC is one example of this; **Figure 12.55** shows another, the Freescale Semiconductor (formerly Motorola) MC3359

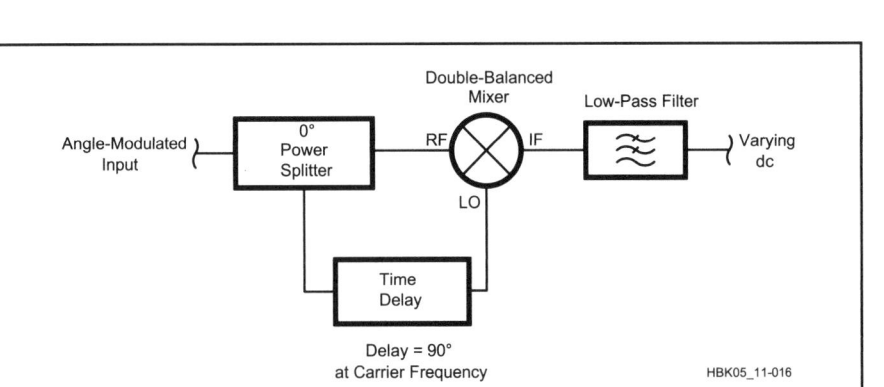

Figure 12.54 — In *quadrature detection*, an angle-modulated signal multiplies with a time-delayed copy of itself to produce a dc voltage that varies with the amplitude and polarity of its phase or frequency excursions away from the carrier frequency. A practical quadrature detector can be as simple as a 0° power splitter (that is, a power splitter with in-phase outputs), a diode double-balanced mixer, a length of coaxial cable ¼-λ (electrical) long at the carrier frequency, and a bit of low-pass filtering to remove the detector output's RF components. IC quadrature detectors achieve their time delay with one or more resistor-loaded tuned circuits (Figure 12.55).

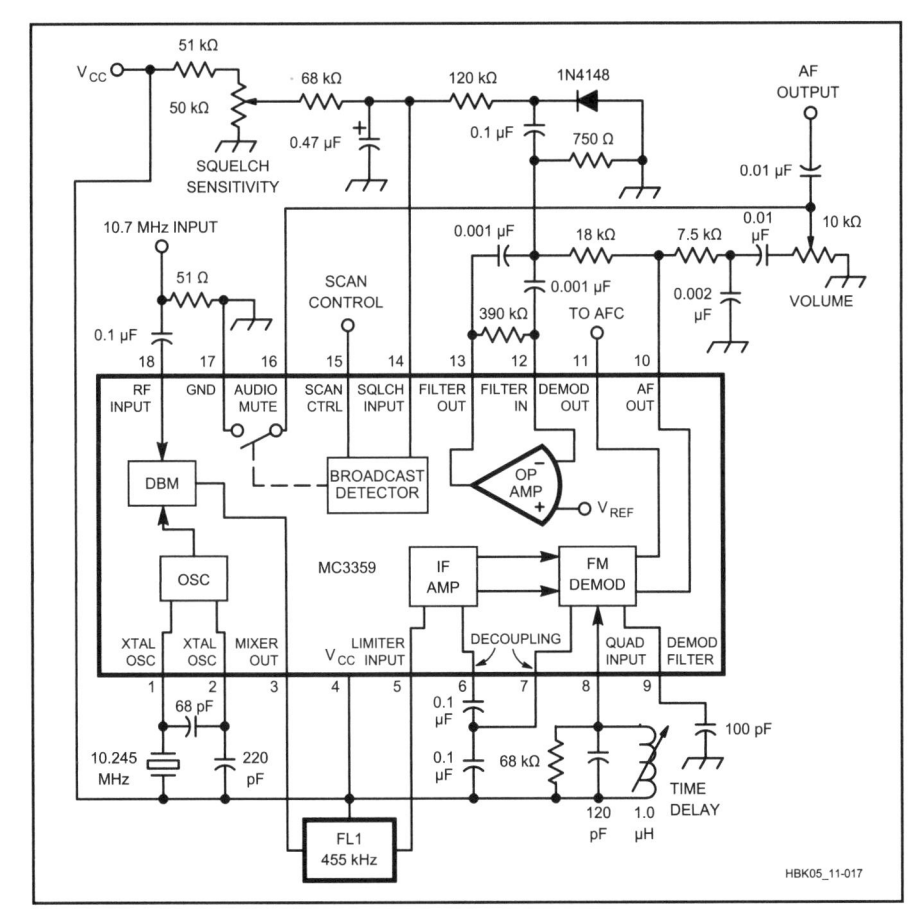

Figure 12.55 — The Freescale MC3359/NTE680 is one of many FM subsystem ICs that include limiter and quadrature-detection circuitry. The TIME DELAY coil is adjusted for minimum recovered-audio distortion.

Receiving 12.47

(equivalent, NTE860). Quadrature detection is also simple to perform in SDR designs.

AMPLITUDE LIMITING

FM radio communication systems are superior to AM in their ability to suppress and ignore static, manmade electrical noise and (through a characteristic called *capture effect*) co-channel signals sufficiently weaker than the desired signal. AM-noise immunity and capture effect are not intrinsic to angle modulation, however; they must be designed into the angle-modulation receiver in the form of signal amplitude *limiting*.

The amplitude of a quadrature detector's input signal affects the amplitude of a quadrature detector's three output signals. A quadrature detector therefore responds to AM, and so does a frequency discriminator. To achieve FM's excellent amplitude noise immunity, then, these angle demodulators must be preceded by *limiter* circuitry that removes all amplitude variations from the incoming signal.

SDR ANGLE DEMODULATION

A popular technique for angle demodulation starts with a phase detector as shown in **Figure 12.56**. The angle-modulated signal is down-converted to a convenient frequency and input to a pair of multipliers where it is mixed with a pair of constant frequency LO signals in quadrature. Low-pass filters then remove signals at the sum frequency, leaving only the I and Q baseband signals.

In PM demodulation, the phase comparison is an absolute comparison against the carrier phase. The phase angle of the input signal, relative to the LO center frequency, can be determined from the I and Q signals as:

$$\varphi = \tan^{-1}\left(\frac{V_Q}{V_I}\right)$$

The arctan function can be computed either by polynomial approximations or a lookup table, depending on system resources. If the signal is a PM signal, the phase signal contains the original modulation and can be filtered and output as audio.

FM demodulation requires additional steps as a special case of PM. The change in angle from the unmodulated carrier is constantly increasing or decreasing and exceeds ±90° as a normal part of operation. For that reason, a simple phase comparator using the recovered carrier will not demodulate FM. FM requires that we measure the rate-of-change of phase and sum those incremental phase changes.

Since frequency is defined as the rate-of-change of phase, it is necessary to differentiate the phase signal to recover the FM modulation signal. Implementing differentiation in DSP involves subtracting each sample from the previous sample. It is necessary to account for the point at which phase passes through 360° and resets to 0°. This can be done through special routines or by scaling of fixed-point data in the computations so that the phase rollover and integer rollover (65535 to 0, for example, in 16-bit math) coincide.

The FM signal will also need a de-emphasis filter (see the **Modulation** and **Transmitting** chapters) to cancel the high-frequency gain that was added during the FM process by the modulator.

Mixer Math: Quadrature Demodulation

Demodulating an angle-modulated signal merely by multiplying it with a time-delayed copy of itself in a double-balanced mixer results in quadrature demodulation (Figure 12.54). To illustrate this mathematically, for simplicity's sake, we'll represent the mixer's RF input signal as just a sine wave with an amplitude, A:

$$A \sin(2\pi f t)$$

and its time-delayed twin, fed to the mixer's LO input, as a sine wave with an amplitude, A, and a time delay of d:

$$A \sin[2\pi f(t+d)]$$

Setting this special mixing arrangement into motion, we see

$$A \sin(2\pi f t) \times A \sin(2\pi f t + d)$$

$$= \frac{A^2}{2}\cos(2\pi f d) - \frac{A^2}{2}\cos(2\pi f d)\cos(2 \times 2\pi f t) + \frac{A^2}{2}\sin(2\pi f d)\sin(2 \times 2\pi f t)$$

Two of the three outputs — the second and third terms — emerge at twice the input frequency; in practice, we're not interested in these, and filter them out. The remaining term — the one we're after — varies in amplitude and sign according to how far and in what direction the carrier shifts away from its resting or center frequency (at which the time delay, d, causes the mixer's RF and LO inputs to be exactly 90° out of phase — in *quadrature* — with each other). We can examine this effect by replacing f in the RF input and LO input sinusoids with the sum term $f_c + f_s$, where f_c is the center frequency and f_s is the frequency shift. A 90° time delay is the same as a quarter cycle of f_c, so we can restate d as

$$d = \frac{1}{4f_c}$$

The first term of the detector's output then becomes

$$\frac{A^2}{2}\cos(2\pi(f_c + f_s)d)$$

$$= \frac{A^2}{2}\cos\left(2\pi(f_c + f_s)\frac{1}{4f_c}\right)$$

$$= \frac{A^2}{2}\cos\left(\frac{\pi}{2} + \frac{\pi f_s}{2f_c}\right)$$

When f_s is zero (that is, when the carrier is at its center frequency), this reduces to

$$\frac{A^2}{2}\cos\left(\frac{\pi}{2}\right) = 0$$

As the input signal shifts higher in frequency than f_c, the detector puts out a positive dc voltage that increases with the shift. When the input signal shifts lower in frequency than fc, the detector puts out a negative dc voltage that increases with the shift. The detector therefore recovers the input signal's frequency or phase modulation as an amplitude-varying dc voltage that shifts in sign as f_s varies around f_c — in other words, as ac. We have demodulated FM by means of quadrature detection.

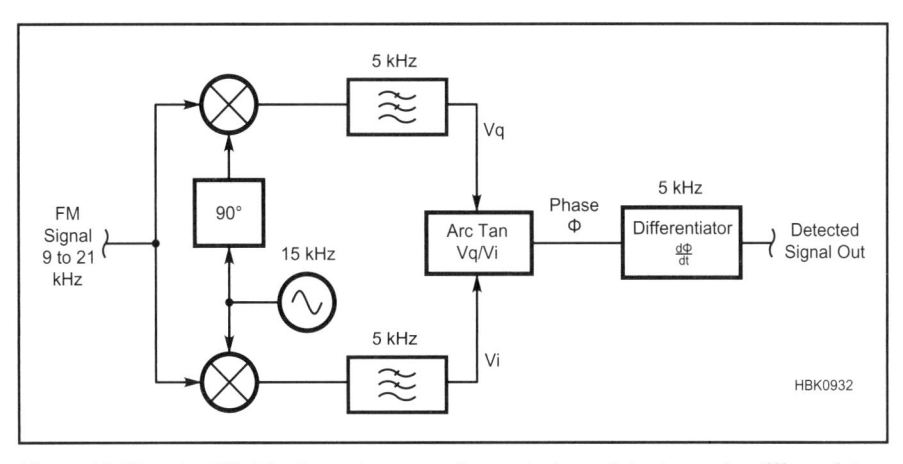

Figure 12.56 — An FM detector using an arctangent phase detector and a differentiator.

12.6 Automatic Gain Control (AGC)

The amplitude of the desired signal at each point in the receiver is generally controlled by the AGC system, although manual control is usually provided as well. Each stage has a distortion versus signal level characteristic that must be known, and the stage input level must not become excessive. The signal being received has a certain signal-to-distortion ratio that must not be degraded too much by the receiver. For example, if an SSB signal has −30 dB distortion products the receiver should create additional distortion no greater than −40 dB with respect to the desired signal. The correct AGC design ensures that each stage gets the right input level. It is often necessary to redesign some stages in order to accomplish this task.

While this chapter deals mostly with AGC in the guise of analog circuits, the same function is also implemented digitally in DSP and SDR receivers. The goal of both is the same — to maintain a signal level at all stages of the receiver that is neither too large nor too small so that the various processing systems operate properly. Whether or not the AGC offset and time constant are implemented by an analog component or by a microprocessor output is immaterial. The point is to manage the RF amplifier gain so that the overall receiver behavior is satisfactory.

AGC in the receive signal chain of an SDR should not be confused with AGC in an analog receiver. AGC in the analog receiver will adjust the fixed dynamic range of the receiver up or down, altering the weak and strong signal performance of the radio dynamically.

The effects of an improperly operating AGC system can be quite subtle or nearly disabling to a receiver and vary with how the AGC system is constructed. This chapter attempts to describe the requirements for proper operation and provides some examples of implementation and common AGC failures in terms of analog circuitry which is somewhat easier to describe than software algorithms, noting that similar behaviors exist even in purely software receivers. The interested student should consider studying the AGC systems of commercial receivers to understand how professional design teams deal with the problem of managing so much gain with such stringent requirements for linearity and distortion.

THE AGC LOOP

Figure 12.57A shows a typical AGC loop that is often used in amateur superhet receivers. The AGC is applied to the stages through RF decoupling circuits that prevent the stages from interacting with each other. The AGC amplifier helps to provide enough AGC loop gain so that the gain-control characteristic of Figure 12.57B is achieved. If effect, the AGC system causes the receiver to act as a compression amplifier with lower overall gain for stronger signals.

The AGC action does not begin until a certain level, called the AGC *threshold*, is reached. The THRESHOLD VOLTS input in Figure 12.57A serves this purpose. After that level is exceeded, the audio level increases more slowly than for weaker signals. The audio rise beyond the threshold value is usually in the 5 to 10 dB range. Too much or too little audio rise are both undesirable for most operators.

As an option, the AGC signal to the RF amplifier is offset by the 0.6 V forward drop of the diode so that the RF gain does not start to decrease until larger signals appear. This prevents a premature increase of the receiver noise figure. Also, a time constant of one or two seconds after this diode helps keep the RF gain steady for the short term.

Figure 12.58 is a typical plot of the signal levels at the various stages of a certain ham band receiver using analog circuitry. Each stage has the proper level and a 115 dB change in input level produces a 10 dB change in audio level. A manual gain control could produce the same effect.

AGC PUMPING

AGC *pumping* can occur in receivers in which the AGC measurement point is located ahead of the stages that determine operating bandwidth, such as when an audio filter is added to a receiver externally and outside the reach of the AGC system. If the weak signal is the only signal within the first IF passband, the AGC will cause the receiver to be at maximum gain and optimum SNR. If an interfering signal is within the first IF passband, but outside the audio DSP filter's passband, we won't hear the interfering signal, but it will enter the AGC system and reduce the gain so we might not hear our desired weak signal. AGC pumping is audible as sudden reductions in signal strength without a strong signal in the passband of the receiver.

AGC pumping is generally not as much of a problem in SDR receivers as it is in heterodyne receivers but the phenomena still exists. The severity depends on the algorithm employed by the SDR and the operating configuration controlled by the user.

AGC TIME CONSTANTS

There are two primary AGC time constants. AGC *attack time* describes the time it takes the AGC system to respond to the presence of a signal. AGC *decay time* describes the response of the AGC system to changes in a

Receiving 12.49

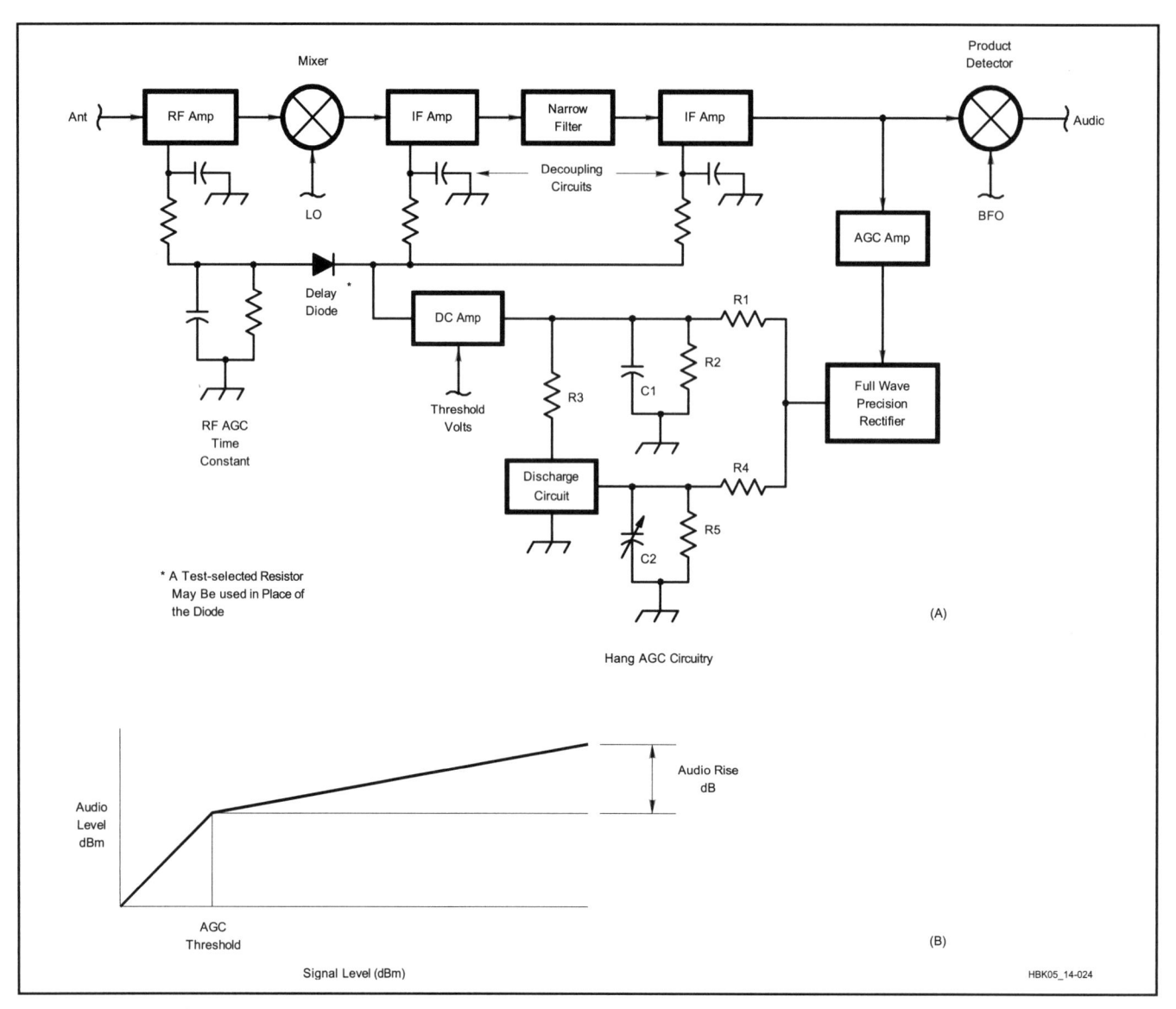

Figure 12.57 — AGC principles. At A: typical superhet receiver with AGC applied to multiple RF and IF stages. At B: audio output level as a function of antenna signal level.

signal that is present. The optimum time constants for the AGC system depends on the type of signal being received, the type of operation being conducted, and the operator's preference.

The operator usually has a control that allows for setting the time that it takes the AGC to recover or decay. If we are listening to two relatively loud stations converse, we may set the AGC to slow. Then as each station stops transmitting, the noise floor is slow to rise and we often hear the next station before the noise floor is again heard. In contrast, we may set the AGC decay time to fast which allows us to hear a weak station immediately after the strong station.

In Figure 12.57, following the precision rectifier, R1 and C1 set an attack time, to prevent excessively fast application of AGC. One or two milliseconds is a good value for the R1 × C1 product. If the antenna signal suddenly disappears, the AGC loop is opened because the precision rectifier stops conducting. C1 then discharges through R2 and the C1 × R2 product can be in the range of 100 to 200 ms. At some point the rectifier again becomes active, and the loop is closed again.

An optional modification of this behavior is the *hang AGC* circuit. If we make R2 × C1 much longer, say 3 seconds or more, the AGC voltage remains almost constant until the R5, C2 circuit decays with a switch selectable time constant of 100 to 1000 ms. At that time R3 quickly discharges C1 and full receiver gain is quickly restored. This type of control is appreciated by many operators because of the lack of AGC pumping due to modulation, rapid fading and other sudden signal level changes.

In an SDR receiver, the typical AGC algorithm has a fast-attack and slow-decay that is adjustable. The AGC algorithm has a gain value that it applies to the receiver buffers which persists from one buffer to the next. If a loud signal appears while the gain is set high, it immediately lowers the gain to prevent a loud sound in our headphones. Once the sound has subsided, the gain is allowed to slowly increase back to its previous value.

AGC LOOP RESPONSE PROBLEMS

If the various stages have the property that each 1 V change in AGC voltage changes the gain by a constant amount (in dB), the AGC loop is said to be *log-linear* and regular feedback principles can be used to analyze and design the loop. But there are some difficulties that complicate this textbook model. One has already been mentioned, that when the

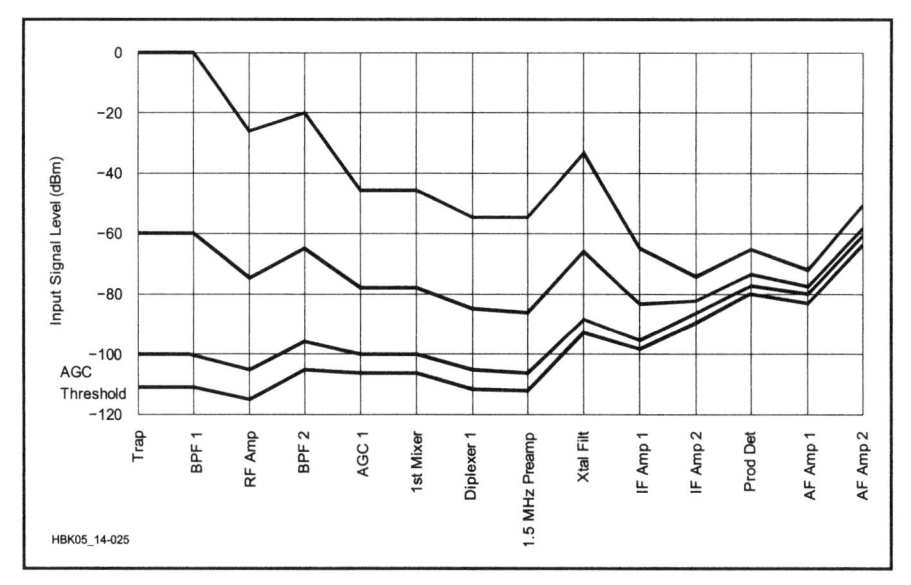

Figure 12.58 — Gain control of a ham-band receiver using AGC. A manual gain control could produce the same result.

12.6.1 Audio-Derived AGC

Some receivers, especially direct-conversion types, use audio-derived AGC. There are problems with this approach as well. At low audio frequencies the AGC control action can be slow to develop. That is, low-frequency audio sine waves take longer to reach their peaks than the AGC time constants. During this time the RF/IF/AF stages can be over-driven. If the RF and IF gains are kept at a low level this problem can be reduced. Also, attenuating low audio frequencies prior to the first audio amplifier should help. With audio AGC, it is important to avoid so-called "charge pump" rectifiers or other slow-responding circuits that require multiple cycles of audio to pump up the AGC voltage. Instead, use a peak-detecting circuit that responds accurately on the first positive or negative half-cycle.

12.6.2 AGC Circuits

Figure 12.59 shows some gain-controllable circuits. Figure 12.59A shows a two-stage 455-kHz IF amplifier with PIN diode gain control. This circuit is a simplified adaptation from a production receiver, the Collins 651S. The IF amplifier section shown is preceded and followed by selectivity circuits and additional gain stages with AGC. The 1.0 µF capacitors aid in loop compensation. The favorable thing about this approach is that the transistors remain biased at their optimum operating point. Right at the point at which the diodes start to conduct, a small increase in IMD may be noticed, but that goes away as diode current increases slightly. Two or more diodes can be used in series, if this is a problem (it very seldom is). Another solution is to use a PIN diode that is more suitable for such a low-frequency IF. Look for a device with $\tau > 10 / (2\pi f)$ where τ is the minority carrier lifetime in ms and f is the frequency in MHz.

Figure 12.59B is an audio derived AGC circuit using a full-wave rectifier that responds to positive or negative excursions of the audio signal. The RC circuit follows the audio closely.

Figure 12.59C shows a typical circuit for the MC1350P RF/IF amplifier. The graph of gain control versus AGC voltage shows the change in dB/V. If the control is limited to the first 20 dB of gain reduction this chip should be favorable for good AGC transient response and good IMD performance. Use multiple low-gain stages rather than a single high-gain stage for these reasons. The gain control within the MC1350P is accomplished by diverting signal current from the first amplifier stage into a *current sink*. This is also known as the *Gilbert cell multiplier* architecture. Another chip of this type is the

signal is rapidly decreasing the loop becomes open and the various capacitors discharge in an open loop manner. As the signal is increasing beyond the threshold, or if it is decreasing slowly enough, the feedback theory applies more accurately.

In SSB and CW receivers rapid changes are the rule and not the exception. It is important that the AGC loop not overshoot or ring when the signal level rises past the threshold. The idea is to design the ALC loop to be stable when the loop is closed. It obviously won't oscillate when open (during decay time). But the loop must have smooth and consistent transient response when the loop goes from open to closed state.

Another problem involves the narrow band-pass analog IF filters. The group delay of analog filters constitutes a time lag in the loop that can make loop stabilization difficult. Moreover, these filters nearly always have much greater group delay at the edges of the passband, so that loop problems are aggravated at these frequencies. Overshoots and undershoots, called *gulping*, are very common. Compensation networks that advance the phase of the feedback help to offset these group delays. The design problem arises because some of the AGC is applied before the filter and some after the filter. It is a good idea to put as much fast AGC as possible after the filter and use a slower decaying AGC ahead of the filter. The delay diode and RC in Figure 12.57A are helpful in that respect. Complex AGC designs using two or more compensated loops are also in the literature. If a second cascaded narrow filter is used in the IF it is usually a lot easier to leave the second or *downstream* filter out of the AGC loop at the risk of allowing AGC pumping as described in the preceding section.

Another problem is that the control characteristic is often not log-linear. For example, dual-gate MOSFETs tend to have much larger dB/V at large values of gain reduction. Many IC amplifiers have the same problem. The result is that large signals cause instability because of excessive loop gain. Variable gain op amps and other similar ICs are available that are intended for gain control loops.

Audio frequency components on the AGC bus can cause problems because the amplifier gains are modulated by the audio and distort the desired signal. A hang AGC circuit (essentially a low-pass filter) can reduce or eliminate this problem.

Finally, if we try to reduce the change in audio levels to a very low value, the required loop gain becomes very large, and stability problems become very difficult. It is much better to accept a 5 to 10 dB variation of audio output.

Because many parameters are involved and many of them are not strictly log-linear, it is best to achieve good AGC performance through an initial design effort and finalize the design experimentally. Use a signal generator, attenuator and a signal pulser (2 ms rise and fall times, adjustable pulse rate and duration) at the antenna and a synchronized oscilloscope to look at the IF envelope. Tweak the time constants and AGC distribution by means of resistor and capacitor decade substitution boxes. Be sure to test throughout the passband of each filter. The final result should be a smooth and pleasant sounding SSB/CW response, even with maximum RF gain and strong signals. Patience and experience are helpful.

Receiving   12.51

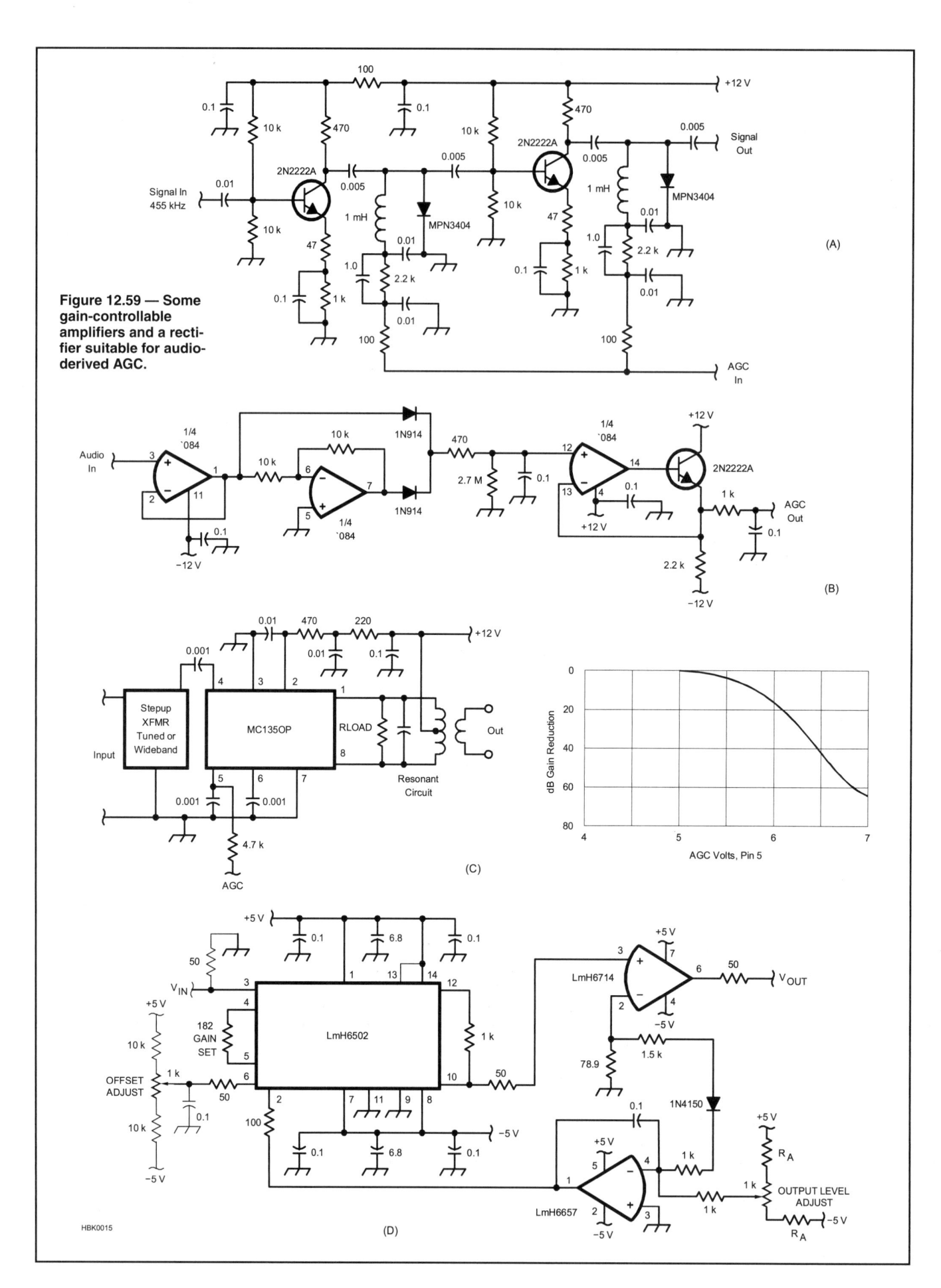

Figure 12.59 — Some gain-controllable amplifiers and a rectifier suitable for audio-derived AGC.

12.52　Chapter 12

NE/SA5209. This type of approach is simpler to implement than discrete circuit approaches, such as dual-gate MOSFETs that are now being replaced by IC designs.

Figure 12.59D shows the high performance National Semiconductor LMH6502MA (14-pin DIP plastic package) voltage controlled amplifier. It is specially designed for accurate log-linear AGC from 0 to 40 dB with respect to a preset maximum voltage gain from 6 to 40 dB. Its ±3 dB bandwidth is 130 MHz. It is an excellent IF amplifier for high performance receiver or transmitter projects.

Additional info on voltage-controlled amplifier ICs can be found on the Analog Devices web site (**www.analog.com**). Search the site for Tutorial MT-073, which describes the operation of various types of gain-controlled amplifiers with numerous product examples.

12.7 Noise Management

A major problem for those listening to receivers has historically been local impulse noise. For HF and VHF receivers it is often from the sparks of internal combustion engine spark plugs, electric fence chargers, light dimmers, faulty power-line insulators and many other similar devices that put out short duration wide band signals. In the UHF and microwave region, radar systems can cause similar problems.

Additional sources of noise are atmospheric and man-made noise with a variety of different profiles — static crashes, power-line buzz, and the ever-increasing white noise and spurious signals from consumer and industrial electronics, particularly switch-mode devices. The capabilities of DSP can be used to combat these diverse types of noise.

Finally, noise canceling by subtracting it from the incoming signals is available as a station accessory using external antennas for sensing and beam-steering. True diversity reception is also available, pioneered for the amateur station, using the spatial characteristics of the arriving noise signals to discriminate between them and the desired signals. All of these techniques provide formidable tools for noise management that were simply unavailable to amateurs of earlier eras.

12.7.1 The Noise Limiter

The first device used in an early (1930s) attempt to limit impulse noise was called a *noise limiter* or *clipper* circuit as originally described by H. Robinson, W3LW. This circuit would *clip* or limit noise (or signal) peaks that exceeded a preset limit. The idea was to have the limit set to about as loud as you wanted to hear anything and nothing louder would get through. This was helpful in eliminating the loudest part of impulse noise or even nearby lightning crashes, but it had two problems. First it didn't eliminate the noise, it just reduced the peak loudness; second, it also reduced the loudness of loud non-noise signals and in the process distorted them considerably.

The second problem was fixed shortly thereafter, with the advent of the *automatic noise limiter* or ANL as described by J. Dickert. The ANL automatically set the clipping threshold to that of a loud signal. It thus would adjust itself as the loudness of signals you listened to changed with time. An ANL was fairly easy to implement and became standard equipment on amateur receivers from the late 1930s on. While ANL circuits are no longer common, simple receivers used today do sometimes incorporate passive clipping circuits to account for their limited AGC ability.

12.7.2 The Noise Blanker

It turned out that improvements in receiver selectivity over the 1950s and beyond, while improving the ability to reduce random noise, actually made receiver response to impulse noise worse. The reason for this is that a very short duration pulse will actually be lengthened while going through a narrow filter. This is due to the filter's different delay times for the pulse's wide spectrum of components, resulting in the components arriving at the filter output at different times. You can demonstrate this in your superhet receiver if it has a narrow crystal filter. Find a frequency with heavy impulse noise and switch between wide and narrow filters. If your narrow filter is 500 Hz or less, the noise pulses will likely be more prominent with the narrow filter. DSP filters with their superior group delay performance exhibit less smearing than their analog counterparts.

The noise limiters described previously were all connected at the output of the IF amplifiers and thus the noise had passed most of the selectivity before the limiter and had been widened by the receiver filters. In SSB receivers, since signals vary in strength as someone talks, the usual AGC responds quickly to reduce the gain of a strong signal and then slowly increases it if the signal is no longer there. This means that a strong noise pulse may reduce the receiver gain for much longer than it lasts.

The solution — a *noise blanker*. An analog noise blanker is almost a separate wideband receiver. It takes its input from an early stage in the heterodyne receiver before much selectivity or AGC has been applied. It amplifies the wideband signal and detects the narrow noise pulses without lengthening them. The still-narrow noise pulses are used to shut off or "blank" the receiver at a point ahead of the selectivity and AGC, thus keeping the noise from getting to the parts of the receiver at which the pulses would be extended. In other words, the receiver is shut off or *gated* during the noise pulse.

In addition to an ON/OFF switch, noise blankers include a control labeled THRESHOLD. The THRESHOLD control adjusts the level of noise that will blank the receiver. If it is set for too low a level, it will blank on signal peaks as well as noise, resulting in distortion of the signal.

An SDR noise blanker can implement the same detect-and-gate technique as an analog receiver. Once the noise impulse is detected, the samples making up the impulse are replaced by an interpolation between the "normal" samples just before and just after the impulse. It is as is the noise impulse was never received.

An alternative technique that also handles longer noise crashes and other large-amplitude, long-duration noise waveforms is described in **Figure 12.60**. The basic idea is to create a filtered average amplitude and watch for incoming signals that exceed the average multiplied by a weighting factor which is how the SDR noise blanker threshold is controlled. When the incoming signal is below this value, it is simply passed along to the rest of the receiver. Above this level, the blanker generates a ramp factor that limits the rate at which the signal can increase. This turns short, sharp impulses into relatively slowly increasing and decreasing ramps, leaving normal signals unaffected.

A well-designed noise blanker can be very effective. Instead of just keeping the noise at the level of the signal as a noise limiter does, the noise blanker can actually *eliminate* the noise. If the pulses are narrow enough, the loss of desired signal during the time the receiver is disabled is not noticeable and the noise may seem to disappear entirely.

Noise blankers can also create problems, particularly in heterodyne receivers. The wide-band circuit that detects noise pulses

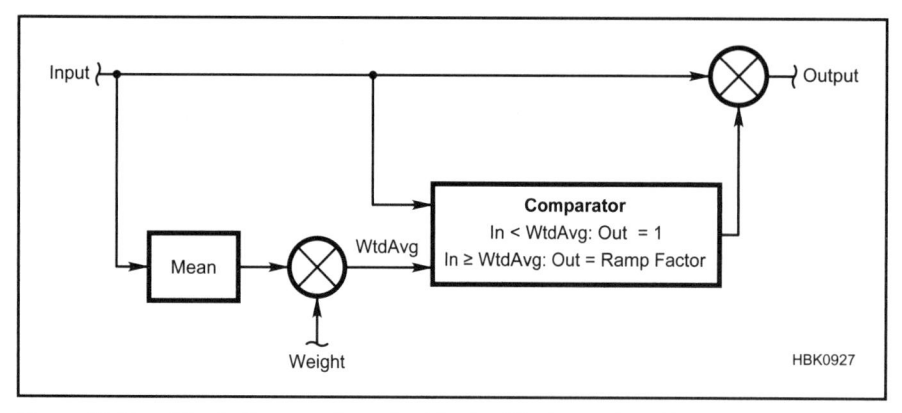

Figure 12.60 — Block diagram of a noise blanker. The input signal is compared to a weighted average. If exceeded, the input signal rise and fall times are limited by a ramp factor. [After *Communications Receivers, 4th ed*]

also detects any signals in that bandwidth. If such a signal is strong and has sharp peaks (as voice and CW signals do), the noise blanker will treat them as noise pulses and shut down the receiver accordingly. This causes tremendous distortion and can make it sound as if the strong signal to which the noise blanker is responding is generating spurious signals that cause the distortion. (This is less of a problem in SDR receivers.) Before you assume that the strong signal is causing problems, turn the noise blanker on and off to check. When the band is full of strong signals, a noise blanker may cause more problems than it solves.

12.7.3 Operating Noise Limiters and Blankers

Many current receivers include both a noise limiter (often labeled NL) and a noise blanker (labeled NB). If your receiver has both, they will have separate controls and it is worthwhile to try them both. There are times at which one will work better than the other, and other times when it goes the other way, depending on the characteristics of the noise. There are other times when both work better than either. In any case, they can make listening a lot more pleasant — just remember to turn them off when you don't need them since either type can cause some distortion, especially on strong signals that should otherwise be easy to listen to.

Recognizing that it is difficult for a single noise blanker to work properly with the wide variations of noise pulses, it is common for current receivers to have two noise blankers with different characteristics that are optimized for the different pulse types. One noise blanker is typically optimized for very short pulses and the other for longer pulses. The operator can switch between the blankers to see which works best on the noise at hand.

The usual approach to operating the noise blanker is to activate it, then adjust the THRESHOLD control until the noise is just blanked. You will probably need to make occasional adjustments as the noise impulse characteristics change. Don't forget to turn the noise blanker off when the noise goes away.

The previous techniques represent the most commonly available techniques to reduce impulse noise. There are a few other solutions as well. Note that we haven't been talking about reducing interference here. By interference, we mean another intended signal encroaching on the channel to which we want to listen. There are a number of techniques to reduce interference, and some also can help with impulse noise.

Many times impulse noise is coming from a particular direction. If so, by using a directional antenna, we can adjust the direction for minimum noise. When we think about directional antennas, the giant HF Yagi springs to mind. For receiving purposes, especially on the lower bands such as 160, 80 and 40 meters (where the impulse noise often seems the worst), a small indoor or outdoor receiving loop antenna as described in the *ARRL Antenna Book* can be very effective at eliminating either interfering stations or noise (both if they happen to be in the same direction).

12.7.4 Noise Canceling

Noise cancellers work by combining signals from our main antenna with the signal from a "sense" antenna and feeding that combination to the receiver. Adjustable gain stages and phasing networks within the unit must then be carefully adjusted so that the two noise signals are equal in level and 180 degrees out of phase. This adjustment is frequency sensitive, so it must be readjusted each time we change frequency. It must also be readjusted for every noise source. Signals coming from the same direction as the noise source will also be canceled, but this effect

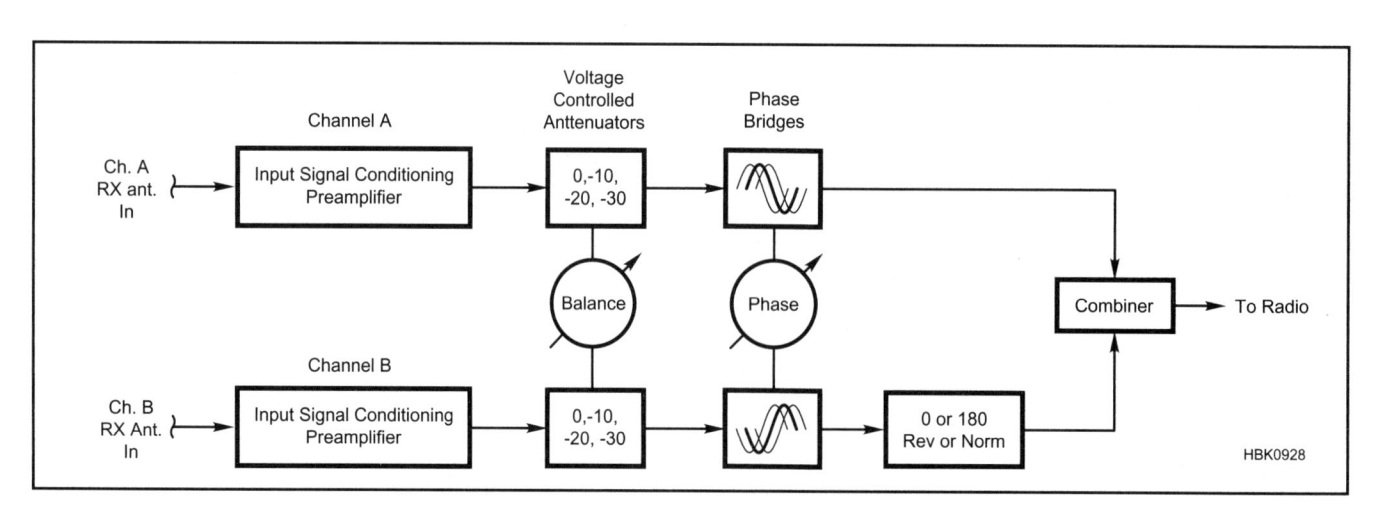

Figure 12.61 — Block diagram of a noise canceling system following the DX Engineering NCC-2. [Courtesy DX Engineering, used by permission]

12.54 Chapter 12

is minimized by placing the sense antenna as close as practical to the noise source. An active noise canceller can greatly reduce a single noise source, but it won't help with more than one source at a time. **Figure 12.61** shows the block diagram of a typical noise canceller and antennas, in this case the DX Engineering NCC-2.

Be careful when using any unit in line with the transceiver output; the carrier detect-driven relay that switches from receive to transmit (that is, bypassing the unit in transmit mode) is known to generate key clicks (transients) in some products. The MFJ 1026 and the DX Engineering NCC-1 and NCC-2 are generally good performers in this regard.

Some transceivers provide connectors where an external preamp or receive antenna can be connected. The click problem can be avoided by connecting the noise canceller at this point. Some SDRs have multiple antenna inputs and the ability to feed them to separate software-defined "receivers", and some software has been written to allow those separate receivers to provide the phasing networks needed to provide noise canceling. In some software, this function is improperly labeled "Diversity Receive." (See the Diversity Reception description below.)

BEAM STEERING

Noise cancellers can also be used to vary the phase of the signals from two receive antennas to vary their directivity. Two vertical antennas, connected to a receiver single receiver by individual feed lines, form a directional antenna. The directional pattern depends on the phase shift provided by the two feed lines (as well as the physical spacing and spatial orientation of the antennas), and it can be adjusted by varying the length of one or both of the feed lines. Used with two omnidirectional verticals, for example, a noise canceller can be used to vary the phase relationship between the two antennas, accomplishing the same result.

SIGNAL FADING

Most periodic (repetitive) fading is the result of the cancellation of signals from the same source taking slightly different paths, so that one is delayed with respect to the other. The direct and reflected signals cancel when they are nearly equal and nearly 180 degrees out of phase with each other. The frequency(ies) at which this 180-degree phase relationship exists is a function of the time difference; the fading interval is longer for lower frequencies. This fading mechanism is heard as very slow fading on the AM broadcast band and 160 meters, and as "picket fencing" at VHF and UHF.

12.7.5 Diversity Reception

Diversity reception has been used since the earliest days of radio to reduce the effects of signal fading. A receiving diversity system consists of two receivers, each connected to its own antenna and to its own loudspeaker (or opposite ears of stereo headphones). When the two antennas are widely separated as a fraction of a wavelength, the probability of cancellation occurring at both antennas at the same time is low, and the operator copies from the receiver providing the best signal.

Diversity reception is also widely used to listen using different receive antennas having different directivity in the horizontal or vertical plane, or aimed in different directions. This use is quite common on the lower HF bands and 160 meters. An operator may listen to the transmit antenna in one ear and a Beverage in the other, or to a loop and a Beverage.

Diversity reception is widely used in consumer FM receivers in vehicles, and in the wireless microphone systems used in live sound and broadcasting. In both of these applications, a circuit called a "voter" chooses the signal from the receiver having the best quality and switches it to the output. Many VHF and UHF repeater systems have receivers at multiple sites that are relayed back to the main transmit site, where a voter chooses between the best signal. Diversity is also used with receive antennas having different wave polarization; cross-polarization between a receive antenna and the wavefront typically results in a 20 dB loss of gain.

12.7.6 DSP Noise Reduction

DSP noise reduction (often labeled NR on the receiver controls) can actually look at the statistics of the signal and noise and figure out which is which and then reduce the noise significantly. These *adaptive filters* can't quite eliminate the noise, and need enough of the desired signal to figure out what's happening, so they won't work if the signal is far below the noise. (See the **DSP and SDR Fundamentals** and **Analog and Digital Filtering** chapters for information on adaptive filters.) Many DSP systems "color" the resulting audio to a degree. Nonetheless, they do improve the SNR of a signal in random or impulse noise.

Noise reduction is designed to reduce non-correlated noise such as atmospheric noise and thermal noise. Most noise reduction blocks rely on the knowledge that noise is much more random in nature than the signals we are attempting to demodulate. A typical NR will use a Least Mean Squares (LMS) or similar algorithm to detect correlated signals and reduce the amplitude of anything else in the passband.

How does this work? The algorithm looks for signals that are highly correlated, meaning that a copy of the signal shifted in time resembles the same signal at a different time. These are the signals that are preserved while the other signals in the passband are judged to be noise and are deemphasized or reduced in volume. Because there are a number of methods for achieving noise reduction in different classes of noise, some vendors often more than one type of noise reduction. Each manufacturer's algorithms for noise reduction are generally proprietary although the *GNU Radio* community's (see the **Transceiver Design Topics** chapter) open-source design approach offers some guidance in how noise reduction is achieved.

As with noise blankers, receivers frequently offer two or more noise reduction settings that apply different noise reduction algorithms optimized for different conditions. Different combinations and types of noise require the operator to select and adjust the noise reduction system for best performance.

12.7.7 DSP Notch Filtering

An Automatic Notch Filter (ANF) is really the opposite of a NR filter. The auto-notch filter looks for the same correlated signals, but instead or preserving these signals, the algorithm attempts to remove these signals. The classic example for which an ANF is useful is when there is a birdie (spur) or undesired CW signal in the passband of a sideband signal. Because the CW signal or spur are much more correlated than the speech we are listening to, these signals are judged to be undesired and the filter deemphasizes them. In this way, the NR and ANF filters are cousins, doing the opposite of each other in support of their specific noise reduction goals.

12.8 References and Bibliography

BOOKS

B. Allison, *Amateur Radio Transceiver Performance Testing*, ARRL, 2013.

W. Hayward, *Introduction to Radio Frequency Design* (Newington, CT: ARRL, 1994).

W. Hayward, R. Campbell, and B. Larkin, *Experimental Methods in RF Design*. (ARRL, Newington, 2009).

P. Horowitz, W. Hill, *The Art of Electronics,* 2nd ed (New York: Cambridge University Press, 1989).

L. E. Larson, *RF and Microwave Circuit Design for Wireless Communication*, (Artech House, 1996).

S. A. Maas, The RF and Microwave Circuit Design Cookbook (Artech House, 1998).

S. A. Maas, *Nonlinear Microwave and RF Circuits*, 2nd ed (Artech House, 2003).

S. A. Maas, *Noise in Linear and Nonlinear Circuits* (Artech House, 2005).

McClanning and Vito, *Radio Receiver Design*, Noble Publishing Corporation, 2001.

RF/IF Designer's Handbook (Brooklyn, NY: Scientific Components, 1992).

RF Communications Handbook (Philips Components-Signetics, 1992).

U. Rohde, D. Newkirk, *RF/Microwave Circuit Design for Wireless Applications* (New York: John Wiley & Sons, 2000). (Large number of useful references in the mixer chapter.)

U. Rohde, J. Whitaker, H. Zahnd, *Communications Receivers, Fourth Edition*, McGraw-Hill, 2017. (Large number of useful references in each chapter, as well.)

Synergy Microwave Corporation Product Handbook (Paterson, NJ: Synergy Microwave Corporation, 2007).

F. E. Terman, *Radio Engineers' Handbook* (New York: McGraw-Hill, 1943).

ARTICLES ABOUT MIXERS

B. Henderson, "Mixers in Microwave Systems (Part 1)", Watkins-Johnson Tech Note, Vol 17 No 1, 1990, Watkins-Johnson.

B. Henderson, "Mixers in Microwave Systems (Part 2)", Watkins-Johnson Tech Note, Vol 17 No 2, 1990, Watkins-Johnson.

B. Gilbert, "Demystifying the Mixer," self-published monograph, 1994.

S. Joshi, "Taking the Mystery Out of Double-Balanced Mixers," *QST,* Dec 1993, pp 32-36.

D. Kazdan "What's a Mixer?" *QST,* Aug 1992, pp 39-42.

F. Kearney and D. Frizelle, "Complex RF Mixers, Zero-IF Architecture, and Advanced Algorithms," *Analog Dialogue*, issue 51-02, Analog Devices.

M. Kossor, "A Digital Commutating Filter," *QEX*, May/Jun 1999, pp 3-8.

U. L. Rohde, "Key Components of Modern Receiver Design," Part 1, *QST,* May 1994, pp 29-32; Part 2, *QST,* Jun 1994, pp 27-31; Part 3, *QST,* Jul 1994, 42-45.

U. L. Rohde, "Testing and Calculating Intermodulation Distortion in Receivers," *QEX*, Jul 1994, pp 3-4.

U. L. Rohde and A. K. Poddar, "High Intercept Point Broadband, Cost Effective and Power Efficient Passive Reflection FET DBM," *EuMIC Symposium*, 10-15 Sep 2006, UK.

U. L. Rohde and A. K. Poddar, "A Unified Method of Designing Ultra-Wideband, Power-Efficient, and High IP3 Reconfigurable Passive FET Mixers," *IEEE/ICUWB*, Sep 24-27, 2006, MA, USA.

U. L. Rohde and A. K. Poddar, "Low Cost, Power-Efficient Reconfigurable Passive FET Mixers", 20th *IEEE CCECE* 2007, 22-26 Apr 2007, British Columbia, Canada.

D. Tayloe, "Letters to the Editor, Notes on 'Ideal' Commutating Mixers (Nov/Dec 1999)," *QEX*, March/April 2001, p 61.

D. Tayloe, "A Low-noise, High-performance Zero IF Quadrature Detector/Preamplifier", March 2003, *RF Design.*

D. Tayloe, US Patent 6,230,000, "A Product Detector and Method Therefore".

J. Vermusvuori, "A Synchronous Detector for AM Transmissions," *QST*, pp 28-33. Uses SA602/612 mixers as phase-locked and quasi-synchronous product detectors.

P. Wiers, "Mirror, Mirror on the Wall — Understanding Image Rejection and Its Impact on Desired Signals," *Analog Dialogue*, issue 51-08, Analog Devices

R. Zavrel, "Using the NE602," Technical Correspondence, *QST,* May 1990, pp 38-39.

ARTICLES ABOUT RECEIVERS

ARRL Lab, "Test Procedures Manual," 2009, **www.arrl.org/files/file/Lab/testproc.pdf**.

B. Brannon, "Sampled Systems and the Effects of Clock Phase Noise and Jitter," Analog Devices, AN-756, **www.analog.com.**

B. Brannon, "Some Recent Development in the Art of Receiver Technology," *Analog Dialogue*, issue 52-08, Analog Devices.

A. Farson, "Noise Power Ratio (NPR) Testing on HF Receivers," *QEX*, Mar 2015, pp. 20-27.

J. Harris, "What's Up With Digital Downconverters — Part 1 and Part 2," *Analog Dialogue*, issue 50-07 and 50-11, Analog Devices.

R. Henderson, "A Rock Bending Receiver for 7 MHz," *QST*, Aug 1995, pp 22-25.

G. Hirshfield, "Ham Notebook: General-Coverage Preselector," *Ham Radio*, Oct 1970, p. 77.

W. Kester, "Understand SINAD, ENOB, SNR, THD, THD+N, and SFDR so You Don't Get Lost in the Noise Floor," Analog Devices, MT-003 Tutorial, 2008, **www.analog.com/static/imported-files/tutorials/MT-003.pdf**.

W. Kester, "Noise Power Ratio (NPR)," Analog Devices, MT-005 Tutorial, 2008. **www.analog.com/media/en/training-seminars/tutorials/MT-005.pdf**.

R. Lyons, "Understanding the 'Phasing Method' of Single Sideband Demodulation," **www.dsprelated.com/showarticle/176.php**.

J. Onate, X. Fortuny, "A Software-Controlled Preselector," *QEX*, May/June 2008, pp. 11-18.

W. Sabin, "Envelope Detection and AM Noise-Figure Measurement," *RF Design*, Nov 1988, p 29.

W. Silver, NØAX, "About FM," *QST*, Jul 2004, pp 38-42.

W. Silver, "About SSB," *QST*, Jan 2016, pp. 51-54.

D. Smith, "Improved Dynamic Range Testing," *QEX*, Jul/Aug 2002, pp. 46-52.

P. Smith, "Little-Known Characteristics of Phase Noise," Analog Devices, AN-741, **www.analog.com**.

Contents

13.1 Characterizing Transmitters
    13.1.1 FCC Rules
    13.1.2 Performance Measurements
    13.1.3 CCS, ICAS, and IMS Ratings

13.2 Transmitter Architecture
    13.2.1 Upconverting Heterodyne Architecture
    13.2.2 SDR Transmitter Architecture

13.3 Modulators
    13.3.1 Amplitude Modulators
    13.3.2 Angle Modulators

13.4 Transmitting CW and Data
    13.4.1 CW Operation
    13.4.2 RF Envelope Shaping
    13.4.3 Break-In CW Operation

13.5 Transmitting AM and SSB
    13.5.1 Amplitude-Modulated Full-Carrier Voice Transmission
    13.5.2 Single-Sideband Suppressed-Carrier Transmission

13.6 Transmitting Angle Modulation
    13.6.1 Angle-Modulated Transmitters
    13.6.2 Frequency Multipliers

13.7 Effects of Transmitted Noise

13.8 Microphones and Speech Processing
    13.8.1 Frequency Content of Speech
    13.8.2 Dynamics Processing
    13.8.3 Types of Microphones
    13.8.4 Using a Professional or PC Microphone
    13.8.5 Optimizing Your Microphone Audio
    13.8.6 Setting Levels for Digital Modes
    13.8.7 Speech Amplification and Processing

13.9 Voice Operation
    13.9.1 Push-To-Talk for Voice
    13.9.2 Voice-Operated Transmit-Receive Switching (VOX)

13.10 Transmitter Power Stages
    13.10.1 Types of Power Amplifiers
    13.10.2 Linear Amplifiers
    13.10.3 Nonlinear Amplifiers
    13.10.4 Hybrid Amplifiers
    13.10.5 Automatic Level Control (ALC)
    13.10.6 Transmit-Receive (TR) Switching

13.11 References and Bibliography

Chapter 13 — Downloadable Supplemental Content

Supplemental Articles and Columns
- "Clean, Punchy, Competitive Contest Audio Without Splatter" by Jim Brown, K9YC
- "SDR: Simplified — A Look at Noise Reduction and Adaptive Filters" by Ray Mack, W5IFS
- "SDR: Simplified — Demystifying PID Control Loops" by Ray Mack, W5IFS
- "Speech Processing: Some New Ideas" by Jim Tonne, W4ENE

HF Transmitter and Transceiver Projects
- Transmitter and transceiver projects from previous editions of the *ARRL Handbook*.
- "The Tuna Tin 2 Today" by Ed Hare, W1RFI
- "The MicroT2 — A Compact Single-Band SSB Transmitter" by Rick Campbell, KK7B
- "The MkII — An Updated Universal QRP Transmitter" by Wes Hayward, W7ZOI
- "Designing and Building Transistor Linear Power Amplifiers" Parts 1 and 2 by Rick Campbell, KK7B
- "The Rockmite — A Simple Single-Band CW Transceiver" by Dave Benson, K1SWL (plus supporting files)
- "The TAK-40 SSB/CW Transceiver" by Jim Veatch, WA2EUJ
- "A Fast TR Switch" by Jack Kuecken, KE2QJ

VHF/UHF Transmitter and Beacon Projects
- "VHF Open Sources" by Rick Campbell, KK7B
- "A 50 MHz CW Beacon" by Michael Sapp, WA3TTS
- "VHF and UHF CW Beacons" by Michael Sapp, WA3TTS
- "A 2-Meter Transmitter for Fox Hunting" by Mark Spencer, WA8SME
- "Simple Frequency Doublers with High Performance" by Paul Wade, W1GHZ
- "A Microwave Controller" by Hamish Kellock, OH2GAQ

The following related items are included with the **Receiving** chapter supplements.
- "Amateur Radio Equipment Development — An Historical Perspective" by Joel Hallas, W1ZR
- Selected SDR: Simplified columns in *QEX* by Ray Mack, W5IFS W5IFS

Chapter 13

Transmitting

Transmitters — the companion to the receivers discussed in the previous chapter. As with receiver design, the analog heterodyne architecture that has dominated for so many years is being challenged and displaced by SDR techniques. Nevertheless, many of the same functions are required, regardless of whether they are implemented in analog electronics or digitally by software. As such, each function is discussed from both the traditional analog perspective and from the SDR perspective where material is available. Subsequent editions will continue to evolve as practices change and standardize on new approaches.

Included in this edition are helpful discussions on microphone selection and audio optimization by Jim Brown, K9YC, and a set of analog audio signal processing circuits by Jim Tonne, W4ENE. Sections on SDR implementations of basic functions are taken from SDR: Simplified columns in *QEX* by Ray Mack, W5IFS and from material contributed by Steve Hicks, N5AC.

The RF power stages of a transmitter are still firmly in the analog camp although design has greatly simplified through integrated circuits and amplifier modules. Circuits for power levels above 100 W (at HF) are covered in the **RF Power Amplifiers** chapter. The **DSP and SDR Fundamentals** chapter has more information on digital techniques and architectures.

Projects included with previous editions have been collected into a set of projects in the online supplemental information accompanying this book.

Transmitter technology has advanced in a parallel process similar to that of the technology of receivers. While transmitters are composed of many of the same named blocks as those used in receivers, it's important to keep in mind that there are significant differences. An RF amplifier in a receiver may deal with amplifying picowatts while one in a transmitter may output up to kilowatts. While the circuits may even look similar, the size of the components, especially cooling systems and power supplies, may differ significantly in scale. Still, many of the same principles apply.

Transmitters also make use of many of the same functional blocks as receivers, such as filters and mixers. You will find additional material on these functions covered in the **Receiving** chapter. Oscillators are covered in the **Oscillators and Synthesizers** chapter. Elements of these functions that are pertinent to transmitter design are covered in this chapter but not duplicated.

Transmitters (and transceivers) using vacuum tubes and solid-state matching circuits are likely to present hazardous voltages. At higher power levels RF exposure issues must be considered — review the **Safety** chapter for more information. Techniques for transmitter measurement are covered in the **Test Equipment and Measurements** chapter.

13.1 Characterizing Transmitters

13.1.1 FCC Rules

A survey of the FCC rules in Part 97 shows that most of them are about transmitted signals! Thus, amateurs should have a clear idea of what required their transmitters are expected to satisfy.

There are two important definitions that FCC Part 97 applies to amateur signals (also known as *emissions*):

97.3(a)(8) *Bandwidth*. The width of a frequency band outside of which the mean power of the transmitted signal is attenuated at least 26 dB below the mean power of the transmitted signal within the band. (See Figure 3.16 later in this chapter.)

97.3(a)(43) *Spurious emission*. An emission, or frequencies outside the necessary bandwidth of a transmission, the level of which may be reduced without affecting the information being transmitted.

There are also some important definitions in Part 2.1031 – 2.1060 that apply to all wireless services:

2.202 *Bandwidths*.

(a) *Occupied bandwidth*. The frequency bandwidth such that, below its lower and above its upper frequency limits, the mean powers radiated are each equal to 0.5 percent of the total mean power radiated by a given emission.

(b) *Necessary bandwidth*. For a given class of emission, the minimum value of the occupied bandwidth sufficient to ensure the transmission of information at the rate and with the quality required for the system employed, under specified conditions. Emissions useful for the good functioning of the receiving equipment as, for example, the emission corresponding to the carrier of reduced carrier systems, shall be included in the necessary bandwidth.

The measurement of bandwidth (and other characteristics) is covered by Part 2.1031-2.1060.

Part 97, Subpart D, sets forth a number of technical standards for signals. Part 97.307 — Emission Standards covers all of the signal characteristics from signal quality through symbol rates. Part 97.313 covers transmitter power limits by band. Parts 97.315 and 97.317 set the standards for certification of external RF power amplifiers.

The FCC rules are easily accessible online via the ARRL website at **www.arrl.org/part-97-amateur-radio** and so are not reproduced here.

13.1.2 Performance Measurements

The ARRL Lab has created a series of standardized tests for product review and compliance testing. The entire test program for receivers and transmitters is described in the book *Amateur Radio Transceiver Performance Testing* by Bob Allison, WB1GCM, ARRL Lab Staff Engineer. Important sections are summarized here. The book also addresses a number of other significant parameters that affect various elements of on-the-air performance. The chapter **Test Measurements and Equipment** also discusses transceiver performance.

EMISSION STANDARDS

A spurious signal is any signal (unwanted) other than the intended (fundamental) transmitted signal. Any oscillator will create unwanted products, such as spurs (spurious emissions) and harmonics (multiples of the fundamental frequency). Some consider harmonics to be spurious emissions but they are addressed separately in this book.

Spurs are usually found near or around the fundamental frequency. They can be reduced with appropriate circuit design and, to some extent, with filtering. Harmonics are suppressed to an acceptable level with the use of band-pass filters. An "acceptable level" is one that will not create interference on two times the fundamental frequency (second harmonic), three times the fundamental frequency (third harmonic), and so on.

The single most important standard any transceiver operating in the amateur bands must meet is the FCC Part 97 rules for emissions. According to Part 97.307(d) and 97.307(e), an HF transceiver's emissions must have at least 43 dB of spurious emission and harmonic suppression below 30 MHz. For 30 MHz through 225 MHz, the spurious and harmonic suppression must be 60 dB. (Emission designators are discussed in the **Modulation** chapter.)

CARRIER AND SIDEBAND SUPPRESSION

While there are no FCC specifications for suppression of the carrier and unwanted sideband for SSB signals, the ARRL Lab has established 60 dB of suppression as good practice. 50 dB of suppression is considered a minimum acceptable level.

INTERMODULATION DISTORTION (IMD)

Spurious emissions caused by IMD are definitely of concern, even though they might satisfy the rules on signal bandwidth. For today's transceivers, a third-order product measurement of 30 dB below PEP is typical, 35 dB is considered good, and 25 dB below PEP is mediocre. A clean signal with the lower possible IMD products should be a key consideration for purchasing or operating a transceiver. It is also important to remember that even the best transmitter can be misadjusted to put out an excessively wide signal that creates a lot of interference.

Figures 13.1 and **13.2** show a typical example of a signal with good IMD performance (Figure 13.1) and an unacceptably wide signal (Figure 13.2). The signal in Figure 13.1 has acceptable 3rd-order IMD products and the higher-order products diminish rapidly farther from the main signal. The signal in Figure 13.2, however, has mediocre performance for the 3rd-order products and the higher-order products are far too high out to ±6 kHz from the carrier frequency. This signal would interfere with at least two SSB contacts to each side of it.

CW KEYING

The shape of a transmitter's keying waveform impacts the quality and effectiveness of its transmissions. By observing the keying waveform, it is possible to assess whether it has characteristics that will affect the quality of the transmitted signal and its impact on adjacent signals.

There are two primary signatures of problems that are can be detected by observing the shape of the keyed waveform. The first is *overshoot* in which the transmitter sends a short high-power transient at the beginning of a transmission (see **Figure 13.3**). This is caused by the power control subsystem not reacting properly to the rapid change in output power. The transient can cause an amplifier's power protection circuitry to activate or trip. It can also cause a key click on adjacent channels. The system at fault can be the ALC system, a software problem, or some other internal power control mechanism.

The second signature is too-rapid rise and fall times or abrupt edges and corners of the

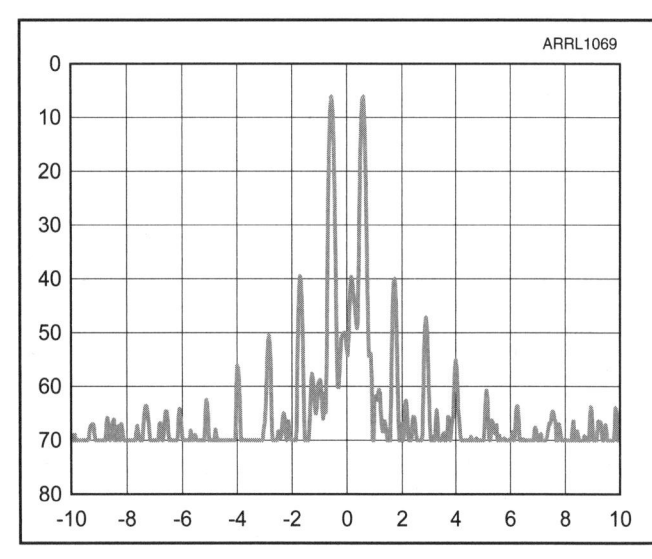

Figure 13.1 — Two-tone IMD test results for a good transmitted signal. The 3rd-order products are close to 40 dB below peak power.

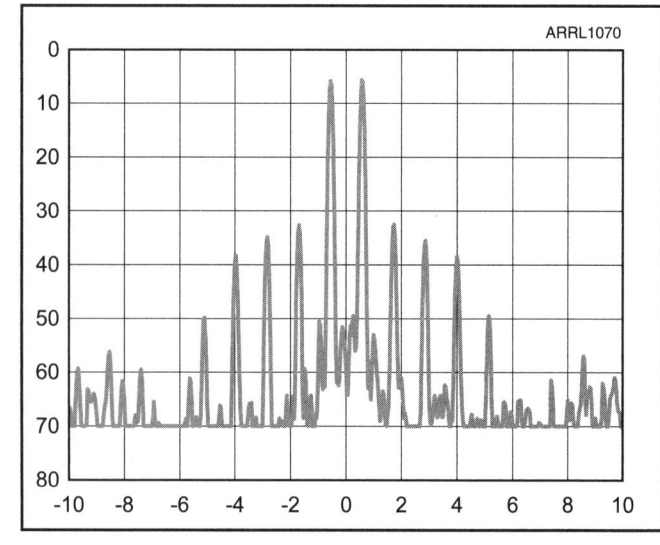

Figure 13.2 — Third-order IMD products are acceptable at 32 dB below PEP but the higher-order products are unacceptably high.

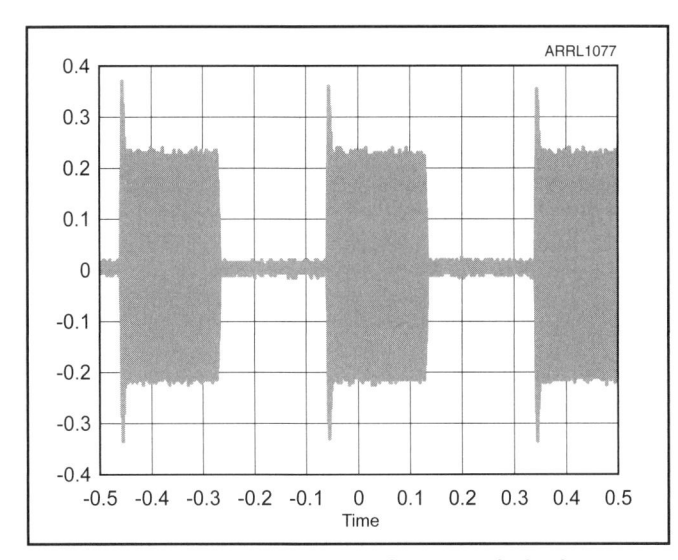

Figure 13.3 — A transient at the leading edge of a keying waveform.

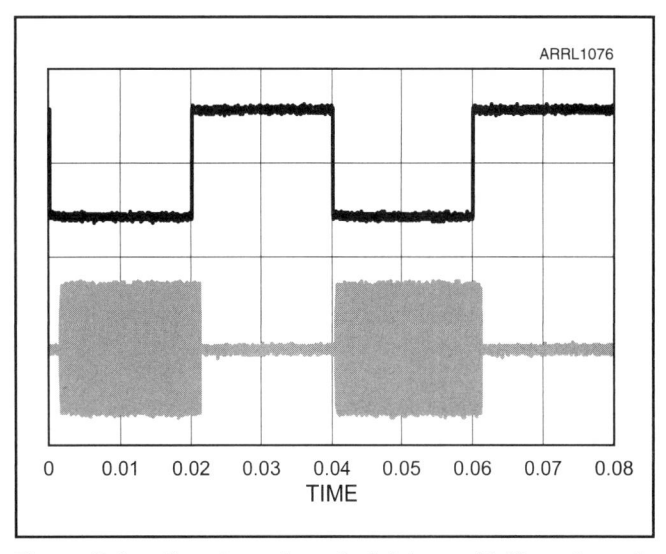

Figure 13.4 — Abrupt, nearly vertical rising and falling edges of "hard" keying.

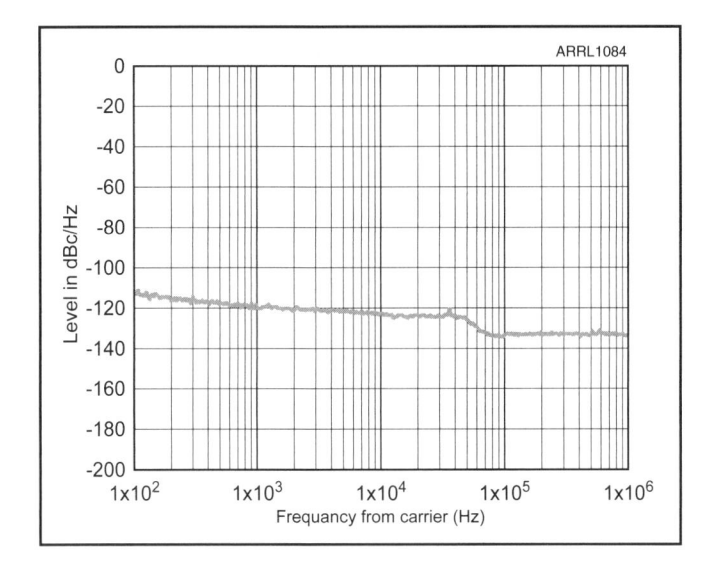

Figure 13.5 — A transmitter with a relatively low composite noise profile. This transmitter is unlikely to cause significant interference on adjacent channels or other bands.

envelope as shown in **Figure 13.4**. There may also be discontinuities or artifacts present during the rising and falling edges of the waveform. These create distortion products that extend well beyond the CW signal's necessary bandwidth as key clicks that cause interference to adjacent channels.

COMPOSITE (PHASE) NOISE

Composite noise is composed of both amplitude and phase noise on the transmitted signal. We are concerned with noise present from 100 Hz to 1 MHz from the carrier frequency of the signal. (See **Figure 13.5**) Composite noise can raise the noise floor of adjacent channels and in severe cases, across an entire band or on multiple bands. (See the discussions on phase noise in this chapter and in the **Transceiver Design Topics** chapter.)

13.1.3 CCS, ICAS, and IMS Ratings

Amateur equipment is usually advertised as being rated at some level of ICAS service. There are several related types of operating service. From the RCA Transmitting Tubes manual (TT-4, 1956), the following definitions are obtained:

Continuous Commercial Service (CCS) covers applications involving continuous tube operation in which maximum dependability and long tube life are the primary considerations.

Intermittent Commercial and Amateur Service (ICAS) covers applications in which high tube output is a more important consideration than long tube life. The term "Intermittent Commercial" in this title applies to types of service in which the operating or "on" periods do not exceed 5 minutes each, and are followed by "off" or stand-by periods of the same or greater duration. The term "Amateur Service" covers other applications where operation is of an infrequent or highly intermittent nature, as well as the use of tubes in "amateur" transmitters. ICAS ratings generally are considerably higher than CCS ratings.

Although the ability of a tube to produce greater output power is usually accompanied by a reduction in tube life, the equipment designer may decide that a small tube operated at its ICAS ratings meets the requirements better than a larger tube operated within CCS ratings.

Intermittent Mobile Service (IMS) covers applications in which very high power output for short periods is required from equipment of the smallest practical size and weight. Tube ratings for IMS service are based on the premise that transmitter "on" periods do not exceed 15 seconds each, and are followed by "off" periods of at least 60 seconds duration. In equipment tests, however, maximum "on" periods of not more than 5 minutes each followed by "off" periods of at least 5 minutes are permissible, provided the total "on" time of such test periods does not exceed 10 hours during the life of the tube. Although tubes operated under IMS ratings may have a life of only about 100 hours, the use of these ratings is economically justified where high power must be obtained intermittently from very small tubes.

If equipment is specified as meeting Continuous Commercial Service requirements, that is exactly how the equipment or device is certified to perform. Very few amateur transmitters or amplifiers, however, are operated that way and if they had to meet the CCS level of service, would be quite expensive.

ICAS, on the other hand, is just a name for the type of service the equipment is expected to provide. The description is intended to apply to use in which the equipment is operated with a 50% duty cycle having equal "on" and "off" periods of 5 minutes or less. Terms like "ICAS 50%" have no standard meaning. That could refer to the original ICAS definition or it could mean a period of 50% duty cycle operation followed by an equal period of no operation at all. The safest choice is to ask the manufacturer directly for their interpretation of ICAS or any similar rating and not assume anything.

Regardless of which rating is used, the intent is to describe the conditions under which the equipment (or devices) may be operated and still be expected to meet the performance specifications. Typically, devices are *de-rated* from their maximum ratings in order to meet the performance specifications but there are many other considerations to take into account when the equipment is designed. For example, equipment designed to operate at a high ambient temperature would have to be de-rated more than equipment operated at a lower temperature.

13.2 Transmitter Architecture

In the following section, "in-band" refers to signal frequencies within the bandwidth of the desired signal. For example, for an upper sideband voice signal with a carrier frequency of 14.200 MHz, frequencies of approximately 14.2003 to 14.203 would be considered in-band. Out-of-band refers to frequencies outside this range, such as on adjacent channels.

13.2.1 Upconverting Heterodyne Architecture

Figure 13.6 shows a traditional superheterodyne architecture for transceivers in which the sideband filter, some amplifiers, and other filters are shared between transmit and receive modes through the use of extensive switching. A limitation of that architecture is that it is difficult to provide operation on frequencies near the first IF. The typical transceiver designer selected a first IF frequency away from the desired operating frequencies and proceeded on that basis.

New amateur bands at 30, 17, and 12 meters were approved at the 1979 ITU World Administrative Radio Conference. The difficulties of managing image rejection on the new bands and the desire for continuous receiver coverage of LF, MF and HF bands (general-coverage receive) required a significant change in the architecture of receivers and transceivers. Thus, the upconverting architecture discussed in the **Receiving** chapter became popular in the 1980s and, with a few notable exceptions, became almost universal in commercial products over the following decade.

The solution was to move to the upconverting architecture shown in **Figure 13.7**. By

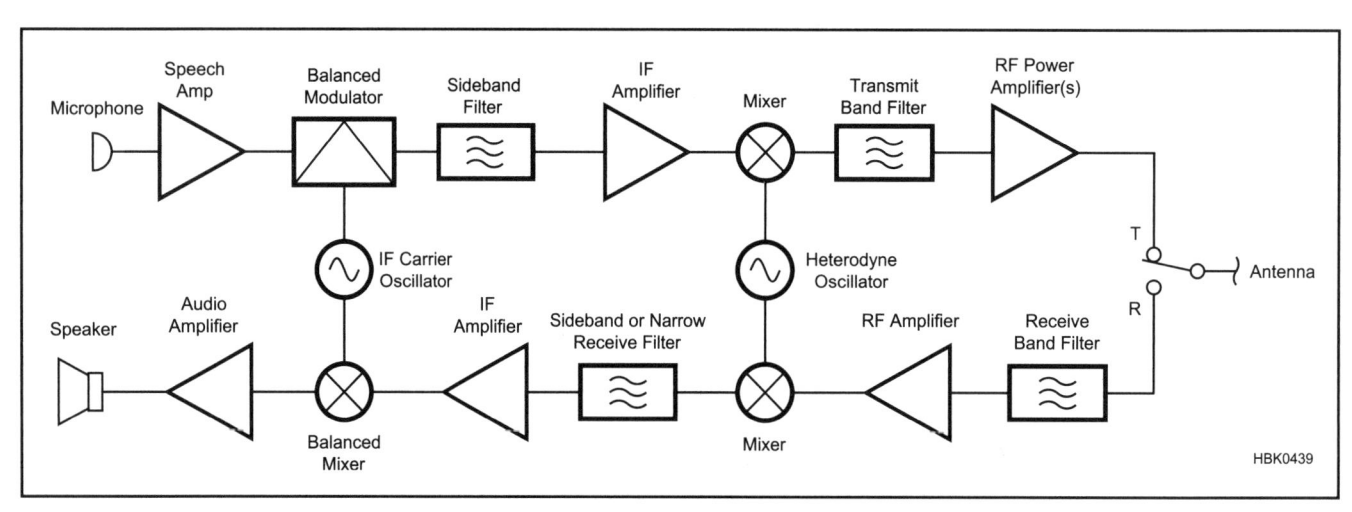

Figure 13.6 — Block diagram of a simple SSB transceiver sharing oscillator frequencies.

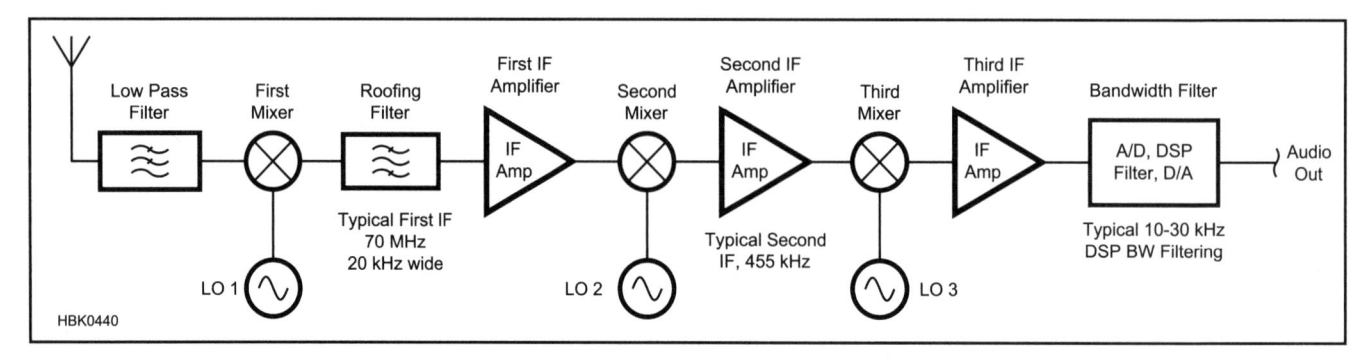

Figure 13.7 — Simplified block diagram of upconverting general coverage transceiver, receiver section shown.

selecting a first IF well above the highest receive frequency, the first local oscillator can cover the entire receive range without any gaps. With the 70 MHz IF shown, the full range from 0 to 30 MHz can be covered by an LO covering 70 to 100 MHz, less than a 1.5:1 range, making it easy to implement with modern PLL or DDS technology. Note that the high IF makes image rejection very easy and, rather than the usual tuned bandpass front end, we can use more universal low-pass filtering. The low-pass filter is generally shared with the transmit side and designed with octave cutoff frequencies to reduce transmitter harmonic content. A typical set of HF transceiver low-pass filter cut-off frequencies would be 1, 2, 4, 8, 16 and 32 MHz.

This architecture offers significant benefits. By merely changing the control system programming, any frequency range or ranges can be provided with no change to the architecture or hardware implementation. Unlike the more traditional transceiver architecture (Figure 13.6), continuous receive frequency coverage over the range is actually easier to provide than to not provide, offering a marketing advantage for those who also like to do shortwave or broadcast listening.

IF FILTERS

The desired IF filter response is shown in **Figure 13.8A**. The reduction of the carrier frequency is augmented by the filter response. It is common to specify that the filter response be down 20 dB at the carrier frequency. Rejection of the opposite sideband should (hopefully) be 60 dB, starting at 300 Hz below the carrier frequency, which is the 300-Hz point on the opposite sideband. The ultimate attenuation should be at least 70 dB. This would represent a very good specification for a high quality transmitter. The filter passband should be as flat as possible (with passband ripple less than 1 dB or so).

Special filters, designated as USB or LSB, are designed with a steeper roll-off on the carrier frequency side, in order to improve rejection of the carrier and opposite sideband. Mechanical filters are available that do this. Crystal-ladder filters (see the **Analog and Digital Filtering** chapter) are frequently called "single-sideband" filters because they also have this property. The steep skirt can be on the low side or the high side, depending on whether the crystals are across the signal path or in series with the signal path, respectively.

Filters require special attention to their terminations. The networks that interface the filter with surrounding circuits should be accurate and stable over temperature. They should be easy to adjust. One very good way to adjust them is to build a narrow-band sweep generator and look at the output IF envelope with a logarithmic amplifier, as indicated in Figure 13.8B. There are three goals:

• The driver stage must see the desired load impedance.

• The stage after the filter must see the desired source (generator) impedance.

• The filter must be properly terminated at both ends.

Lack of any of these conditions will result in loss of specified filter response. Figure 13.8B shows two typical approaches. This kind of setup is a very good way to make sure the filters and other circuitry are working properly.

Finally, overdriven filters (such as crystal or mechanical filters) can become nonlinear and generate distortion. Thus it is necessary to stay within the manufacturer's specifications. Magnetic core materials used in the tuning networks must be sufficiently linear at the signal levels encountered. They should be tested for IMD separately.

IF Linearity and Noise

Figure 13.9 indicates that after the last SSB filter, whether it is just after the SSB modulator or after the IF clipper, subsequent BPFs are considerably wider. For example, the 70 MHz crystal filter may be 15 to 30 kHz wide. This means that there is a "gray region" in the transmitter in which out-of-band IMD that is generated in the IF amplifiers and mixers can cause adjacent-channel interference.

A possible exception, not shown in Figure 13.9, is that there may be an intermediate IF

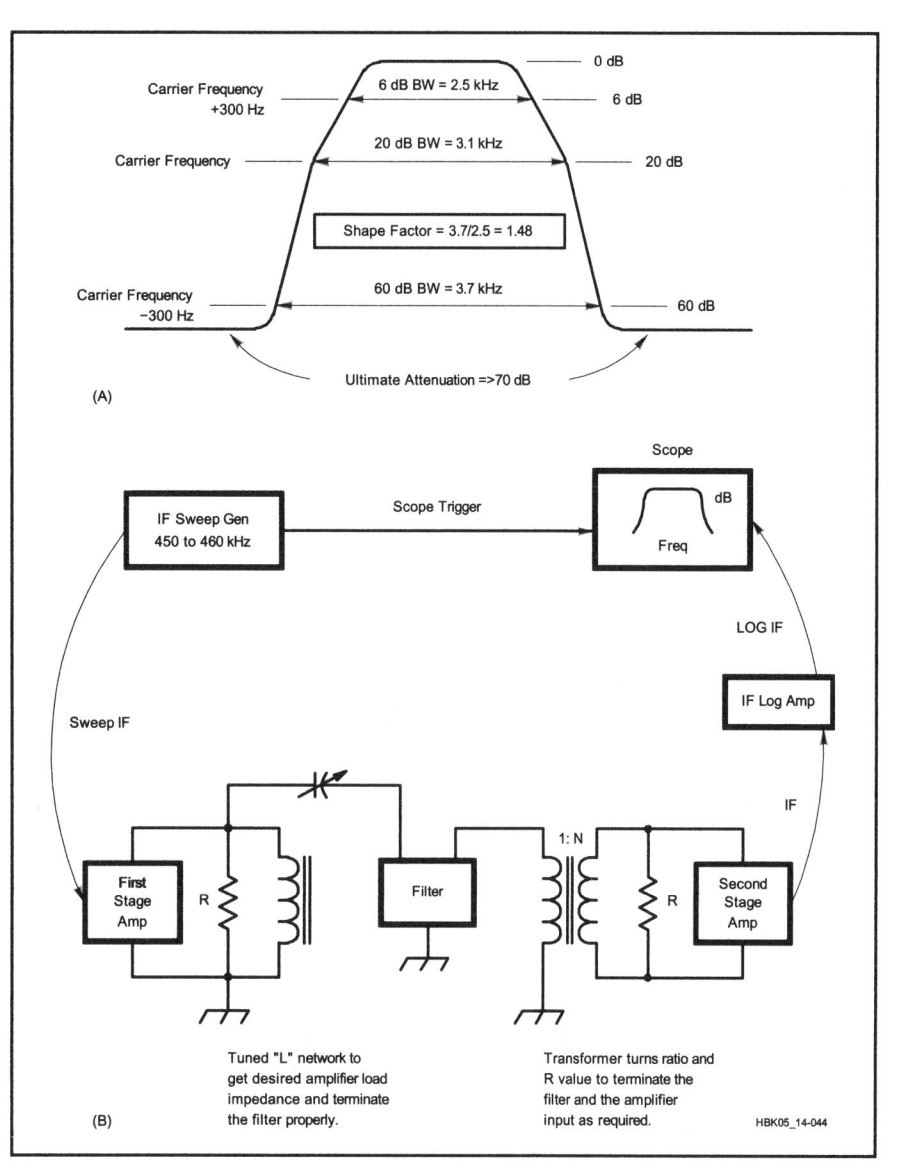

Figure 13.8 — At (A), desired response of a SSB IF filter. At (B), one method of terminating a mechanical filter that allows easy and accurate tuning adjustment and also a possible test setup for performing the adjustments.

in the 10 MHz region that also contains a narrow filter.

The implication is that special attention must be paid to the linearity of these circuits. It's the designer's job to make sure that distortion in this gray area is much less than distortion generated by the PA and also less than the phase noise generated by the final mixer. Recall also that the total IMD generated in the exciter stages is the result of several amplifier and mixer stages in cascade; therefore, each element in the chain must have at least 40 to 50 dB IMD quality. The various drive levels should be chosen to guarantee this. This requirement for multistage linearity is one of the main technical and cost burdens of the SSB mode.

Of interest also in the gray region are additive white, thermal and excess noises originating in the first IF amplifier after the SSB filter and highly magnified on their way to the output. This noise can be comparable to the phase noise level if the phase noise is low, as it is in a high-quality radio. Recall also that phase noise is at its worst on modulation peaks, but additive noise may be (and often is) present even when there is no modulation. This is a frequent problem in co-located transmitting and receiving environments. Many transmitter designs do not have the benefit of the narrow filter at 70 MHz, so the amplified noise can extend over a much wider frequency range.

TRANSMIT MIXER LINEARITY AND NOISE

The last IF and the last mixer LO in Figure 13.9 are selected so that, as much as possible, harmonic IMD products are far enough away from the operating frequency that they fall outside the passband of the low-pass filters and are highly attenuated. This is difficult to accomplish over the transmitter's entire frequency range. It helps to use a high-level mixer and a low enough signal level to minimize those products that are unavoidable. Low-order crossovers that cannot be sufficiently reduced are unacceptable, however; the designer must go back to the drawing board.

13.2.2 SDR Transmitter Architecture

SDR transmitter architecture looks a lot like the SDR receiver architecture as described in the **DSP and SDR Fundamentals** and **Receiving** chapters "turned around." For example, the FFT can be reused as its own inverse to translate back and forth between the time and frequency domains. I/Q modulation looks very much like I/Q demodulation. Substitute a DAC for the ADC to change digital to analog and vice versa. Digital filters just need a data stream and enough clock speed to handle the throughput.

The main question is one of providing enough computing resources and deciding where to make the jump from analog to digital. As the speed and resolution of data converters increases while the cost plummets, the transition between the analog and digital realms is moving ever closer to the antenna. Commercial mainstream transceiver designs being introduced in 2017 are no longer based on the traditional analog superheterodyne architecture. It is only a matter of time before the superheterodyne becomes a legacy technology.

Superheterodyne techniques are still used at points in the signal path, however. **Figure 13.10** shows the progression of transmitter architectures from all-superheterodyne through direct-sampled. If you think they look like the SDR receiver architectures of Figures 8.3 through 8.6 in the **DSP and SDR Fundamentals** chapter, you're right. They

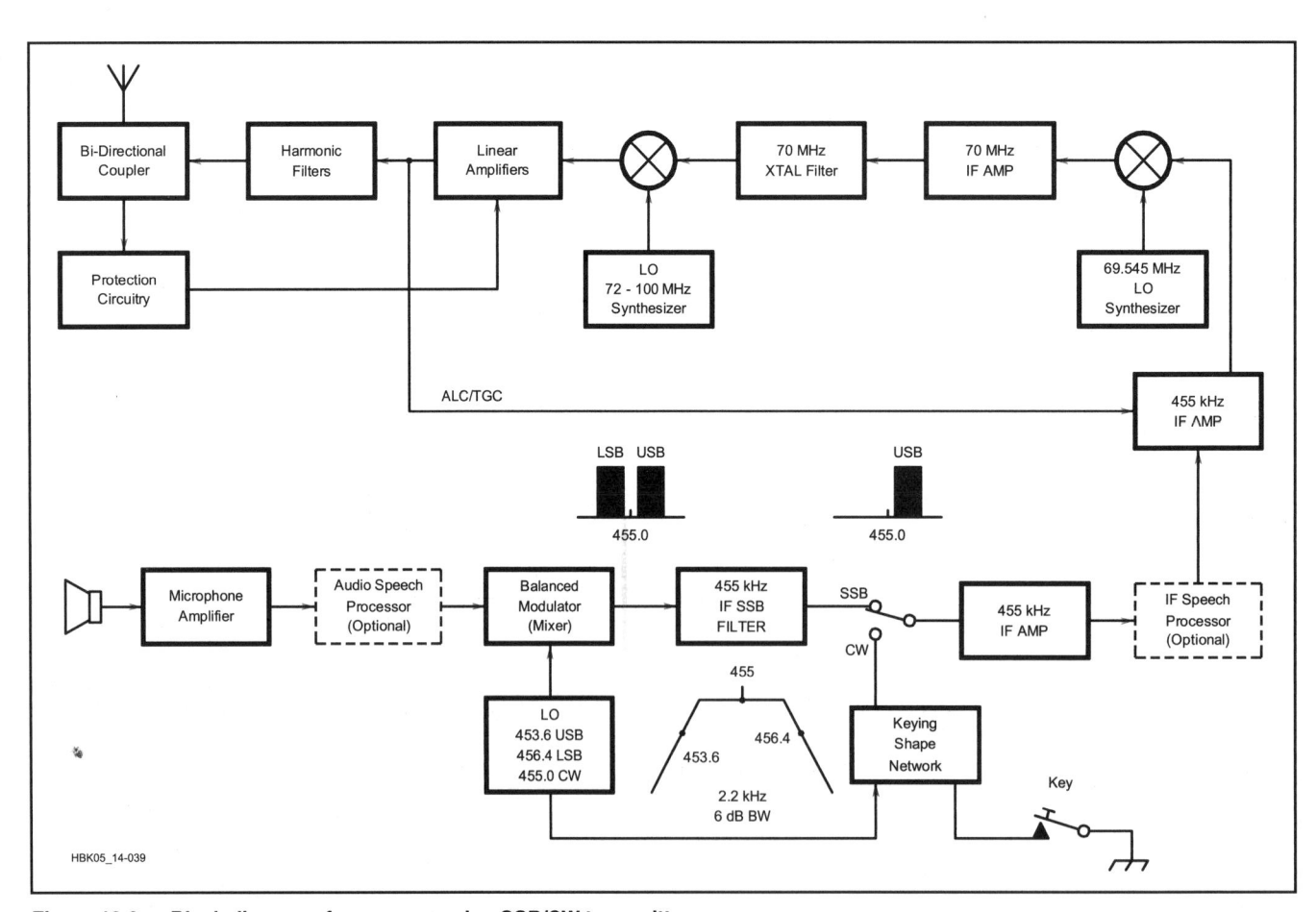

Figure 13.9 — Block diagram of an upconversion SSB/CW transmitter.

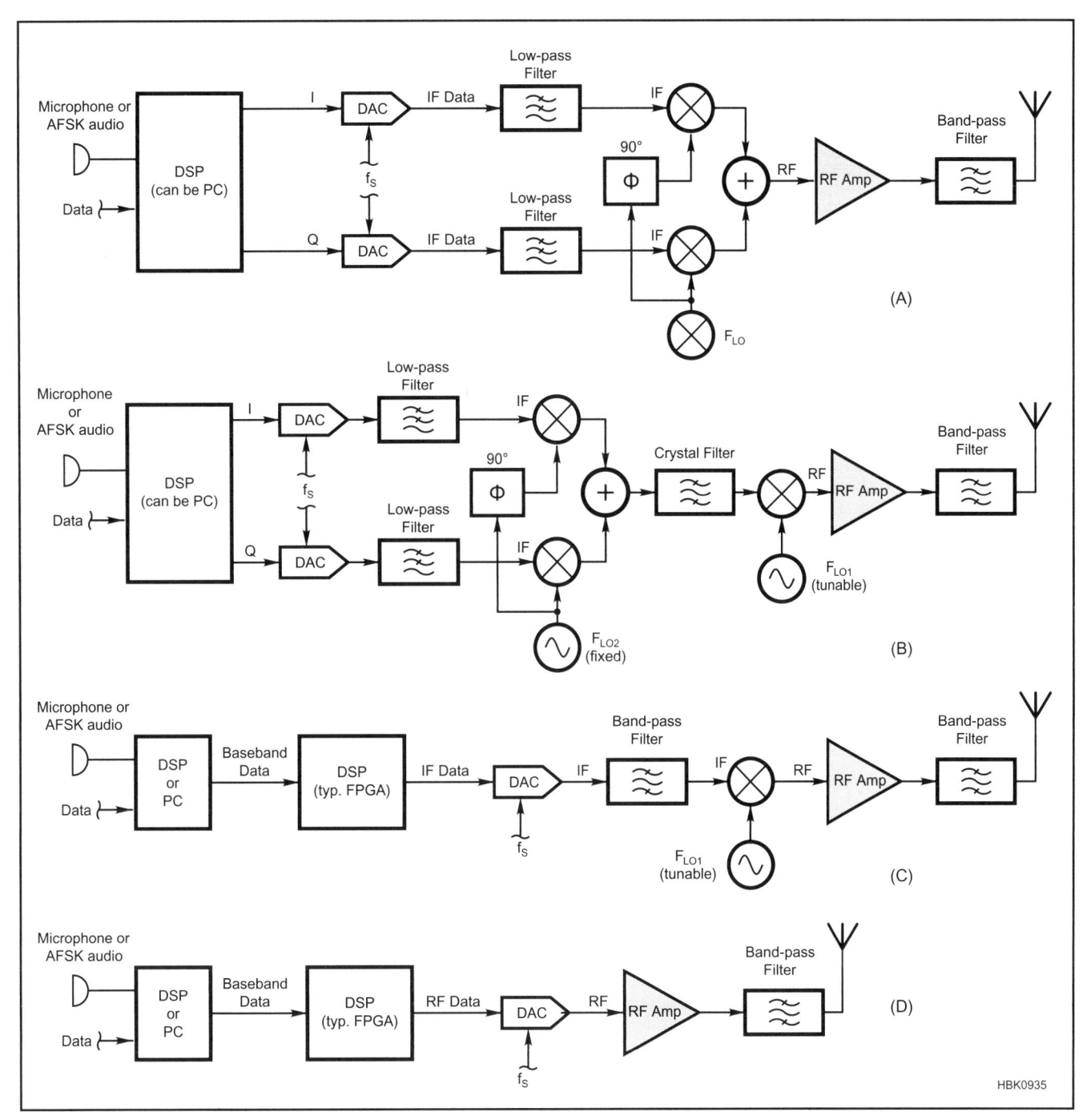

Figure 13.10 — Several SDR transmitter architectures. Direct-from-baseband (A), Hybrid superhet/SDR combination (B), Hybrid DSP-at-IF (C), Direct-sampled (B).

are essentially the same processes used for receiving but converting signals to RF instead of vice versa. (See the **Receiving** chapter for a discussion of the architecture pros and cons.) All of these architectures are in use by amateurs in homebuilt and commercial equipment today.

In any specific transceiver, the receiver and architectures are complementary in that they make use of the same DSP components and convert between analog and digital at roughly the same point in the signal path. The architecture is largely driven by the cost and availability of the data converters and the FPGA or similar DSP computing devices. (Some transceivers are based on generic FPGA parts while others make use of specialized DSP or graphics processors.) Tradeoffs involved with the various architectures are discussed in the **Transceiver Design Topics** chapter.

SDR technology is evolving rapidly so it is premature to make blanket statements about expected levels of performance. The best approach is to read the *QST* Product Reviews, review comparisons such as by Rob Sherwood, NCØB (**www.sherweng.com/table.html**) and Jim Brown, K9YC (**k9yc.com/publish.html**), ask experienced operators for their opinions, and then try the equipment for yourself!

Transmitting 13.7

13.3 Modulators

Previous editions of the *Handbook* covered modulators in a general treatment of mixers. Much of that discussion is now included in the **Receiving** chapter where you can find more detailed information on mixer operation.

13.3.1 Amplitude Modulators

You can see how an AM signal is constructed as illustrated in **Figure 13.11**. Figure 13.11A shows the carrier, and the sidebands from a modulating tone are shown in 13.11B and 13.11C. The waveform of an AM signal appears to vary the carrier amplitude but this is not the case. The varying envelope of the AM signal results from the signal's three components — the carrier and the two sidebands — adding together. As the components reinforce and cancel each other, their sum (which appears as the envelope) rises and falls.

If you look closely, you can see that the waveforms in Figures 13.11B and 13.11C have slightly different frequencies than the carrier. If the two sidebands are added together, the signal of Figure 13.11D is produced. This is what the two sidebands look like as waveforms without the carrier. This is a *double-sideband, suppressed carrier* (DSBSC).

When the carrier signal is added, the full AM signal is produced in Figure 13.11D. When all of the signals are in-phase, the resulting signal has its maximum amplitude. When all of the signals are out of phase, the resulting signal goes to zero. If the carrier's phase is used as our reference, the phase of each sideband can be viewed as slipping behind (lower sideband) or moving ahead (upper sideband) of the carrier. The sidebands are out of phase with each other at the frequency of the tone so the resulting envelope reproduces the modulating tone's sine wave.

In the transmitter, the SSB modulator must suppress both the carrier and the unwanted sideband. Carrier suppression is normally accomplished with a *balanced modulator*, a

Figure 13.11 — At A is an unmodulated carrier. If the upper (B) and lower (C) sidebands are added together a double-sideband suppressed carrier (DSBSC) signal results (D). If each sideband has half the amplitude of the carrier, then the combination of the carrier with the two sidebands results in a 100%-modulated AM signal (E). Whenever the two sidebands are out of phase with the carrier, the three signals sum to zero. Whenever the two sidebands are in phase with the carrier, the resulting signal has twice the amplitude of the unmodulated carrier.

Mixer Math: Amplitude Modulation

We can easily allow the carrier to be part of the mixer along with the sidebands merely by adding enough *dc level shift* into the information we want to mix so that its waveform never goes negative. In the sidebar "Mixer Math: Mixing as Multiplication" in the **Receiving** chapter, mixer math was kept relatively simple by setting the peak voltage of the input signals directly equal to their sine values. Each input signal's peak voltage therefore varies between +1 and −1, so all we need to do to keep our modulating- signal term (provided with a subscript *m* to reflect its role as the modulating or information waveform) from going negative is add 1 to it. Identifying the carrier term with a subscript c, we can write

$$\text{AM signal} = (1 + m \sin 2\pi f_m t) \sin 2\pi f_c t \qquad (A)$$

Notice that the modulation ($2\pi f_m t$) term has company in the form of a coefficient, *m*. This variable expresses the modulating signal's varying amplitude — variations that ultimately result in amplitude modulation. Expanding the equation gives us:

$$\text{AM signal} = \sin 2\pi f_c t + \frac{1}{2} m \cos(2\pi f_c - 2\pi f_m)t - \frac{1}{2} m \cos(2\pi f_c - 2\pi f_m)t \qquad (B)$$

The modulator's output now includes the carrier ($\sin 2\pi f_c t$) in addition to sum and difference products that vary in strength according to m. According to the conventions of talking about modulation, we call the sum product, which comes out at a frequency higher than that of the carrier, the *upper sideband (USB)*, and the difference product, which comes out a frequency lower than that of the carrier, the *lower sideband (LSB)*.

Why We Call It Amplitude Modulation

This process is called *amplitude modulation* because the complex waveform consisting of the sum of the sidebands and carrier varies with the information signal's magnitude (m). Concepts long used to illustrate AM's mechanism may mislead us into thinking that the *carrier* varies in strength with modulation, but careful study of the equation above shows that this doesn't happen. The carrier, $\sin 2\pi f_c t$, goes into the modulator as a sinusoid with an unvarying maximum value of |1|. The modulator multiplies the carrier by the dc level (+1) that we added to the information signal (m $\sin 2\pi f_m t$). Multiplying $\sin 2\pi f_c t$ by 1 merely returns $\sin 2\pi f_c t$. Thus, the carrier's amplitude does not vary as a result of amplitude modulation.

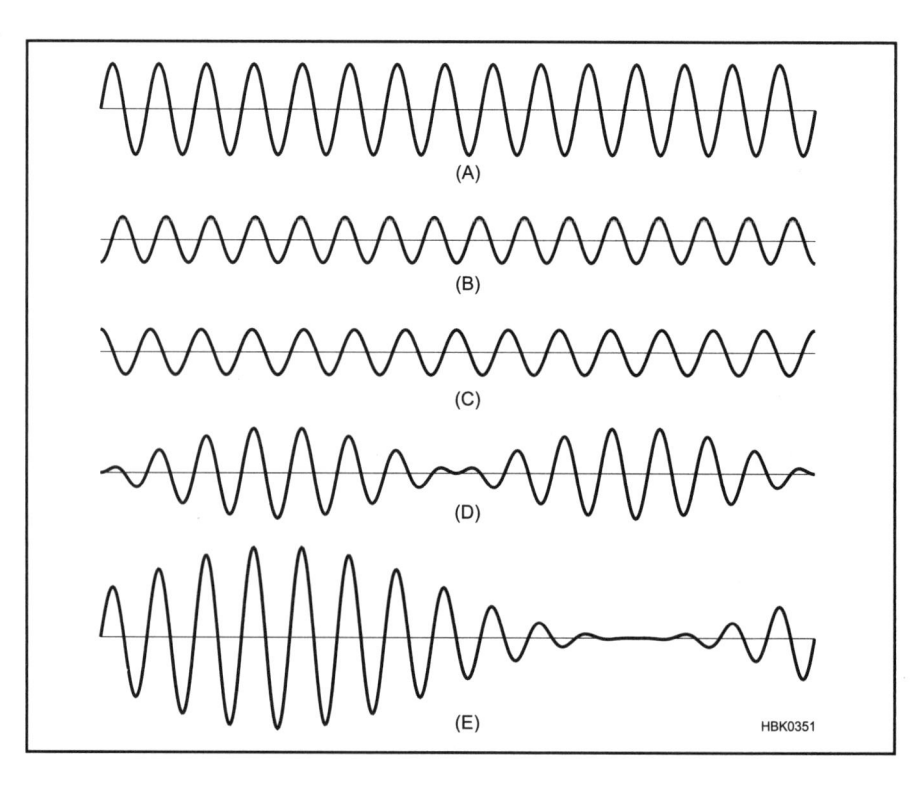

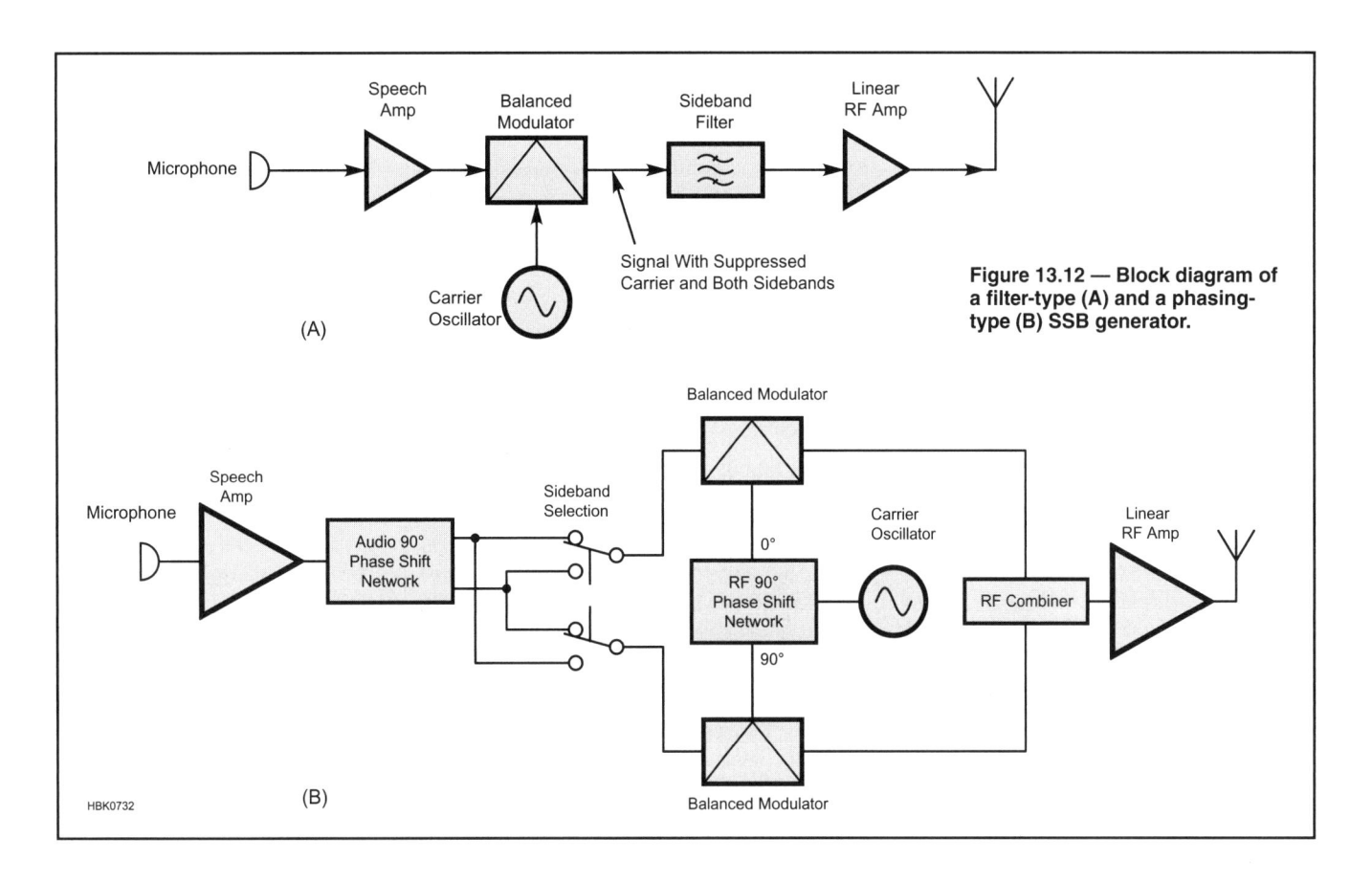

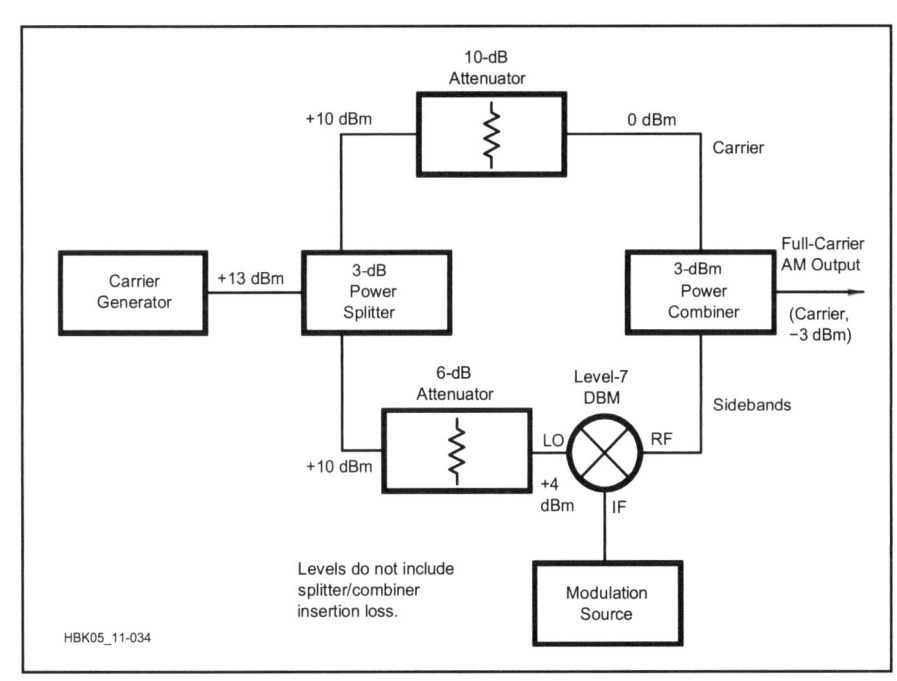

Figure 13.12 — Block diagram of a filter-type (A) and a phasing-type (B) SSB generator.

Figure 13.13 — Generating full-carrier AM with a diode DBM. A practical modulator using this technique is described in *Experimental Methods in RF Design*.

type of mixer whose output contains the sum and difference frequencies of the two input signals (the modulating signal and the carrier) but not the input signals themselves. There are several ways to eliminate the unwanted sideband, but the most common, shown in **Figure 13.12A**, is to pass the output of the balanced mixer through a crystal filter that passes the wanted sideband while filtering out the unwanted one. This is convenient in a transceiver since the same filter can be used in the receiver by means of a transmit-receive switch.

Another method to generate single sideband is called the *phasing method*. See Figure 13.12B. Using trigonometry, it can be shown mathematically that the sum of the signals from two balanced modulators, each fed with audio signals and RF carriers that are 90° out of phase, consists of one sideband only. The other sideband is suppressed. The output can be switched between LSB and USB simply by reversing the polarity of one of the inputs, which changes the phase by 180°. The phasing method eliminates the need for an expensive crystal filter following the modulator or, in the case of a transceiver, the need to switch the crystal filter between the transmitter and receiver sections. In addition, the audio quality is generally better because it eliminates the poor phase dispersion that is characteristic of most crystal filters. Using analog techniques, designing and building an audio phase-shift network that accurately maintained a 90° differential over a decade-wide frequency band (300 Hz to 3000 Hz) was rather complicated. With modern DSP techniques, the task is much easier.

BALANCED MODULATORS

A balanced modulator is a mixer. Briefly, the IF frequency LO (455 kHz in the example of Figure 13.9) translates the audio frequencies up to a pair of IF frequencies — the LO plus the audio frequency and the LO minus the audio frequency. The balance from the

Transmitting 13.9

LO port to the IF output causes the LO frequency to be suppressed by 30 to 40 dB. Adjustments are provided to improve the LO null.

The filter method of SSB generation uses an IF band-pass filter to pass one of the sidebands and block the other. In Figure 13.9 the filter is centered at 455.0 kHz. The LO is offset to 453.6 kHz or 456.4 kHz so that the upper sideband or the lower sideband (respectively) can pass through the filter. This creates a problem for the other LOs in the radio, because they must now be properly offset so that the final transmit output's carrier (suppressed) frequency coincides with the frequency readout on the front panel of the radio.

Various schemes have been used to create the necessary LO offsets. One method uses two crystals for the 69.545 MHz LO that can be selected. In synthesized radios, the programming of the microprocessor controls the various LOs. Some synthesized radios use two IF filters at two different frequencies, one for USB and one for LSB, and a 455.0 kHz LO, as shown in Figure 13.9. These radios can be designed to transmit two independent sidebands (ISB) resulting in two separate channels in the spectrum space of the usual AM channel.

The data sheets for balanced modulators and mixers specify the maximum level of audio for a given LO level. Higher audio levels create excessive IMD. The IF filter following the modulator removes higher-order IMD products that are outside its passband but the in-band IMD products should be at least 40 dB below each of two equal test tones. Speech clipping (AF or IF) can degrade this to 10 dB or so, but in the absence of speech processing the signal should be clean, in-band.

AMPLITUDE MODULATION WITH A DBM

We can generate DSB, suppressed-carrier AM with a DBM (double balanced mixer) by feeding the carrier to its RF port and the modulating signal to the IF port. (See the **Receiving** chapter for a detailed discussion of the DBM.) This is a classical *balanced modulator*, and the result — sidebands at radio frequencies corresponding to the carrier signal plus audio and the RF signal minus audio — emerges from the DBM's LO port. If we also want to transmit some carrier along with the sidebands, we can dc-bias the IF port (with a current of 10 to 20 mA) to upset the mixer's balance and keep its diodes from turning all the way off. (This technique is sometimes used for generating CW with a balanced modulator otherwise intended to generate DSB as part of an SSB-generation process.) **Figure 13.13** shows a more elegant approach to generating full-carrier AM with a DBM.

As we saw earlier when considering the many faces of AM, two DBMs, used in conjunction with carrier and audio phasing, can be used to generate SSB, suppressed-carrier AM. Likewise, two DBMs can be used with RF and LO phasing as an image-reject mixer.

AN MC1496P BALANCED MODULATOR

Although it predates the SA602/612, Freescale's MC1496 Gilbert cell multiplier remains a viable option for product detection and balanced modulator service. It has been around for decades and is still one of the best and least expensive. **Figure 13.14** is a typical balanced modulator circuit using the MC1496. The circuit of **Figure 13.15** includes an MC1496-based balanced modulator that is capable of carrier suppression greater than 50 dB. Per its description in Hayward, Campbell, and Larkin's *Experimental Methods in RF Design*, its output with audio drive should be kept to about –20 dBm with this circuit. LO drive should be 200 to 500 mV P-P.

SDR SSB GENERATORS

(This section is taken from the SDR: Simplified column by Ray Mack, W5IFS in the September/October 2012 issue of *QEX*.) The structure of this SDR SSB generator software is the same as if it were implemented in analog hardware. **Figure 13.16** shows the block diagram of the system. The program operates in a serial fashion: first an audio baseband filter limits the audio to a band of 300 Hz to 3 kHz. Second, the DDS phase step value to determine the carrier frequency is computed. Following that is the multiplication for the balanced mixer. Finally the undesired sideband is removed. Once the single sideband signal has been created, up-conversion is used to translate it to RF.

The audio band-pass filter response is only useful with 200 taps or more (See **Figure 13.17**). At 100 taps the rejection is only on the order of 12 dB below 100 Hz. Likewise, the opposite sideband filter requires on the order of 700 to 1000 taps to give approximately 60 dB of opposite sideband suppression. The large number of taps also makes the skirts very steep, so that we can use the filter to also further reduce any carrier feedthrough. **Figure 13.18** illustrates how steep the skirts can be. If the low-frequency carrier is at 18 kHz, carrier suppression is approximately 52 dB and the unwanted sideband more than that.

One alternative to reduce taps required in the audio filter is to simply use a dc block in the analog portion of the audio chain to set a lower boundary on the frequency. The response will be zero at 0 Hz and rise very rapidly to the frequency we set. This reduces the need for a sharp cutoff in DSP.

The close-in rejection of audio above 3 kHz is 45 dB or more with the 200-tap filter. Additionally, there is almost no energy above 3 kHz in the human voice, so energy in that region will likely be at least 60 dB below the lower frequencies after filtering.

Limiting the higher frequencies allows the use of a 6 kHz wide sideband selection filter instead of the normal 3 kHz filter to get bet-

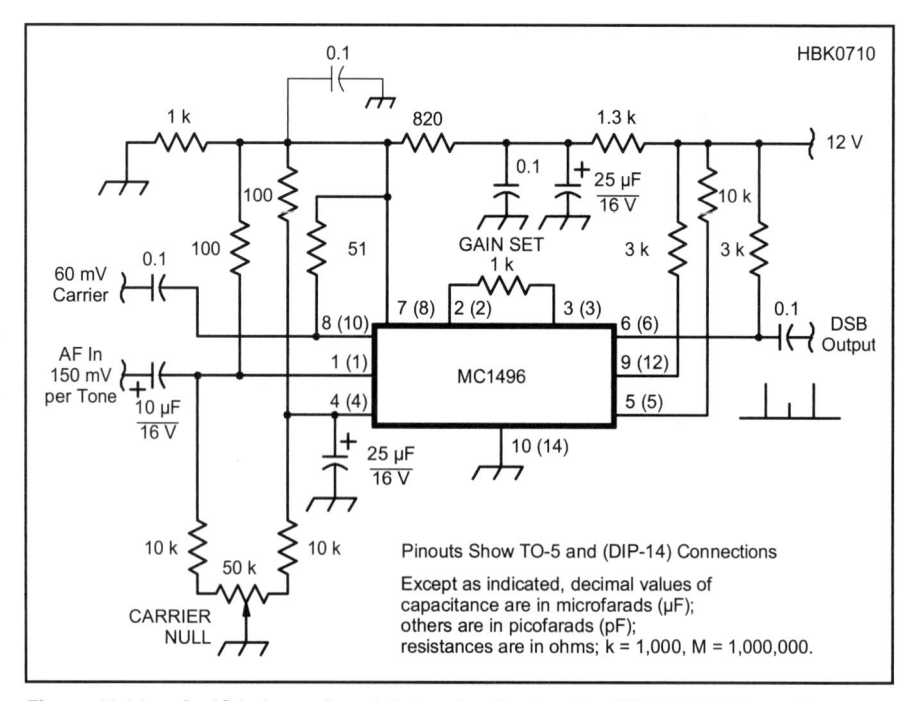

Figure 13.14 — An IC balanced modulator circuit using the MC1496 IC. The resistor between pins 2 and 3 sets the subsystem gain.

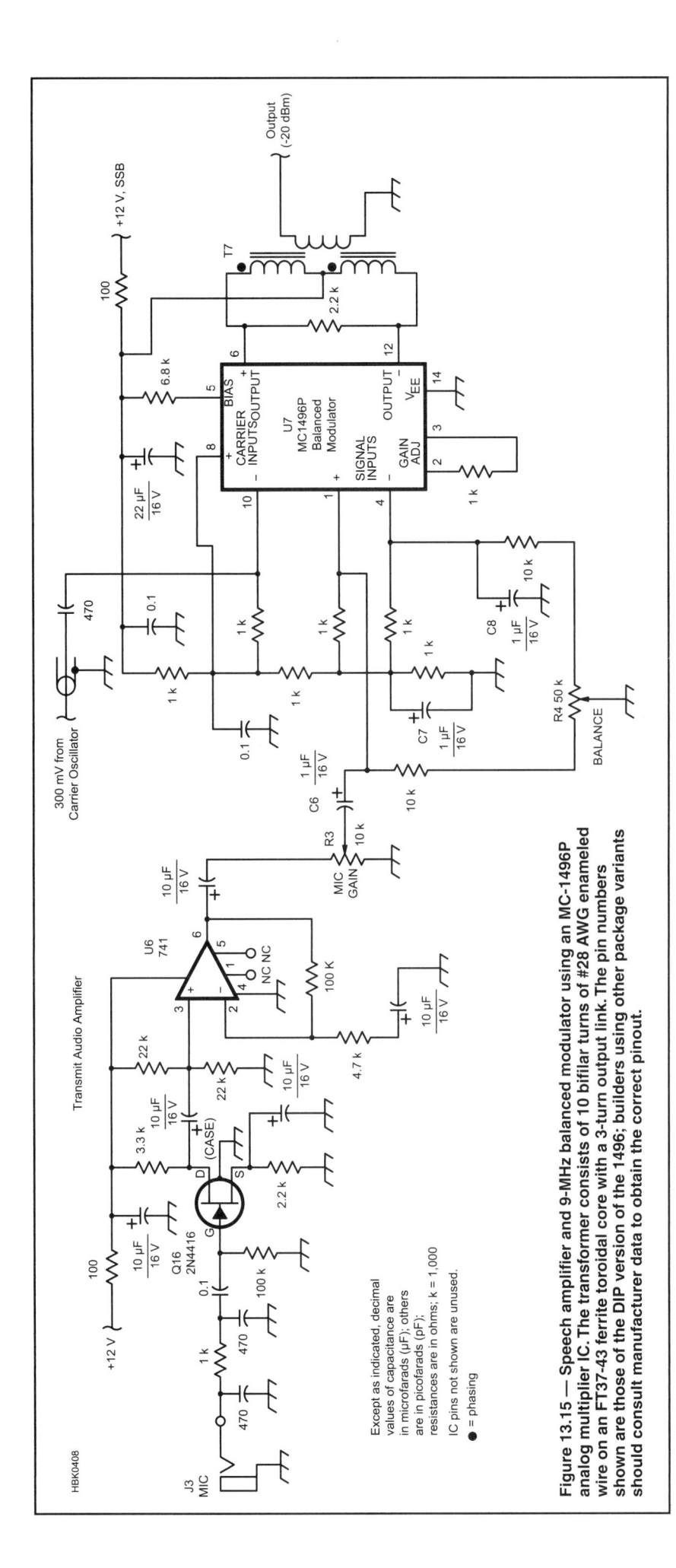

Figure 13.15 — Speech amplifier and 9-MHz balanced modulator using an MC-1496P analog multiplier IC. The transformer consists of 10 bifilar turns of #28 AWG enameled wire on an FT37-43 ferrite toroidal core with a 3-turn output link. The pin numbers shown are those of the DIP version of the 1496; builders using other package variants should consult manufacturer data to obtain the correct pinout.

ter skirt response. A low-pass or high-pass filter would also work and give approximately the same skirt response, but we want to be sure to eliminate any residual energy at baseband in the case of a lower sideband transmission. The wider bandwidth limits the lower frequency for our carrier. We want the carrier frequency to be as high as possible in order to limit image response when we up-convert to our final RF signal.

There is a practical limit with respect to the number of taps in the filters. Each tap requires one multiply-accumulate operation, which is a MAC in the DSP world. (MAC also means Media Access Control to a networking hardware person!) The DSP is capable of one MAC for each MHz of clock frequency for each portion of the hardware chain. If voice is digitized at a 48 kHz sample rate, a transmitter filter with 200 taps for audio and 1000 taps for sideband selection will need 57.6 MMACs to do its job. (See the **Receiving** chapter note from KA9Q regarding fast convolution to implement the filter method as a more efficient method if the hardware can support it.) In addition, a large number of taps can create latency. In this case, for a 48 kHz sample stream, 1000 taps represents 20 msec. Depending on how the SDR is implemented, this could add to overall microphone-to-RF latency.

OVERMODULATION

Since the information we transmit using AM shows up entirely as energy in its sidebands, it follows that the more energetic we make the sidebands, the more information energy will be available for an AM receiver to "recover" when it demodulates the signal. Even in an ideal modulator, there's a practical limit to how strong we can make an AM signal's sidebands relative to its carrier, however. Beyond that limit, we severely distort the waveform we want to translate into radio form.

We reach AM's distortion-free modulation limit when the sum of the sidebands and carrier at the modulator output *just reaches zero* at the modulating wave-form's most negative peak (**Figure 13.19**). We call this condition *100% modulation*, and it occurs when *m* in equation A in the sidebar "Mixer Math: Amplitude Modulation" equals 1. (We enumerate *modulation percentage* in values from 0 to 100%. The lower the number, the less information energy is in the sidebands. You may also see modulation enumerated in terms of a *modulation factor* from 0 to 1, which directly equals *m*; a modulation factor of 1 is the same as 100% modulation.) Equation B in the sidebar shows that each sideband's voltage is half that of the carrier. Power varies as the square of voltage, so the power in each sideband of a 100%-modulated signal is therefore $(½)^2$ times, or ¼, that of the carrier.

Transmitting 13.11

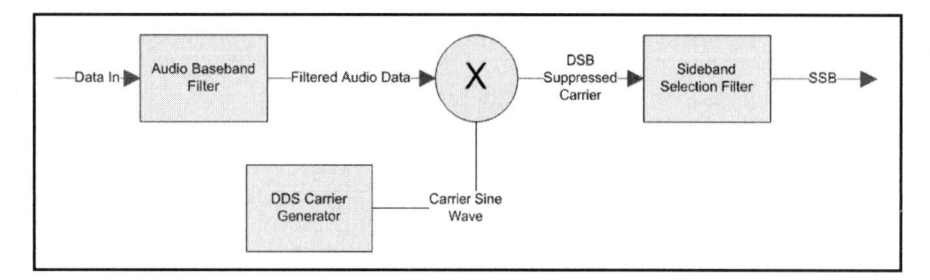

Figure 13.16 — This block diagram shows the software SSB transmit generator using the filter method.

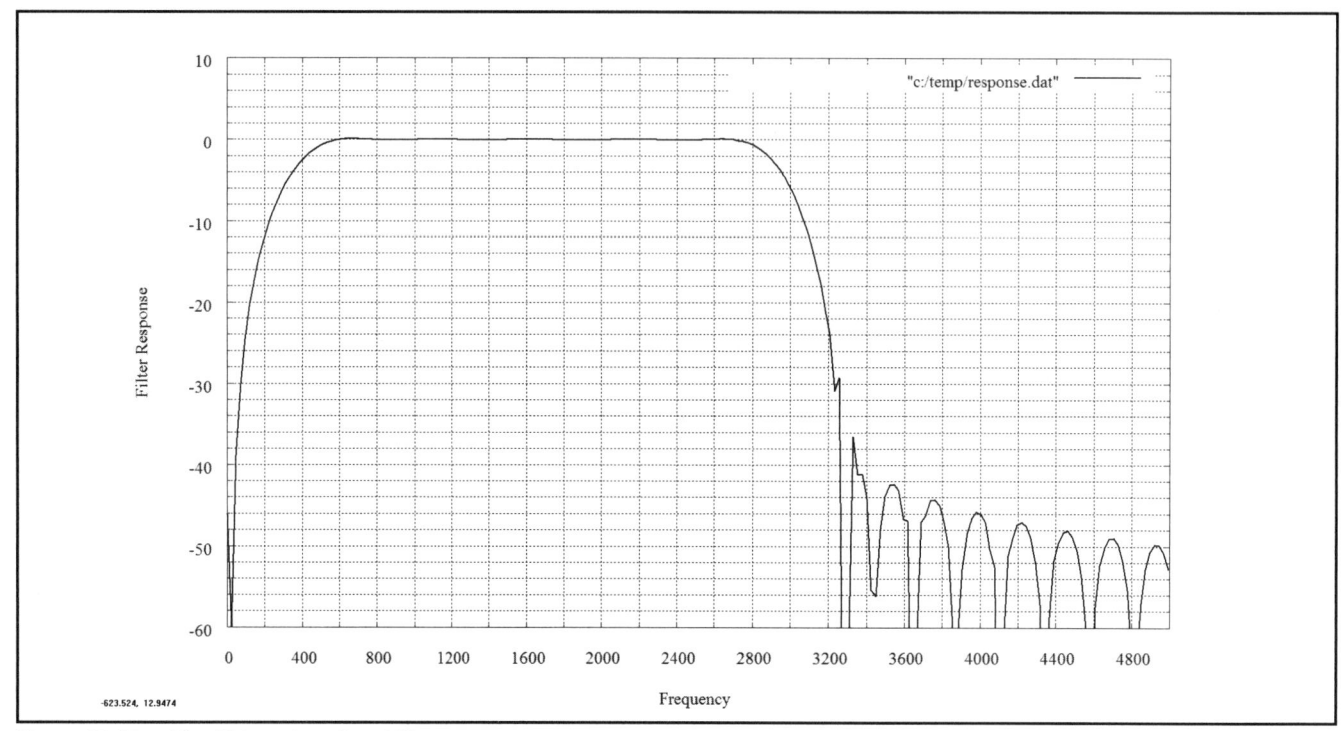

Figure 13.17 — The 200-tap baseband filter response.

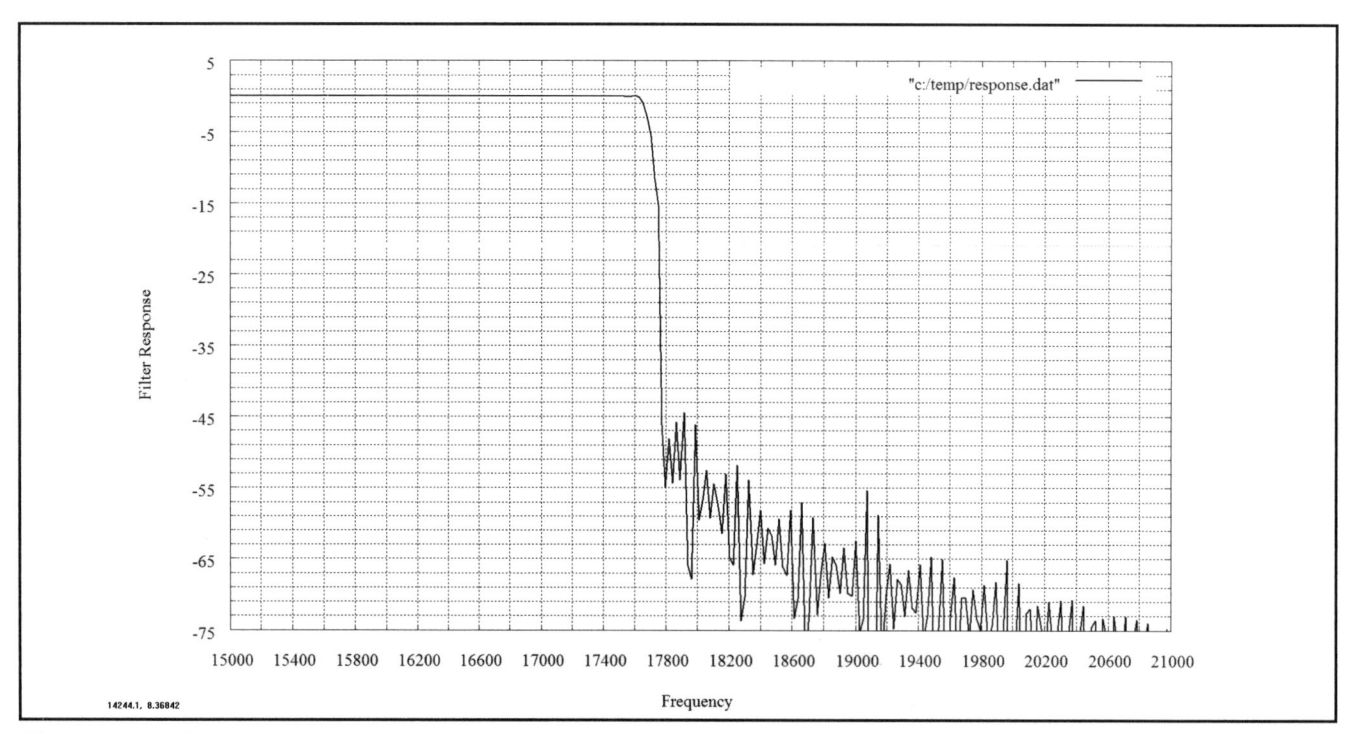

Figure 13.18 — The response of a 700-tap filter, showing a wider frequency view. The filter is 6 kHz wide to allow for a steep skirt on the carrier side. The 6 dB cutoff point is set at 300 Hz away from the low-frequency carrier, which is at 18,000 Hz (see text).

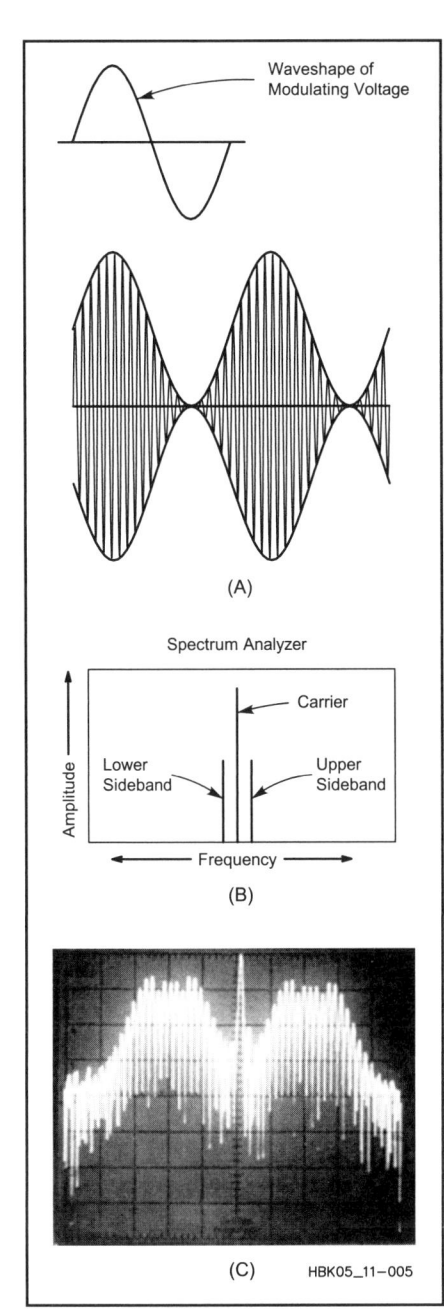

Figure 13.19 — Graphed in terms of amplitude versus time (A), the *envelope* of a properly modulated AM signal exactly mirrors the shape of its modulating waveform, which is a sine wave in this example. This AM signal is modulated as fully as it can be — 100% — because its envelope *just* touches zero on the modulating wave's negative peaks. Graphing the same AM signal in terms of amplitude versus frequency (B) reveals its three spectral components: Carrier, upper sideband and lower sideband. B shows sidebands as single-frequency components because the modulating waveform is a sine wave. With a complex modulating waveform, the modulator's sum and difference products really do show up as bands on either side of the carrier (C).

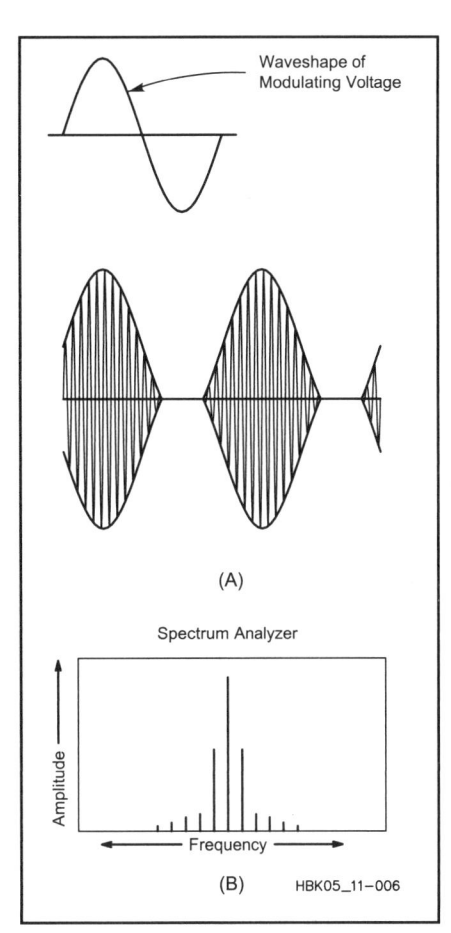

Figure 13.20 — Negative-going overmodulation of an AM transmitter results in a modulation envelope (A) that doesn't faithfully mirror the modulating waveform. This distortion creates additional sideband components that broaden the transmitted signal (B). Positive-going modulation beyond 100% is used by some AM broadcasters in conjunction with negative-peak limiting to increase "talk power" without causing negative overmodulation.

A transmitter capable of 100% modulation when operating at a carrier power of 100 W therefore puts out a 150-W signal at 100% modulation, 50 W of which is attributable to the sidebands. (The *peak* envelope power [PEP] output of a double-sideband, full-carrier AM transmitter at 100% modulation is four times its carrier PEP. This is why our solid-state, "100-W" MF/HF transceivers are usually rated for no more than about 25 W carrier output at 100% amplitude modulation.)

One-hundred-percent negative modulation is a brick-wall limit because an amplitude modulator can't reduce its output to less than zero. Trying to increase negative modulation beyond the 100% point results in *overmodulation* (**Figure 13.20**), in which the modulation envelope no longer mirrors the shape of the modulating wave (Figure 13.20A). A

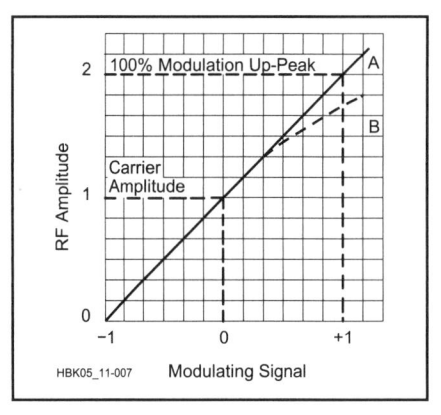

Figure 13.21 — An ideal AM transmitter exhibits a straight-line relationship (A) between its instantaneous envelope amplitude and the instantaneous amplitude of its modulating signal. Distortion, and thus an unnecessarily wide signal, results if the transmitter cannot respond linearly across the modulating signal's full amplitude range (B).

negatively overmodulated wave contains more energy than it did at 100% modulation, but some of the added energy now exists as *harmonics of the modulating waveform* (Figure 13.20B). This distortion makes the modulated signal take up more spectrum space than it needs. In voice operation, overmodulation commonly happens only on syllabic peaks, making the distortion products sound like transient noise we refer to as *splatter*.

MODULATION LINEARITY

If we increase an amplitude modulator's modulating-signal input by a given percentage, we expect a proportional modulation increase in the modulated signal. We expect good *modulation linearity*. Suboptimal amplitude modulator design may not allow this, however. Above some modulation percentage, a modulator may fail to increase modulation in proportion to an increase in its input signal (**Figure 13.21**). Distortion, and thus an unnecessarily wide signal, results.

13.3.2 Angle Modulators

Amplitude modulation served as our first means of translating information into radio form because it could be implemented as simply as turning an electric noise generator on and off. (A spark transmitter consisted of little more than this.) By the 1930s, we had begun experimenting with translating information into radio form and back again by modulating a radio wave's angular velocity (frequency or phase) instead of its overall amplitude. The result of this process is *frequency modulation (FM)* or *phase modulation (PM)*, both of which are often grouped

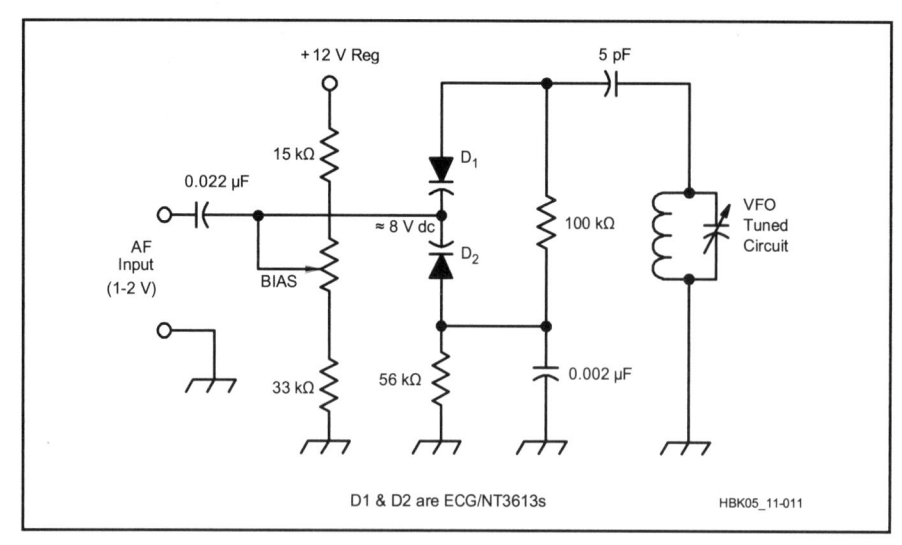

Figure 13.22 — One or more tuning diodes can serve as the variable reactance in a reactance modulator. This HF reactance modulator circuit uses two diodes in series to ensure that the tuned circuit's RF-voltage swing cannot bias the diodes into conduction. D1 and D2 are "30-volt" tuning diodes that exhibit a capacitance of 22 pF at a bias voltage of 4. The BIAS control sets the point on the diode's voltage-versus-capacitance characteristic around which the modulating waveform swings.

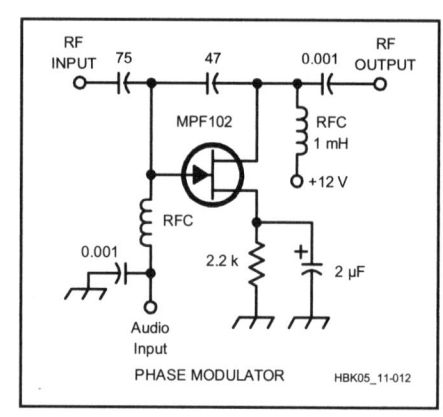

Figure 13.23 — A series reactance modulator acts as a variable shunt around a reactance — in this case, a 47-pF capacitor — through which the carrier passes.

under the name *angle modulation* because of their underlying principle.

A change in a carrier's frequency or phase for the purpose of modulation is called *deviation*. An FM signal deviates according to the amplitude of its modulating waveform, independently of the modulating waveform's frequency; the higher the modulating wave's amplitude, the greater the deviation. A PM signal deviates according to the amplitude *and frequency* of its modulating waveform; the higher the modulating wave's amplitude and/or frequency, the greater the deviation. See the sidebar, "Mixer Math: Angle Modulation" for a numerical description of these processes.

If you vary a reactance in or associated with an oscillator's frequency-determining element(s), you vary the oscillator's frequency. If you vary the tuning of a tuned circuit through which a signal passes, you vary the signal's phase. A circuit that does this is called a *reactance modulator*, and can be little more than a tuning diode or two connected to a tuned circuit in an oscillator or amplifier (**Figure 13.22**). Varying a reactance through which the signal passes (**Figure 13.23**) is another way of doing the same thing.

The difference between FM and PM depends solely on how, and not how much, deviation occurs. A modulator that causes deviation in proportion to the modulating wave's amplitude and frequency is a phase modulator. A modulator that causes deviation only in proportion to the modulating signal's amplitude is a frequency modulator.

ANGLE MODULATION SIDEBANDS

Although angle modulation produces uncountable sum and difference products, most of them are vanishingly weak in practical systems. They emerge from the modulator spaced from the average ("resting," unmodulated) carrier frequency by integer multiples of the modulating frequency (**Figure 13.24**). The strength of the sidebands relative to the carrier, and the strength and phase of the carrier itself, vary with the degree of modulation — the modulation index. (The *overall* amplitude of an angle-modulated signal does not change with modulation, however; when energy goes out of the carrier, it shows up in the sidebands, and vice versa.) In practice, we operate angle-modulated transmitters at modulation indexes that make all but a few of their infinite sidebands small in amplitude.

Mixer Math: Angle Modulation

An angle-modulated signal can be mathematically represented as

$$f_c(t) = \cos(2\pi f_c t + m \sin(2\pi f_m t))$$

$$= \cos(2\pi f_c t) \cos(m \sin(2\pi f_m t)) - \sin(2\pi f_c t) \sin(m \sin(2\pi f_m t))$$

In this equation, we see the carrier frequency ($2\pi f_c t$) and modulating signal ($\sin 2\pi f_m t$) as in equation A shown in the sidebar Mixer Math: Amplitude Modulation. We again see the modulating signal associated with a coefficient, m, which relates to degree of modulation. (In the AM equation, *m* is the modulation factor; in the angle-modulation equation, *m* is the *modulation index* and, for FM, equals the deviation divided by the modulating frequency.) We see that angle-modulation occurs as the cosine of the sum of the carrier frequency ($2\pi f_c t$) and the modulating signal ($\sin 2\pi f_m t$) times the modulation index (*m*). In its expanded form, we see the appearance of sidebands above and below the carrier frequency.

Angle modulation is a multiplicative process, so, like AM, it creates sidebands on both sides of the carrier. Unlike AM, however, angle modulation creates an *infinite* number of sidebands on either side of the carrier! This occurs as a direct result of modulating the carrier's angular velocity, to which its frequency and phase directly relate. If we continuously vary a wave's angular velocity according to another periodic wave's cyclical amplitude variations, the rate at which the modulated wave repeats *its* cycle — its frequency — passes through an infinite number of values. (How many individual amplitude points are there in one cycle of the modulating wave? An infinite number. How many corresponding discrete frequency or phase values does the corresponding angle-modulated wave pass through as the modulating signal completes a cycle? An infinite number!) In AM, the carrier frequency stays at one value, so AM produces two sidebands — the sum of its carrier's unchanging frequency value and the modulating frequency, and the difference between the carrier's unchanging frequency value and the modulating frequency. In angle modulation, the modulating wave shifts the frequency or phase of the carrier through an infinite number of different frequency or phase values, resulting in an infinite number of sum and difference products.

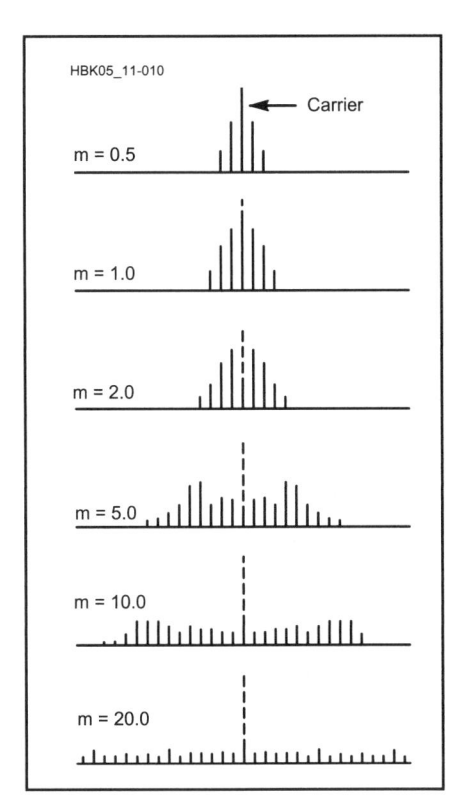

Figure 13.24 — Angle-modulation produces a carrier and an infinite number of upper and lower sidebands spaced from the average ("resting," unmodulated) carrier frequency by integer multiples of the modulating frequency. (This drawing is a simplification because it only shows relatively strong, close-in sideband pairs; space constraints prevent us from extending it to infinity.) The relative amplitudes of the sideband pairs and carrier vary with modulation index, *m*.

(A mathematical tool called *Bessel functions* helps determine the relative strength of the carrier and sidebands according to modulation index. The **Modulation** chapter includes a graph to illustrate this relationship.) Selectivity in transmitter and receiver circuitry further modify this relationship, especially for sidebands far away from the carrier.

BIPHASE-SHIFT KEYING (BPSK) MODULATION WITH A DBM

Back in our discussion of square-wave mixing, we saw how multiplying a switching mixer's linear input with a square wave causes a 180° phase shift during the negative part of the square wave's cycle. As **Figure 13.25** shows, we can use this effect to produce *biphase-shift keying (BPSK)*, a digital system that conveys data by means of carrier phase reversals. A related system, *quadrature phase-shift keying (QPSK)* uses two DBMs and phasing to convey data by phase-shifting a carrier in 90° increments.

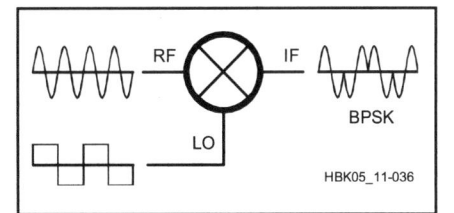

Figure 13.25 — Mixing a carrier with a square wave generates biphase-shift keying (BPSK), in which the carrier phase is shifted 180° for data transmission. In practice, as in this drawing, the carrier and data signals are phase-coherent so the mixer switches only at carrier zero crossings.

DEVIATION AND FREQUENCY MULTIPLICATION

Maintaining modulation linearity is just as important in angle modulation as it is in AM, because unwanted distortion is always our enemy. A given angle-modulator circuit can frequency- or phase-shift a carrier only so much before the shift stops occurring in strict proportion to the amplitude (or, in PM, the amplitude and frequency) of the modulating signal.

If we want more deviation than an angle modulator can linearly achieve, we can operate the modulator at a suitable sub-harmonic — submultiple — of the desired frequency, and process the modulated signal through a series of *frequency multipliers* to bring it up to the desired frequency. The deviation also increases by the overall multiplication factor, relieving the modulator of having to do it all directly. A given FM or PM radio design may achieve its final output frequency through a combination of mixing (frequency shift, no deviation change) and frequency multiplication (frequency shift *and* deviation change).

"TRUE FM"

Something we covered a bit earlier bears closer study: "An FM signal deviates according to the amplitude of its modulating waveform, independently of the modulating wave-form's frequency; the higher the modulating wave's amplitude, the greater the deviation. A PM signal deviates according to the amplitude *and frequency* of its modulating waveform; the higher the modulating wave's amplitude *and/or frequency*, the greater the deviation."

The practical upshot of this excerpt is that we can use a phase modulator to generate FM. All we need to do is run a PM transmitter's modulating signal through a low-pass filter that (ideally) halves the signal's amplitude for each doubling of frequency (a reduction of "6 dB per octave," as we sometimes see such responses characterized") to compensate for its phase modulator's "more deviation with higher frequencies" characteristic. The result is an FM, not PM, signal. FM achieved with a phase modulator is sometimes called *indirect FM* as opposed to the *direct FM* we get from a frequency modulator.

We sometimes see claims that one piece of gear is better than another solely because it generates "true FM" as opposed to indirect FM. We can debunk such claims by keeping in mind that direct and indirect FM *sound exactly alike in a receiver* when done correctly.

CONVEYING DC LEVELS WITH ANGLE MODULATION

Depending on the nature of the modulation source, there *is* a practical difference between a frequency modulator and a phase modulator. Answering two questions can tell us whether this difference matters: Does our modulating signal contain a dc level or not? If so, do we

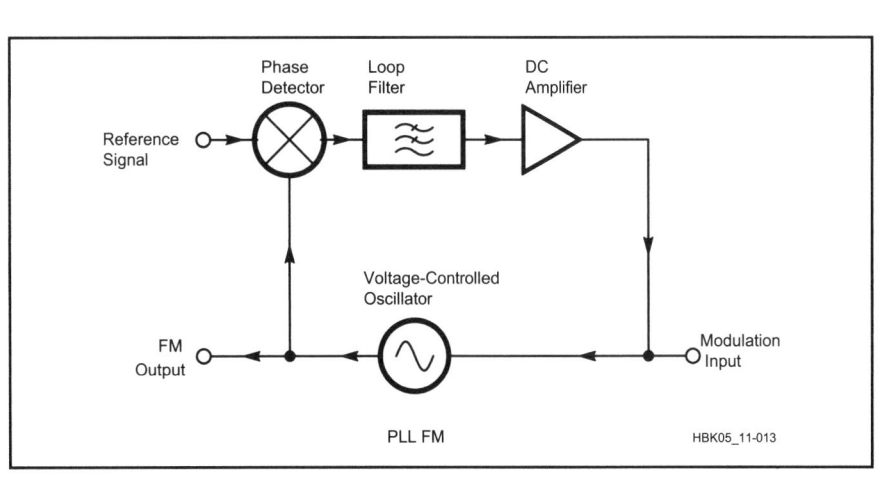

Figure 13.26 — Frequency modulation using a phase-locked loop (PLL).

Transmitting 13.15

need to accurately preserve that dc level through our radio communication link for successful communication? If both answers are *yes*, we must choose our hardware and/or information-encoding approach carefully, because a frequency modulator can convey dc-level shifts in its modulating waveform, while a phase modulator, which responds only to instantaneous changes in frequency and phase, cannot.

Consider what happens when we want to frequency-modulate a phase-locked-loop-synthesized transmitted signal. **Figure 13.26** shows the block diagram of a PLL frequency modulator. Normally, we modulate a PLL's VCO because it's the easy thing to do. As long as our modulating frequency results in frequency excursions too fast for the PLL to follow and correct — that is, as long as our modulating frequency is outside the PLL's *loop bandwidth* — we achieve the FM we seek. Trying to modulate a dc level by pushing the VCO to a particular frequency and holding it there fails, however, because a PLL's loop response includes dc. The loop, therefore, detects the modulation's dc component as a correctable error and "fixes" it. FMing a PLL's VCO therefore can't buy us the dc response "true FM" is supposed to allow.

We *can* dc-modulate a PLL modulator, but we must do so by modulating the frequency of the loop *reference*. The PLL then adjusts the VCO to adapt to the changed reference, and our dc level gets through. In this case, the modulating frequency must be *within* the loop bandwidth — which dc certainly is — or the VCO won't be corrected to track the shift.

SDR ANGLE MODULATORS

Figure 13.27 shows the block diagram of an FM transmitter using DSP to produce the carrier, and using addition to create true FM from the audio input. An FM signal can be generated directly through the DDS by simply adding or subtracting a small value that corresponds to the audio voltage to the tuning value used for the DDS accumulator. The frequency deviation is adjusted by controlling the gain applied to the audio signal. This method produces true frequency modulation. If the audio signal is used to control the phase accumulation of the DDS, the result is PM.

Angle modulation can also be produced using I/Q modulation as in **Figure 13.28**. A DSB-SC (double-sideband, suppressed-carrier) signal is produced by a balanced modulator or DSP multiplier (see SDR SSB Generators earlier in this chapter). The DSB-SC signal is then added to the carrier signal with a 90° phase difference. The result is a PM signal.

Frequency modulation requires that an integrator (low-pass filter) be applied to the modulating signal. This is because frequency is the time-derivative of phase. By applying the integrated signal to a phase modulator, FM is produced with a deviation that does not depend on signal amplitude — only frequency.

Because of the low-pass filter, speech is usually given a high-frequency boost by a high-pass pre-emphasis network. A corresponding de-emphasis (low-pass) network must be applied to the recovered modulation in the receiver to restore the original modulating signal's frequency response. This improves intelligibility and signal-to-noise ratio of the received audio.

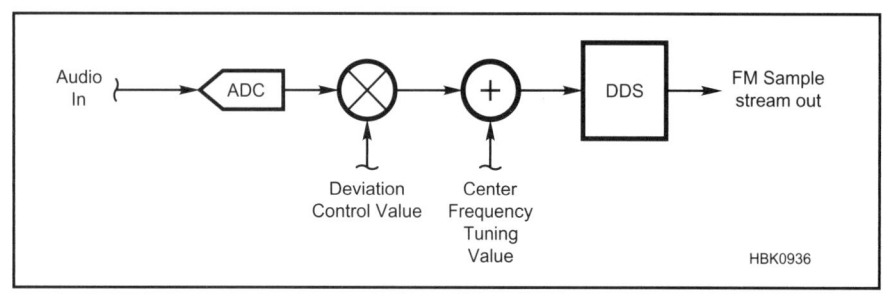

Figure 13.27 — Creating FM by controlling the frequency of a DDS signal source. By controlling the phase step instead of the frequency, PM would be created.

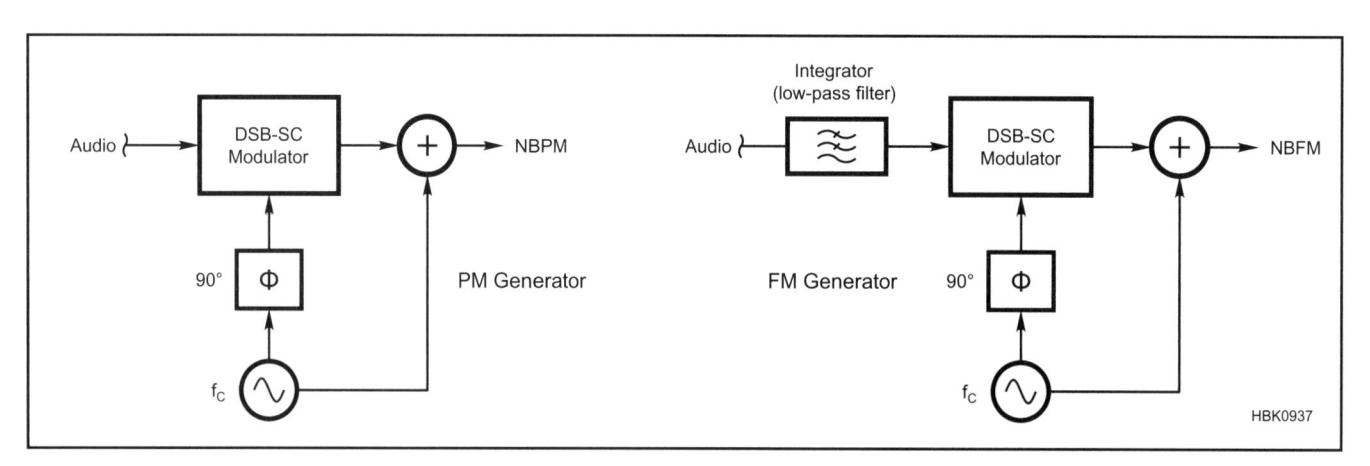

Figure 13.28 — Two methods of using I/Q modulation to produced angle-modulated signals. The block diagram includes a DSB generator (Figure 13.16) with the additional step of mixing (multiplying) the DSB signal with a phase-shifted carrier signal to produce PM (A) or FM (B). FM requires applies an integrator (low-pass filter) to the modulating signal so that output frequency depends only on the amplitude of the modulating signal and not its frequency.

13.4 Transmitting CW

Earlier in this chapter, the importance of shaping the time envelope of the keying pulse of an on-off keyed transmitter is discussed. There are serious ramifications of not paying close attention to this design parameter. The optimum shape of a transmitter envelope should approach the form of a sinusoid raised to a power with a tradeoff between occupied bandwidth and overlap between the successive pulses. This can be accomplished either through filtering of the pulse waveform before modulation in a linear transmitter, or through direct generation of the pulse shape using DSP.

The differences between well-designed and poor pulse shaping can perhaps be best described by looking at some results. The following figures are from recent *QST* product reviews of commercial multimode 100 W HF transceivers. **Figure 13.29** shows the CW keying waveform of a transmitter with good spectrum control. The top trace is the key closure, with the start of the first contact closure on the left edge at 60 WPM using full break-in. Below it is the nicely rounded RF envelope. **Figure 13.30** shows the resultant signal spectrum. Note that the signal amplitude is about 80 dB down at a spacing of ±1 kHz, with a floor of –90 dB over the 10 kHz shown. **Figures 13.31** and **13.32** are similar data taken from a different manufacturer's transceiver. Note the sharp corners of the RF envelope, as well as the time it takes for the first "dit" to be developed. The resulting spectrum is not even down 40 dB at ±1 kHz and shows a floor that doesn't quite make –60 dB over the 10 kHz range. It's easy to see the problems that the latter transmitter will cause to receivers trying to listen to a weak signal near its operating frequency. The unwanted components of the signal are heard on adjacent channels as sharp clicks when the signal is turned on and off, called *key clicks*. Note that even the best-shaped keying waveform in a linear transmitter will become sharp with a wide spectrum if it is used to drive a stage such as an external power amplifier beyond its linear range. This generally results in clipping or limiting with subsequent removal of the rounded corners on the envelope. Trying to get the last few dB of power out of a transmitter can often result in this sort of unintended signal impairment.

13.4.1 CW Operation

Figure 13.33A closely resembles what we see when a properly adjusted CW transmitter sends a string of dots. Keying a carrier on and off produces a wave that varies in amplitude and has double (upper and lower) sidebands that vary in spectral composition according

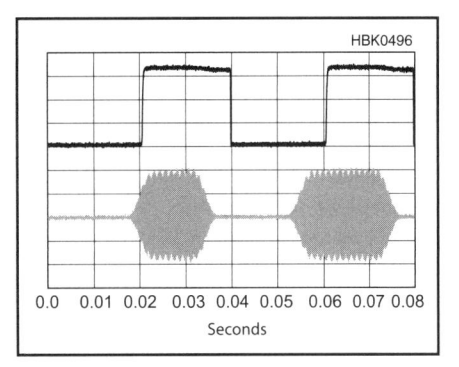

Figure 13.29 — The CW keying waveform of a transmitter with good spectrum control. The top trace is the key closure, with the start of the first contact closure on the left edge at 60 WPM using full break-in. Below that is the nicely rounded RF envelope.

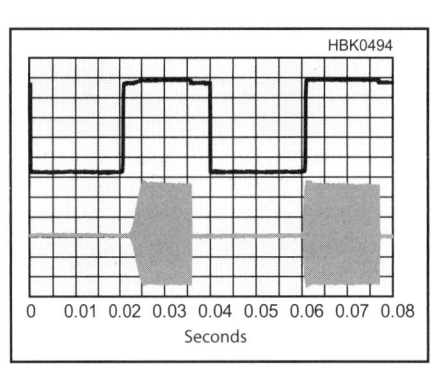

Figure 13.31 — The CW keying waveform of a transmitter with poor spectrum control. The top trace is the key closure, with the start of the first contact closure on the left edge at 60 WPM using full break-in. Note the sharp corners of the RF envelope that result in excessive bandwidth products.

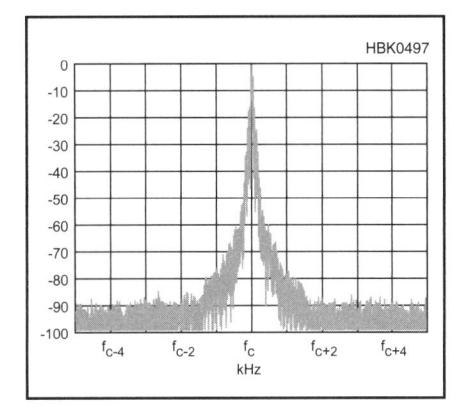

Figure 13.30 — The resultant signal spectrum from the keying shown in Figure 13.29. Note that the signal amplitude is about 80 dB down at a spacing of ±1 kHz, with a floor of –90 dB over the 10 kHz shown.

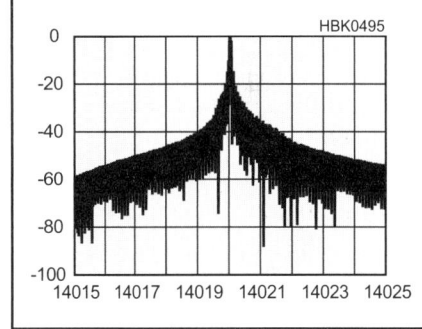

Figure 13.32 — The resultant signal spectrum from the keying shown in Figure 13.31. The resulting spectrum is not even down 40 dB at ±1 kHz and shows a floor that doesn't quite make 60 dB below the carrier across the 10 kHz.

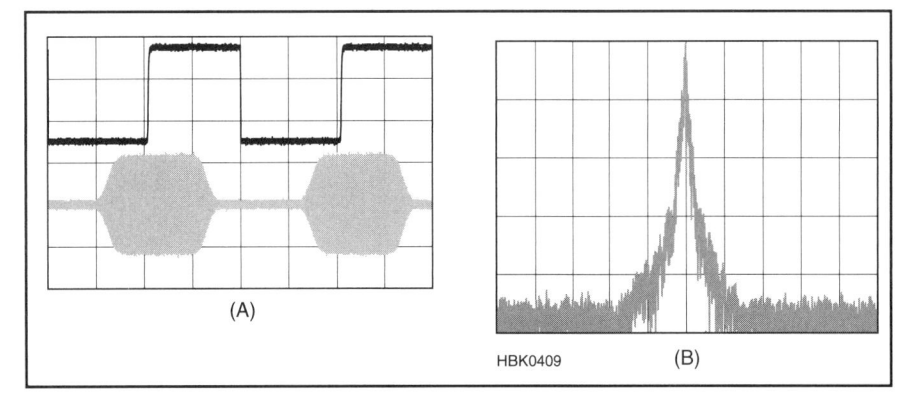

Figure 13.33 — Waveshaping in a CW transmitter often causes a CW signal's RF envelope (lower trace in the amplitude-versus-time display at A) to contain less harmonic energy than the abrupt transitions of its key closure waveform (upper trace in A) suggest should be the case. B, an amplitude-versus-frequency display, shows that even a properly shaped CW signal has many sideband components.

to the duration and envelope shape of the on-off transitions. The emission mode we call CW is therefore a form of AM. The concepts of modulation percentage and overmodulation are usually not applied to generating an on-off-keyed Morse signal, however. This is related to how we copy CW by ear, and the fact that, in CW radio communication, we usually don't translate the received signal all the way back into its original pre-modulator (*baseband*) form, as a closer look at the process reveals.

In CW transmission, we usually open and close a keying line to make dc transitions that turn the transmitted carrier on and off. See Figure 13.33B. CW reception usually does not entirely reverse this process, however. Instead of demodulating a CW signal all the way back to its baseband self — a shifting dc level — we want the presences and absences of its carrier to create long and short audio tones. Because the carrier is RF and not AF, we must mix it with a locally generated RF signal — from a *beat-frequency oscillator (BFO)* — that's close enough in frequency to produce a difference signal at AF (this BFO can, of course, also be inserted at an IF stage). What goes into our transmitter as shifting dc comes out of our receiver as tone bursts of dot and dash duration.

It so happens that we always need to hear one or more harmonics of the fundamental keying waveform for the code to sound sufficiently crisp. If the transmitted signal will be subject to fading caused by varying propagation — a safe assumption for any long-distance radio communication — we can *harden* our keying by making the transmitter's output rise and fall more quickly. This puts more energy into keying sidebands and makes the signal more copyable in the presence of fading — in particular, *selective fading*, which linearly distorts a modulated signal's complex waveform and randomly changes the sidebands' strength and phase relative to the carrier and each other. The appropriate keying hardness also depends on the keying speed. The faster the keying in WPM, the faster the on-off times — the harder the keying — must be for the signal to remain ear- and machine-readable through noise and fading.

Instead of thinking of this process in terms of modulation percentage, we just ensure that a CW transmitter produces sufficient keying-sideband energy for solid reception. Practical CW transmitters usually do not do their keying with a modulator stage as such. Instead, one or more stages are turned on and off to modulate the carrier with Morse, with rise and fall times set by *R* and *C* values associated with the stages' keying and/or power supply lines. A transmitter's CW *waveshaping* is therefore usually hardwired to values appropriate for reasonably high-speed sending (35 to 55 WPM or so) in the presence of fading.

However, some transceivers allow the user to vary keying hardness at will as a menu option. Rise and fall times of 1 to 5 ms are common; 5-ms rise and fall times equate to a keying speed of 36 WPM in the presence of fading and 60 WPM if fading is absent.

The faster a CW transmitter's output changes between zero and maximum, the more bandwidth its carrier and sidebands occupy. See Figure 13.33B. Making a CW signal's keying too hard is therefore spectrum-wasteful and inconsiderate of other stations because it makes the signal wider than it needs to be. Keying sidebands that are stronger and wider than necessary are traditionally called *clicks* because of what they sound like on the air.

Radiotelegraph or CW operation can be easily obtained from the transmitter architecture design shown in Figure 13.9. For CW operation, a carrier is generated at the center of the SSB filter passband. There are two ways to make this carrier available. One way is to unbalance the balanced modulator so that the LO can pass through. Each kind of balanced modulator circuit has its own method of doing this. The approach chosen in Figure 13.9 is to go around the modulator and the SSB filter.

A shaping network controls the envelope of the IF signal to accomplish two things: control the shape of the Morse code character in a way that limits wideband spectrum emissions that can cause interference, and make the Morse code signal easy and pleasant to copy.

13.4.2 RF Envelope Shaping

On-off keying (CW) is a special kind of low-level amplitude modulation (a low signal-level stage is turned on and off). It is special because the sideband power is subtracted from the carrier power, and not provided by a separate "modulator" circuit, as in high-level AM. It creates a spectrum around the carrier frequency whose amplitude and bandwidth are influenced by the rates of signal amplitude rise and fall and by the curvature of the keyed waveform.. For additional infor-

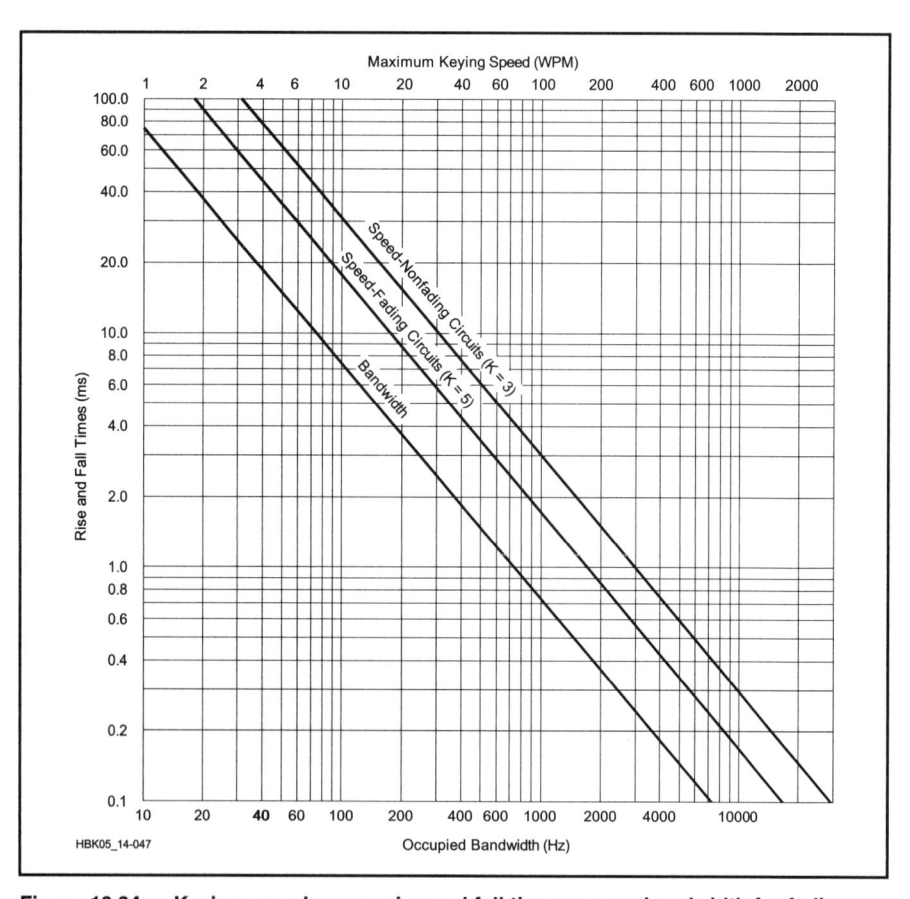

Figure 13.34 — Keying speed versus rise and fall times versus bandwidth for fading and nonfading communications circuits. For example, for transmitter output waveform rise and fall times of approximately 6 ms, draw a horizontal line from 6.0 ms on the rise and fall times scale to the bandwidth line. Then draw a vertical line to the occupied bandwidth scale at the bottom of the graph. In this case the bandwidth is about 130 Hz. Also extend the 6.0 ms horizontal line to the K = 3 line for a nonfading circuit. Finally draw a vertical line from the K = 3 line to the WPM axis. The 6 ms rise and fall time should be suitable for keying speeds up to about 50 WPM in this example.

mation see the article by Sabin on IF signal processing in the References section of this chapter.

Now look at **Figure 13.34**. The vertical axis is labeled Rise and Fall Times (ms). For a rise/fall time of 6 ms (between the 10% and 90% values) go horizontally to the line marked Bandwidth. A –20 dB bandwidth of roughly 120 Hz is indicated on the lower horizontal axis. Continuing to the K = 5 and K = 3 lines, the upper horizontal axis suggests code speeds of 30 WPM and 50 WPM respectively.

These code speeds can be accommodated by the rise and fall times displayed on the vertical axis. For code speeds greater than these the Morse code characters become "soft" sounding and difficult to copy, especially under less-than-ideal propagation conditions.

The ITU Classification of Emission Standards for determining necessary bandwidths of signals uses a value of 0.8 for the conversion between baud and WPM and suggests a typical value for K of 5 on an HF channel where the signal is subjected to fading. The bandwidth for a 13 WPM signal would then be:

BW = WPM × 0.8 × 5 = 10.4 × 5 = 52 Hz

For a narrow spectrum and freedom from adjacent channel interference, a further requirement is that the spectrum must fall off very rapidly beyond the –20 dB bandwidth indicated in Figure 13.34. A sensitive narrowband CW receiver that is tuned to an adjacent channel that is only 1 or 2 kHz away can detect keying sidebands that are 80 to 100 dB below the key-down level of a strong CW signal.

An additional consideration is that during key-up a residual signal, called *backwave*, should not be noticeable in a nearby receiver. A backwave level at least 90 dB below the key-down carrier is a desirable goal.

Microprocessor-controlled transceivers manufactured today control CW keying rise- and fall-time through software. The operator generally accesses the keying shape parameter through a menu selection and adjustment process. Three to four ms is a typical value for most transceivers that balances crisp keying characteristics against excessive off-channel artifacts. See *QST* Product Reviews for waveforms and discussions of rise- and fall-time settings.

Homebrew equipment usually relies on analog circuitry to control keying waveforms. **Figure 13.35** is the schematic of one waveshaping circuit that has been used successfully. A Sallen-Key third-order op amp low-pass filter (0.1 dB Chebyshev response) shapes the keying waveform, produces the rate of rise and fall and also softens the leading and trailing corners just the right amount. The key closure activates the CMOS switch, U1, which turns on the 455-kHz IF signal. At the key-up time, the input to the wave-shaping filter is turned off, but the IF signal switch remains closed for an additional 12 ms.

The keying waveform is applied to the gain control pin of a CLC5523 amplifier IC. This device, like nearly all gain-control amplifiers, has a *logarithmic* control of gain; therefore some experimental "tweaking" of the capac-

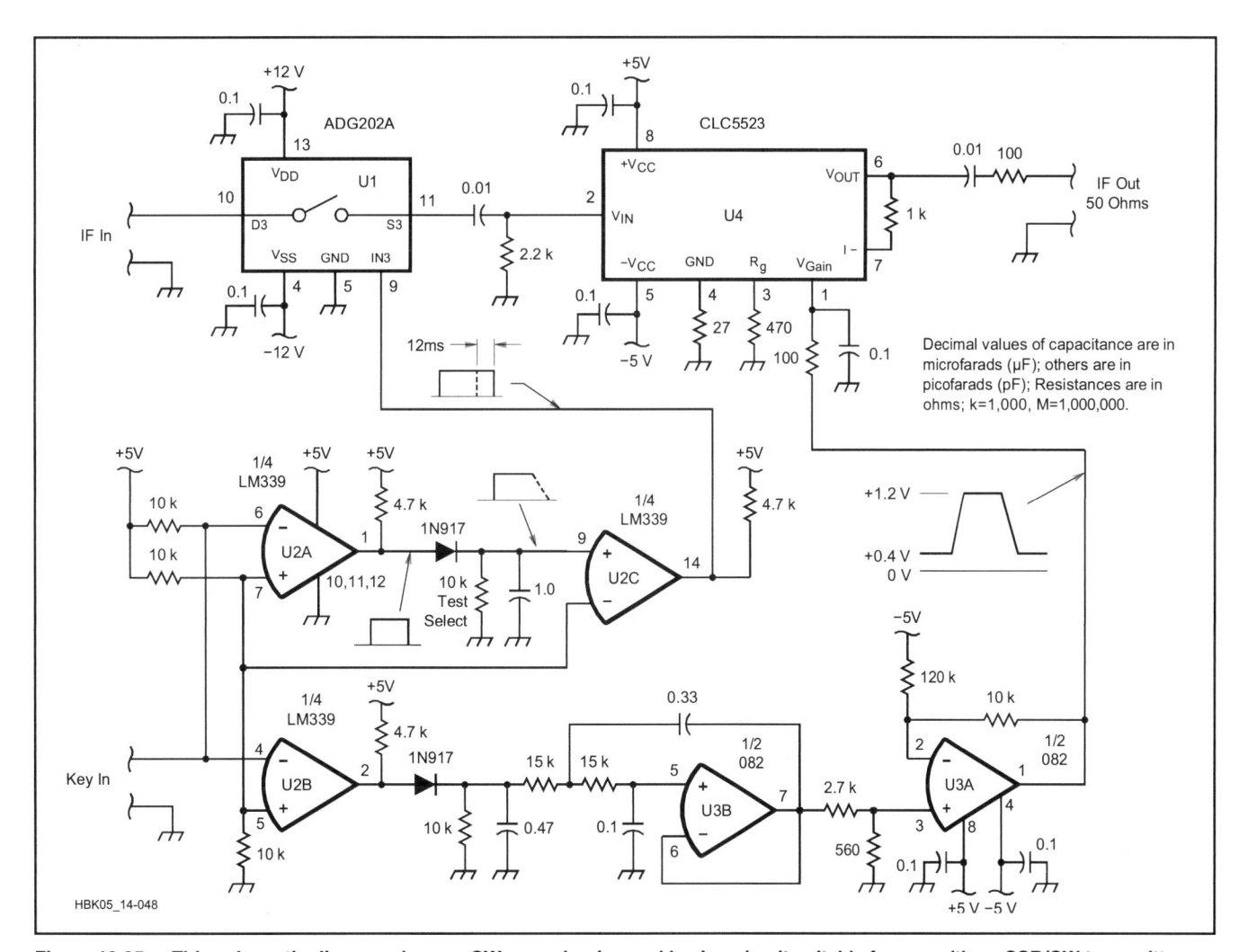

Figure 13.35 — This schematic diagram shows a CW waveshaping and keying circuit suitable for use with an SSB/CW transmitter such as is shown in Figure 13.9.

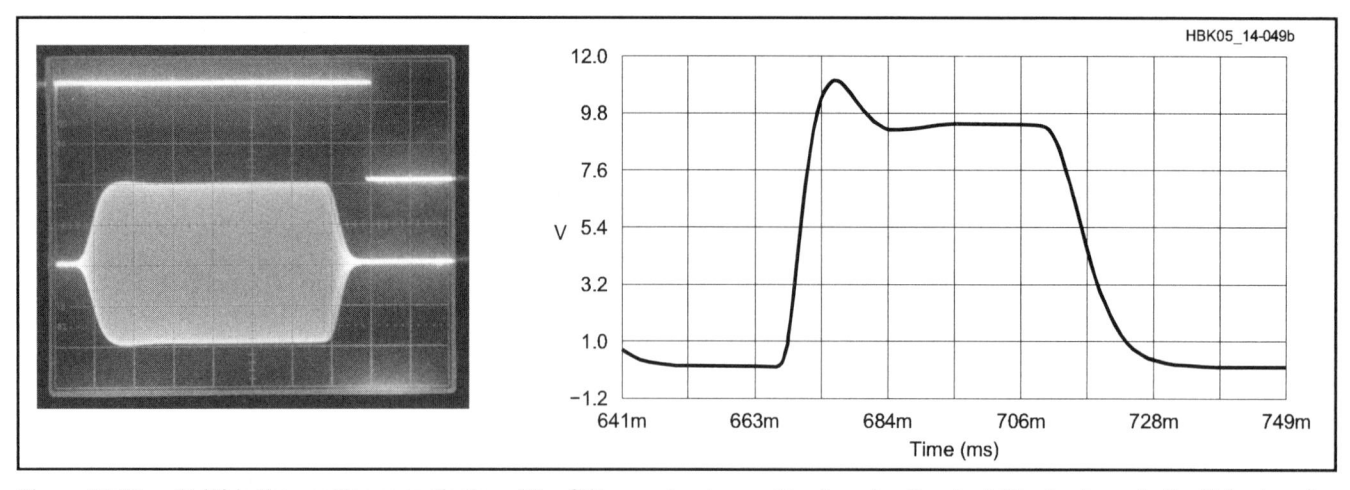

Figure 13.36 — At (A) is the oscilloscope display of the CW waveshaping and keying circuit output. The top trace is the IF keying signal applied to S1 of Figure 13.35. The bottom trace is the transmitter output RF spectrum. At (B) is a *SPICE* simulation of the waveshaping network. When this signal is applied to the logarithmic control characteristic of the CLC5523 amplifier, the RF envelope is modified slightly to the form shown in A.

itor values was used to get the result shown in **Figure 13.36A**. The top trace shows the on/off operation of the IF switch, U1. The signal is turned on shortly before the rise of the keying pulse begins and remains on for about 12 ms after the keying pulse is turned off, so that the waveform falls smoothly to a very low value. The result is an excellent spectrum and an almost complete absence of backwave. Compare this to the factory transmitter waveshapes shown in Figures 13.29 and 13.31. The bottom trace shows the resulting keyed RF output waveshape. It has an excellent spectrum, as verified by critical listening tests. The thumps and clicks that are found in some CW transmitters are virtually absent. The rise and fall intervals have a waveshape that is approximately a cosine. Spread-spectrum frequency-hop waveforms have used this approach to minimize wideband interference.

Figure 13.36B is an accurate *SPICE* simulation of the wave shaping circuit output before the signal is processed by the CLC5523 amplifier. To assist in adjusting the circuit, create a steady stream of 40 ms dots that can be seen on an RF oscilloscope that is looking at the final PA output envelope. It is important to make sure that the excellent waveshape is not degraded on its way to the transmitter output. Single-sideband linear power amplifiers are well suited for a CW transmitter, but they must stay within their linear range, and the backwave problem must be resolved.

When evaluating the spectrum of an incoming CW signal during on-the-air operations, a poor receiver design can contribute problems caused by its vulnerability to a strong but clean adjacent channel signal. Clicks, thumps, front end overload, reciprocal mixing, and other issues can be created in the receiver. It is important to put the blame where it really belongs.

13.4.3 Break-In CW Operation

Most current 100 W class HF transceivers use high-speed relays (with the relay actually following the CW keying) or solid-state PIN diodes to implement full break-in CW. Some RF power amplifiers use high-speed vacuum relays for the TR switching function. See the section on TR Switching later in this chapter for more information about circuits to perform this function. Two projects for adding QSK switching to linear amplifiers are included in the **Station Accessories** chapter.

The term *semi-break-in* is used to designate a CW switching system in which closing the key initiates transmission, but switching back to receive happens between words, not between individual dits. Some operators find this less distracting than full break-in, and it is easier to implement with less-expensive relays for the TR switching.

13.5 Transmitting AM and SSB

13.5.1 Amplitude-Modulated Full-Carrier Voice Transmission

A popular form of voice amplitude modulation is called *high-level amplitude modulation*. It is generated by mixing (or modulating) an RF carrier with an audio signal. **Figure 13.37** shows the conceptual view of this. **Figure 13.38** is a more detailed view of how such a voice transmitter would actually be implemented. The upper portion is the RF channel and the lower portion is the audio frequency or AF channel, usually called the *modulator*. The modulator is nothing more than an audio amplifier designed to be fed from a microphone and with an output designed to match the anode or collector impedance of the final RF amplifier stage.

The output power of the modulator is

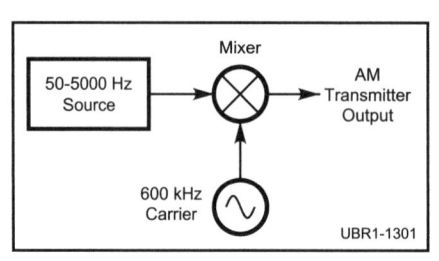

Figure 13.37 — Block diagram of a conceptual AM transmitter.

applied in series with the dc supply of the output stage (only) of the RF channel of the transmitter. The level of the voice peaks needs to be just enough to vary the supply to the RF amplifier collector between zero volts, on negative peaks, and twice the normal supply voltage on positive voice peaks. This usually requires an AF amplifier with about half the average power output as the dc input power (product of dc collector or plate voltage times the current) of the final RF amplifier stage.

The output signal, called *full-carrier double-sideband AM*, occupies a frequency spectrum as shown in **Figure 13.39**. The spectrum shown would be that of a standard broadcast station with an audio passband from 50 Hz

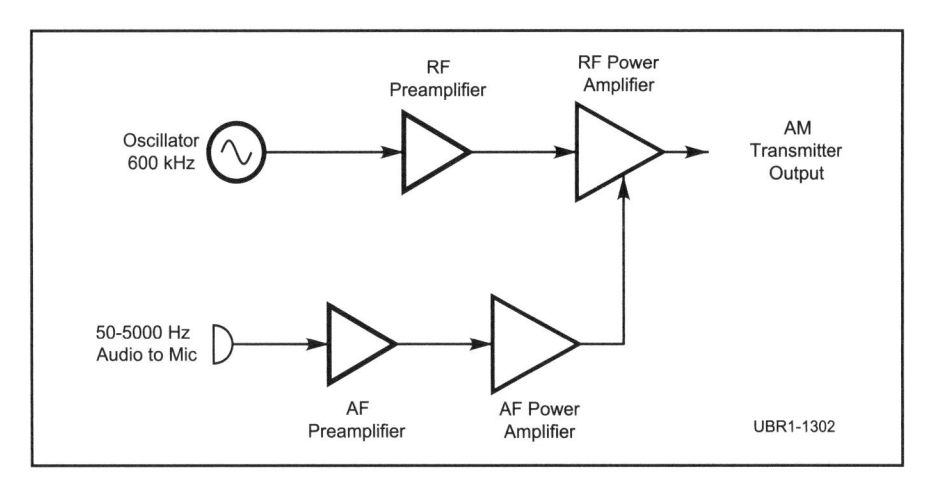

Figure 13.38 — Block diagram of a 600 kHz AM broadcast transmitter.

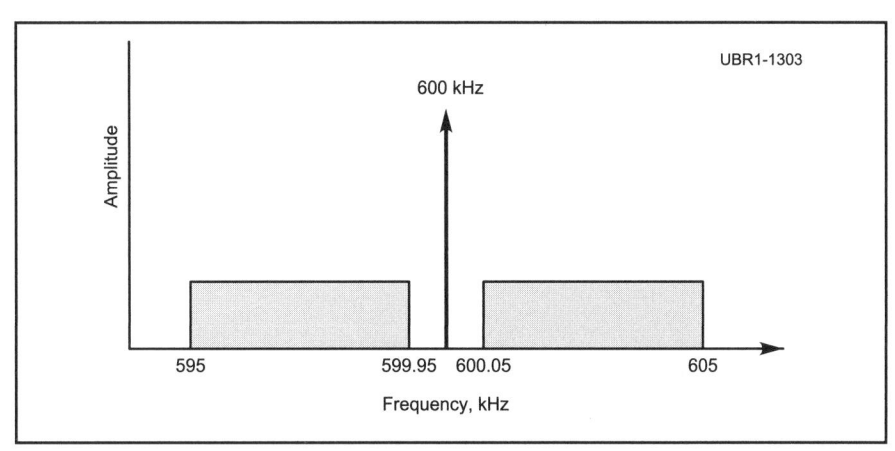

Figure 13.39 — The range of spectrum used by a 600 kHz AM broadcast signal showing sidebands above and below a carrier at 600 kHz.

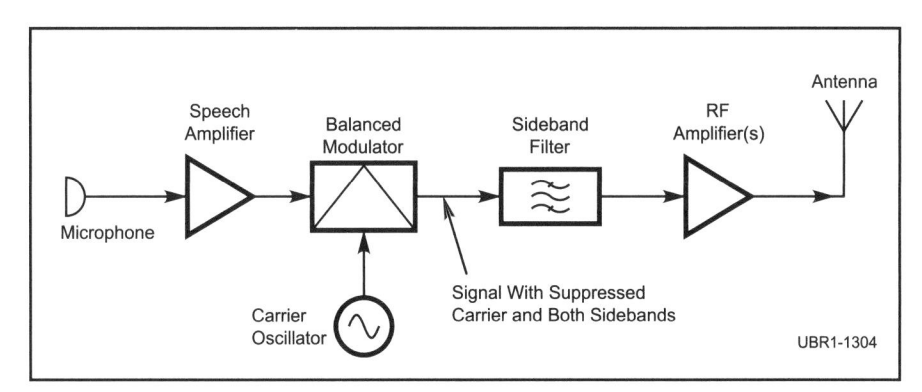

Figure 13.40 — Block diagram of a filter type single-sideband suppressed-carrier (SSB) transmitter.

than single sideband (SSB), and the equipment becomes quite costly as power is increased. The primary application is in broadcasting — largely because AM transmissions can be received on the simplest and least expensive of receivers. With a single transmitter and thousands of receivers, the overall system cost may be less and the audience larger than for systems that use more efficient modulation techniques. While the PEP output of an AM transmitter is four times the carrier power, none of the carrier power is necessary to carry the information, as we will discuss in the next section.

13.5.2 Single-Sideband Suppressed-Carrier Transmission

The two sidebands of a standard AM transmitter carry (inverted) copies of the same information, and the carrier carries essentially no information. We can more efficiently transmit the information with just one of the sidebands and no carrier. In so doing, we use somewhat less than half the bandwidth, a scarce resource, and also consume much less transmitter power by not transmitting the carrier and the second sideband.

SSB — THE FILTER METHOD

The block diagram of a simple single-sideband suppressed-carrier (SSB) transmitter is shown in **Figure 13.40**. This transmitter uses a balanced mixer as a *balanced modulator* to generate a double sideband suppressed carrier signal without a carrier. That signal is then sent through a filter designed to pass just one (either one, by agreement with the receiving station) of the sidebands.

Depending on whether the sideband above or below the carrier frequency is selected, the signal is called *upper sideband* (*USB*) or *lower sideband* (*LSB*), respectively. The resulting SSB signal is amplified to the desired power level and we have an SSB transmitter. Amateur practice is to use USB above 10 MHz and LSB on lower frequencies. The exception is 60 meter channels, on which amateurs are required to use USB for data and voice signals.

While a transmitter of the type in Figure 13.40 with all processing at the desired transmit frequency will work, the configuration is not often used. Instead, the carrier oscillator and sideband filter are often at an intermediate frequency that is heterodyned to the operating frequency as shown in **Figure 13.41**. The reason is that the sideband filter is a complex narrow-band filter and most manufacturers would rather not have to supply a new filter design every time a transmitter is ordered for a new frequency. Many SSB trans-

to 5 kHz. Note that the resulting channel width is twice the highest audio frequency transmitted. If the audio bandwidth were limited to typical "telephone quality speech" of 300 to 3300 Hz, the resulting bandwidth would be reduced to 6.6 kHz. Note also that while a perfect multiplication process would result in just two sidebands and no carrier, this implementation actually provides the sum of the carrier and the sidebands from the product terms. (See the **Receiving** chapter for the mathematical description of signal multiplication.)

Full-carrier double-sideband AM is used in fewer and fewer applications. The spectral and power efficiency are significantly lower

Transmitting 13.21

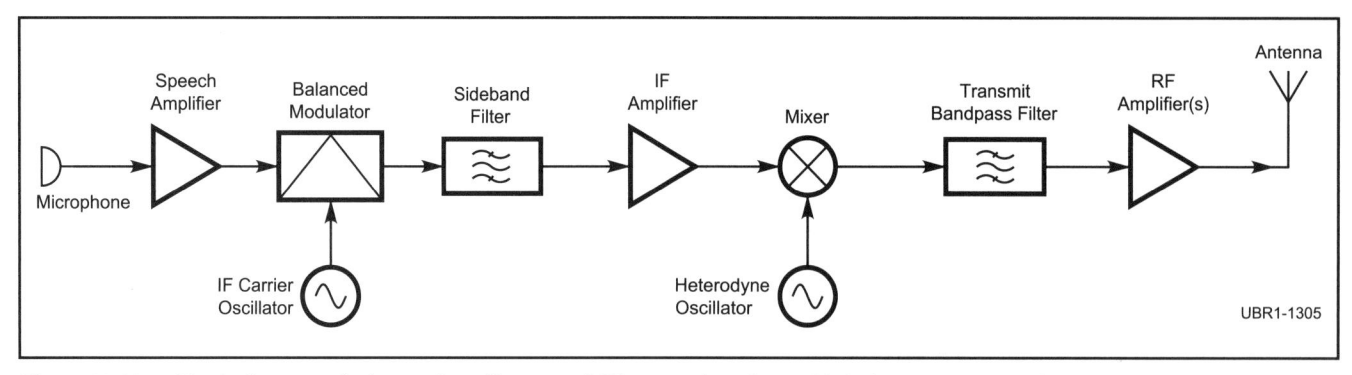

Figure 13.41 — Block diagram of a heterodyne filter-type SSB transmitter for multiple frequency operation.

mitters can operate on different bands as well, so this avoids the cost of additional mixers, oscillators and expensive filters.

Note that the block diagram of our SSB transmitter bears a striking resemblance to the diagram of a superheterodyne receiver except that the signal path is reversed to begin with information and produce an RF signal. The same kind of image rejection requirements for intermediate frequency selection that were design constraints for the superhet receiver applies here as well.

The filter method can be implemented by analog circuitry, using high-quality crystal filters to remove the unwanted sideband and a carefully adjusted balanced modulator to eliminate the carrier. An SDR can also implement the filter method by using very sharp DSP filters at a low frequency (carrier frequency less than 100 kHz) and then up-converting the signal to the desired RF frequency. As DSP hardware continues to improve in speed, this method should continue to grow in popularity

SSB — THE PHASING METHOD

Most current transmitters use the method of SSB generation shown in Figure 13.40 to generate the SSB signal. That is the *filter method*, but really occurs in two steps — first a balanced modulator is used to generate sidebands and eliminate the carrier, then a filter is used to eliminate the undesired sideband, and often to improve carrier suppression as well.

The *phasing method* of SSB generation is exactly the same as the image-rejecting mixer described in the **Receiving** chapter. This uses two balanced modulators and a phase-shift network for both the audio and RF carrier signals to produce the upper sideband signal as shown in **Figure 13.42A**. By a shift in the sign of either of the phase-shift networks, the opposite sideband can be generated. This method trades a few phase-shift networks and an extra balanced modulator for the sharp sideband filter of the filter method.

While it looks deceptively simple, a limitation is in the construction of an analog phase-shift network that will have a constant 90° phase shift over the whole audio range. Errors in phase shift result in less than full carrier and sideband suppression. Nonetheless, there have been some successful examples offered over the years.

The 90° phase shift network is also known as a Hilbert transformer after the mathematical operation it performs. Difficult to implement well in analog form, the phase shift is

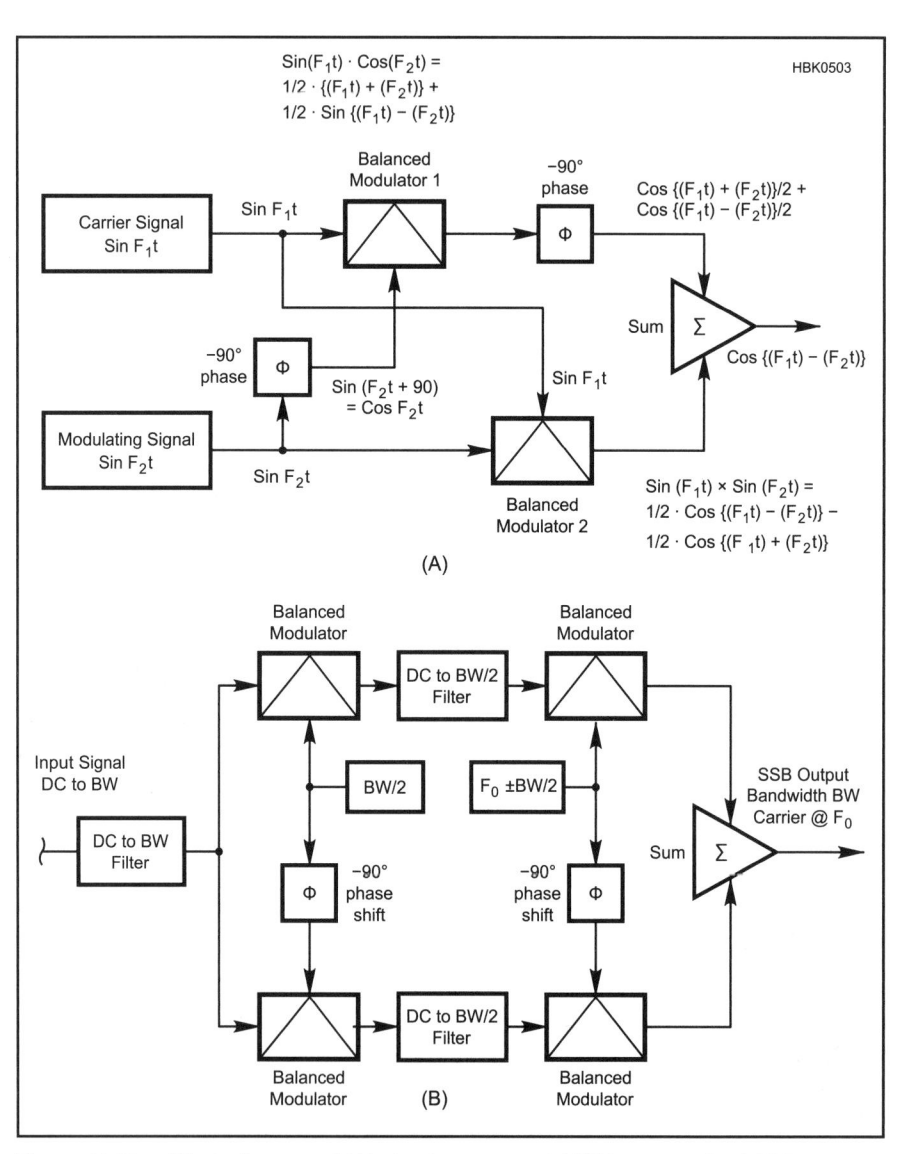

Figure 13.42 — Block diagram of (A) phasing type and (B) Weaver method SSB generators for single-frequency operation.

straightforward to implement digitally. That makes the phasing method a good choice for SSB generation by an SDR transmitter.

SSB — THE WEAVER METHOD

Taking the phasing method one step further, the Weaver method solves the problem of requiring phase-shift networks that must be aligned across the entire audio range. Instead, the Weaver method, shown in Figure 13.42B, first mixes one copy of the message (shown with a bandwidth of dc to BW Hz) with an in-band signal at BW/2 Hz and another copy with a signal at BW/2 Hz that is phase-shifted by –90°. Instead of phase-shifting the message, only the signal at BW/2 Hz must be phase-shifted — a much simpler task!

The output of each balanced modulator is filtered, leaving only components from dc to BW/2. These signals are then input to a second pair of balanced modulators with a more conventional LO signal at the carrier frequency, f_0, offset by +BW/2 for USB and –BW/2 for LSB. The output of the balanced modulators is summed to produce the final SSB signal.

The Weaver method is difficult to implement in analog circuitry, but is well-suited to digital signal processing systems. The Weaver method has become common in DSP-based equipment that generates the SSB signal digitally.

13.6 Transmitting Angle Modulation

13.6.1 Angle-Modulated Transmitters

Transmitters using frequency modulation (FM) or phase modulation (PM) are generally grouped into the category of *angle modulation* since the resulting signals are often indistinguishable. An instantaneous change in either frequency or phase can create identical signals, even though the method of modulating the signal is somewhat different. To generate an FM signal, we need an oscillator whose frequency can be changed by the modulating signal.

We can make use of an oscillator whose frequency can be changed by a "tuning voltage." If we apply a voice signal to the TUNING VOLTAGE connection point, we will change the frequency with the amplitude and frequency of the applied modulating signal, resulting in an FM signal.

The phase of a signal can be varied by changing the values of an R-C phase-shift network. One way to accomplish phase modulation is to have an active element shift the phase and generate a PM signal. In **Figure 13.43**, the drain current through the field-effect transistor is varied with the applied modulating signal, varying the phase shift at the stage's output. Because the effective load on the stage is changed, the carrier is also amplitude-modulated and must be run through an FM receiver-type limiter in order to remove the amplitude variations.

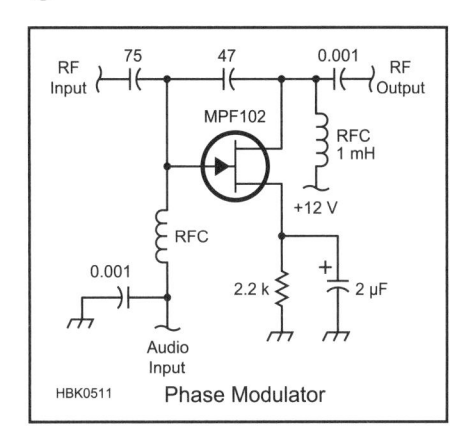

Figure 13.43 — Simple FET-based phase modulator circuit.

FREQUENCY MODULATION TRANSMITTER DESIGN

Frequency modulation is widely used as the voice mode on VHF for repeater and other point-to-point communications. **Figure 13.44** shows the phase-modulation method, also known as *indirect FM*, as used in many FM transmitters. It is the most widely used approach to FM. Phase modulation is performed at a low frequency, say 455 kHz. Prior to the phase modulator, speech filtering and processing perform four functions:

1. Convert phase modulation to frequency modulation (see below).

2. Apply pre-emphasis (high-pass filtering) to the speech audio higher speech frequencies for improved signal-to-noise ratio after de-emphasis (low-pass filtering) of the received audio.

3. Perform speech processing to emphasize

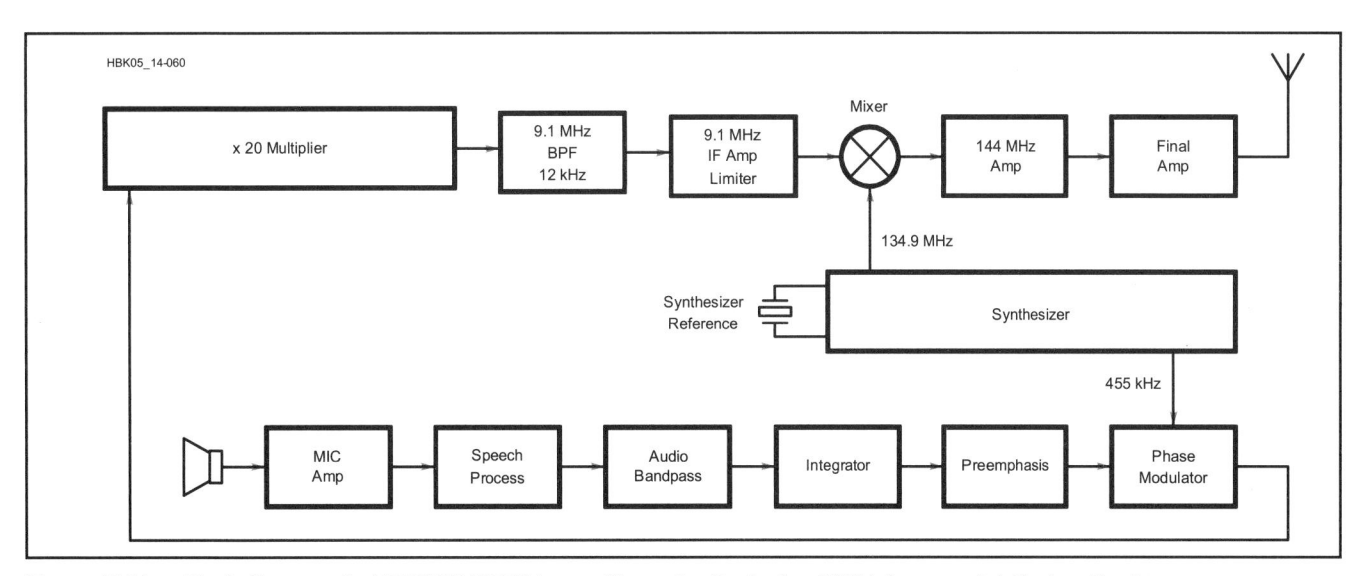

Figure 13.44 — Block diagram of a VHF/UHF NBFM transmitter using the indirect FM (phase modulation) method.

the weaker speech components.

4. Compensate for the microphone's frequency response and possibly also the operator's voice characteristics.

Multiplier stages then move the signal to some desired higher IF and also multiply the frequency deviation to the desired final value. If the FM deviation generated in the 455 kHz modulator is 250 Hz, the deviation at 9.1 MHz is 20 × 250, or 5 kHz.

13.6.2 Frequency Multipliers

Frequency multipliers are frequently used in FM transmitters as a way to increase the deviation along with the carrier frequency. They are composed of devices that exhibit high levels of harmonic distortion, usually an undesired output product. In this case the desired harmonic is selected and enhanced through filtering. The following examples show the way this can be done, both with amplifiers and with passive diode circuits. (Additional discussion of frequency multipliers can be found in Chapter 5.4 of *Experimental Methods in RF Design* and in the "VHF Signal Sources" article by Rick Campbell, KK7B which is included in this book's downloadable supplemental content.)

A passive multiplier using diodes is shown in **Figure 13.45A**. The full-wave rectifier circuit can be recognized, except that the dc component is shorted to ground. If the fundamental frequency ac input is 1.0 V_{RMS}, the second harmonic is 0.42 V_{RMS} or 8 dB below the input, including some small diode losses. This value is found by calculating the Fourier series coefficients for the full-wave-rectified sine wave, as shown in many textbooks.

Transistor and vacuum-tube frequency multipliers operate on the following principle: if a sine wave input causes the plate/collector/drain current to be distorted (not a sine wave) then harmonics of the input are generated. If an output resonant circuit is tuned to a harmonic, the output at the harmonic is emphasized and other frequencies are attenuated. For a particular harmonic the current pulse should be distorted in a way that maximizes that harmonic. For example, for a doubler the current pulse should look like a half-wave rectified sine wave (180° of conduction). A transistor with Class B bias would be a good choice. For a tripler, use 120° of conduction (Class C).

An FET, biased at a certain point, is very nearly a *square-law* device as described in the **Electrical Fundamentals** chapter. That is, the drain-current change is proportional to the square of the gate-voltage change. It is then an efficient frequency doubler that also de-emphasizes the fundamental.

A push-push doubler is shown in Figure 13.45B. The FETs are biased in the square-

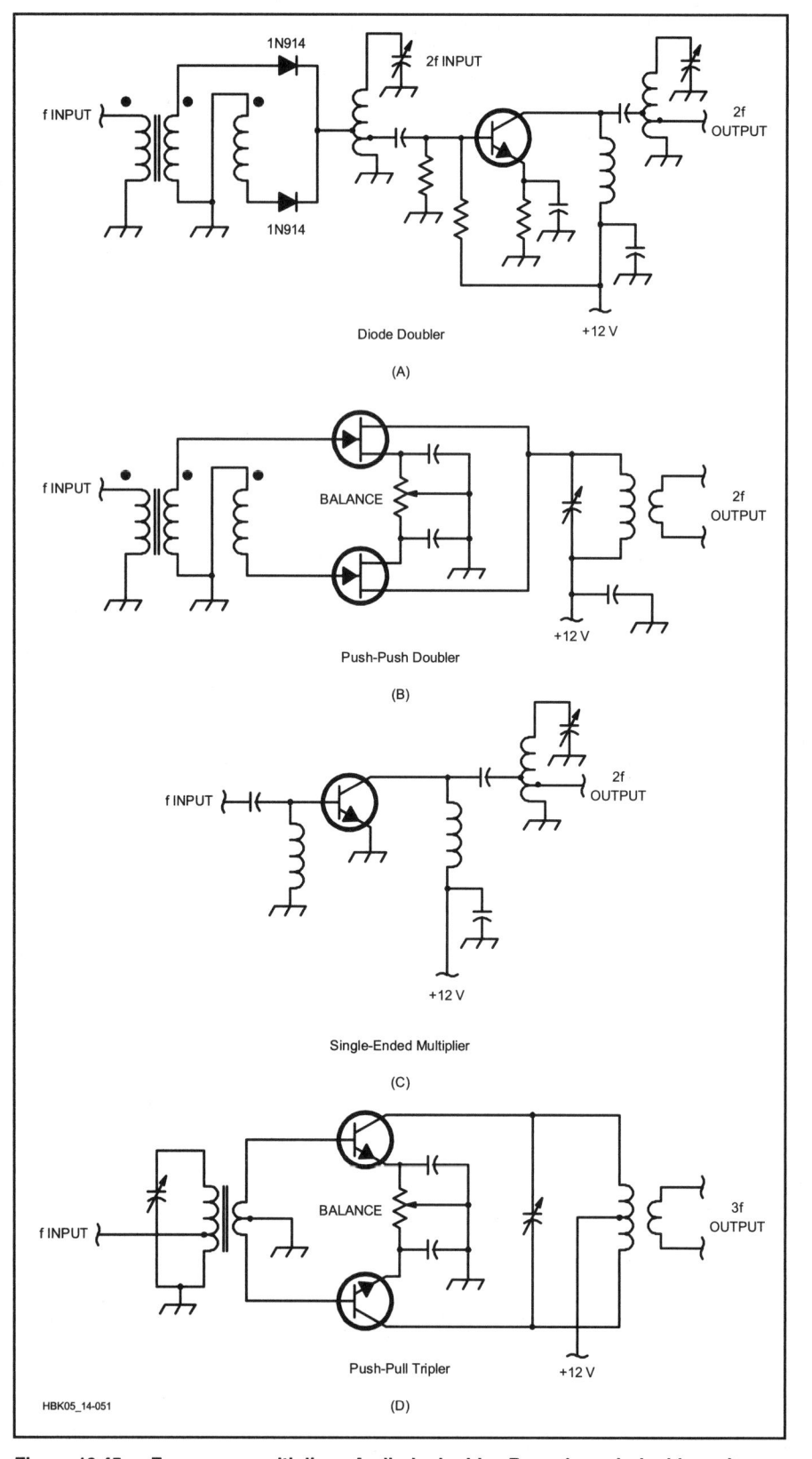

Figure 13.45 — Frequency multipliers. A: diode doubler. B: push-push doubler using JFETS. C: single-ended multiplier using a BJT. D: push-pull tripler using BJTs.

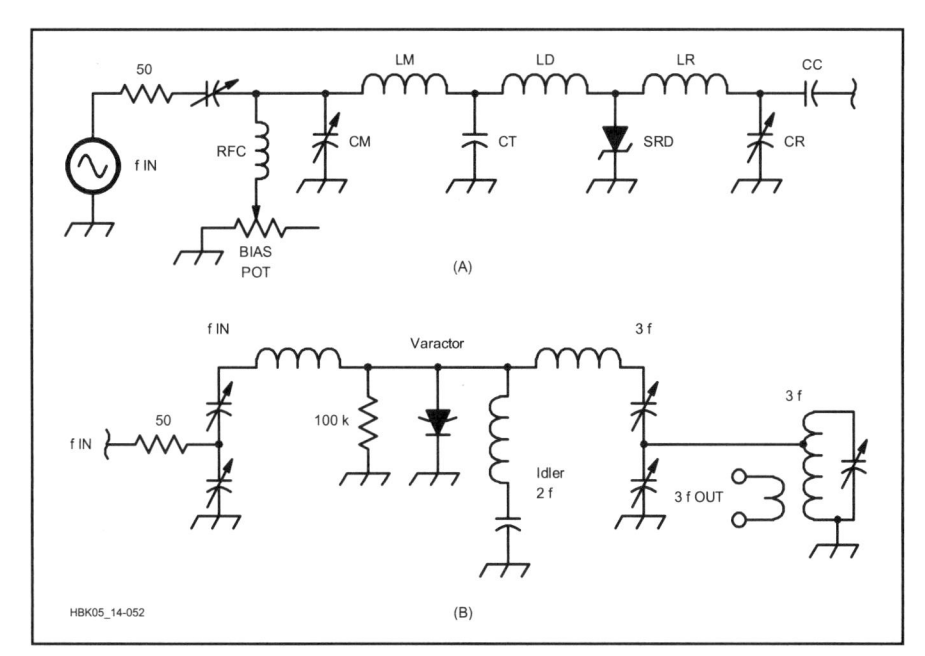

Figure 13.46 — Specialized diode frequency multipliers. A: step-recovery diode multiplier. B: varactor diode multiplier.

law region and the BALANCE potentiometer minimizes the fundamental frequency. Note that the gates are in push-pull and the drains are in parallel. This causes second harmonics to add in-phase at the output and fundamental components to cancel.

Figure 13.45C shows an example of a single-ended doubler using a bipolar transistor. The efficiency of a doubler of this type is typically 50%, that of a tripler 33%, and of a quadrupler 25%. Harmonics other than the one to which the output tank is tuned will appear in the output unless effective band-pass filtering is applied. The collector tap on L1 is placed at the point that offers the best compromise between power output and spectral purity.

A push-pull tripler is shown in Figure 13.45D. The input and output are both push-pull. The balance potentiometer minimizes even harmonics. Note that the transistors have no bias voltage in the base circuit; this places the transistors in Class C for efficient third-harmonic production. Choose an input drive level that maximizes harmonic output.

The step recovery diode (SRD) shown in **Figure 13.46A** is an excellent device for harmonic generation, especially at microwave frequencies. The basic idea of the SRD is as follows: When the diode is forward conducting, a charge is stored in the diode's diffusion capacitance, and if the diode is quickly reverse-biased, the stored charge is very suddenly released into an LC harmonic-tuned circuit. The circuit is also called a "comb generator" because of the large number of harmonics that are generated. (The spectral display looks like a comb.) A phase-locked loop (PLL) can then lock onto the desired harmonic.

A varactor diode can also be used as a multiplier. Figure 13.46B shows an example. This circuit depends on the fact that the capacitance of a varactor changes with the instantaneous value of the voltage across it, in this case the RF excitation voltage. This is a nonlinear process that generates harmonic currents through the diode. Power levels up to 25 W can be generated in this manner.

Following frequency multiplication, a second conversion to the final output frequency is performed. Prior to this final translation, IF band-pass filtering is performed in order to minimize adjacent channel interference that might be caused by excessive frequency deviation. This filter needs good phase linearity to assure that the FM sidebands maintain the correct phase relationships. If this is not done, an AM component is introduced to the signal, which can cause nonlinear distortion problems in the PA stages. The final frequency translation retains a constant value of FM deviation for any value of the output signal frequency.

The IF/RF amplifiers can be nonlinear Class C amplifiers because the signal in each amplifier contains, at any one instant, only a single value of instantaneous frequency and not multiple simultaneous frequencies whose relationship must be preserved as in SSB. These amplifiers are not sources of IMD, so they need not be "linear." The sidebands that appear in the output are a result only of the FM process. (The spectrum of an FM signal is described by Bessel functions.)

In phase modulation, the frequency deviation is directly proportional to the frequency of the audio signal. (In FM, the deviation is proportional to the audio signal's amplitude.) To make deviation independent of the audio frequency, an audio-frequency response that rolls off at 6 dB per octave is needed. An op-amp low-pass circuit in the audio amplifier accomplishes this function. This process converts phase modulation to frequency modulation.

In addition, audio speech processing helps to maintain a constant value of speech amplitude, and therefore constant IF deviation, with respect to audio speech levels. Pre-emphasis of speech frequencies (a 6 dB per octave high-pass response from 300 to 3000 Hz) is commonly used to improve the signal-to-noise ratio at the receive end. Analysis shows that this is especially effective in FM systems when the corresponding de-emphasis (complementary low-pass response) is used at the receiver. (See reference for Schwartz.) By increasing the amplitude of the higher audio frequencies before transmission and then reducing them in the receiver, high-frequency audio noise from the demodulation process is also reduced, resulting in a "flat" audio response with lower hiss and high-frequency noise.

An IF limiter stage may be used to ensure that any amplitude changes that are created during the modulation process are removed. The indirect-FM method allows complete frequency synthesis to be used in all the transmitter local oscillators (LOs), so that the channelization of the output frequency is very accurate. The IF and RF amplifier stages are operated in a highly efficient Class-C mode, which is helpful in portable equipment operating on small internal batteries.

FM is more tolerant of frequency misalignments between the transmitter and receiver than is SSB. In commercial SSB communication systems, this problem is solved by transmitting a *pilot carrier* with an amplitude 10 or 12 dB below the full PEP output level. The receiver is then phase-locked to this pilot carrier. The pilot carrier is also used for squelch and AGC purposes. A short-duration "memory" feature in the receiver bridges across brief pilot-carrier dropouts, caused by multipath nulls.

In a "direct FM" transmitter, a high-frequency (say, 9 MHz or so) crystal oscillator is frequency-modulated by varying the voltage on a varactor diode. The audio is pre-emphasized and processed ahead of the frequency modulator as for indirect-FM.

Transmitting 13.25

13.7 Effects of Transmitted Noise

With receiver sensitivity, selectivity, and linearity having reached extraordinary levels of performance, a reduction in transmitted spurious emissions is clearly in the best interests of all amateurs. It does us no good to spend time and effort creating an exceptional receiver if the channel is filled with transmitted noise and distortion products! (See the article by Grebenkemper in the Reference section.)

In heterodyne transmitters the last mixer and the amplifiers after it are wideband circuits, limited only by the harmonic filters and by any selectivity that may be in the antenna system. Wide-band phase noise transferred onto the transmitted modulation by the last LO (almost always a synthesizer of some kind) can extend over a wide frequency range; therefore LO cleanliness is always a matter of great concern.

The amplifiers after this mixer are also sources of wide-band "white" or additive noise. This noise can be transmitted even during times when there is no modulation, and it can be a source of local interference. To reduce this noise, use a high-level mixer with as much signal output as possible, and make the noise figure of the first amplifier stage after the mixer as low as possible.

SDR transmitters may not have analog mixers but they certainly have data converters and many processes that generate phase noise through clock jitter, non-linear data conversion, and other causes, even rounding errors! The result — heard on the air as transmitted noise — causes the same problems as noise generated by an analog transmitter. **Figure 13.47** is a collection of composite noise (phase noise) and CW keying sideband noise from several current transceivers evaluated by the ARRL Lab during product review assessments. The data is from a single band (14 MHz) and does not represent either the best or worst performance. This chart was initially created in 2014 from that data by Jim Brown, K9YC, to compare the noise performance of several transceivers. (The FT1000MP Mark V Field legacy spectrum shows the improved performance available today.) The data points on the graph represent noise peaks from the measured noise spectra. For the CW sideband noise data, a comparison of averaged and smoothed data is available in K9YC's online paper referenced at the end of this section. The paper also includes data for several older transceiver models.

There is quite a bit of difference between the various models as described in the *QST* Product Reviews. The variation shows why it is important for amateurs to pay attention to noise performance specifications, especially if they plan on operating in the crowded HF bands. With many transceivers now offering upgradable firmware, amateurs are strongly encouraged to install the latest version. This will improve performance on both receive and transmit, as well as help all of us transmit cleaner signals on the air.

Transmitted noise plays the same role in interference as receiver phase noise. The two are ultimately additive and interference becomes a "weakest link" problem in that poor noise performance of the receiver or the

Noise Consideration for Antenna Layout

By Steve Hicks, N5AC

Transmitted noise is a point to consider when laying out the antennas at a multi-transmitter site like Field Day or a contest station. For every 10 dB stronger any given signal appears in the receiver, another 10 dB improvement in phase noise performance is required to ensure interference-free operation. A poor antenna layout that produces very strong signals in receivers when local transmitters are operating can render even the best phase noise performance receivers inoperable. George Cutsogeorge, W2VJN's book *Managing Interstation Interference* (available from Inrad (**www.inrad.net**) is an excellent reference for station planning and interference mitigation techniques.

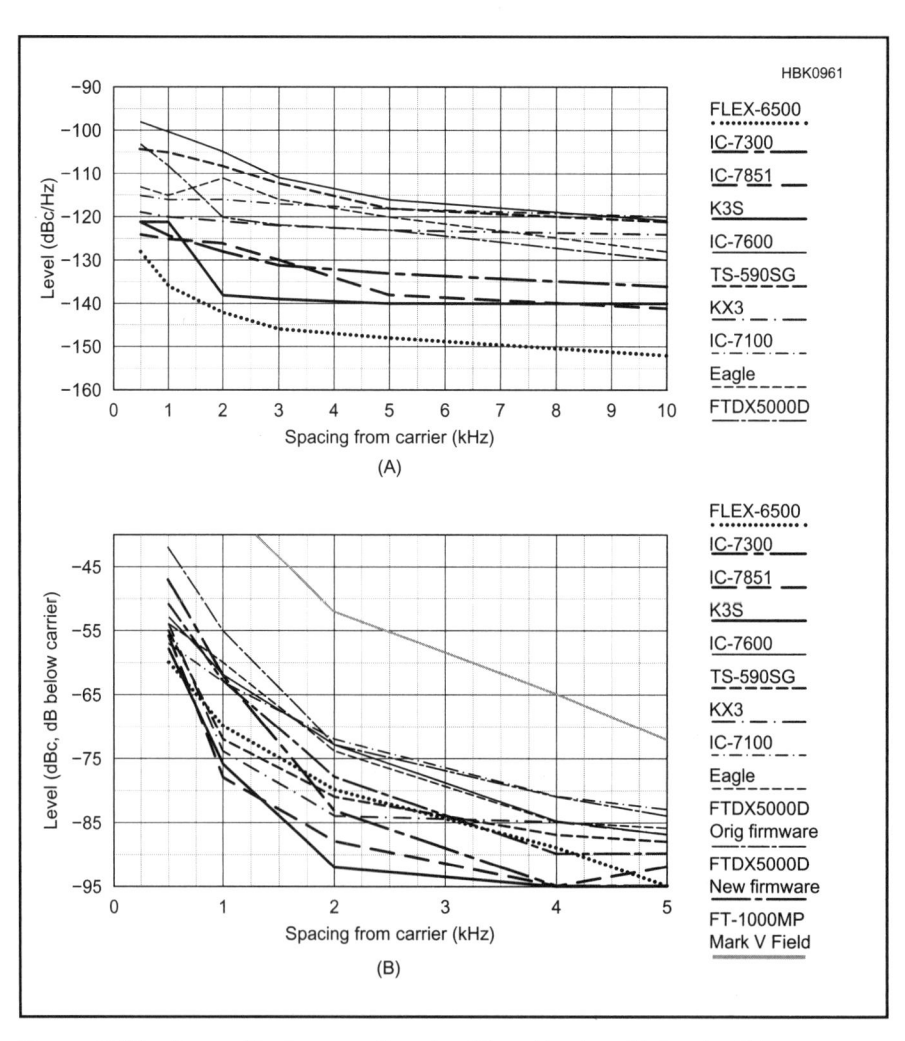

Figure 13.47 — Transmitted composite noise (A) and keying sidebands (B) from a selection of representative modern transmitters measured by the ARRL Lab. These graphs are based on ARRL Lab test data published in *QST* Product Reviews, following graphs originally created by Jim Brown, K9YC

transmitter can be the culprit in an interference problem. While both amplitude and phase noise contribute to transmitted composite noise, most of the noise contribution is phase noise from the various oscillators and clock signals in the transceiver. (The effects of receiver phase noise are addressed in the **Receiving** chapter.)

In a multiple-transmitter operation such as Field Day or a contest station, a single radio with poor transmitted noise performance can render all of the receivers at the site useless. Similarly, a receiver with poor phase noise performance can suffer from interference issues regardless of how good the performance of co-located transmitters is. In situations where multiple radios are brought to a single location for a joint operation, transmit phase noise is typically more strongly scrutinized since a single poor performer in the transmit phase noise arena can render the whole operation a failure.

Transmitted noise is not just a problem when multiple stations are at one site. Poor noise performance at full power can have an adverse effect on other stations for miles around. In competitive environments, noise from a closely-spaced strong signal can render adjacent channels nearly unusable. Under normal circumstances, transmitted noise raises the noise floor everywhere there is propagation. After decades of receiver improvement, it is important for amateurs to pay closer attention to transmitted noise performance.

The ARRL Lab measures transmitted noise as part of Product Reviews for *QST* magazine. These tests are described in the **Test Measurements and Equipment** chapter and in the book *Amateur Radio Transceiver Performance Testing* by Bob Allison, WB1GCM, ARRL Lab Staff Engineer. Individual transceiver performance is documented in the *QST* Product Review. In addition to creating Figure 13.47, Jim Brown, K9YC has compiled the information from these reviews in an online paper, "Comparison of ARRL Lab Data for Selected Transceivers" which is available at **k9yc.com/publish.html**. Figure 13.47 is typical of the many figures in the paper comparing various noise measurements.

13.8 Microphones and Speech Processing

13.8.1 Frequency Content of Speech

Human speech has content from about 100 Hz to 8 kHz, but only the energy between about 400 Hz and 4 kHz contributes to speech intelligibility. Vocal content below 400 Hz provides "body" to the voice (great for singers and radio announcers), but that low frequency output of the microphone also contains breath pops, room noise, microphone handling noise, wind noise, and reverberation. This low frequency energy can easily be as much as half of the power picked up by the microphone, but it contributes nothing to communications, so it wastes transmitter power.

Likewise, speech content above 3 kHz provides "presence" and helps communications a bit, but the added bandwidth adds noise (and QRM to and from other stations). Most SSB transmitting filters are 2.7 kHz wide, so a well-adjusted radio will align those filters so that they pass audio between 400 Hz and 3.1 kHz. A few radios allow the user to adjust this setting via a configuration menu.

These bandwidth limits for speech communications were established in the earliest days of long distance telephony — they allow what's necessary, but nothing extra. Over more than a century, they have allowed more and more conversations to be packed into less and less bandwidth.

Thus, our first rule is to minimize any part of the audio signal below about 400 Hz, and to not waste bandwidth transmitting sound above 3 kHz. We have several controls over this. First, we can choose a microphone without excess low frequency response. See "Choosing a Microphone" later in this section. Many transceivers provide menu settings to tailor the audio frequency response. Study the manual to understand and choose settings for your radio.

Some newer transceivers make it even easier to tailor the frequency response — they have a built-in octave-band equalizer covering the speech range. (An octave is a 2:1 frequency step). Each band can be set for up to 18 dB of boost or cut in 1 dB steps. A good starting point for most microphones and voices is maximum cut of the three lowest bands (50, 100, 200 Hz), and 3–6 dB cut of the fourth band (400 Hz) leaving all other bands set flat (no boost or cut). Some microphone or voices may benefit from a bit more cut at 400 Hz or from 3-6 dB of cut or boost in the two highest bands. Save these adjustments for when you have a trained listener to advise you.

13.8.2 Dynamics Processing

The loudness of speech varies over a wide range as we speak, sometimes by as much as 20 dB. The audio section of our transmitter must be adjusted so that we never overmodulate, which causes interference on adjacent frequencies (splatter), but keeping audio level as close as practical to 100% modulation makes our signal louder at the other end. Modern transceivers include peak limiters to prevent overmodulation on loudness peaks and compressors to increase the audio gain for quieter parts of speech. When well-designed and carefully adjusted, these circuits work well, increasing our "talk power," but when badly adjusted, cause transmitted audio to be distorted, mushy, dull, and hard to understand.

The strength of sound falls off with distance from the source by inverse square law, just as RF field strength falls off with distance from the antenna. Doubling (or halving) the distance between microphone and mouth causes loudness to change by 6 dB. A boom microphone attached to a headset helps maintain more constant level by keeping the microphone element at a fixed distance.

To adjust these circuits, first set equalization as in the previous section, then set microphone gain so that normal speech causes near 100% modulation with compression disabled. Then set the transceiver display to show compression and adjust compression (or processing) to provide about 10 dB gain reduction on voice peaks. While radios can be set for more compression, few sound very good with more than 10 dB, and too much compression can make speech hard to copy. (On some transceivers, compression may be called "processing.") The combined effect of equalization to eliminate speech content below 400 Hz and using 10 dB of compression is about 13 dB, which is equivalent to multiplying transmitter power by a factor 20!

13.8.3 Types of Microphones

Most common microphones in the amateur station are one of two basic types:

Dynamic microphones operate on the same principle as a loudspeaker, (a coil mounted to a diaphragm is moved by varying magnetic field that surrounds it makes air vibrate) but in reverse (vibration moves a diaphragm in the microphone, generating a voltage in the coil as it moves within the magnetic field). A loudspeaker works pretty well as a microphone, and has been used that way for more than half a century in intercom systems.

Electret condenser microphones are very different — the diaphragm is one plate of a capacitor; a voltage is applied between the two plates (the other being fixed). The source impedance is quite high (megohms), and must be transformed to a lower impedance by a FET follower built into the microphone (so that what it feeds doesn't load down the microphone). The electret capsule is pre-polarized, but the FET follower needs a small positive voltage fed through a load resistor to operate. This is referred to as *bias voltage* and it is applied to the output of the microphone: 8 V dc through a 5.6 kΩ resistor is typical. (Note that if bias voltage is applied to a dynamic microphone element, the result will be muffled, low-volume audio. If the radio's microphone connection supplies bias voltage, a series blocking capacitor of 0.1 to 1 µF should be used to remove the bias voltage.)

Both electrets and dynamic microphones are available with an *omnidirectional* pattern (picks up equally in all directions) or a *cardioid* pattern (picks up better in front of the microphone with a null to the rear). Cardioids can be thought of as "half space" microphones, meaning they pick up sounds from anywhere in front of the microphone but reject sound from all directions to the rear.

Cardioid microphones have an important characteristic called *proximity effect*, which is a very strong bass boost for sound sources very close to the microphone. In addition to making voices "bass heavy," proximity effect magnifies breath pops, wind noise, and handling noise. Virtually all microphones used in live sound are cardioids, and those intended for use by singers have a strong low frequency rolloff that partially compensates proximity effect. Although cardioids reduce room noise pickup, proximity effect generally makes them a poor choice in the ham shack. A microphone designed for radio communications is a better choice.

Cardioids work on the principle of acoustic cancellation between sound reaching the element via front and rear openings of the microphone housing. (Omnidirectional microphones have a single opening). Proximity effect is the result of that process and there being a single front opening and a single rear opening.

An important variation of the cardioid microphone is built with extra openings spaced along the length of the handle, which greatly reduces proximity effect. The ElectroVoice (EV) 664 and 666 were the first popular microphones of this type, which are called "variable-D" (for the variable distant openings), as opposed to "single-D" cardioids with a single rear opening. If you're looking for a good used pro-quality microphone for your ham station, the variable-D EV RE10, 11, 15, 16, 18, 20, and 27, and the Shure SM53 and SM54 are great choices. All but the RE16, 20, and 27 are long discontinued, but dynamic microphones last indefinitely as long as they are not badly mistreated, so buying used from a trustworthy source is a good option.

An omnidirectional microphone, whether dynamic or an electret, or one of the variable-D models listed above, are the best choice for ham radio. They have no proximity effect, so can be used close to the mouth. This minimizes breath pops, while still being close enough to minimize room noise. The soft foam supplied with many microphones is intended to reduce breath pops.

MICROPHONE EQUALIZATION

Beginning in the late 1950s, Shure introduced the model 440, the first microphone designed specifically for SSB transmission. The modern version is the 444D. These are omni-directional mics with the recommended equalization built in — low frequency response rolling off below 400 Hz and a pronounced peak around 3 kHz that compensates for some of the loss in the SSB transmit filter. These are excellent sounding microphones and are primarily desktop models. Most microphones in the Heil line use the same concepts.

13.8.4 Using a Professional or PC Microphone

Pro microphones are balanced and are designed to feed balanced inputs using shielded, twisted pair cables, while ham microphones and rigs use unbalanced wiring. Pro electret microphones cannot easily be used with ham gear (because of the method used to power the balanced microphone's FET follower output stage).

Pro dynamic microphones work well and are easy to connect with ham gear. Their 3-pin XL-connector comes wired for balanced circuits — Pin 1 is the shield, Pins 2 and 3 carry the signal. To connect them to your ham rig with shielded twisted pair, wire the shield to the shell of the microphone connector and connect the signal pair to MIC and MIC RETURN (or MIC GND).

Alternatively, with coaxial cable between the microphone and the radio, wire the cable shield to pin 1 and 3 at the microphone and the center conductor to pin 2. At the radio's microphone connector, wire the center conductor to the radio's MIC input and wire the cable shield both to MIC RETURN and to the connector shell.

Pro microphones generally have uniform ("flat") frequency response. They have more bass response than communications microphones and lack the boost around 3 kHz, so they generally require more equalization. The low frequency rolloff in audio circuits is set by the time constant of interstage coupling capacitors and their resistive load. Using a smaller value capacitor raises the –3dB frequency ($X_C = R$) producing a gentle low frequency rolloff (6 dB/octave). In transmitters that lack an equalizer, raising the –3dB frequency to 1-2 kHz (by reducing those time constants) can provide much of the equalization needed to make a pro microphone produce good communications audio.

Headsets with a microphone attached made for use with computers work well with ham transceivers. **Figure 13.48** illustrates good placement that minimizes breath pops and allows an occasional sip of water or coffee. Most of these microphones are electrets with both headphones and microphone wired to 3.5-mm (⅛-inch) phone plugs (also known as TRS or tip-ring-sleeve plugs). Almost any of these headsets will work with ham transceivers, but some are far more comfortable than others. The Yamaha CM500 and Koss SB-45 and CS-100 are popular with contesters and DXers. All that is needed is a cable adapter to a Foster plug (the round 8-pin connector used on most transceivers) to mate with the 8-pin microphone connector on transceivers that lack a 3.5 mm microphone jack.

Figure 13.48 — Using a computer-style headset electret boom microphone. Place the microphone far enough from your mouth to avoid picking up excessive noise from breathing and pops from speech. Balance the placement for normal speech levels while minimizing pickup of room and fan noise. On-the-air testing is important to account for your station circumstances and speaking style.

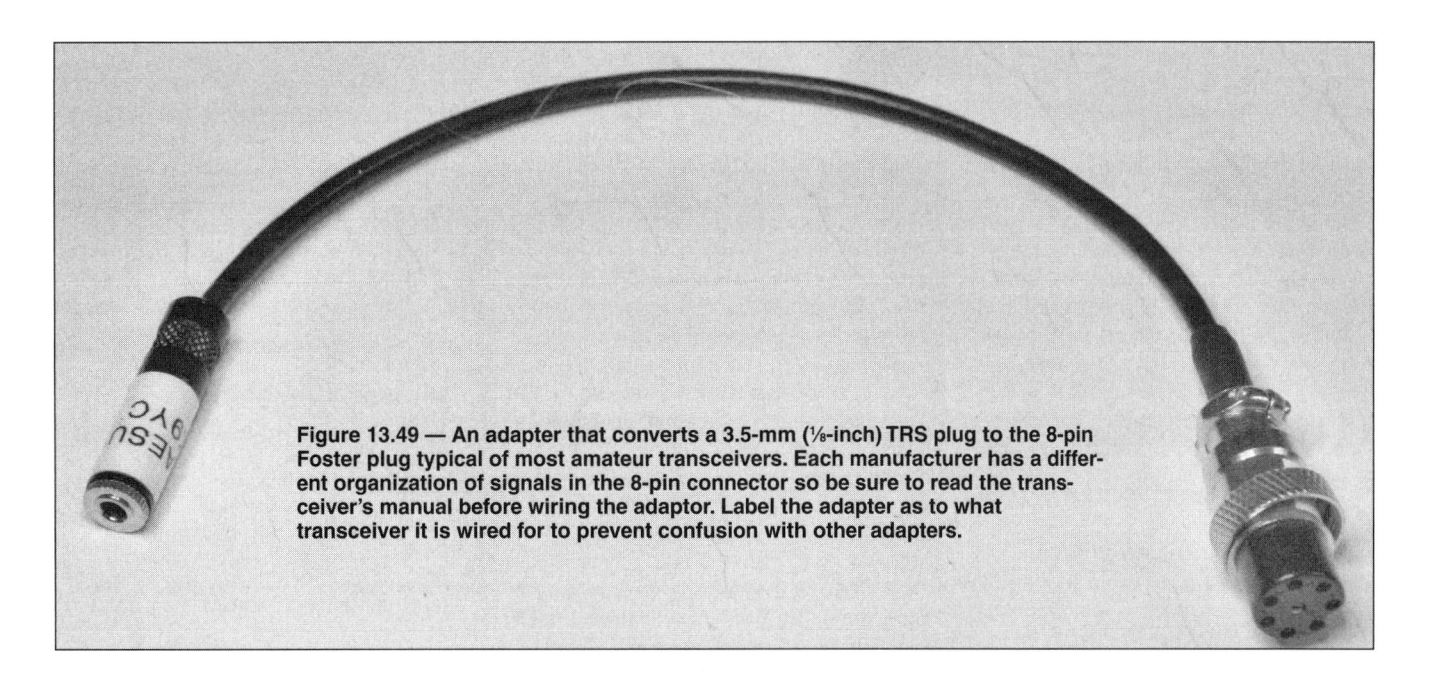

Figure 13.49 — An adapter that converts a 3.5-mm (⅛-inch) TRS plug to the 8-pin Foster plug typical of most amateur transceivers. Each manufacturer has a different organization of signals in the 8-pin connector so be sure to read the transceiver's manual before wiring the adaptor. Label the adapter as to what transceiver it is wired for to prevent confusion with other adapters.

Adapters for RJ-45 microphone connectors are also available. **Figure 13.49** shows a typical adapter you can build yourself.

To make the adapter, you'll need a cable-mount plug to mate with your radio and a female ⅛-in TRS jack to mate with the TRS plug on the headset. Check the manual for your transceiver for wiring of the microphone connector and label the adapter.

To connect the microphone to the radio, run a single-conductor shielded cable (such as mini-coax or braid-shielded audio cable) from the tip of the TRS jack to the microphone input pin of the Foster plug, connecting the cable shield to the sleeve of the TRS jack and the shell of the Foster plug.

Nearly all modern radios supply bias voltage in the range of 8 V on one pin of the microphone connector; wire a 5.6 kΩ resistor between that pin and the MIC pin. This resistor can have a very low power rating, so it's usually possible to fit it inside the Foster plug. Buy Foster plugs from ham vendors; female TRS jacks can be bought from pro audio vendors such as Full Compass and Sweetwater. (Neutrik part number NYS240BG is typical.)

13.8.5 Optimizing Your Microphone Audio

Summarizing the steps to optimize audio for communications:

1) Set your radio to minimize audio content below 400 Hz and above 3.2 kHz.

2) Keep the distance between microphone and mouth as constant as possible. A boom microphone attached to a headset solves this problem.

3) Get audio gains set right: adjust the mic input of the radio (or of the computer), the

Computer Audio Formats

Bits and Kilobits Per Second

The number of bits in a digital system (called the bit depth) sets the limit for its maximum dynamic range. An ideal 16-bit system would provide 96 dB of dynamic range (the difference between the highest and lowest instantaneous voltage that it can accurately reproduce). The dynamic range of real products is a few dB less. Each additional bit doubles the range of voltage that can be reproduced, and double (or half) the voltage is a change of 6 dB. Thus, a 12-bit system should be capable of a few dB less than 72 dB dynamic range.

The bit rate of a digital system, expressed in kilobits/sec (kbps), sets the limit for its audio bandwidth, which is 90% of half the numerical value, in kHz. Thus, a 48 kHz system can provide about 22 kHz audio bandwidth. When a sound card is used as part of a spectrum display, the maximum displayed bandwidth in kHz is equal to the maximum bit rate in kbps. Most computer sound cards and sound recording software can operate at standard sample rates and bit depth less than their maximum value, and most software that uses a computer sound system can vary these settings either automatically or as desired by the user.

The size of a sound file depends both on its bit depth and bit rate. A 12-bit sound file recorded at 12 kbps provides audio bandwidth of about 5 kHz with about 70 dB of dynamic range, and is a good choice for use in Amateur Radio. Uncompressed sound files recorded in this format require about 16 kB on a hard drive for each second of recording time for each channel of audio recorded.

Audio Data Compression

Audio and video signals in digital form can be compressed to reduce both the bandwidth needed to transmit them and the size of files needed to contain them. Compression systems like MP3 use smart algorithms to approximate the audio by leaving out parts of the waveform that the ear/brain is unlikely to miss. On playback, the system guesses at what parts were left out and adds them back in. Such systems are referred to as lossy compression because they do not provide a perfect copy of the original digital signal. Lossless systems like the ZIP or FLAC (Free Lossless Audio Codec) formats, do provide an exact copy of the original. ZIP provides very little compression of uncompressed sound files, but FLAC can reduce file size by about one half.

While file compression can save space on a hard drive, it takes time for the compression and de-compression algorithms to operate. MP3 compression is a great choice for recording a QSO, but a poor choice for recording messages for playback during a contest. MP3 compression can reduce file size (and transmission bandwidth) by 75-95% (that is, files and bandwidth between 5% and 25% of their uncompressed size).

USB sound cards designed for semi-pro audio users and even for gamers are usually good performers. They are often significantly better that the sound cards built into computers, especially laptops. An inferior quality sound card can degrade the decoding capability of software for digital modes. Some semi-pro units have LEDs to indicate safe signal levels — for example, green for good level, red for overload (also called "digital clip").

output gain of the computer sound card, and/or the line input of the radio.

4) Set processing for an indicated 10 dB on voice peaks.

5) Resist the urge to turn up mic gain or compression — once levels have been set as described here, turning it up louder makes your voice sound *worse*, not better.

You should also make sure the transmitter RF controls are set properly:

6) Tune the RF power amp carefully.

7) Don't overdrive the RF amp, and don't use ALC to set TX power.

8) If your radio requires a nominal 13.8 V dc power supply, make sure the supply is as close to 14 V as possible.

13.8.6 Setting Levels for Digital Modes

SETTING SOUND CARD INPUT LEVEL

This is important to achieving maximum signal-to-noise performance. For units with a digital clip indicator (see the sidebar), simply turn up the input gain until the red light flashes with the loudest signals, then back it off slightly so that it never flashes. Then set the digital gain in your encode/decode software as directed by the manual.

SETTING SOUND CARD OUTPUT LEVEL

It is just as important to avoid transmitting a distorted or overmodulated signal. There are three steps, all of which are important: (1) making the output of the computer clean, (2) not overdriving the radio's audio input stage, and (3) setting the audio input gain in the radio. There are (at least) four good ways to set output level from the computer, depending on what test equipment is available.

The first method uses an oscilloscope connected to the output of the sound card (in this case, the USB interface) that feeds the radio. Set the sweep so that you see clearly defined sine waves that make up the signal from the digital program (RTTY, PSK, WSJT modes, and so on) in transmit mode. Because these modulation schemes include multiple frequencies, you probably won't get the display to sync. Increase the output level until you see squaring at the top of the sine waves or "spiky" digital distortion, then reduce the output level by half the voltage.

The second method uses an audio spectrum analyzer connected to the output of the sound card. With the digital program in transmit mode and output level set fairly low, note the spectrum lines. With JT65, you should see only the tones that you would see on the WSJT-X or JT65-HF display, roughly 200 Hz wide. With RTTY, you should see only two tones spaced by 170 Hz. With JT9 or PSK, you should only see a single tone. Now, increase levels until you begin to see additional lines spread out from the normal tones. These additional lines are distortion products, and will cause QRM. Note the *difference* in strength (in dB) between the signal tones and the distortion, then gradually increase output level until you see the difference become smaller (which indicates that the percentage distortion is rising). Now, back off the output level until the difference is larger (the distortion is much less). With proper adjustment, the distortion products should be at least 40 dB below the tones.

The third method uses an audio voltmeter connected to the output of the sound card. With the digital program in transmit mode, start with very low output, and gradually increase it until you no longer see voltage increasing, then back off the output level to one-half the maximum measured voltage.

The fourth method uses your ears and headphones connected to the output of the sound card. Start with the output of the sound card set low, gradually increasing it until you hear harshness or sharpness in the tones. That harshness is the distortion products. Now, reduce the output of the sound card until the tones sound half as loud. This works because a change of 6-10 dB is perceived as half (or twice) as loud.

FEEDING COMPUTER AUDIO TO THE RADIO

To avoid overdriving the radio's audio input, feed the computer sound card to the radio's LINE IN input (if there is one). In older rigs, this may be labeled as a phone patch input, or for use with a hardware RTTY interface.

If the rig has no line input, you'll need to feed the microphone input through a simple voltage divider (often called a "pad" — see the sidebar) so that you don't overload the microphone preamp. All it takes is two resistors, one in series with the audio path, and one in parallel with the input of the radio. 20 dB (a 10:1 voltage divider) of attenuation should be enough for most radios, and calls for a 10:1 ratio between the two resistors. The values are not critical, but 10 kΩ for the series resistor and 1 kΩ for the parallel resistor, or 4.7 kΩ and 470 Ω are good choices. Low-wattage resistors may be used here, and can fit within the connectors of the patch cable between the computer and the radio if you use the right connector. RCA and 1/8-inch connectors made by Switchcraft have the most space inside them. Neutrik is also a good brand.

With all of these methods, adjust the input gain control of your radio according to the user manual for the radio for transmitting digital modes. Always make sure that any processing in the radio is turned off.

As a final check, ask another amateur who is receiving your signal fairly well to look carefully for sidebands in the received waterfall display (first making sure that the noise blanker is turned off, and that you are not overloading the receiver).

Microphone Pads

(The following material was contributed by Ethan Winer. More design information is available on his website: ethanwiner.com/gadgets.html.)

The balanced microphone attenuator or *pad* shown in **Figure 13.A1**. is about as basic a circuit as you're likely to encounter. But finding the optimum resistor values can be a challenge for the beginner, and a time consuming nuisance for the more advanced.

Figure 13.A2.shows the same general configuration, except this circuit yields a low-end rolloff beginning at a frequency dictated by the resistor and capacitor values. Notice that the designation "R1" does not appear in this diagram. The same component numbering is used throughout the figures to make the formulas easier to understand. Also note that the low-cut circuit in Figure 2 will not pass bias voltage (also known as *phantom power* in professional audio).

Exchanging the capacitors and resistor in Figure 13.A2 results in a high-frequency loss (**Figure 13.A3**), while adding an inductor allows adjusting the midrange response for boosting presence or controlling sibilance (**Figures 13.A4A** and **13.A4B**).

One problem with inductors is their inherent series resistance, which is

$$R2 = \frac{R_{IN} \times R}{R_{IN} - R}$$

Where: $R = \frac{2 R1}{(10^{\frac{A}{20}})-1}$

A = Desired loss in dB
R_{IN} = Your console's input impedance

Pin numbers are for XL connector

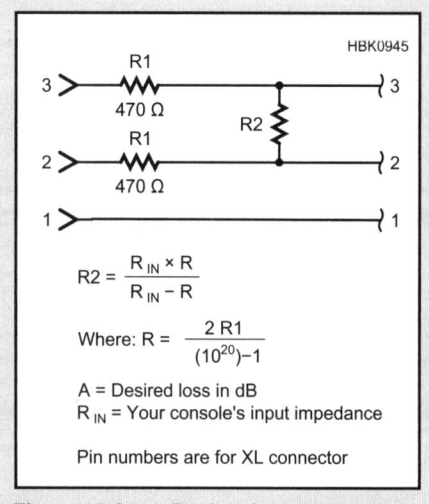

Figure 13.A1 — Basic microphone attenuation pad.

13.8.7 Speech Amplification and Processing

AUDIO SIGNAL LEVELS

The output level of most modern microphones ranges from about 10 mV to a few hundred mV when used close to the mouth. Microphone inputs are designed to accept signals in this range and are likely to be overloaded by stronger signals. In addition to microphone inputs, most ham equipment also features line-in inputs that are designed to accept signals between about 100 mV and 2 V.

IMPEDANCE IN AUDIO CIRCUITS

Since solid-state electronics became standard, audio circuits are no longer impedance-matched. Instead, audio circuits are voltage-matched. *Output* circuits have a low source impedance, typically around 100 Ω for pro line level, 300 Ω for consumer line level, and around 200 Ω for most modern microphones. Audio *input* circuits have a high input impedance, typically 10 kΩ for pro line level inputs, 50 kΩ for consumer line level inputs, and at least 1 MΩ for microphone inputs.

---

inevitable due to the wire they're made from. The smaller (physically) a given inductor is built, the higher the resistance since the wire must be a smaller diameter. The Mouser 43LH and 43LJ series inductors minimize this by winding the wire around a ferrite core. At low currents the ferrite core does a great job of increasing the inductance without requiring as many turns of wire, which keeps the series resistance relatively low. Also, these coils are encapsulated in a rugged phenolic case which eliminates the danger of damaging the hair-thin wires during assembly.

For the midrange networks shown in this sidebar you can expect to alter the response by about 4 or 5 dB, though this can be varied by adjusting R2 up or down in value. With the high- and low-end rolloffs, the cutoff slope is 6 dB. per octave beyond the chosen frequency. This rolloff rate is hard to change because additional capacitors and resistors would be needed. That not only complicates the design, but also reduces the signal level overall.

Construction Notes

The pads can be constructed in the usual metal enclosures. Note that the S3FM connector assembly made by Switchcraft — a 3.5-inch tube fitted with a male XL (or XLR) at one end and a female at the other — has enough room in the middle to build a mike pad, low-end rolloff network, polarity reverser, or any number of other useful little gadgets.

With space generally at a premium in any small enclosure, you must use the smallest components you can find. For microphone-level signals you can use ⅛-watt resistors. Another space saver is to use low-voltage capacitors. When the component values are large, such as the low-frequency rolloff, tantalum capacitors are the best choice and you may be able to find ultra-miniature types rated as low as 6 or even 3 V. Tantalums cost more than standard electrolytics, but they are smaller and generally higher quality.

Use shrink-fit sleeving over all of the components or otherwise ensure that the components don't short out to one another. The S3FM comes with a plastic-coated cardboard tube that lines the inside of the case, and this prevents any wires from touching the grounded case. Clear shrink tubing lets you see what parts are inside — a definite advantage if you have to take it apart for repair or just to see what's in there. Avoid black electrical tape for insulation; not only can't you see through it, but after a while it can turn into a sticky mess that's difficult to unwrap. Draw the schematic on a small piece of paper, and roll it up to serve as the outer insulation.

$$C1 = 2 \times \frac{1}{2 \pi f R}$$

Where: f = Desired cutoff frequency

$$R = \frac{R_{IN} \times 2000}{R_{IN} + 2000}$$

Pin numbers are for XL connector

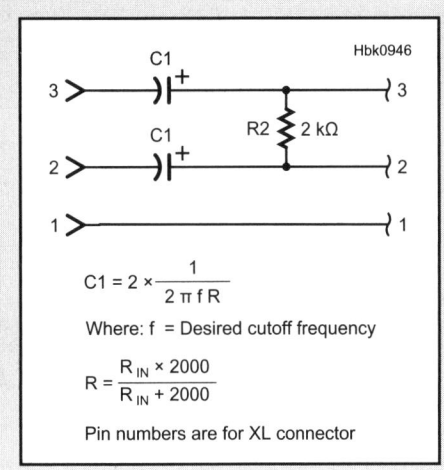

Figure 13.A2 — Low-frequency rolloff pad.

$$C1 = \frac{1}{2 \pi f R}$$

Where: f = Desired cutoff frequency

$$R = \frac{940 \times R_{IN}}{940 - R_{IN}}$$

Pin numbers are for XL connector

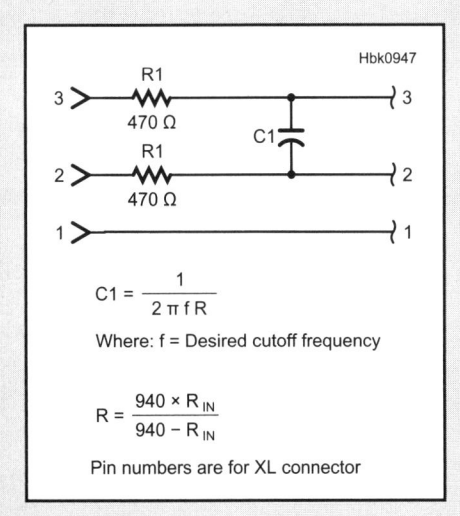

Figure 13.A3 — High-frequency rolloff pad.

$$C1 = \frac{1}{2000 \pi f}$$

$$L1 = C = 10^6$$

Where: f = Desired cutoff frequency

Also $f = \frac{1}{2 \pi \sqrt{LC}}$

Pin numbers are for XL connector

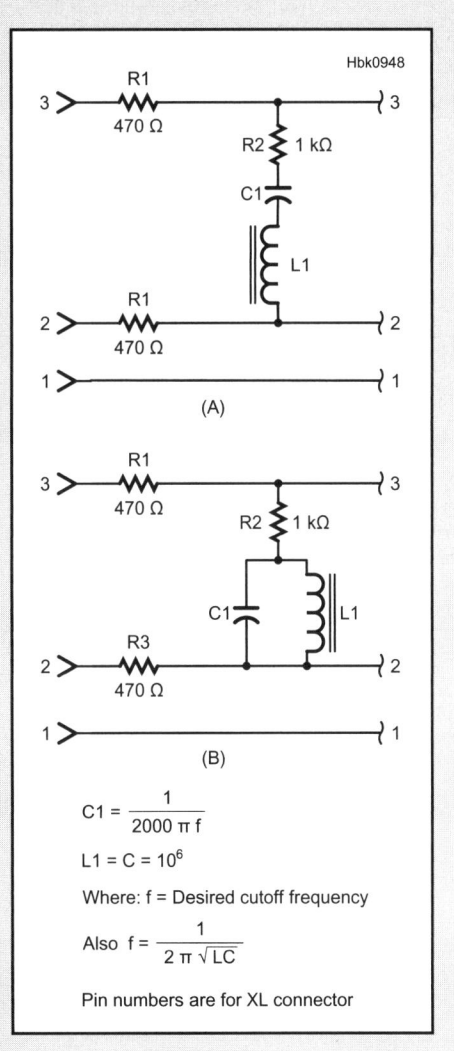

Figures 13.A4 — Midrange cut (A) and boost (B) pads.

Thanks to these impedance relationships, very little current flows in microphone and line circuits. Output stages are constant voltage sources, so they can easily drive multiple inputs in parallel. While output circuits are usually *rated* for a 600 Ω load, loading them with 600 Ω degrades their performance.

Loudspeaker amplifiers are different, in that they *do* provide power. They are still constant voltage sources, and those that drive loudspeakers typically have output impedance of a few tens of milliohms, designed to drive loads in the range of 4-16 Ω. Since they are constant voltage sources, they will deliver four times more power into a 4-Ω load than into a 16-Ω load. The ratio of load impedance to source impedance is the *damping factor*.

Headphone amplifiers also supply power but a lot less of it. Headphones range in impedance from 8 Ω to more than 600 Ω, and most will be pretty loud with only a few volts drive. Most headphone amplifiers can drive more than one pair of headphones in parallel. Most headphone amplifiers have a resistor in series with their output so that they are not damaged when a plug is not inserted properly.

Computer sound cards have stereo *outputs* designed to drive headphones and line level inputs. The sound cards built into many laptop computers have only a mono *input*, often designed only for microphone levels. Most outboard sound cards, and better built-in sound cards, provide both a mono microphone and a stereo line input, or a single stereo input that can be switched to microphone or line level via the computer's operating system or the software that uses the audio signal.

SPEECH PROCESSING

Transmitters generally require audio signals in the volt region and it will be found advantageous to shape the frequency response prior to transmission. ("Amplified" microphones are outside this discussion.) Before being applied to the modulator circuits in the transmitter the audio signal is applied to a clipper or compressor for amplitude control. Such circuits along with their associated filtering increase the average value of signal level into the transmitter and so make the signal sound louder and define the occupied bandwidth.

PREAMPLIFIER

The output of the microphone is amplified and its frequency response shaped in a pre-amplifier as shown in **Figure 13.50**. R4 allows coarse gain adjustment and it can be a 100 kΩ potentiometer if various microphones are to be accommodated. The low-pass filter has a flat response out to about 3 kHz, including a peak of several dB at 2500 Hz (discussed below). The filters work in concert with the following treble peaking circuit to produce a response very suitable for communications as shown in **Figure 13.51**. The magnitude of the peak at 2500 Hz may be adjusted by simply changing the value of R12. This treble peaking circuit only affects speech signals in the 2500 Hz region.

The response as shown has a rise of 15 dB at 2500 Hz relative to 400 Hz but is nevertheless down 30 dB at 10 kHz. Very low frequencies have been rolled off. The output of the preamplifier is applied to a level control and then to a clipper or compressor for level control.

CLIPPER

After the speech signal has been increased in level and the basic response has been shaped, it may be applied to a clipper to increase its average volume level. At this point it must be pointed out that clipping must be used with great care if the transmitter is operating in the single-sideband mode. SSB transmitters cannot handle clipped waveforms gracefully. Clipping can always be used to catch occasional overshoots resulting from sluggish AGC systems, as an example, but in SSB systems should not be used as a routine method of volume maximization. However, clipping can be used in AM systems with great effect. A clipper followed by a low-pass filter sets the occupied bandwidth of the transmitter, assuming the following stages are operating cleanly.

Figure 13.52 shows the schematic of a speech clipper with its associated filtering.

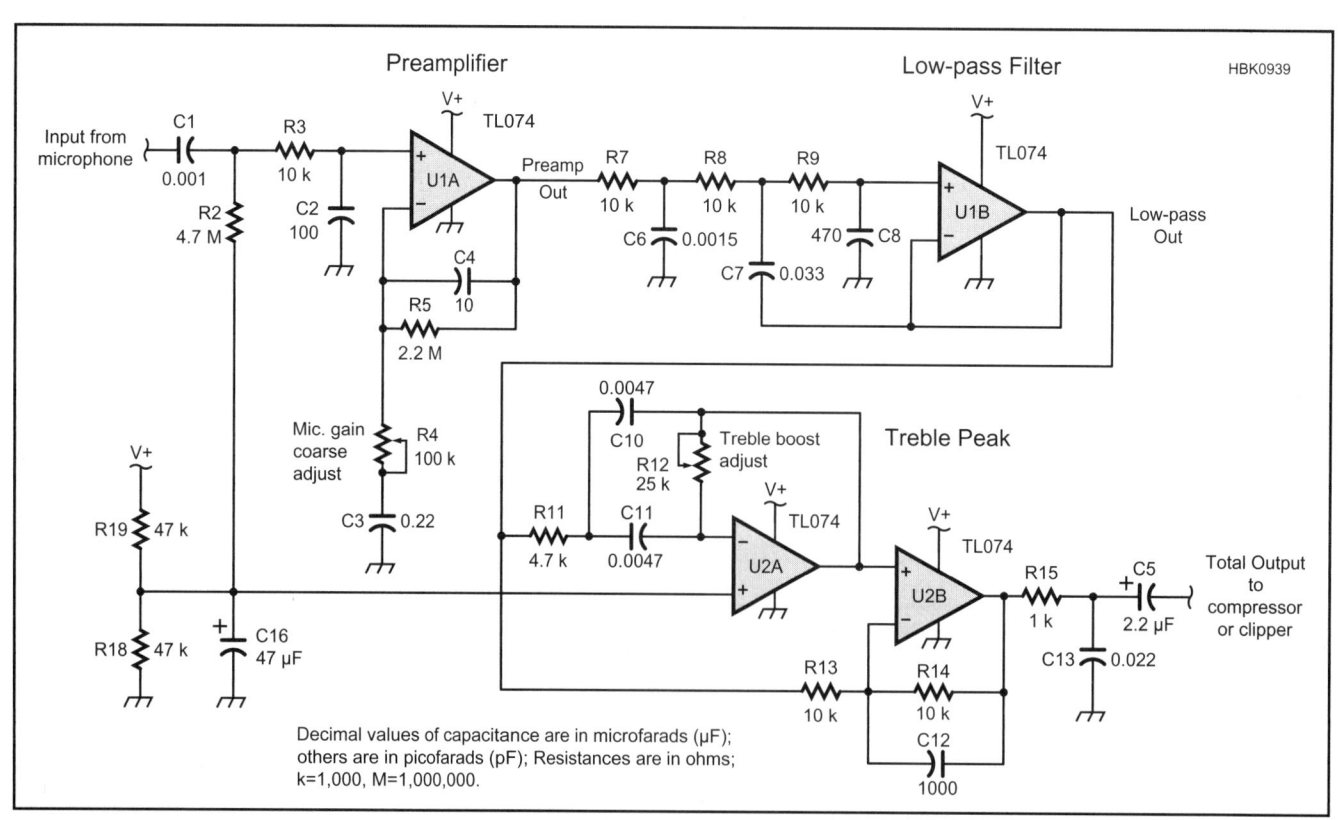

Figure 13.50 — Schematic of a microphone preamplifier with a gain stage, a low-pass filter and a treble peaking stage.

The "preclip" filters are optional but recommended. The "postclip" low-pass filter is a mandatory requirement to limit the transmitted bandwidth.

The 200 Hz high-pass filter ahead of the clipper greatly reduces low-frequency intermodulation distortion. The 3 kHz low-pass filter ahead of the clipper prevents high-frequency audio (sibilants) from being clipped and similarly causing high-frequency intermodulation distortion.

This circuit uses an over-driven op-amp as a clipper. Its sensitivity may be changed by changing the value of R8. The output is reduced by a factor of two (R11 and R12) so the following low-pass filter can handle the signal in a linear mode.

This filter has a sharp cutoff which would ordinarily have overshoots in its transient response when a clipped waveform is applied to its input. This can result in overmodulation, but it has been modified to have a step in its frequency response with the result that the overshoots have been turned into "undershoots" and so are rendered harmless. The overall response of the filtering in this block including the high-pass and both low-pass filters is shown in **Figure 13.53.**

AUDIO COMPRESSOR

Another way to increase the average modulation level is to use automatic gain control (AGC) or a compressor. Such a circuit is shown in **Figure 13.54.** Compressors can be used for any mode of speech transmission. Compression should *never* be used with digital modes using AFSK modulation.

On the output of the op-amp are two LEDs in parallel but with opposite polarities. Audio voltages of either polarity illuminate a photoconductor causing its resistance to decrease. The photoconductor will then adjust the gain of the associated op-amp circuit. As audio levels increase, the LEDs illuminate the photoconductor more, reducing its resistance.

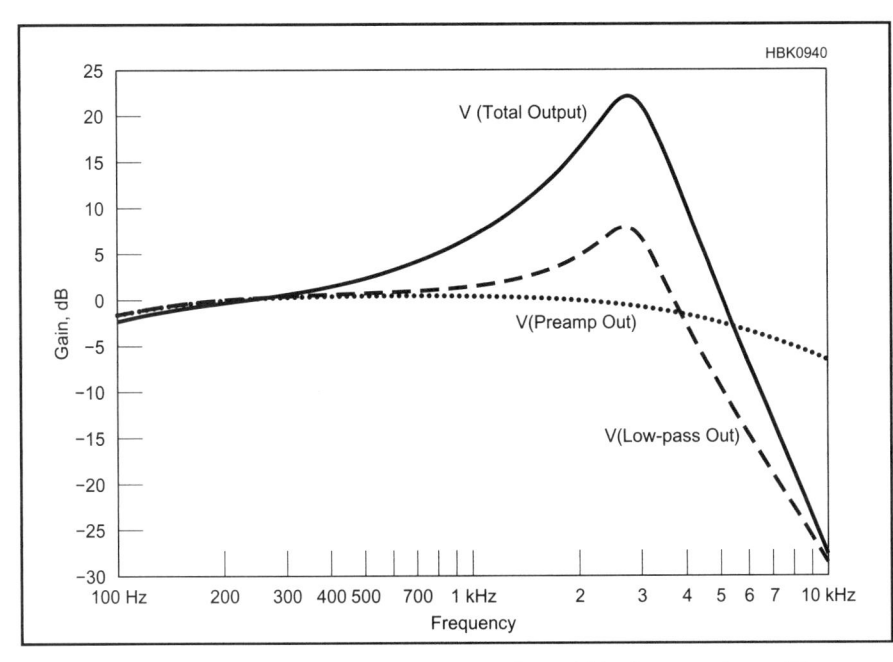

Figure 13.51 — Frequency response at various points within the speech amplifier.

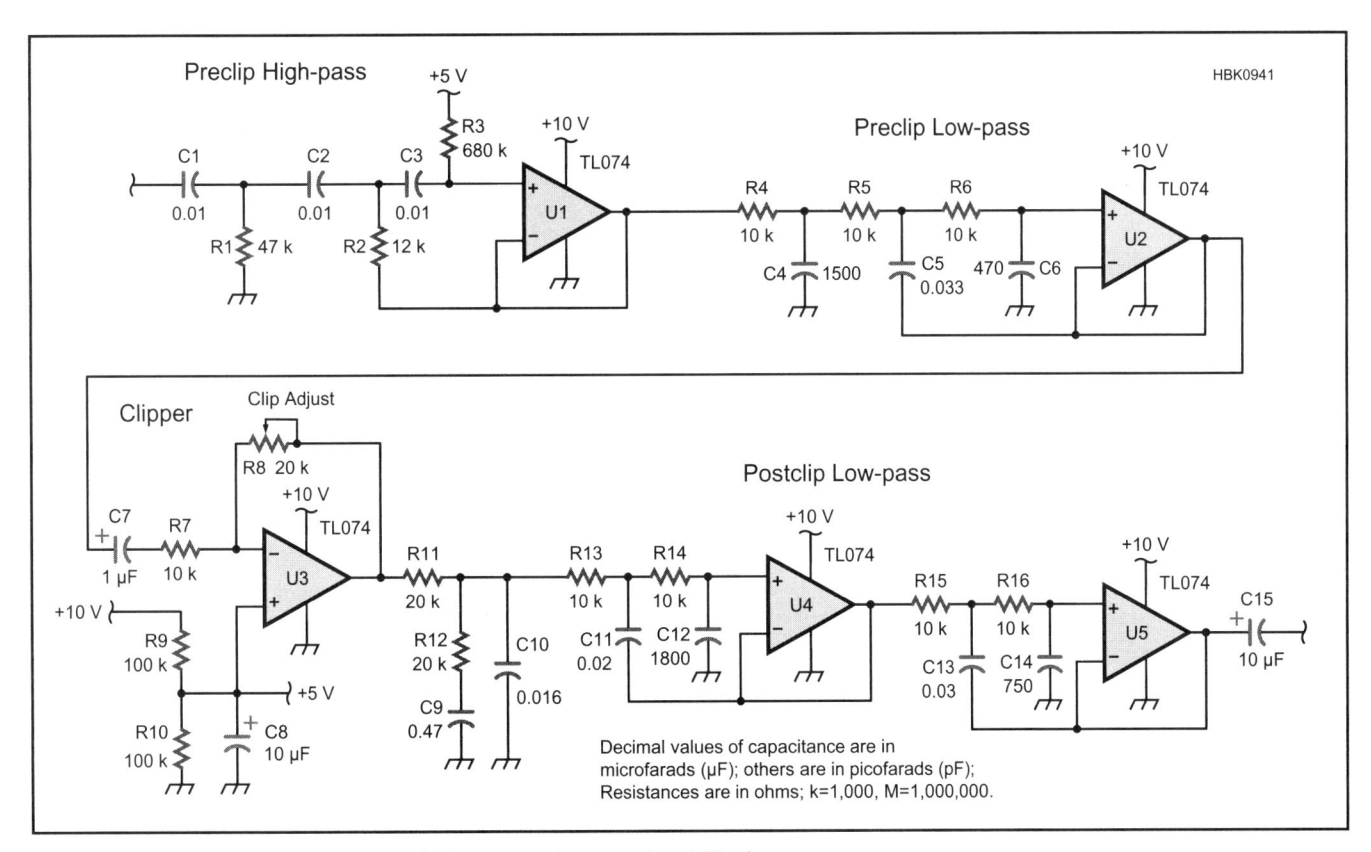

Figure 13.52 — Schematic of the speech clipper and its associated filtering.

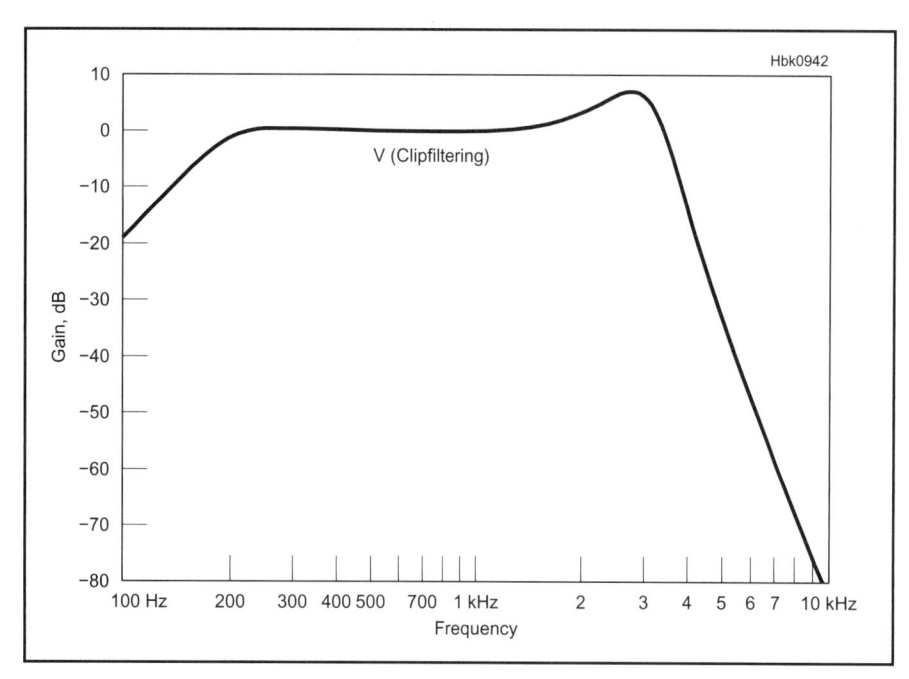

Figure 13.53 — Overall response of the clipper-filtering block.

This causes the photoconductors to reduce the circuit gain, maintaining a constant audio output level. A second photoconductor monitors the illumination and so shows the degree of compression. The photoconductors (Luna PDV-P8101 or equivalent) are mounted directly on top of the white LEDs (Cree C503D-WAN-CCBEB152 or equivalent). This is shown in the inset for Figure 13.54.

This circuit responds to signal level increases within 2 or 3 milliseconds. After a transient, it increases the gain back to normal in less than 100 milliseconds. The result is a very high average modulation level with far lower distortion than a clipper. Some signal overshoots will escape while gain reduction is underway but time-wise, on a percentage basis, they are quite small. If this block of circuitry is followed by a clipper to catch the overshoots then even those small overshoots will be of no concern.

The pre-clip high-pass and pre-clip low-pass filters shown in the clipper block may be used in the compressor; they were not shown here. If used, they must be on the input to the compressor.

IF SPEECH CLIPPER

Audio clipper speech processors can generate a considerable amount of in-band harmonics and IMD (involving different simultaneously occurring speech frequencies). The total distortion detracts somewhat from speech intelligibility. IF clippers (also known as RF speech processors) overcome most of these problems, especially the Hilbert Transform problem. (See Sabin and Schoenike in the References section.)

Figure 13.55A is a schematic diagram of a 455 kHz IF clipper using high-frequency op-amps. 20 dB of gain precedes the diode clippers. A second amplifier establishes the desired output level. The clipping produces a wide band of IMD products close to the IF frequency. Harmonics of the IF frequency are easily rejected by subsequent selectivity. "Close-in" IMD distortion products are band-limited by the 2.5 kHz wide IF filter so that out-of-band splatter is eliminated. The in-band IMD products are at least 10 dB below the speech tones.

Figure 13.55B shows a block diagram of an adaptation of the above system to an audio in-audio out configuration that can be inserted into the mic input of any transmitter to provide the benefits of RF speech processing. These are sometimes offered as aftermarket accessories.

Figure 13.56 shows oscilloscope pictures

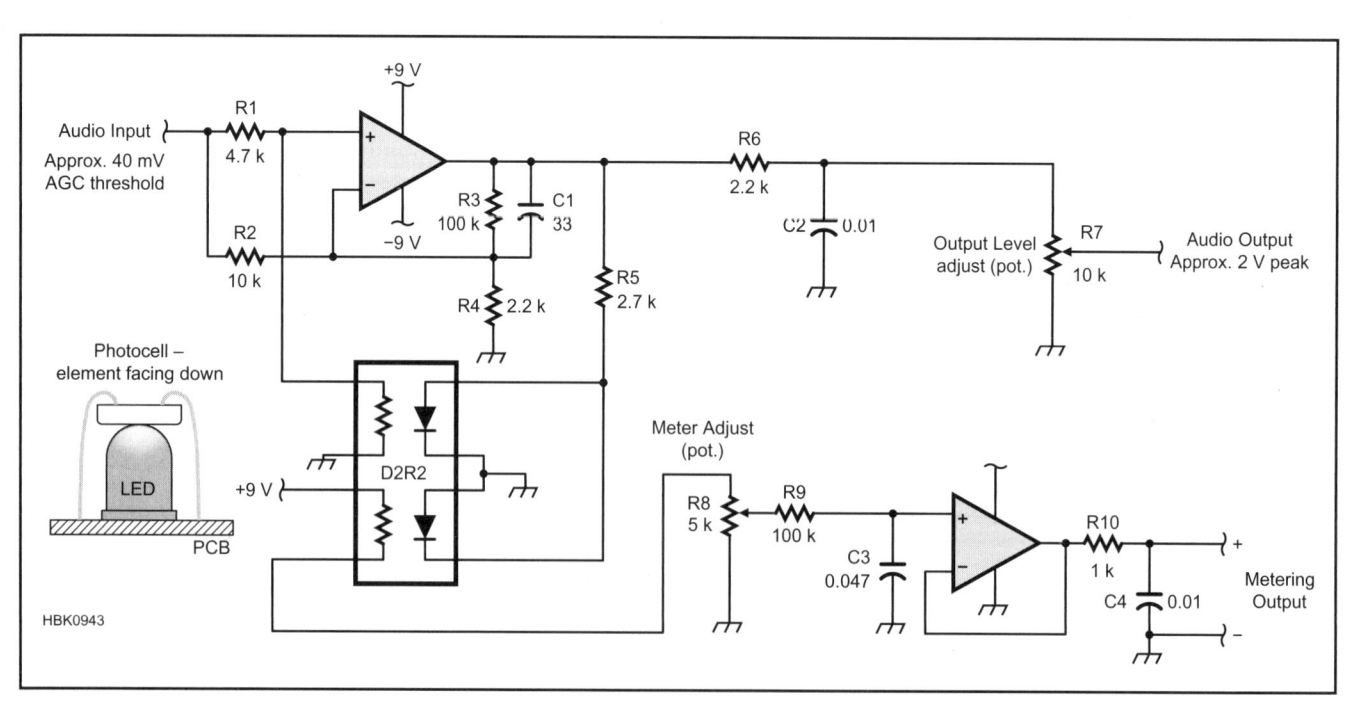

Figure 13.54 — Compressor circuit based on LEDs shining on photoconductors (cadmium sulfide photocells). See the text for a description of how to fabricate D2R2.

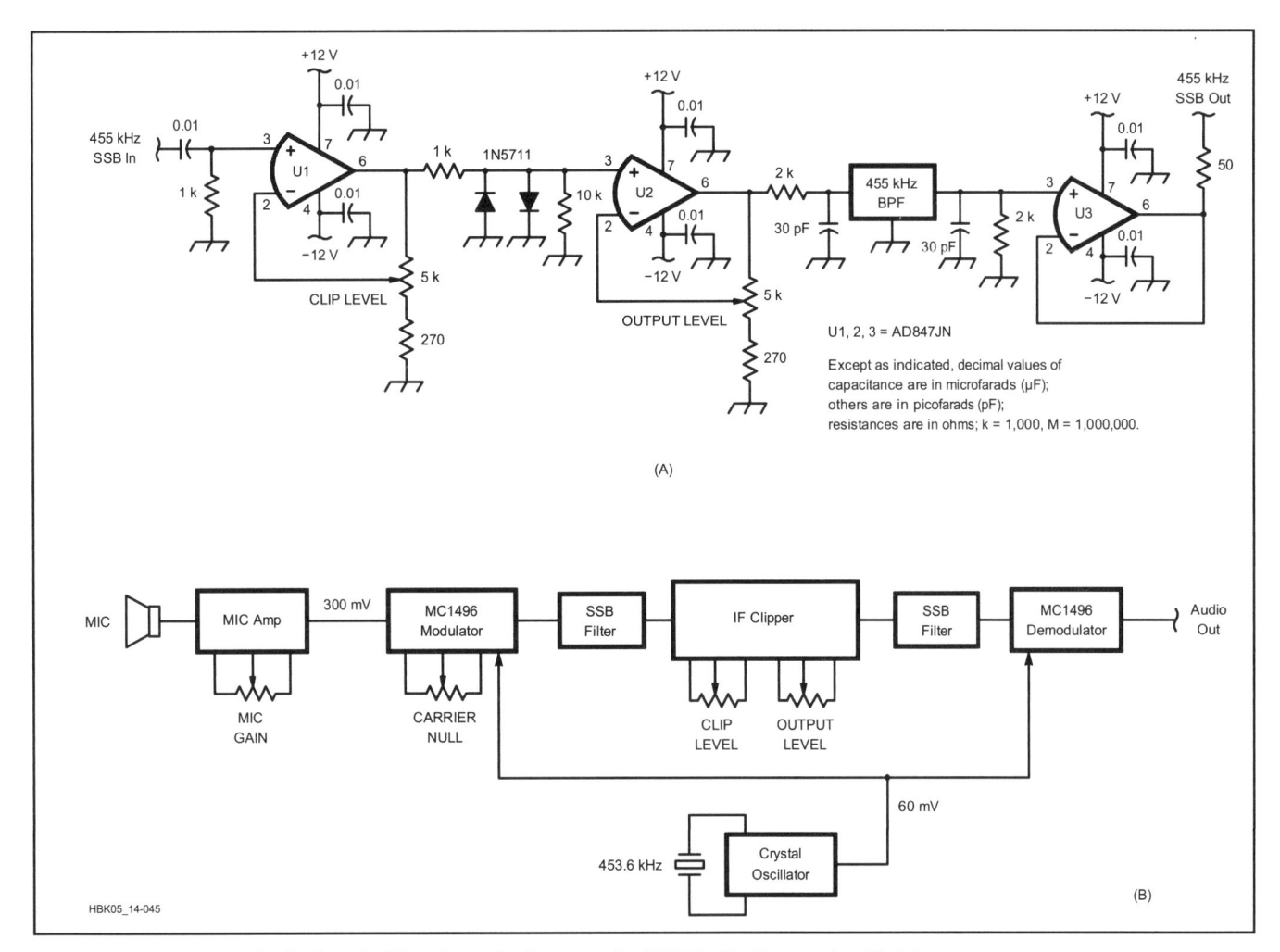

Figure 13.55 — IF speech clipping. At (A), schematic diagram of a 455 kHz IF clipper using high-frequency op amps. At (B) block diagram of an adaptation of the above system to an audio in-audio out configuration.

of an IF clipped two-tone signal at various levels of clipping. The level of clipping in a radio can be estimated by comparing with these photos. Listening tests verify that the IMD does not sound nearly as bad as harmonic distortion. In fact, processed speech sounds relatively clean and crisp. Tests also verify that speech intelligibility in a noise background is improved by 8 dB. (See the article on RF clippers by Sabin in the References section.)

The repeaking effect from band-pass filtering the clipped IF signal occurs, and must be accounted for when adjusting the output level. A two-tone audio test signal or a speech signal should be used. The ALC circuitry (discussed later) will reduce the IF gain to prevent splattering in the power amplifiers. If the IF filter is of high quality and if subsequent amplifiers are clean, the transmitted signal is of very high quality and is very effective in noisy situations and often also in pile-ups.

The extra IF gain implies that the IF signal entering the clipper must be free of noise,

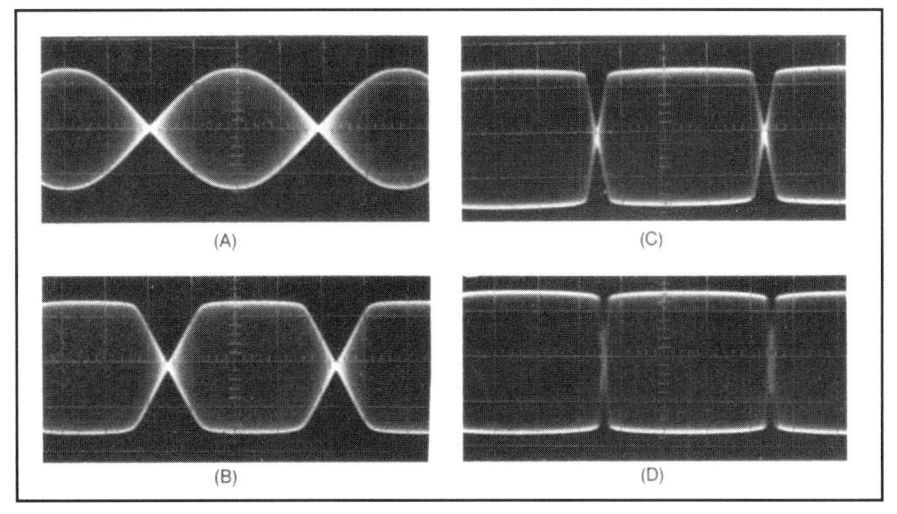

Figure 13.56 — Two-tone envelope patterns with various degrees of RF clipping. All envelope patterns are formed using tones of 600 and 1000 Hz. At A, clipping threshold; B, 5 dB of clipping; C, 10 dB of clipping; D, 15 dB of clipping.

Transmitting   13.35

hum and spurious products. The cleanup filter also helps reduce the carrier frequency, which is outside the passband.

An electrically identical approach to the IF clipper can be achieved at audio frequencies. If the audio signal is translated to, say 455 kHz, processed as described and translated back to audio, all the desirable effects of IF clipping are retained. This output then plugs into the transmitter's microphone jack. Figure 13.55B shows the basic method. The mic amplifier and the MC1496 circuits have been previously shown and the clipper circuit can be the same as in Figure 13.55A.

The interesting operating principle in all of these examples is that the characteristics of the IF clipped (or equivalent) speech signal do not change during frequency translation, even if translated down to audio and then back up to IF in a balanced modulator.

13.9 Voice Operation

13.9.1 Push-To-Talk for Voice

Another advance in amateur station switching followed longstanding practices of aircraft and mobile voice operators who had other things to contend with besides radio switches. Microphones in those services included built-in switches to activate TR switching. Called push-to-talk (PTT), this function is perhaps the most self-explanatory description in our acronym studded environment.

Relays controlled the various switching functions when the operator pressed the PTT switch. Some top-of-the-line transmitters of the period included at least some of the relays internally and had a socket designed for PTT microphones. **Figure 13.57** is a view of the ubiquitous Astatic D-104 microphone with PTT stand, produced from the 1930s to 2004, and still popular at flea markets and auction sites. PTT operation allowed the operator to be out of reach of the radio equipment while operating, permitting "easy chair" operation for the first time.

Modern transceivers include some form of PTT (or "one switch operation"). Relays, diodes, transistors and other components seamlessly handle myriad transmit-receive changeover functions inside the transceiver. Most transceivers have additional provisions for manually activating PTT via a front-panel switch. And many have one or more jacks for external PTT control via foot switches, computer interfaces or other devices.

13.9.2 Voice-Operated Transmit-Receive Switching (VOX)

How about break-in for voice operators? SSB operation enabled the development of voice operated transmit/receive switching, or VOX. During VOX operation, speaking into the microphone causes the station to switch from receive to transmit; a pause in speaking results in switching back to receive mode. Although VOX technology can work with AM or FM, rapidly turning the carrier signal on and off to follow speech does not provide the smooth operation possible with SSB. (During SSB transmission, no carrier or signal is sent while the operator is silent.)

VOX OPERATION

VOX is built into current HF SSB transceivers. In most, but not all, cases they also provide for PTT operation, with switches or menu settings to switch among the various control methods. Some operators prefer VOX, some prefer PTT and some switch back and forth depending on the operating environment.

VOX controls are often considered to be in the "set and forget" category and thus may be controlled by a software menu or by controls on the rear panel, under the top lid or behind an access panel. The following sections discuss the operation and adjustment of radio controls associated with VOX operation. Check your transceiver's operating manual for the specifics for your radio.

Before adjusting your radio's VOX controls, it's important to understand how your particular mic operates. If it has no PTT switch, you can go on to the next section! Some mics with PTT switches turn off the audio signal if the PTT switch is released, while some just open the control contacts. If your mic does the former, you will need to lock the PTT switch closed, have a different mic for VOX, or possibly modify the internal mic connections to make it operate with the VOX. If no audio is provided to the VOX control circuit, it will never activate. If the mic came with your radio, or from its manufacturer, you can probably find out in the radio or mic manual.

VOX Gain

Figure 13.58 shows some typical transceiver VOX controls. The VOX gain setting determines how loud speech must be to initiate switchover, called "tripping the VOX." With a dummy load on the radio, experiment with the setting and see what happens. You should be able to advance it so far that it switches with your breathing. That is obviously too sensitive or you will have to hold your breath while receiving! If not sensitive enough, it may cause the transmitter to switch

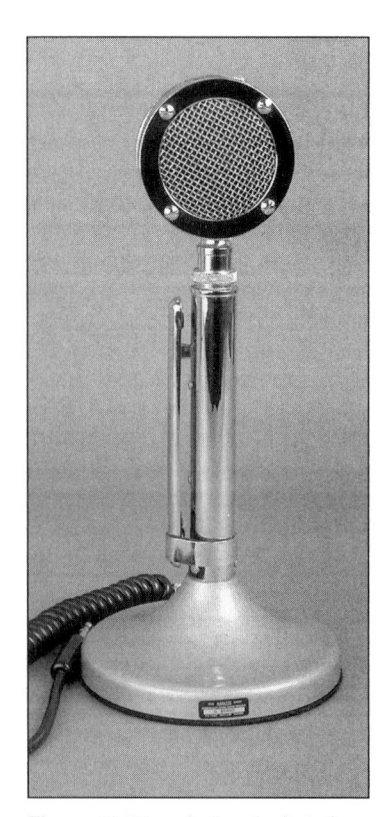

Figure 13.57 — A classic Astatic D-104 mic with PTT stand.

Figure 13.58 — The function of VOX controls is described in the text. They require adjustment for different types of operating, so front-panel knobs make the most convenient control arrangement. In some radios, VOX settings are adjusted through the menu system.

off during softly spoken syllables. Notice that the setting depends on how close you are to the microphone, as well as how loud you talk. A headset-type microphone (a "boom set") has an advantage here in that you can set the microphone distance the same every time you use it.

The optimum setting is one that switches to transmit whenever you start talking, but isn't so sensitive that it switches when the microphone picks up other sounds, such as a cooling fan turning on or normal household noises.

VOX Delay

As soon as you stop talking, the radio can switch back to receive. Generally, if that happens too quickly, it will switch back and forth between syllables, causing a lot of extra and distracting relay clatter. The VOX delay control determines how long the radio stays in the transmit position once you stop talking. If set too short, it can be annoying. If set too long, you may find that you miss a response to a question because the other station started talking while you were still waiting to switch over.

You may find that different delay settings work well for different types of operation. For example, in a contest the responses come quickly and a short delay is good. For casual conversation, longer delays may be appropriate. Again, experiment with these settings with your radio connected to a dummy load.

Anti-VOX

This is a control with a name that may mystify you at first glance! While you are receiving, your loudspeaker is also talking to your microphone — and tripping your VOX — even if you aren't! Early VOX users often needed to use headphones to avoid this problem. Someone finally figured out that if a sample of the speaker's audio signal were fed back to the mic input, out-of-phase and at the appropriate amplitude, the signal from the speaker could be cancelled out and would not cause the VOX circuit to activate the transmitter. The ANTI-VOX (called ANTI-TRIP in the photo) controls the amplitude of the sampled speaker audio, while the phase is set by the transceiver design.

As you tune in signals on your receiver with the audio output going to the speaker, you may find that the VOX triggers from time to time. This will depend on how far you turn up the volume, which way the speaker is pointed and how far it is from the mic. You should be able to set the anti-VOX so that the speaker doesn't trip the VOX during normal operation.

Generally, setting anti-VOX to higher values allows the speaker audio to be louder without activating the VOX circuit. Keep in mind that once you find a good setting, it may need to be changed if you relocate your microphone or speaker. With most radios, you should find a spot to set the speaker, microphone and anti-VOX so that the speaker can be used without difficulty.

13.10 Transmitter Power Stages

The functions described so far that process input data and information and result in a signal on the desired output radio frequency generally occur at a low level. The one exception is full-carrier AM, in which the modulation is classically applied to the final amplification stage. More modern linear transmitter systems generate AM in the same way as SSB at low levels, typically between 1 mW and 1 W.

13.10.1 Types of Power Amplifiers

The **RF Power Amplifiers** chapter provides a detailed view of power amplifiers; however, we will take a quick peek here to set the stage for the following discussions. Amplifiers use dc power applied to active devices in order to increase the power or level of signals. As will all real devices, they introduce some distortion in the process, and are generally limited by the level of distortion products. Power amplifiers can be constructed using either solid-state devices or vacuum tubes as the active device. At higher powers, typically above a few hundred watts, vacuum tubes are more frequently found, although there is a clear trend toward solid state at all amateur power levels.

Independent of the device, amplifiers are divided into classes based on the fraction of the input cycle over which they conduct. A sinusoidal output signal is provided either by the *flywheel* action of a resonant circuit or by other devices contributing in turn. The usual amplifier classes are summarized in **Table 13.1**. Moving from Class A toward Class C, the amplifiers become progressively less linear but more efficient. The amplifiers with a YES in the LINEAR column thus are not all equally linear however A, AB or Class B amplifiers can be suitable for operation in a linear transmitter chain. Class C amplifiers can be used only for amplification of signals that do not have modulation information contained in the amplitude, other than on-off keyed signals. Thus class C amplifiers are useful for amplification of sinusoids, CW, FM, or as the nonlinear stage at which high-level AM modulation is employed.

Recent developments in switching-type amplifiers and in single-band matching network design have created several additional classes. Class D is a switchmode amplifier most often used for high-efficiency audio amplification. Class E and F use tuned output networks that let the amplifying device act like a switch but prevent high voltage and high current at the same time. Class G is similar to a Class B amplifier, but switches between two voltage levels to reduce power dissipation at low signal levels. Class I uses two devices driven with complementary pulse duty cycles to cancel harmonics and follow the input waveform. Class S is a variation on Class D, and Class T uses DSP to optimize pulse widths in a Class D amplifier for better performance. More information on amplifier classes is available in the online tutorial "Amplifier Classes" at **www.electronics-tutorials.es/amplifier/amplifier-classes.html**. See also the references at the end of this chapter for Rosu and for Silver.

Table 13.1
Characteristics of Transceiver Power Amplifier Classes
Values are typical

Class	Conduction	Linear	Efficiency
A	360°	Yes	30%
AB	270°	Yes	55%
B	180°	Yes	65%
C	90°	No	74%

13.10.2 Linear Amplifiers

While transmitters at power levels of 1 mW to 1 W have been successfully used for communication across many portions of the spectrum, most communications systems operate with more success at higher powers. The low level stage is usually referred to as an exciter, while higher power is provided by one or more linear amplifier stages as shown in **Figure 13.59**.

The power levels shown at the various points in Figure 13.59 are fairly typical for a high powered amateur station. The 1500 W PEP output represents the legal limit for US amateurs in most bands (200 W PEP on 30 meters and 100 W ERPD on the 60 meter channels are notable exceptions). The first amplifier block may contain more than one stage, while the final output amplifier is often composed of multiple parallel active devices.

Typical power supply requirements for the amplifier stages are noted for a number of reasons. First, while power is rarely an issue at the exciter level, often it is a significant issue at the power levels shown for the amplifiers. The power supplies represent a large portion of the cost and weight of the system as the power increases. Some manufacturers are beginning to use switching-type power supplies for high-power amplifiers, resulting in a major reduction in size and weight.

Note also that a gross amplifier efficiency of about 50% is assumed for the amplifiers, taking into account ancillary subsystems as well as the inefficiency of the active devices in linear mode. The 50% that doesn't result in actual RF output is radiated as heat from the amplifier and must be removed from the amplifier as it is generated to avoid component damage. This represents another cost and weight factor that increases rapidly with power level.

The voltages shown for the supplies are those typical of modern solid state amplifiers. While virtually all commercial equipment now includes solid state amplifiers at the 100 W level, vacuum tube active devices are frequently found at higher levels, although the trend is clearly moving toward solid state. Vacuum tube amplifiers typically operate at voltages in the 2 to 4 kV range, requiring stringent measures be taken to avoid arcing across components. In addition, vacuum tube amplifiers typically dissipate up to 100 W of filament power that must be added to the power supply and heat dissipation planning.

13.10.3 Nonlinear Amplifiers

Nonlinear transmitters are somewhat different in architecture than the linear systems discussed previously. The configuration of a high-level AM modulated transmitter is shown in **Figure 13.60**. Note that none of the upper RF stages (the "RF chain") need to be particularly linear. The final stage must be nonlinear to have the modulation applied. Thus the RF stages can be the more power-efficient Class C amplifiers if desired.

There are some observations to be made here. Note that the RF chain is putting out the full carrier power whenever in transmit

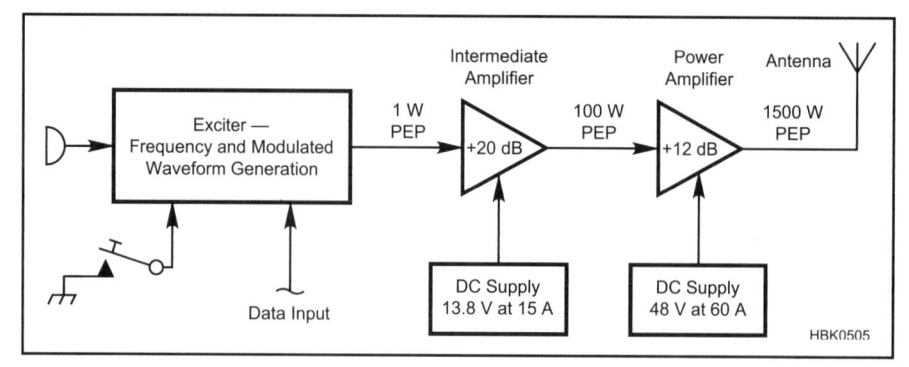

Figure 13.59 — Block diagram of a solid-state linear transmitter chain with multiple amplifier stages.

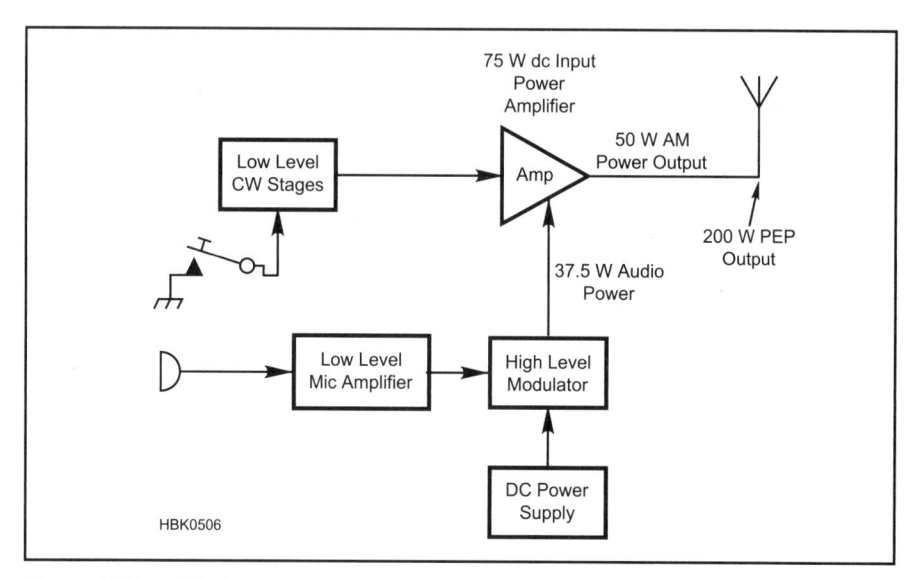

Figure 13.60 — Block diagram of a high level AM modulated transmitter.

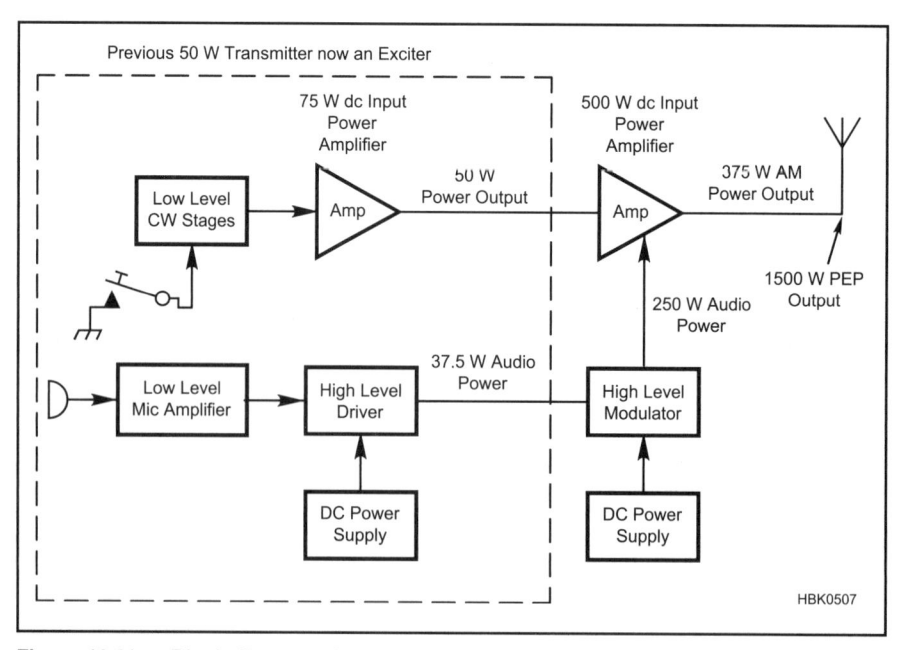

Figure 13.61 — Block diagram of a high level AM modulated transmitter with added output stage.

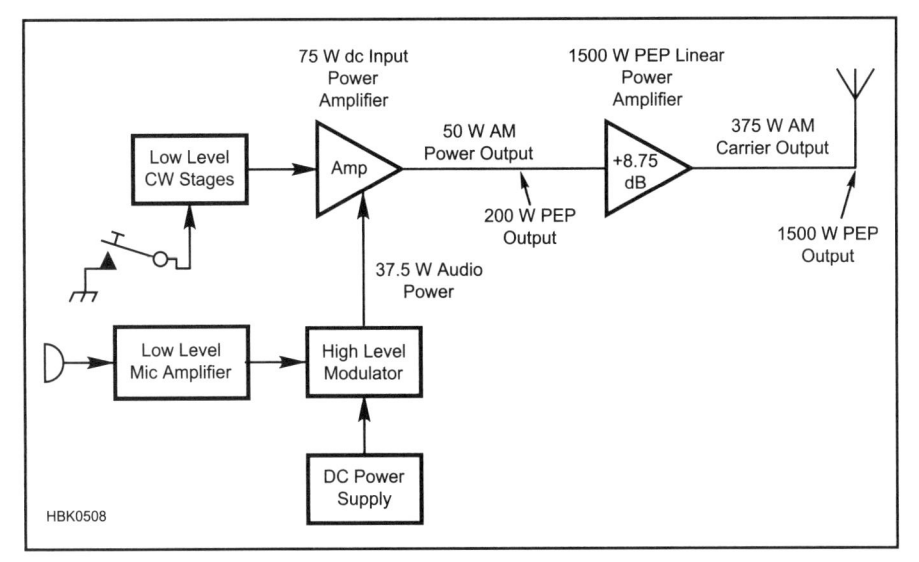

Figure 13.62 — Block diagram of a hybrid nonlinear/linear AM transmission system.

13.10.5 Automatic Level Control (ALC)

The purpose of ALC is to prevent the various stages in the transmitter from being overdriven. Over-drive can generate too much out-of-band distortion or cause excessive power dissipation, either in the amplifiers or in the power supply. ALC does this by sampling the peak amplitude of the modulation (the envelope variations) of the output signal and then developing a dc gain-control voltage that is applied to an early amplifier stage, as suggested in Figure 13.9.

ALC is usually derived from the last stage in a transmitter. This ensures that this last stage will be protected from overload. However, other stages prior to the last stage may not be as well protected; they may generate excessive distortion. It is possible to derive a composite ALC from more than one stage in a way that would prevent this problem. But designers usually prefer to design earlier stages conservatively enough so that, given a temperature range and component tolerances, the last stage can be the one source of ALC. The gain control is applied to an early stage so that all stages are aided by the gain reduction.

Note that ALC should be minimally active with most digital mode transmissions. The modulation of these signals requires linear amplification to preserve the waveform shape and minimize distortion products. ALC action creates distortion as it alters the power level of the signal. Adjust the radio drive levels so that the ALC is at its minimum level of activity — usually shown as the lower bar of a multi-segment LCD meter or a needle position just above zero. (The same caution applies to any form of audio or speech processing if the digital signal is generated by audio tones applied to the transmitter's microphone input.)

Figure 13.63 shows how a dual directional

mode, requiring a 100% duty cycle for power and amplifier components, unlike the SSB systems discussed previously. This imposes a considerable weight and cost burden on the power supply system. Note also that the PEP output of a 100% modulated AM system is equal to four times the carrier power.

The typical arrangement to increase the power of such a system is to add not only an RF amplifier stage capable of handling the desired power, but also to add additional audio power amplification to fully modulate the final RF stage. For 100% high-level plate modulation, an audio power equal to half the dc input power (plate voltage times plate current of a vacuum tube amplifier) needs to be provided. This arrangement is shown in **Figure 13.61**. In the example shown, the lower level audio stages are provided by those of the previous 50 W transmitter, now serving as an exciter for the power amplifier and as a driver for the modulating stage. This was frequently provided for in some transmitters of the AM era, notably the popular E. F. Johnson Ranger series, which provided special taps on its modulation transformer for use as a driver for higher-power systems.

It is worth mentioning that in those days the FCC US amateur power limit was expressed in terms of dc *input* to the final stage and was limited to 1000 W, rather than the 1500 W PEP *output* now specified. A fully modulated 1000 W dc input AM transmitter would likely have a carrier output of 750 W or 3000 W PEP — 3 dB above our current limit. If you end up with that classic Collins KW-1 transmitter, throttle it back to make it last and stay out of trouble!

13.10.4 Hybrid Amplifiers

Another alternative that is convenient with current equipment is to use an AM transmitter with a linear amplifier. This can be successful if the relationship that PEP = 4 × Carrier Power is maintained. **Figure 13.62** shows a 1500 W PEP output linear amplifier following a typical 50 W AM transmitter. In this example, the amplifier would be adjusted to provide a 375 W carrier output with no modulation applied to the exciter. During voice peaks the output seen on a special PEP meter, or using an oscilloscope, should be 1500 W PEP.

Note that during AM operation, the amplifier is producing a higher average power than it would without the carrier being present, as in SSB mode. The duty cycle specification of the amplifier should be checked to be sure it can handle the heavier load. If the amplifier has an RTTY rating, it should be safe to run an AM carrier at 66% of the RTTY output, following the required on and off time intervals.

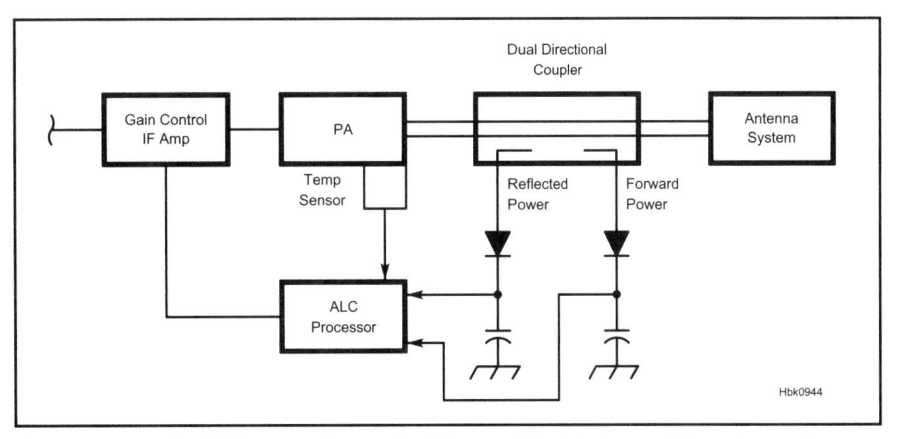

Figure 13.63 — An ALC protection method for a solid-state transmitter using a directional coupler to sense power level.

Transmitting 13.39

coupler can be used to provide ALC for a solid-state power amplifier (PA). The basic idea is to protect the PA transistors from excessive SWR and dissipation by monitoring both the forward power and the reflected power.

13.10.6 Transmit-Receive (TR) Switching

As the complexity of a transceiver increases, the business of switching between receive and transmit becomes quite complex. In commercially built equipment, this function is usually controlled by a microprocessor that manages any necessary sequencing and interlock functions that would require an excessive amount of circuitry to implement with discrete components. For an example of just how complex TR switching could be in an advanced transceiver, look at the schematic for any mid-level or top-of-the-line solid-state transceiver sold since the 1980s!

Nevertheless, the basic functions of TR switching are well within scope for the amateur building a transceiver. Understanding TR switching will also assist in troubleshooting a more complex commercial radio. Even full break-in keying is possible: Two schematics of circuits for fast TR switching from an article by Jack Kuecken, KE2QJ, are included below, and the full article is included in the downloadable supplemental information provided with this book.

Numerous schemes are popular for switching an antenna between transmitter and receiver functions. But these schemes tend to get in the way when one is developing both simple receivers and transmitters, perhaps as separate projects. A simple relay-based TR scheme is then preferred and is presented here. In this system, used in the MkII Updated Universal QRP Transmitter by Wes Hayward, W7ZOI (see the full article in this book's downloadable supplemental content), the TR relay not only switches the antenna from the receiver to the transmitter, but disconnects the headphones from the receiver and attaches them to a sidetone oscillator that is keyed with the transmitter.

The circuitry that does most of the switching is shown in **Figure 13.64**. A key closure discharges capacitor C1. R2, the 1 kΩ resistor in series with C1, prevents a spark at the key. Of greater import, it also does not allow us to "ask" that the capacitor be discharged instantaneously, a common request in similar published circuits. Key closure causes Q6 to saturate, causing Q7 to also saturate, turning the relay on. The relay picked for this example has a 700 Ω, 12 V coil with a measured 4 ms pull-in time.

Relay contacts B switch the audio line. R17 and R18 suppress clicks related to switching. A depressed key turns on PNP switch Q1, which then turns on the side-tone multivibrator, Q2 and Q3. The resulting audio is routed to switching amplifier Q4 and Q5. Although the common bases are biased to half of the supply voltage, emitter bias does not allow any static dc current to flow. The only current that flows is that related to the sidetone signal during key down intervals. Changing the value of R16 allows the audio volume to be adjusted, to compensate for the particular low-impedance headphones used.

Depending on the architecture of the transceiver, there will likely have to be some additional control circuitry in order to avoid annoying switching artifacts. These gener-

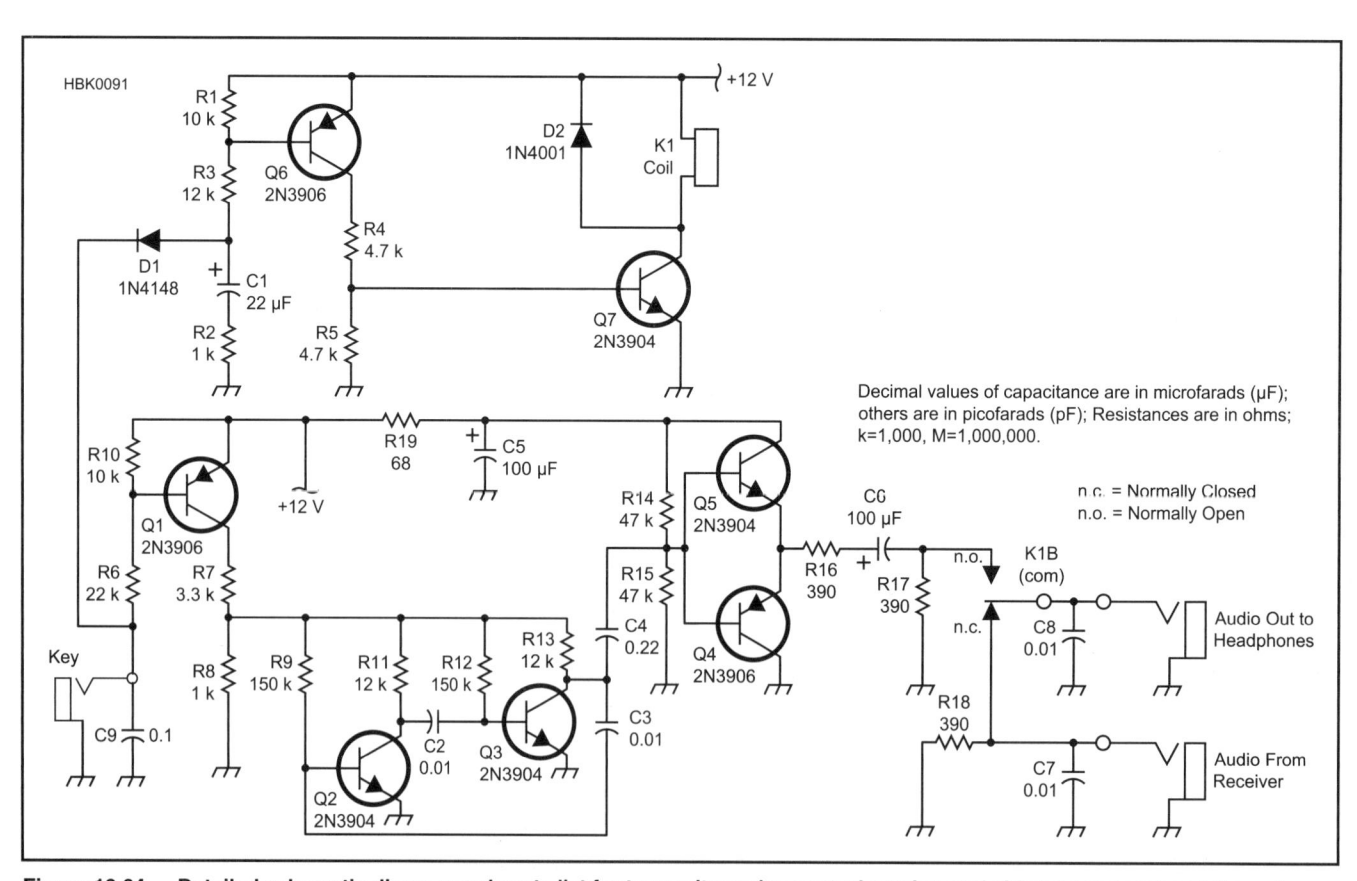

Figure 13.64 — Detailed schematic diagram and parts list for transmit-receive control section and sidetone generator of the universal QRP transmitter. Resistors are ¼ W, 5% carbon film.

C1 — 22 µF, 25 V electrolytic
C2, C3, C7, C8 — 0.01 µF, 50 V ceramic
C4 — 0.22 µF, 50 V ceramic
C5, C6 — 100 µF, 25 V electrolytic
C9 — 0.1 µF, 50 V ceramic
K1 — DPDT 12 V coil relay. An NAIS DS2Y-S-DC12, 700 Ω, 4 ms relay was used in this example.
Q1, Q4, Q6 — 2N3906, PNP silicon small signal transistor
Q2, Q3, Q5, Q7 — 2N3904, NPN silicon small signal transistor

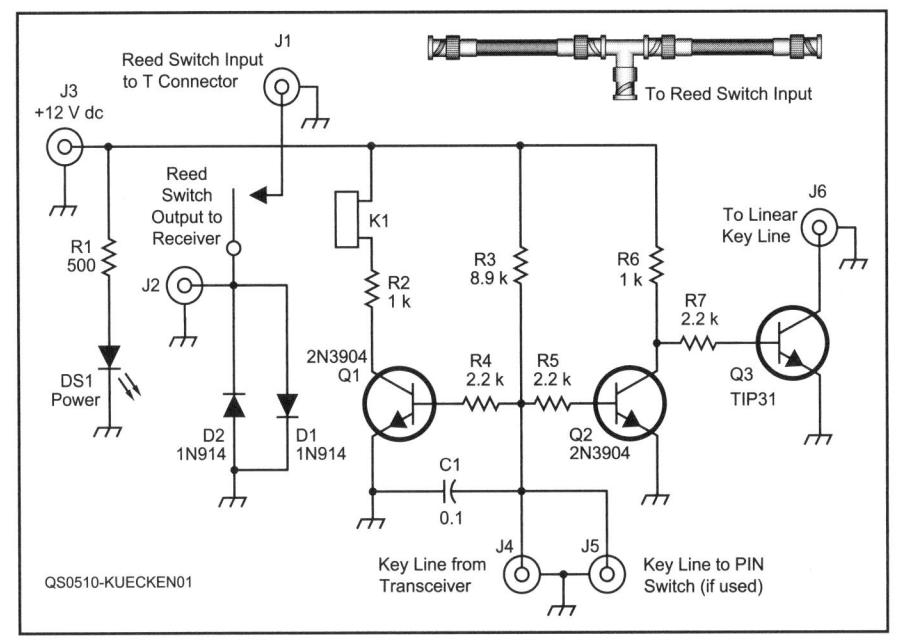

Figure 13.65 — Schematic and parts list for the reed relay TR switch. Resistors are ¼ W.

D1, D2 — High speed switching diode, 1N914 or equivalent
DS1 — LED
J1, J2 — Chassis mount BNC connectors
J3-J6 — Chassis mount phono connectors
K1 — SPST normally open reed relay with 12 V coil
Q1, Q2 — Small signal PNP transistor, 2N3904 or equivalent
Q3 — NPN power transistor, TIP31 or equivalent

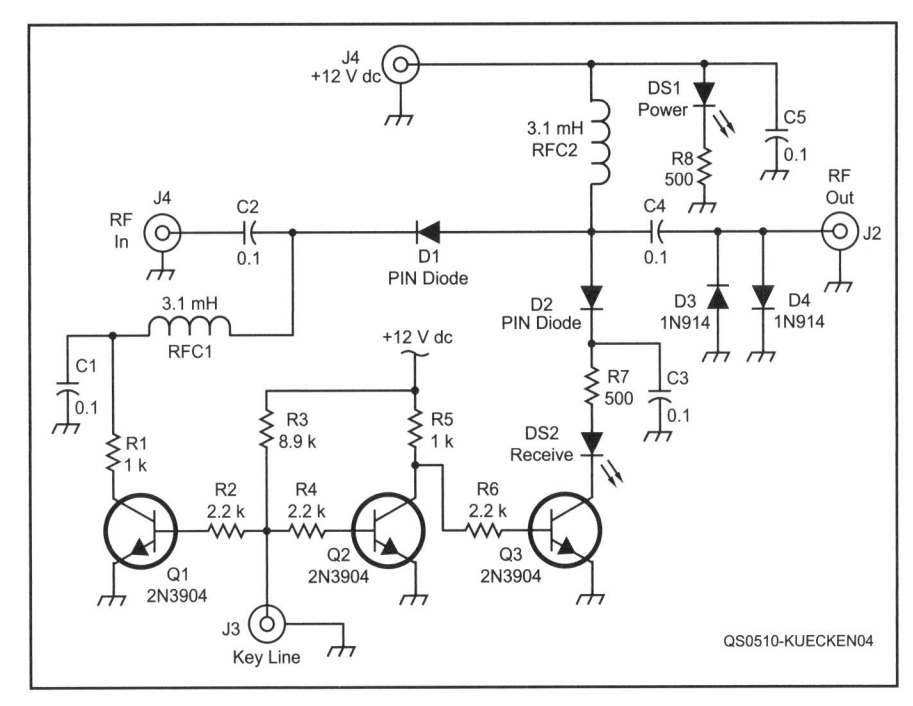

Figure 13.66 — Schematic and parts list for the PIN diode TR switch. Resistors are ¼ W.

C1-C5 — 0.1 µF ceramic capacitor
D1, D2 — PIN diode
D3, D4 — Switching diode, 1N914 or equivalent
DS1, DS2 — LED
J1, J2 — Chassis mount BNC connector
J3, J4 — Chassis mount phono connector
Q1-Q3 — Small signal PNP transistor, 2N3904 or equivalent
RFC1, RFC2 — 3.1 mH RF choke, 225 turns #30 AWG enameled wire wound on a 5⁄16 inch diameter, 5⁄8 inch long plastic tube

ally fall into the category of transients in the receiver audio and turning on the transmitter too slowly to capture initial code elements, also known as "dot shortening." A review of the transceiver design from which this circuit is taken and of other homebuilt transceiver designs will illustrate the problem and the methods used to address it.

If full break-in TR switching is required, high-speed switching components such as a reed relay or PIN diodes are required. KE2QJ provided a pair of such circuits (**Figure 13.65** and **Figure 13.66**) that can be adapted for internal use in a home-built transceiver, although their original purpose was to integrate a stand-alone receiver with a transceiver and linear amplifier. The full article is available with this book's downloadable supplemental content.

If you already have a receiver and transmitter and want to integrate them under the control of a separate TR switch, the K8IQY "Magic Box" (**www.4sqrp.com/MagicBox.php**) is available as a kit. This is a microprocessor-controlled design that can handle up to 10 W of transmitter power, switches at up to 50 WPM, and includes an audio sidetone output, as well. Complete documentation for the kit is available online, including schematics and design information. The kit could be extended to handle more transmit power with heavier components and the appropriate circuit changes.

TR SWITCHING WITH A LINEAR AMPLIFIER

Virtually every amateur HF transceiver includes a rear panel jack called something along the lines of KEY OUT, intended to provide a contact closure while in transmit mode. This jack is intended to connect to a corresponding jack on a linear amplifier called something like KEY IN. Check the transceiver and amplifier manuals to find out what they are called on your units. A diagram of the proper cabling to connect the transceiver and amplifier will be provided in the manual.

AMPLIFIER-TRANSCEIVER COMPATIBILITY

While you're there, check the ratings to find out how much voltage and current the transceiver can safely switch. In earlier days, this switching was usually accomplished by relay contacts. More modern radios tend to use solid-state devices to perform the function. Although recent amplifiers are usually compatible with the switching capabilities of current transceivers, the voltage and/or current required to switch the relays in an older linear amplifier may exceed the ratings. Fortunately, it is pretty easy to find out what your amplifier requires, and almost as easy to fix if it's not compatible with your radio.

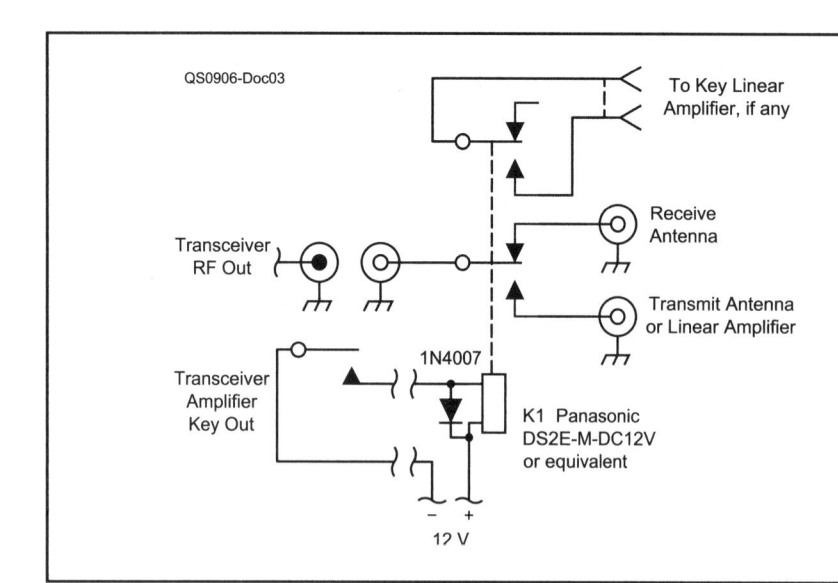

Figure 13.67 — Schematic of an external box that allows a modern transceiver to key a linear amplifier with TR switch voltage or current requirements that exceed the transceiver's ratings. As a bonus, it can also be used to allow reception from a low-noise receiving antenna.

If your amplifier manual doesn't say what the switching voltage is, you can find out with a multimeter or DMM. Set the meter to read voltage in a range safe for 250 V dc or higher. Connect the positive meter probe to amplifier key jack's center conductor, and connect the negative meter probe to the chassis ground (or other key jack terminal if it's not grounded). This will tell you what the open circuit voltage is on the amplifier key jack. You may need to try a lower voltage range, or an ac range, or switch the probes (if the key line is a negative dc voltage) to get a reading.

Now set the meter to read current. Start with a range that can read 1 A dc, and with the leads connected as before, you should hear the amplifier relay close and observe the current needed to operate the TR relay or circuit. Adjust the meter range, if needed, to get an accurate reading.

These two levels, voltage and current, are what the transceiver will be asked to switch. If *either* reading is higher than the transceiver specification, do not connect the transceiver and amplifier together. Doing so will likely damage your transceiver. You will need a simple interface circuit to handle the amplifier's switching voltage and current.

The simple, low-cost relay circuit shown in **Figure 13.67** can be used to key an older amplifier with a modern transceiver. It offers an added benefit: Another potential use of the transceiver KEY OUT jack is to switch to a separate low-noise receive antenna on the lower bands. While most high-end transceivers have a separate receive-only antenna connection built in, many transceivers don't. If you don't need one of the extra functions, just leave off those wires.

13.11 References and Bibliography

See also the list of Books in the **Receiving** chapter references along with a list of articles about Mixers.

J. Grebenkemper, KI6WX, "Phase Noise and its Effect on Amateur Communications," *QST*, Part 1, Mar 1988, pp 14-20; Part 2, Apr 1988, pp 22-25.

J. Hallas, W1ZR, *Basic Radio* (ARRL, 2005).

W. Hayward, W7ZOI, R. Campbell, KK7B, and B. Larkin, W7PUA, *Experimental Methods in RF Design* (ARRL, 2003).

W. Hayward, W7ZOI, "Crystal Oscillator Experiments," Technical Correspondence, *QST*, Jul 2006, pp 65-66.

W. Hayward, W7ZOI, and D. DeMaw, W1FB (SK), *Solid State Design for the Radio Amateur* (ARRL, 1977), pp 26-27.

B. P. Lathi, *Modern Digital and Analog Communication Systems*, Oxford University Press.

D. Pozar, *Microwave Engineering*, Fourth Edition (John Wiley and Sons, 2012).

I. Rosu, YO3DAC/VA3IUL, "RF Power Amplifiers," **www.qsl.net/va3iul**.

W. Sabin, WØIYH, "A 455 kHz IF Signal Processor for SSB/CW," *QEX*, Mar/Apr 2002, pp 11-16.

W. Sabin and E. Schoenike, Editors, *Single-Sideband Systems and Circuits* (McGraw-Hill, 1987).

W. Sabin, WØIYH, "RF Clippers for SSB," *QST*, Jul 1967, pp 13-18.

W. Silver, NØAX, Hands-On Radio, Experiment #174 "Switching Amplifiers," *QST*, July 2017, pp. 58-59.

J. Scarlett, KD7O, "A High-Performance Digital-Transceiver Design," Parts 1-3, *QEX*, Jul/Aug 2002, pp 35-44; Mar/Apr 2003, pp 3-12; and Nov/Dec 2003, pp 3-11.

M. Schwartz, *Information Transmission, Modulation and Noise*, Third edition (McGraw-Hill, 1980).

Contents

14.1 Signal Chains in SDR Transceivers
    14.1.1 Receive Signal Chain
    14.1.2 Transmit Signal Chain
14.2 User Interfaces
    14.2.1 The Panadapter Display
    14.2.2 The Waterfall Display
    14.2.3 User Control Interfaces

14.3 Configuration and Control Interfaces
    14.3.1 Icom CI-V
    14.3.2 CAT (Computer Aided Transceiver) Interface
14.4 SDR Design Tools
    14.4.1 *GNU Radio*
    14.4.2 FPGA Data Engines

**Chapter 14 —
Downloadable Supplemental Content**

- "Digital Signal Processing and GNU Radio Companion" by John Petrich, W7FU
- "Digital Signal Processing (DSP) Projects: Examples of GNU Radio and GRC Functionality" by John Petrich, W7FU, and Tom McDermott, N5EG
- Hands-On SDR, *QEX* columns by Scotty Cowling, WA2DFI
- Chapter 14 – Audio Oscillator example.grc *GNU Radio* design file
- Also see the **Transmitting** chapter downloadable supplemental content for transmitter and transceiver projects from previous *ARRL Handbooks*.

Chapter 14

Transceiver Design Topics

This chapter is intended to capture system-level concerns that deal with integrating the functions of receiving and transmitting into an effective transceiver. It is anticipated that this chapter will grow as more material becomes available along with the expansion of SDR technology in Amateur Radio. Innovations in digital systems and networks by amateurs will also find an initial home in this *Handbook* chapter. Since the topics are not expected to overlap, reference sections will be created for each topic if appropriate.

This edition's chapter primarily includes high-level material on SDR design. Steve Hicks, N5AC, contributed the sections on signal chains and interfaces. John Petrich, W7FU, updated the introductory material on *GNU Radio* and expanded the list of reference materials. The additional short introduction to FPGA data engines is based on the series of *QEX* columns "Hands-On SDR" by Scotty Cowling, WA2DFI.

There is a great of deal of material that doesn't fit neatly into the categories of receiving, transmitting, DSP/SDR fundamentals, or any of the major radio functions. This information is still required, however, to integrate all of the functions into a single package — the transceiver. There are questions of architecture, interfaces, development tools, and many other topics that must be addressed to build an effective transceiver or communications system. That is the purpose of this general-purpose chapter, to create a home in the *Handbook* for material that would be inappropriate for a chapter focused on a particular aspect of the radios themselves. Amateur Radio is poised at the threshold of great innovation and change — it's a bright future!

14.1 Signal Chains in SDR Transceivers

In an SDR, most work in both transmit and receive signal processing is performed in a computing or processing element that operates on digital samples. **Figure 14.1** shows a simplistic diagram of a transceiver setup for phone operation. Looking first at the transmit side of the radio, the analog microphone audio is converted to digital samples in an analog to digital converter (ADC). These digital samples are passed to the processing element where they enter the *transmit signal chain*. The transmit signal chain typically has a series of functional blocks that perform various functions on the signal including the modulator. While it is possible to use a purely digital exciter, most radios then pass the digital samples into a digital to analog converter (DAC) which turns the digital signal back into analog form. The resulting analog signal is amplified by an RF power amplifier and transmitted through the antenna.

In the receiver, the direction of flow is the opposite: analog RF data enters through the antenna and is turned into digital signals in an ADC. This data is passed to the receive *signal chain* where it is filtered, demodulated and processed into a signal we can hear. In some digital modes, such as RTTY, the demodulated signals are filtered and turned directly into digital symbols without ever being turned back into analog. For modes that we are expected to hear, the digital samples are sent into a codec where a DAC turns them back into analog for playback through headphones, speakers, or via a line-level output.

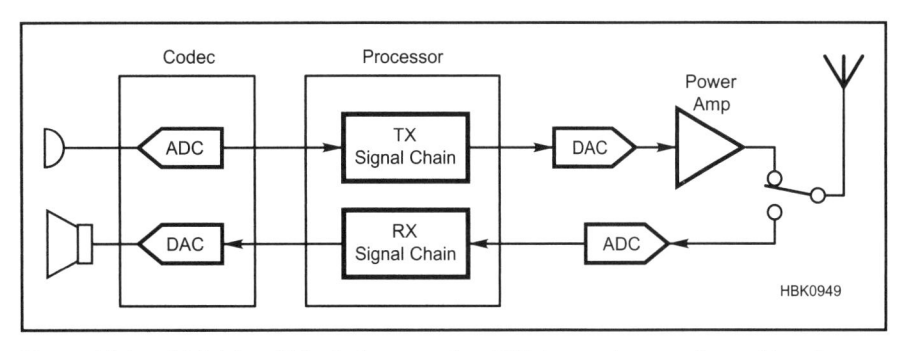

Figure 14.1 — A high-level block diagram of an SDR transceiver configured for phone operation.

The transmit signal chain and receive signal chain are at the heart of an SDR. Let's take a closer look at how they operate.

14.1.1 Receive Signal Chain

Most receivers will capture more digital samples than are needed for a single receiver. This can happen for many reasons. For example, we might have a wideband sampling receiver that captures a substantial portion of the spectrum and places several receivers in that spectrum. In this case, each individual narrowband receiver only requires a portion of the captured data. When we use the term narrowband receiver, we're talking about a receiver that will be used to demodulate signals in a 50-20,000 Hz slice of the RF spectrum. In another example, the receiver might be designed using an analog or digital mixing technique that reduces the bandwidth to an "audio" range (such as 0-192 kHz). The radio may preserve this larger bandwidth to plot a spectrum display, but will reduce it for narrowband receiver processing.

To understand the next steps, it's important to first understand the relationship between sampling rate and available bandwidth. Generally, in a sampled RF system we will either be using real or complex samples. (See the **DSP and SDR Fundamentals** chapter) *Real samples* will be used for audio input and output. Real samples consist of a single fixed or floating point number that represents each sample.

According to the Nyquist sampling theorem, we can represent at most one half of our sampling rate in bandwidth. For example, if we sample a microphone signal at 48 ksps (real samples), we can represent audio from 0-24 kHz. As a practical matter, the filters we use to process the audio will have a transition band that will further restrict this to something around 20 kHz.

If we sample using the in-phase and quadrature sampling (I/Q) commonly used in RF systems, then each sample consists of a pair of fixed or floating point numbers, one for I and one for Q. This is also commonly referred to as *complex sampling*. In a complex sampled system, sample speed and sampled bandwidth are equal, ignoring filter transition bands. For example, if the sample rate is 48 ksps (complex samples), the samples can represent almost of 48 kHz of RF spectrum (again accounting for filter transition bands). For a better understanding of the reasons behind these general rules there are several excellent references including Richard Lyons' book *Understanding Digital Signal Processing* that can be consulted. (See the Reference sections of the **DSP and SDR Fundamentals**, **Receiving**, and **Transmitting** chapters for a comprehensive set of references rather than reproducing them in this chapter.)

In either situation, the primary need to reduce the bandwidth for the receiver signal chain is driven by the processing resources required to process the receiver signals. The more bandwidth that is captured digitally, the higher the sampling rate and consequently the more processing power required in our signal chain. If we plan to ultimately discard the extra bandwidth in a filter, then we are wasting valuable processing resources by processing a wider bandwidth than we ultimately need.

In any of these cases, our first step is generally to reduce the bandwidth of the incoming signals through decimation. (See the **DSP and SDR Fundamentals** chapter) By decimation, we reduce the number of samples in the receiver by combining multiple samples and producing an output that has fewer samples, but with more bits per sample (greater bit width). After decimation, the receiver will typically have a sampling rate of somewhere between 24 and 48 ksps. We will then process all elements of our signal chain at this rate. While this is not strictly necessary, it is the most convenient. If our sampling rate varies in each block of our signal chain, we will be constantly buffering and re-sampling, again wasting valuable time and computing resources.

A typical receiver signal chain is shown in **Figure 14.2**, again computing from right to left. (This is the same direction as signal flow in the block labeled "Receive Signal Chain" in Figure 14.1.) Each DSP block in the chain will take input samples, generally in a buffer or block of samples, process the samples using the algorithm for the block, and then pass the resulting samples to the next block. It is a requirement of the receive signal chain that all blocks are processed in less than the time it takes before another buffer of samples arrives.

What does this mean? Let's say that our system is running at 48 ksps and our sample buffers are 512 samples each. We will receive a new buffer every 10.67 ms. If we are not able to process the next sample buffer because we are still processing the last buffer we received, then the buffers will stack up forming a queue of samples needing processing. Even worse, our DAC at the output of the signal chain has the responsibility for turning a stream of sample buffers into a continuous audio signal. If we "starve" it by not sending a buffer when it has exhausted the previous buffer, it will be forced to play empty audio or repeat previous buffers. If you've ever used digital electronics built this way, you've likely experienced the effects first-hand. Here are some examples of how other engineers dealt with a similar problem:

1. In XM satellite radio, when the satellite signal is briefly lost some satellite radios play "comfort noise," a low-level hiss that sounds like a normal AM or FM signal that has faded away. This noise is completely synthetic and doesn't represent any actual noise in the receiver. Since the source signal is digital, the receiver knows when the signal has faded and could easily play "blank audio," but it was probably judged that this sound would best convey to the consumer that the radio is working, but has lost a signal.

2. Many CD players, when starved for digital data from the disc due to a scratch and the inability to recover the signal, will replay the contents of the last digital buffer, resulting in a repetitive sound reminiscent of a skipping vinyl record player. This sound conveys to traditional (analog) vinyl users that there is a problem with the disc. (Data however, does not warp when left in the sunlight on a vehicle's back seat!)

It is, therefore, important to budget processing power to ensure all blocks can be processed in the time it takes to collect a new buffer. If our radio has more than one receiver, but a single processing element, our requirement will be to process all the DSP blocks for all receivers in the requisite time for a single buffer. While beyond the scope of this discussion, it's worth mentioning that multi-core processors, both symmetric and asymmetric, can provide a platform for some unique solutions that stagger or pipeline DSP blocks and receivers and allow spreading the processing requirements across different cores.

PASS-BAND FILTER

Next, we filter the buffered data. The filter removes unneeded signals from the buffer, limiting it to just our bandwidth of interest, called the *receiver pass-band*. Since the samples entering the filter are 48 ksps of I/Q data, we start out with something on the order of 40 kHz of audio bandwidth. If we are using sideband, we're only typically interested in a bandwidth of 2-5 kHz. If we're using CW we might want to reduce the bandwidth down to 50-100 Hz. The filter achieves this reduction in bandwidth by employing DSP filtering techniques. (See the **Analog and Digital Filtering** chapter)

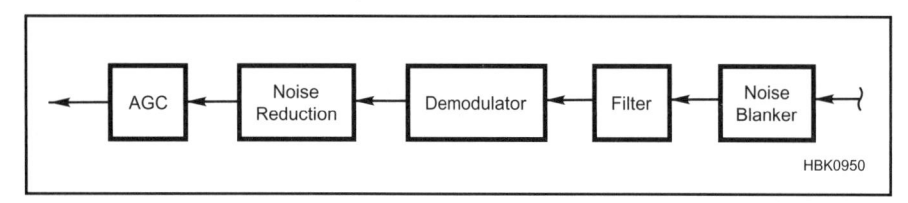

Figure 14.2 — Typical functional blocks that make up a receive signal chain.

The filter may need to accumulate several buffers of time-domain samples before performing the filter processing depending on how steep or sharp the filter skirts are required to be in order to create the filter's required shape factor. As mentioned previously, it is also required that once we have accumulated the requisite buffers, we must process the filter within the duration of our buffering. For example, if our buffer size is 512 samples and we are using an overlap-and-save FIR filter with 2048 taps, we will need to accumulate 2048 samples before processing the filter. After this, 1024 samples will be added to the filter for the next processing, since 1024 samples are saved from the last processing. In aggregate, we must be able to process this filter in under 1024/48 ksps = 20.3 ms of CPU time (including all other signal chain operations).

Filters used in receivers can be of many different topologies including finite impulse response (FIR) and infinite impulse response (IIR). Even within these two broad categories there are a plenty of additional variations that affect passband and stop-band ripple, phase distortion (detrimental to some digital modes), group delay, and other parameters. Also, this filter which is often called the *final filter* since it is the last filter before the signals are presented to the operator, will determine a significant part of the receiver latency (the delay between the input of an RF signal to the output of the data or audio). Why is this? The slower the sampling rate, the more impact collecting samples and filtering them will have on latency.

Some radios allow the operator to make tradeoffs in filter parameters, favoring low latency at one time and favoring the best filtering at another. A sizable FIR filter using 4096 taps will add roughly 1.5 x 4096 / 48 ksps = 128 ms of latency. This is not a large amount for phone conversations, but would be significant for CW contesting.

One of the great triumphs of SDR is that we have eliminated our dependency on needing a collection of electronic or mechanical filters. We now have continuously variable filters that let us tailor our pass-band to meet our operating demands without worrying about the design cost or space for our old electronic and mechanical filter collection. In some radios, we can also adjust the taps in the filter to select better filter shape factor or lower latency as our operations dictate.

DEMODULATOR

The demodulator performs the conversion of on-air signal to the baseband audio signal that we will be hearing. For example, with FM we must convert a fixed-amplitude carrier changing frequency according to the amplitude of the audio into a time-domain amplitude-varying signal that we can understand with our ears and brain. The output of the demodulator is audio that we can hear and understand.

The demodulator block is selected based on the mode being used. When you change the mode of the radio on the front panel, you are switching one demodulator with another for the mode you have just selected. Of course, the filtering and noise mitigation techniques may vary by mode also, and so we may be switching other blocks in the DSP chain based on the requirements of each mode.

14.1.2 Transmit Signal Chain

For phone, the transmit signal chain will prepare spoken audio for transmission over the air. If our mode is CW or other digital modes, the transmit signal chain will be very different, perhaps just a single or a pair of software oscillators that produce the tones that we will send on air. **Figure 14.3** shows a typical signal chain for phone transmission.

GAIN

Depending on how the designer has implemented the ability to change output power in the radio, a gain stage may exist at the start of the signal chain that can be adjusted to raise or lower the power of the transmitter. This gain stage could be implemented at other places in the radio as well. A gain stage will multiply all samples in the buffer by an input level value, raising or lowering the level of all audio samples in the buffer.

EQUALIZATION

In a software defined radio, it is easy to isolate frequency bands in an audio buffer and allow each band's relative power to be raised or lowered. This equalization function can be used to tailor a person's voice to produce the best sound on the receiving end. This function is known as equalization or simply EQ. The input to the equalization function is the relative increase or decrease for each band of interest. A typical equalizer panel with vertical sliders for each audio band is shown in **Figure 14.4**. At the output of the equalization stage, we have audio prepared for transmission, but it may exceed required output levels that have been set in the radio. For example, we may independently have set a maximum output power for the radio to prevent overshooting an amplifier input. This is where a clipper becomes useful.

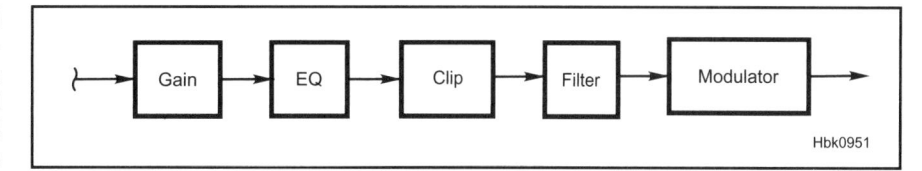

Figure 14.3 — Typical functional blocks that make up a transmit signal chain.

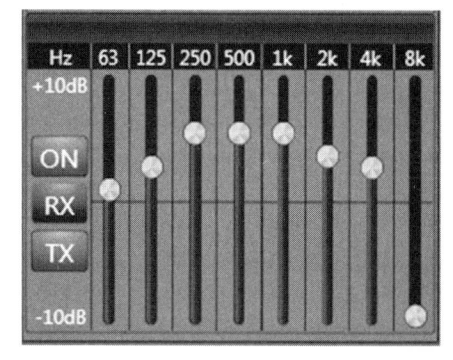

Figure 14.4 — An equalizer control window showing the adjustments for each frequency band of interest.

CLIPPER / ALC

A clipper may be employed to reduce the level of any signals that exceed required power levels. It generally does this by checking each sample in the buffer for the maximum allowable level and replacing any samples that exceed the threshold with a corresponding sample of the maximum level, thereby clipping the peak value of that sample.

While clipping can produce undesirable effects, it may be necessary to prevent the radio from operating outside the limits provided by the operator. Automatic level control (ALC) may also be used to reduce signal levels if a downstream amplifier provides voltage to the radio requesting a lowering of the levels.

Generally, a series of meter displays or values derived at different stages in the signal chain will provide the operator with information on undesired effects occurring within the signal chain. This allows the operator to make adjustments to correct any undesired effects. Since we have absolute control over the signal level by altering samples in the radio, it is generally better to set a maximum power out in the radio and allow the signal chain to make the appropriate adjustments than to rely on ALC to adjust the levels when they are too high for an amplifier.

An ALC subsystem that is too active can modulate the transmit signal. This results in distortion that could be prevented by adjusting the proper levels in the signal chain to start with. This is why many digital mode guidelines specify that the ALC system be switched off — to avoid unintentional distortion of the signal by power control systems.

FILTER

Since our audio input may contain frequency components well above those required or that comply with good practices, a filter is employed to remove them. For normal SSB operation, we could set the filter to pass audio from 100 Hz–2.8 kHz. For Extended Signal Sideband (ESSB), we may set the filter to pass audio from 50 Hz-4 kHz or more. The transmit filter setting may also be set to comply with communication laws in the country where the transmission is occurring.

The filter will remove the unneeded frequency components of the signal before transmission using similar DSP techniques to those in the receive signal chain filter.

MODULATOR

The modulator will then take the audio signal and create a modulated RF or IF signal required by the operating mode. The modulator takes care of placing the audio in the proper sideband for SSB, producing the carrier for AM and performing frequency modulation for FM. After modulation, the signal is ready to be transmitted.

SUMMARY

Signal chains are the heart of the software defined radio. This overview provides the basics of how a signal chain is put together and the requirements on each of the DSP functions. A typical signal chain in an SDR may have many more blocks including blocks to meter samples, providing valuable feedback to the operator, more audio tailoring and filtering blocks, oscillators for in-air testing, speech compressors, and so on.

14.2 User Interfaces

Many years ago, the knob we used to tune our radios was often attached to a frequency indicator stenciled on a piece of plastic that would rotate into view as the knob was turned. The plastic marker displayed an offset into a band selected by a band switch. The strength of any incoming signal would be displayed on an S meter, a magnetic meter movement excited by the voltage from the AGC circuit. In the 1970s and 1980s, the *liquid crystal display* (LCD) and *light emitting diode* (LED) display came into popularity and most radio manufacturers adopted some form of display device that used LCD and or LEDs. Both technologies were used to show frequency, mode selections, and simulated S meters without their mechanical counterparts.

These technologies of the past provided only minimal *situational awareness*. We only had a narrow view of the spectrum limited to the instruments at hand showing us the signal strength in our narrow receiver along with a display of our current frequency. There was no way to see how many signals were on the band, how strong they were, whether the noise floor in the band was rising, or if we might just be listening where some local noise was causing us interference.

With *panadapters* now available on modern transceivers, we can see all the signals across the band. Finding a place to call CQ can be difficult when the bands are busy. With a panadapter, we can glance at the band and notice where there are gaps, quickly tune to an empty frequency, and call CQ. We can also instantly tell where the strong and weak signals are in the band. If we're looking for signals arriving at our location through particular propagation, we can search for signals that look alike or share the similar power levels.

The *waterfall display* provides the same information with a time-historical twist. In the waterfall we can see how signals and noise are changing over time. Imagine working a DX pileup where a few hundred amateurs are all trying to work the same station. We can watch the DX station systematically contact every station and observe the operating patterns. We know where the DX station is listening because we can see each station in the pileup respond to the DX station as they are called. Observing this pattern, we now know where the DX will listen next and can simply drop our call in this location and make the contact. Those enjoying panadapters today lament: how did we survive without this capability?

The tools available today for gaining a situational awareness of the bands and our receiver have dramatically changed. Let's look at each of these tools in some more detail.

14.2.1 The Panadapter Display

The *panadapter*, or spectrum display, shown in **Figure 14.5** displays the amplitude

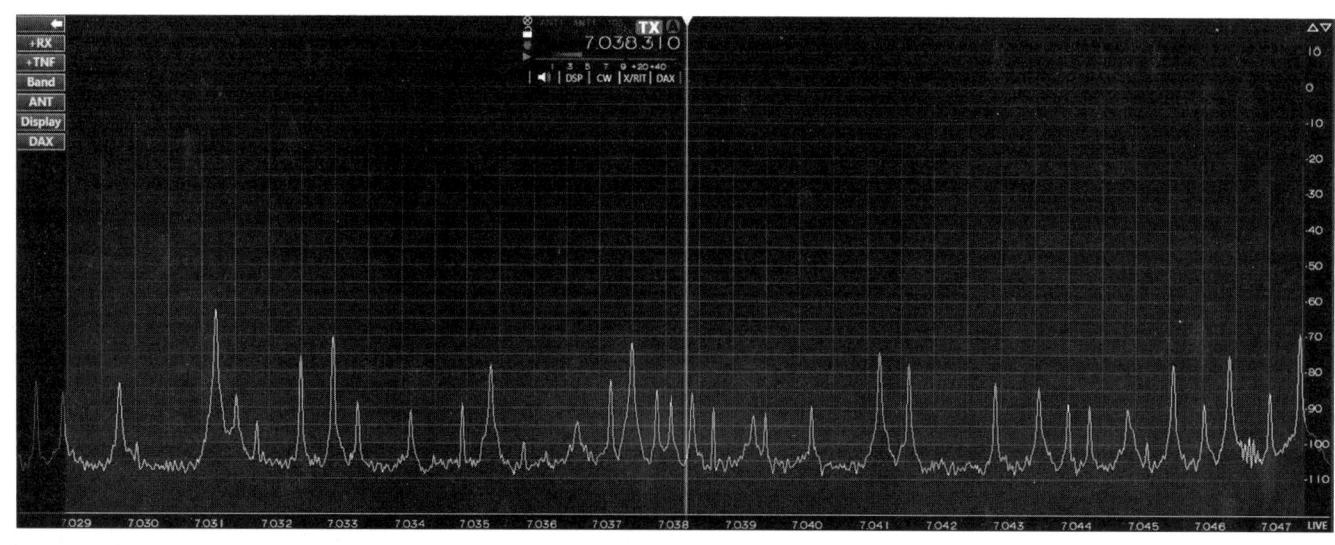

Figure 14.5 — A typical panadapter display showing a number of signals over about 18 kHz of the 40 meter CW segment.

of signals across a range of frequencies. The panadapter's design roots come from spectrum analyzers that were designed in the 1950s and 1960s. These instruments featured a swept receiver that tuned across the band. As the receiver tuned the band, the signal level in the receiver was captured and displayed. The resulting display is a graph with frequency on the x-axis and amplitude on the y-axis.

The spectrum analyzer has proven its worth in many areas from radio design and troubleshooting to the analysis of on-air interference problems. The almost-continuous view of the spectrum allows the operator to quickly understand the spectrum and act accordingly. A spectrum analyzer's controls allow alteration of the bandwidth of the sweep receiver, known as *resolution bandwidth (RBW)*, the *sweep rate* of the receiver, the total bandwidth displayed and other parameters. (See the **Test Measurements and Equipment** chapter for more details about spectrum analyzers.)

In the absence of a signal, the swept receiver would return the higher of the noise from the input port of the analyzer or the spectrum analyzer's noise floor. This noise floor visualized or painted is partly a function of the bandwidth of the sweep receiver itself: the wider the bandwidth, the more noise was input to the receiver and the higher the noise floor appears. If the noise floor visualized on the sweep was higher than signals of interest, the resolution bandwidth of the receiver could be lowered, reducing the noise let into the receiver and lowering the noise floor of the display.

In the absence of a signal and assuming evenly distributed noise, the noise floor will drop by 3 dB each time the resolution bandwidth is halved since the total noise in the receiver was cut in half by the bandwidth filter. Typically, as the display is "zoomed in" to show less bandwidth on the screen, the instrument will automatically reduce the receiver bandwidth in the sweep (resolution bandwidth) and the noise floor of the display will drop. The swept receiver approach to a spectrum display is used in radios designed in the early 2000s, such as the Icom 756 Pro-series.

The swept receiver design has some key drawbacks, though. First, time is required for the receiver to settle, a measurement to be taken, and the receiver tuned to the next frequency. This limits the speed at which the receiver can tune and often results in a slow "painting" of the display that lacks the full-motion look of modern panadapters.

The slower sweep rate reduces situational awareness. For example, imagine someone sitting sending a series of CW dits. In the swept design, the receiver will typically hear a signal or no signal as it passes the CW dit signal. We will either see a nice signal out of the noise – or nothing – depending on the timing of the dits in relation to our sweep receiver. With a modern panadapter refreshing many times per second, we can see the signal rise and fall with the CW dits, giving us a clear view of what's going on.

The second drawback of the swept receiver design is the tradeoff between sweep speed and resolution bandwidth. As we reduce RBW to see more detail in the spectrum, the sweep rate must slow because the measurement takes longer; primarily because the narrower filter requires more time for signals to pass through and stabilize before the measurement takes place. The more detail we want to see, the slower our display updates, and the lower our situational awareness.

Today's transceiver panadapter displays are built on many of the same principles of the spectrum analyzer with one notable exception: today's receiver panadapters are almost always built from a Fast Fourier Transform or FFT (See the **DSP and SDR Fundamentals** chapter). The FFT accepts a wide bandwidth of time domain samples from an analog-to-digital converter and translates the time-domain signals into the frequency spectrum.

PANADAPTER TYPES

There are two main panadapter types available in current amateur products; the *dependent* and *independent* panadapter. In a dependent panadapter design, the data for the panadapter is from the receiver's IF signal. In this scenario, the panadapter will always show the spectrum to either side of our received frequency which is shown in the center. For example, if the panadapter display spans 192 kHz, our receive frequency will be in the center and we will see 96 kHz of spectrum on either side of the receiver.

In contrast, an independent display operates independently of the receiver. The panadapter display frequencies can be moved and the received frequency can be moved without being in the center of the display. This allows showing a DX pileup with the DX station on the left, the pileup on the right and tune our transmitter across the pileup without shifting the spectrum display. Internally, this requires a separate receiver just for the panadapter that is tuned independent of the receiver(s) in the radio.

The FFT used to build the panadapter is always measured in *points* or *bins*, each of which is essentially a collection of receiver channels like our sweep receiver in the spectrum analyzer. The bins are spaced evenly across the range of frequencies output by the FFT. The bandwidth of each bin is determined by the total sampling width presented to the FFT divided by the number of FFT points. For example, if our input is 192 kilosamples per second (abbreviated ksps), and we use a 4096-point FFT, each bin of the FFT would represent a receiver that is 192,000 / 4096 = 46.875 Hz in width. In other words, each point in the display of our FFT represents the signal and noise heard by a receiver with a bandwidth of about 47 Hz. In this way, you can think of the panadapter as a series of equally spaced S meters, laying on their sides continually showing the signal level in each of our FFT bins.

To compute an FFT for a panadapter, the FFT must first collect enough time-domain samples to fill the input registers of the FFT. Using the previous example, a 4096-point FFT required 4096 time-domain input samples in order to create a 4096-point frequency-domain output. For a receiver operating at 192 ksps, the time required to collect these samples is 4096 / 192,000 = 21.3 ms. After this time, the FFT can be computed and a *frame* can be displayed for the operator. The maximum possible frame rate for the display is the reciprocal of the time to fill the input. In this example, 1/21.3ms = 46.875 frames per second (46.875 Hz refresh or update rate). Note that this frame rate is exactly equal to the bin width of the FFT.

Considering a typical sideband signal with a bandwidth of 3 kHz, the panadapter just described would show 3,000 Hz / 46.875 Hz = 64 different points across the audio range of a received signal. Since a sideband signal is the audio in the operator's voice shifted in frequency to the RF spectrum, we can see the energy in the operator's voice at each of 64 different frequencies as the operator talks. Outside of the operator's intended transmit bandwidth we can also observe any RF that is transmitted unintentionally. This allows us to observe the cleanliness of signals on the band in significant detail.

Figure 14.6 shows a transmitted SSB signal that is fairly clean, that has little RF outside of the transmitted band of interest, and **Figure 14.7** shows a significantly less clean signal displaying splatter caused by an improperly configured amplifier. This capability is particularly useful for assisting another amateur to diagnose a transmitter that has signal anomalies. The visual representation of their transmission can make quick work of identifying intermodulation distortion, splatter, and other problems.

For CW or narrowband digital mode operation, a panadapter with a higher resolution than 47 Hz is desired. There are two ways to achieve higher resolution:

1. An increase in the number of points in the FFT directly reduces the bandwidth of each FFT bin, both lowering the noise floor and increasing the resolution.

2. A reduction in the bandwidth of the samples presented from the ADC also directly affects the resolution. For example, if we simultaneously reduce the ADC bandwidth to 96ksps and increase the FFT to 8192 points, our bin size is now 96,000 / 8192 = 11.7 Hz, a reduction factor of four in the bin size. The noise floor of the narrower bin will decrease by 6 dB as well.

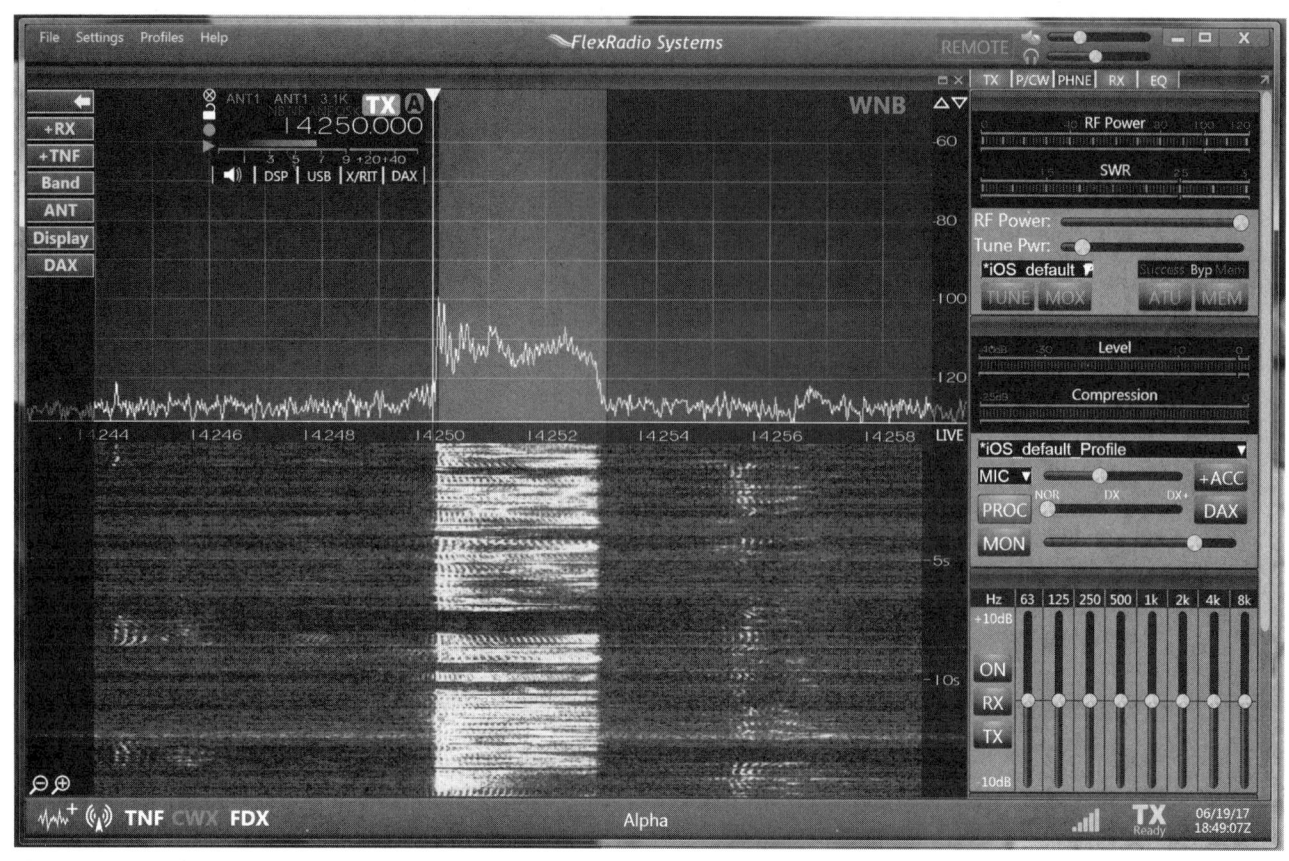

Figure 14.6 — A panadapter display showing a cleanly transmitted SSB signal.

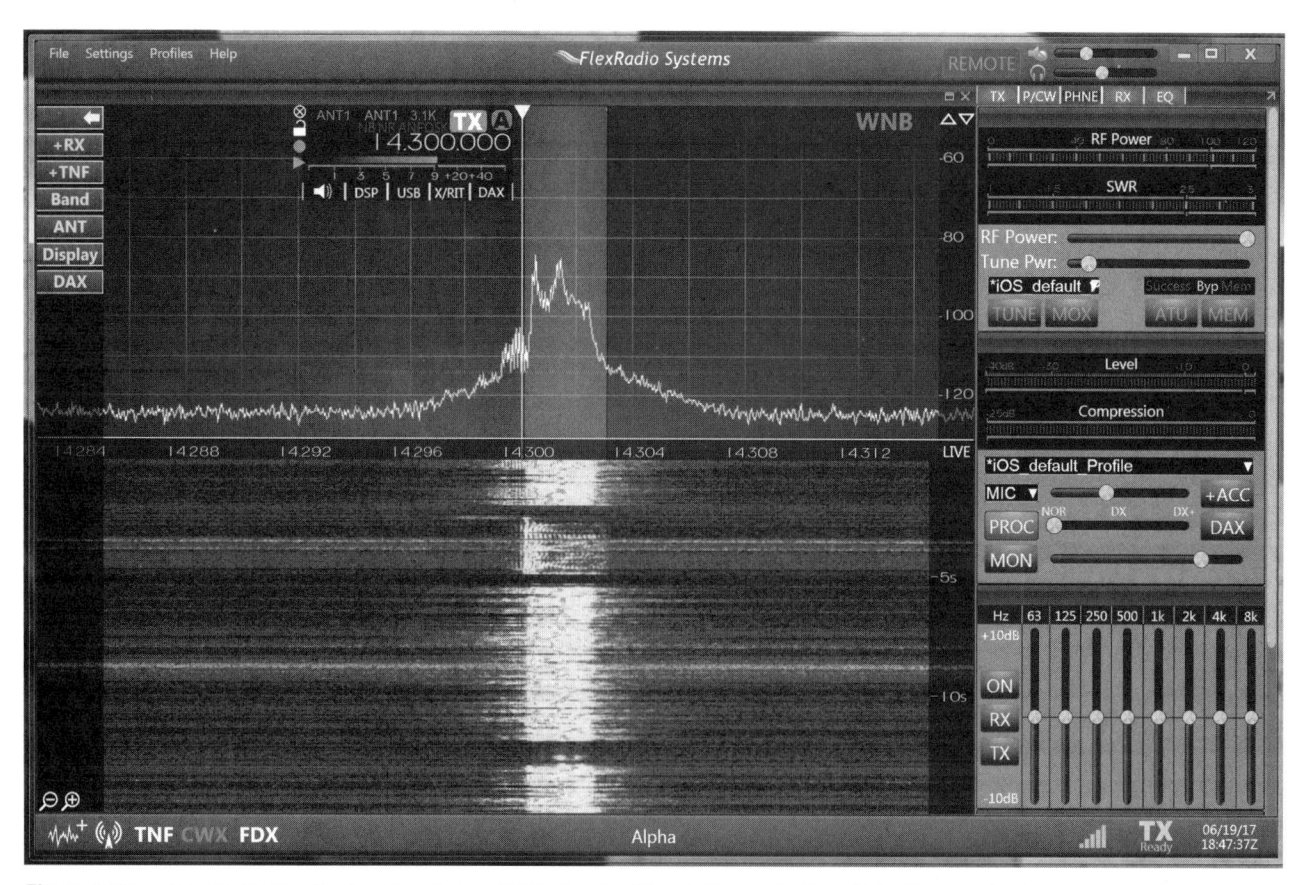

Figure 14.7 — A panadapter display showing an SSB signal with splatter and other distortion products.

The resulting display shows higher resolution but this comes at a price. First, the frame rate of our FFT is now 11.7 frames per second. This is because we must now collect 8192 / 96,000 = 85.3 ms of data before calculating the FFT. Also, because the FFT is now based on a larger time period of data, fine temporal (moment-to-moment) details are lost in the display. For example, a 60 WPM CW signal is composed of 20 ms dits and 20 ms spaces between elements. A string of dits at this speed could be visible as individual pulses in our first FFT example, but would be somewhat lost in the new FFT since several transitions would occur during each FFT frame. This time limit tends to place practical limits on how fine-grained an FFT can be used in a panadapter. The other practical limit is computational complexity. As the number of points in the FFT is increased, more computing power is required to calculate the FFT that is the basis for the panadapter.

How far we might "zoom in" to a panadapter display is a function of what we want to observe. For SSB with signals approximately 3 kHz wide, we often want to observe many tens of kilohertz of spectrum to get a good view of other signals on the bands. In contrast, with CW we might only want to see a few kHz of bandwidth to determine the exact frequency of each CW signal. With two-tone FSK (RTTY) and PSK (PSK31) signals, it can be helpful to see both components clearly to aid in tuning, but not at such a fine resolution that the display operates slowly or incurs temporal distortion. A properly designed modern panadapter will allow us to make these tradeoffs to get the panadapter tuned "just right" to give us the view of the spectrum we need to help most in our operating mode.

PANADAPTER CONSTRUCTION

There are several methods for building panadapter displays, but the two key pieces of a panadapter display are the receiver and the FFT. As mentioned earlier, dependent panadapters (**Figure 14.8A**) are derived from the same receiver we use to demodulate and copy stations we are trying to work. In this case, the primary decision is how wide to make the receiver (sampling rate) since this will determine the bandwidth of our panadapter.

In radio systems with dependent panadapters for which the processing of the receiver signal chain is performed on a PC, the designer must be careful to limit the panadapter bandwidth since all this data will need to be sent to the PC and processed using the PC's main CPU. The dependent panadapter architecture was invented with *PowerSDR* and first shown on the original FlexRadio transceivers such as the FLEX-5000. This panadapter architecture is also used in the HPSDR and several other radios.

With the independent panadapter architecture shown in Figure 14.8B, we see that the receiver and panadapters are separate. This architecture allows tuning the panadapter independently of the receiver and gives rise to more flexibility in setting up the panadapter display and receivers. The other key consideration is the rate of the sample stream from the receiver into the FFT. As discussed above, this affects the bin width of the display along with the refresh rate of the display. It also affects the amount of processing power required to process the raw data from the receiver. The wider the panadapter, the higher the sampling rate data is required to produce the display and the more computing power is required, assuming no loss of data.

To implement a "simple" panadapter display using the independent panadapter architecture, we could use a signal receiver with a bandwidth of, say 1 MHz, running into a FFT with 16,384 FFT points (the FFT algorithm requires the number of bins to be a power of two, in this case 2^{14}). This would give us bin sizes of 61 Hz. If our radio display has, say, a horizontal width of 600 pixels we can implement a zoom-in and zoom-out feature by simply discarding or using a MAX function across bins we are consolidating into a single pixel. This type of display will also have a consistent noise floor, commensurate with a 61 Hz receiver bandwidth.

To implement a more advanced panadapter using the independent panadapter architecture, we could implement a variable rate decimation function as shown in **Figure 14.9**. The decimator or resampler can take in a sample

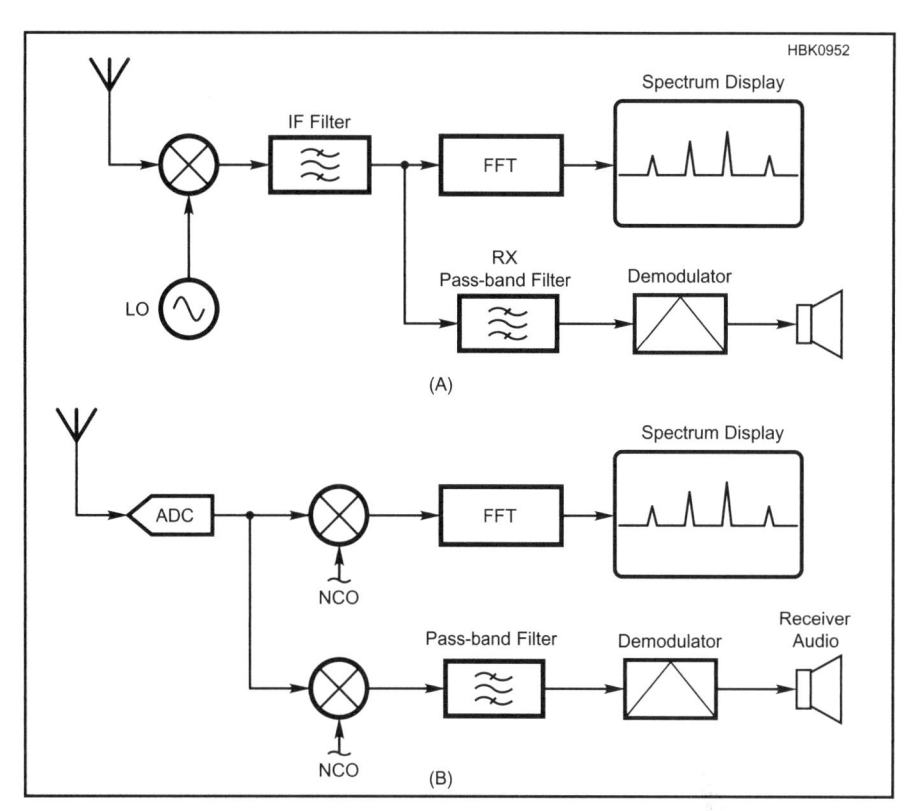

Figure 14.8 — Panadapter architecture. (A) Dependent architecture in which the panadapter and main receiver signal chain share common tuning and filtering mechanisms. The panadapter and receiver are tuned together. Dependent panadapters can be implemented both as superheterodyne and as direct sampling receivers. (B) shows an independent architecture in which the panadapter and receiver have their own signal chain. The panadapter and receiver can be tuned independently of each other.

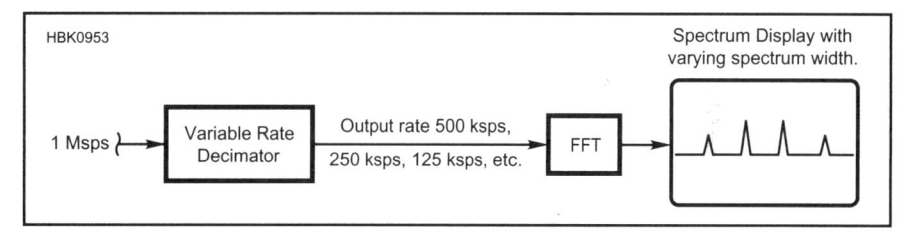

Figure 14.9 — Variable rate decimation.

stream at one sample rate and output a stream at other rates. In this way, we can zoom-in and zoom-out by varying the decimation rate. For example, let's assume out input rate to the decimator is 1 Mbps. We could output 1 Mbps, 500 kbps, 250 kbps, and so on. down to any rate we needed. This data could then be input to the same FFT function.

The resulting FFT output frame rate will be the input sampling rate divided by the number of FFT points and will have a bin width equal to the sampling rate divided by the number of bins (assuming I/Q input data). This architecture is used in the FLEX-6000 Signature Series transceivers and requires substantially more computing resources than the simple implementation, but provides a more capable panadapter that can expand to many MHz of spectrum or zoom in to just a few kHz.

PANADAPTER APPLICATIONS

The benefits of a panadapter can be wide-reaching. In the simplest of cases, the instantaneous view of the spectrum can quickly demonstrate where the band is and is not in use. Watching the band for just a few seconds gives the operator an idea for a good place to call CQ. It's always a good idea to check if the band is use before calling since only one side of a conversation may be audible from your QTH, but this same awareness of the band is difficult to achieve by spinning the dial.

When operating on microwave weak signal bands, it can be hard to find other signals. Rover (mobile) stations using crystal-controlled rigs in very cold or very hot weather may have drifted many kHz from their dial frequency due to the multiplicative effect of crystal error on higher bands and temperature changes in the rover. A panadapter makes quick work of locating these operators. A common methodology is to ask a rover to "send dashes" on a microwave band and then watch the waterfall for the tell-tale dashes to appear. Because signals deep into the 500 Hz noise floor can be seen on the waterfall display, we can see signals from stations before we can hear them and this can also be used to assist in pointing antennas. As a fixed station, we can tell the rover operator on a liaison frequency to rotate his antennas as we watch the panadapter for a rise or fall of signal strength. Some panadapters have increased their FFT bins to 2^{17} to reduce their bin size and allow them to see even further into the noise floor.

In contesting, there are often advantages to working stations in a particular order. For example, weaker stations that have reduced signals in the panadapter may be DX stations that would result in a multiplier. Stronger stations are easier to work and bagging these stations first might be a strategy worthy of consideration. In some sprint-style contests *running*, continually calling CQ on the band and working stations that respond to your CQ, is not permitted. Finding other stations quickly becomes paramount in this type of operating event. With a panadapter, finding stations quickly is simplified to looking for peaks in the panadapter display.

Interference in contests is a frequent problem and rapid identification and resolution of interference sources is important. An adjacent splattering station is obvious in a panadapter and can allow an operator to make a quick comment to the right station, asking for the other operator to check the transmitting equipment. In some situations, changing frequency may be required and again the panadapter can help locate where to move. From a competitive standpoint, having a panadapter is akin to having extra mirrors on a race car to see where other competitors are and what they are up to.

For panadapters displayed on a computer monitor, tuning can often be achieved by placing the a cursor on a signal or specific frequency and clicking. Quickly working stations in this manner bypasses the required tuning on traditional receivers. In this situation, the panadapter can provide a significant advantage. This is also true of panadapters on touch-screen devices where tuning can be accomplished by just tapping on a signal seen on the panadapter display.

Interference and noise are common in today's RF landscape. The panadapter offers the same capabilities of a spectrum analyzer by showing instantaneous views of the spectrum to help with isolation and characterization of noise. Some noise is limited to a narrow range of frequencies while other noise sources may repeat on a specific frequency interval. Knowing the repeating frequency interval of a noise source or the similarities of the noise across the band can aid in diagnosis of the type of noise. Some types of noise drift over time while others remain fairly constant with time. Other noise is broadbanded and raises the noise floor of the entire band. All of these different characteristics of noise can be easily observed in a panadapter, giving the amateur a thorough view of the type of noise under investigation.

14.2.2 The Waterfall Display

The *waterfall* display is similar to the panadapter in that it has frequency along the x-axis. The y-axis in a waterfall is time rather than amplitude as shown in **Figure 14.10**. The waterfall display is typically created line-by-line, starting at the top of the display. A new line is added to the display with each unit of time and all previous lines of the display are shifted down one line. In this way, the waterfall shows what has happened in the spectrum over time. It is this flowing motion of the waterfall that gives the display its name since it gives the impression of a band of slowly falling water.

Let's build on the earlier analogy of a panadapter as equally spaced S meters lying on their sides. Similarly, the waterfall display can be envisioned as a series of panadapter frames, equally spaced in time and lying on their sides so we view them "from the top." What we see in the waterfall is color or intensity representing the height of the signal (amplitude) in the panadapter. Each line of the waterfall has either different colors or different intensities on each frequency that represent the signal level from the panadapter during that period of time. Typically, brighter or more intense colors represent stronger signals. By looking at the waterfall display, we can see the occupation of frequencies across the spectrum over time. The historical view of the waterfall can assist

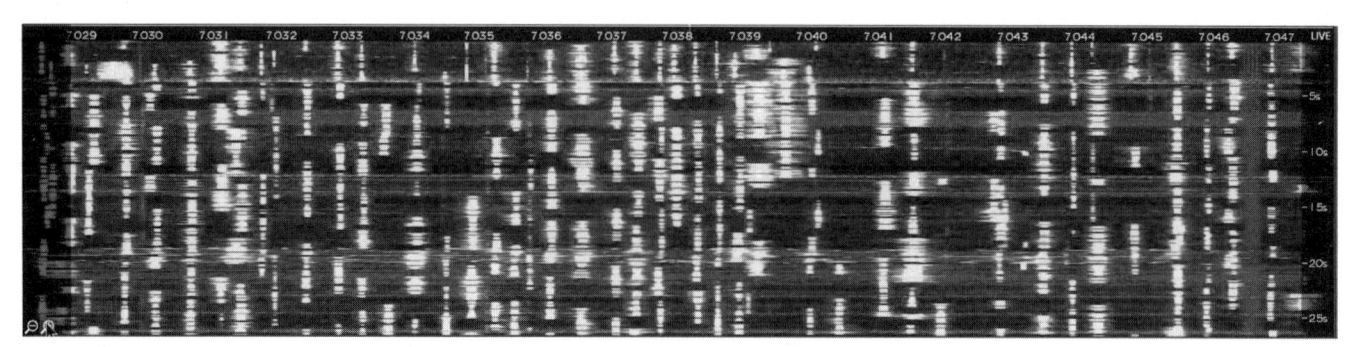

Figure 14.10 — A waterfall display showing the same spectrum as the panadapter in Figure 14.5 with CW and digital signals. More recent data is at the top of the display and signal strength is indicated by brightness.

in locating a frequency that is either has been or has not been in use depending on the need.

Like its cousin the panadapter, waterfall displays are also calculated from an FFT, sometimes from the same data used to produce the panadapter. The waterfall also uses the same FFT bins and follows the same rules as the panadapter. The noise floor visible in the waterfall is determined by the bin size of the FFT. The narrower the bins in the FFT, the less noise in the bin and the more weak signals can be observed in the waterfall. In Amateur Radio, we generally refer to the noise floor as the noise observed in a receiver with a 500 Hz bandwidth. If our FFT bin width is 50 Hz, our noise floor would be 10 dB lower, calculated as $10\log_{10}(500/50)$. Similarly, a 5 Hz bin would have a noise floor 20 dB lower than for a 500 Hz receiver bandwidth. To see signals "below the noise floor" is a useful capability in both the panadapter and waterfall displays.

The historical view of a waterfall can provide an additional level of information not always visible in a panadapter. Using the same microwave operating example, assume that we are attempting to hear 10 GHz signal from a microwave rover with the dish antenna slightly off our bearing. A common technique is to ask the rover to send a series of slow CW dashes "please send dashes" using a VHF liaison frequency. By watching the noise floor in the waterfall carefully, we may be able to see a faint line representing those dashes. We can then ask the rover to rotate the dish one way or the other and see if the intensity increases. The final outcome would hopefully be to align the dish where we can hear the rover.

Using an HF example, the waterfall can provide unique insight into the patterns used by a DXpedition station operator. Knowing these patterns and where the DX station is transmitting can help the DXer pick a frequency that is likely to be heard, and worked, by the DX station. For example, by observing the DX station working several stations across a pileup, the DXer can immediately put the information to use and "tailgate" the last contact hoping to work the DX entity before the listening frequency changes. Consistently locating the DX entity on a traditional receiver by spinning the dial is futile in comparison.

COMBINING THE PANADAPTER AND WATERFALL

A common way to show both a panadapter and a waterfall display at the same time is to position the panadapter above the waterfall, both lining up in frequency so that a common frequency axis is used for both. In this way, we can see what's happening now in the panadapter and what happened in the past in the waterfall.

A vast amount of information is presented to the operator with both displays present simultaneously. A short burst of noise heard in the receiver could be anything, but close examination of the panadapter and waterfall can show that it is a signal slowly moving across the spectrum (perhaps an ionosonde) or maybe it's a spread-spectrum signal that is 10 kHz wide moving around the ham bands. The difference will be apparent looking at a wider view of the waterfall and seeing the same signal move around the band. Most operators find that after using a panadapter and waterfall for a while they are not able to easily go back to using a radio without these features that enhance situational awareness.

14.2.3 User Control Interfaces

The front panel of the radio, referred to here as the *user interface* or simply, *interface*, provides for control, meters, status, frequency indicators and displays such as a panadapter and/or waterfall to visualize the spectrum. Typical controls allow for changing the frequency, mode, mode-specific settings and other features of the radio.

THICK CLIENTS

The SDR-1000, an amateur SDR designed by Gerald Youngblood, K5SDR, was featured in a 2002 series of *QEX* articles listed in the references for the **DSP and SDR Fundamentals** chapter. The SDR-1000 hardware did not have an interface itself, but relied instead on a computer program as its interface. This first SDR interface, *PowerSDR*, was designed to display the spectrum and control the radio. *PowerSDR* is not only the interface for the SDR-1000, it also performs all of the signal processing required to both modulate and demodulate audio and produce all of the spectrum and other displays in the software. This type of interface is known as a *thick client* in the computer industry. The term thick client is used when substantial work must be done in the client software. **Figure 14.11** shows how

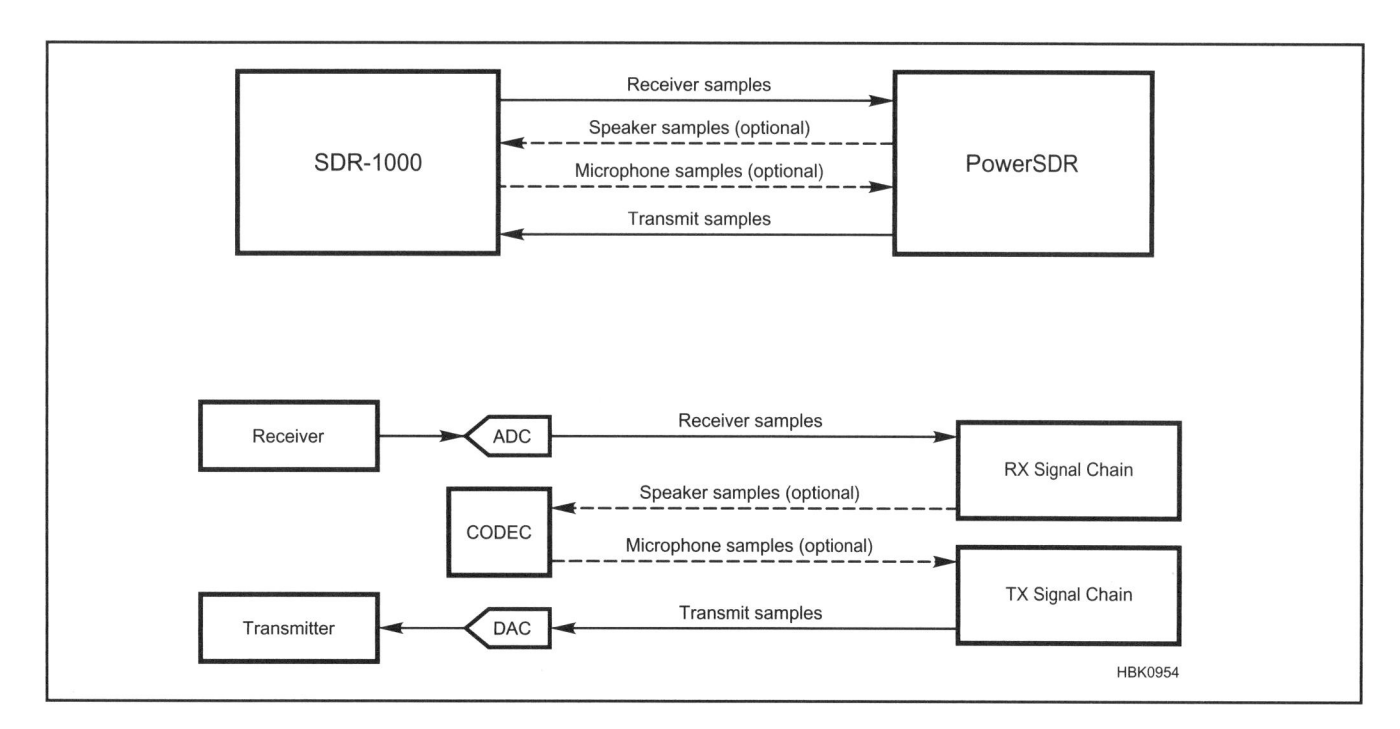

Figure 14.11 — A block diagram of the SDR-1000 showing the main data flows for signal processing.

the signal processing software in *PowerSDR* works with the radio.

There are generally four streams of real-time data that flow between a thick client and the SDR hardware:

1) Receiver samples are time-domain samples collected by the SDR hardware. The hardware itself can be direct-sampling, a superheterodyne (followed by an ADC), or direct conversion. The samples sent to the software for processing are generally in the range of 48 ksps to 384 ksps. Since the samples are often sent as both in-phase and quadrature (I/Q) and are often 16-32 bits each, a 384 ksps stream can contain as much as 25 Mbps of data.

2) The receiver samples are tuned, demodulated, filtered and ultimately provided to the radio hardware for audio output, usually from headphones or speakers.

3) Microphone samples are captured in the radio hardware and sent to the software for processing and preparation for transmission.

4) Transmit samples are sent from the software back to the radio for transmission when the radio is transmitting.

Some radios require both the speakers and microphone to reside on the computer rather than the radio. In this case, both the speaker and microphone streams are generally not sent to and from the radio, respectively.

Once the interface software has the samples collected from the receiver, it can perform the DSP functions required to create the audio signal. (See the sections on Receive and Transmit Chains earlier in this chapter.)

Similarly, the transmit signal chain commonly has a modulator, filter and limiter. When the radio is transmitting CW or FSK, the SDR software generally synthesizes the waveforms for both of these modes directly without the need for many of the other transmit signal chain elements. For this reason, it is common for there to be a separate signal chain for each mode.

The thick client SDR interfaces such as *PowerSDR* place a higher demand on the computing hardware since many of the DSP functions are performed in the computer. There is also a stringent set of requirements around timing to ensure that the constant flow of samples on both the receive and transmit sides is not interrupted. If an interruption occurs on the receive side, it will result in audio dropouts. Interruptions on the transmit side can result in discontinuities in the transmit signal. Depending on the hardware involved, discontinuities in the transmit signal can result in high frequency components that cause the transmitted signal to reside outside of the desired transmit passband. There are advantages to the thick client architecture, specifically:

1) Since computing and software requirements for the radio itself are minimal, the radio hardware can be less expensive.

2) Software that runs on the PC is typically easier to develop, test and debug.

3) As PC hardware has continued to achieve higher price-performance ratios, more power for more capabilities can be added without changing the radio..

The thick client architecture is now common, due in a large part to the availability of open source *PowerSDR* and the ease of adapting it to other radios. More than one HPSDR radio has been designed using this architecture as have the ANAN radios, adapted from the HPSDR designs.

THIN CLIENTS

In contrast to a thick client interface are *thin client* interfaces. In a thin client, all or most of the work required to modulate, demodulate and produce the displays for the radio is performed inside the radio hardware. The thin client is used, then, to display the interface and accept control commands which as passed to the radio for processing. An example of the thin client approach is the FLEX-6000 Signature Series radios by FlexRadio Systems.

In the FLEX-6000, all modulation, demodulation and radio control are performed in the radio in the *SmartSDR* software running under *Linux*. This reduces the performance requirements on the client system used for the interface. In turn, the interface can easily be run on cellular phones, tablet computers and other less expensive computing hardware. Key advantages of the thin client architecture are:

1) A wide array of computing hardware can serve as the interface due to the low computing demands.

2) Reduction of network bandwidth between the client and radio due to the processing occurring in the radio. This allows remote operation over low-speed network interfaces making remote directly to a cell phone possible, for example.

3) The client software is considerable simpler since it is just responsible for display and control and can, therefore, be easily ported to new computing devices resulting in a wide array of available interfaces and interface platforms.

4) Availability of an applications programming interface (API) due to the necessity of an API for the client. This API can then be used by other amateur applications wishing to use the radio as a server or utility.

14.3 Configuration and Control Interfaces

Computer control interfaces for radios play a key role in use of our radios beyond all but the simplest of operation. These interfaces allow us to check the status of our radios, change their settings, tune them and operate from a distance. Logging programs often use them during contests to automatically acquire frequency and other data for the contest log. In combination with logging programs, the interfaces can be used to automatically select antennas, turn rotators, and control other equipment in the station.

Each radio manufacturer has selected or designed an interface to work with their radios. Typically a manufacturer will use a common interface across their product lines. The user's manual and service manual contain complete information on the commands and data that are exchanged via the interface protocol.

14.3.1 Icom CI-V

Icom's control interface, CI-V, named as the fifth (V) Communications Interface (CI) is a serial "one-wire" protocol that uses the RS-232 electrical interface (generally with 5 V rather than the RS-232 standard ±12 V), but allows multi-drop or multiple transceivers on a single CI-V communications line.

By using CSMA/CD (carrier sense, multiple access, collision detect), multiple radios can avoid using the communications interface at the same time, detecting when a collision occurs and retransmitting data. This is the same technique used in 10Base2 Ethernet in which coaxial cable was used and multiple computers used the same communications bus.

In CI-V, each radio has an address (which can be changed) and the computer can communicate with any of the radios on the CI-V bus. The CI-V protocol allows tuning the radio, changing modes, selecting memory channels, and other functions. CI-V generally treats the RS-232 data as bytes and references commands using their hexadecimal values. It is essentially a binary communications protocol. CI-V is also used in newer Ten-Tec radios, but with additional commands specific to Ten-Tec transceivers.

14.3.2 CAT (Computer Aided Transceiver) Interface

CAT is a control interface based on the RS-232 electrical standard. Most manufacturers such as Kenwood, Yaesu, Elecraft, and FlexRadio implement CAT via RS-232 or via a USB interface that emulates RS-232 signals. The protocol used by each manufacturer is proprietary to that line of equipment. Unlike CI-V, CAT is a point-to-point protocol meaning the expectation is that there is a single computer controlling a single radio on the line. CSMA/CD protocols are no longer required, but an additional communications port must be used for each radio. CAT is not a binary communications interface, but uses ASCII characters. As with CI-V, each radio implements only commands that are meaningful to that radio.

With the advent of USB, many radios now make their CAT interfaces available over USB in the form of a USB communications port. When the USB cable is plugged into a computer, the USB protocol recognizes the device as a communication port and adds a new port to the computer. In this way, many radios can be added to a single computer using a USB hub.

As Ethernet and the Internet have been added to our computing palette, CAT has been implemented over TCP/IP, an Internet standard communications protocol pair. For example, with the FLEX-6000's *SmartSDR* CAT program, a TCP/IP port can be added that responds to CAT commands. The base protocol remains the same, but the communications transport mechanism is TCP/IP over Ethernet rather than RS-232. This allows a relatively simple conversion for programs wishing to access radios over Ethernet rather than either RS-232 or USB.

FlexRadio Systems, although adopting CAT to allow for interoperation with legacy software such as existing loggers and digital mode programs, also added a new computer control interface, the *SmartSDR* API. CAT is restricted to commands relating to two variable frequency oscillators (VFO), typically called VFO A and VFO B. Since the FLEX-6000 can currently have up to eight slice receivers (synonymous with a VFO for the purposes of controlling the radio), the CAT standard could not sufficiently provide for control of the radio. The SmartSDR API is also based on ASCII commands and allows full control of the radio over a TCP/IP port or using a Microsoft *Windows* .NET DLL interface. FlexRadio's *SmartSDR* thin client running on a *Windows* PC achieves all of its display and control capabilities using the *SmartSDR* API.

14.4 SDR Design Tools

A description of how SDR works and the opportunities it presents are interesting but not of much use unless the reader can acquire and use the necessary tools to work with SDR technology. This section discusses *GNU Radio*, a popular software development environment for working with digital signal processing (DSP) and applying it to SDR. A short introduction to working with FPGA technology is also included. DSP software is key to working effectively with SDR at the level to which amateurs are accustomed with traditional analog technology and a soldering iron.

14.4.1 GNU Radio

INTRODUCTION TO GNU RADIO

The ability to create and work with software for SDR projects is a new skill for many hams. Professional programmers have many options to pursue. For hams without a programming background, software packages are now available that create a gateway for ordinary hams to build custom DSP software. Software authoring has been vastly simplified. The software packages feature graphic user interfaces (GUI) and offer useful DSP functions in DSP source code libraries.

The ham experimenter has choices of graphically based DSP software packages: the proprietary packages, *Matlab / Simulink* by MathWorks and *LabVIEW* by National Instruments, or the open source *GNU Radio / GNU Radio Companion* (*GRC*) DSP library package. This section introduces the combination of *GNU Radio* and *GRC* package as a powerful, "ham friendly," development environment for SDR projects. The material is based on a pair of *QEX* articles by John Petrich, W7FU (see the *GNU Radio* references) which are included in the online supplemental information for this book.

GNU Radio was conceived as a development tool intended for advanced educational programs, and commercial product development labs. With a little effort, hobbyists can use these tools as well. *GNU Radio* can be used as a simulation tool to study DSP without being connected to an SDR. *GNU Radio* can also be used to develop practical and operationally satisfying DSP software for SDR transmitters, receivers, and transceivers as well as test equipment.

To make DSP authoring accessible for all levels of users, the *GNU Radio* developers include the user option of *GNU Radio Companion (GRC)*. *GRC* is the graphical DSP library interface, an integral part of *GNU Radio*. The foundational *GNU Radio* DSP library is accessed with character-based command line entries. *GRC* is a graphical overlay to the *GNU Radio* DSP library with the same full functionality as the command line approach. *GRC* emulates the command line entries and represents each DSP function as a graphical icon without command line entries. (For the sake of completeness, a very few of the *GRC* DSP parameters in are expressed as simple Python code commands. These Python commands are covered in the section **Learning Resources: DSP Competency and *GNU Radio***)

An arrangement of DSP icons and digital data links is termed a *flow graph*. When executed, the *GRC* flow graph is compiled to a Python code file, which itself is a wrapper for C++ executable DSP code. This artful layered construction, like a set of nesting dolls, provides a high level, user friendly, graphical interface for DSP authoring with the speed and efficiency of lower level code for DSP process speed and efficiency. More information from the developers about the construction of this DSP library environment is available at **wiki.gnuradio.org/index.php/What_is_GNU_Radio%3F**

GNU RADIO AND THE GRC TOOL

GRC, the easy to use graphical interface, makes this DSP library particularly appealing. Reduced to the basics, the step-by-step design of a functional DSP begins with envisioning or drawing a block diagram pattern of a traditional analog signal processing circuit. Once the general signal processing pattern is conceived, select the desired DSP function(s) from the DSP library (filter, mixer, oscillator, amplifier, etc.), arrange the DSP function(s) as graphical blocks in the work screen according to the design pattern, connect the blocks with an appropriate type of data link, add the DSP parameters in each block, and execute the program. The details of constructing a DSP flow graph are covered in the **Success with *GNU Radio* Tools** section and in the on-line tutorials referenced in the section **Learning Resources: DSP Competency and *GNU Radio***. The process is straightforward.

Let's examine the *GRC* work environment and flow graph composition at the highest level or block level. The *GRC* work environment consists of four parts: the work area, the control bar, the library, and the console. **Figure 14.12** illustrates the *GRC* user graphic user interface (GUI). The DSP is authored in the work area in the center of the GUI screen. The *GRC* control bar is located across the top of the work area. The *GNU Radio* DSP library runs along the right margin of the screen. The operating console is visible at the very bottom of the work environment and becomes active when a DSP function is executed.

Figure 14.14 — A screen showing how parameters are managed for a typical DSP filter block.

Centered in the work area are six DSP blocks which, in aggregate constitute a DSP flow graph. The flow graph implements, in DSP, a 1 kHz audio tone output to both an audio sink (computer speaker) and to an FFT panadapter display (on screen). **Figure 14.13** is the FFT display output once the flow graph has been executed. Note the signal spike is accurately centered at 1 kHz on the FFT display and the 1 kHz tone would be heard via the computer sound card.

Continuing to the parameter level, one step below the block level, each DSP library item is displayed as a rectangular shaped "block" with input / output ports. Each block must be "opened" with a mouse right-click to gain access to the parameter fields that define that DSP function. Each parameter has a field in which the values are either added or selected from a menu.

Figure 14.14 displays the parameter screen for a low-pass filter DSP block. Note how the digital data type (*FIR Type*), sample rate, filter bandwidth and filter shape, and other parameters can be selected or specified. Some parameter values are intuitive, direct carry-overs from analog design. For example, the bandwidth and shape factor parameters for a DSP filter block are specified in kHz in the same way an analog filter is specified. Other parameter values are not as intuitive and refer to parameters unique to DSP. Examples of these parameters are the DSP *Sample Rate* and *FIR Type* choices. More detail about the most commonly used DSP blocks and appropriate parameter choices are explained in greater detail in the section below, **The Rest of the Story: Basic DSP Theory Applied to a Flow Graph Segment**.

Figure 14.15 depicts the more complex flow graph of an SDR broadcast FM receiver. This flow graph uses an RTL-SDR as the receiver source. Other SDR receiver hardware

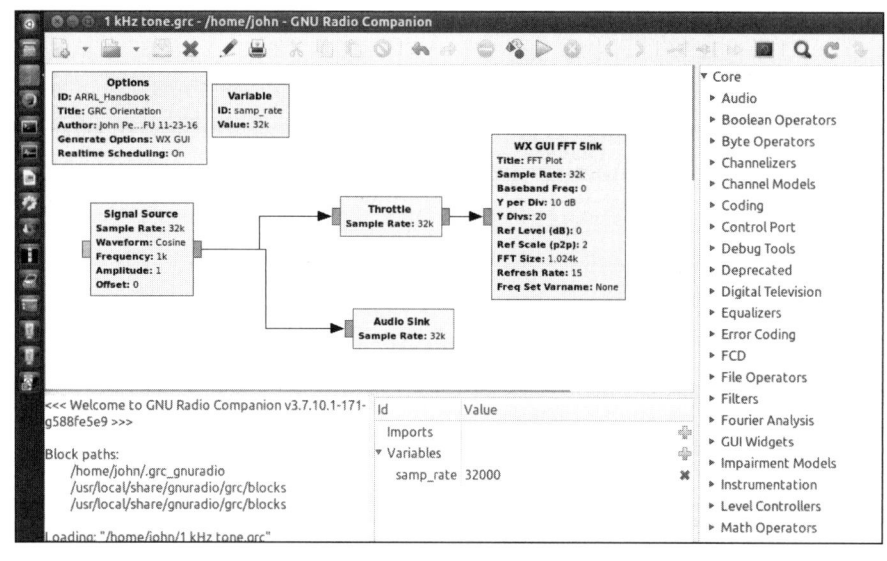

Figure 14.12 — The development window user interface for *GNU Radio* functional blocks.

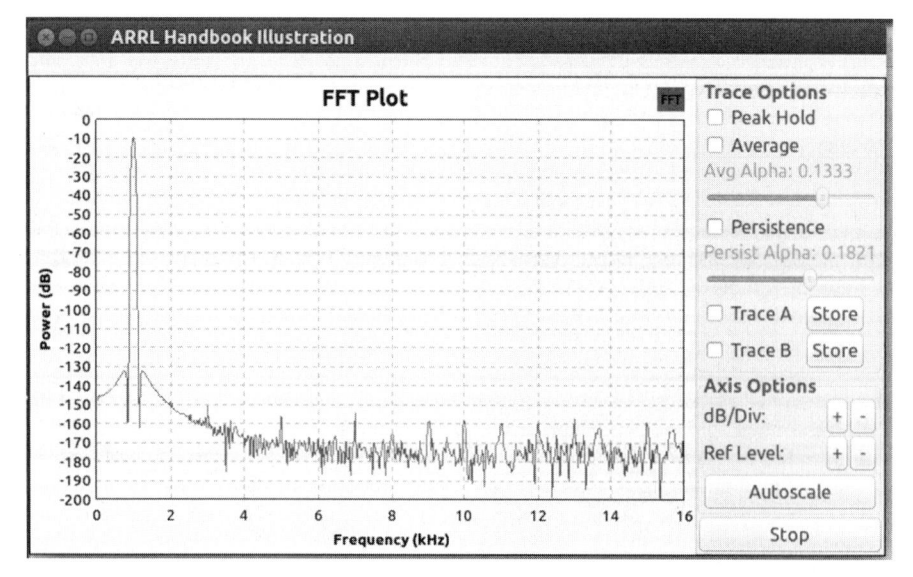

Figure 14.13 — The user interface window showing an operating 1 kHz audio tone FFT.

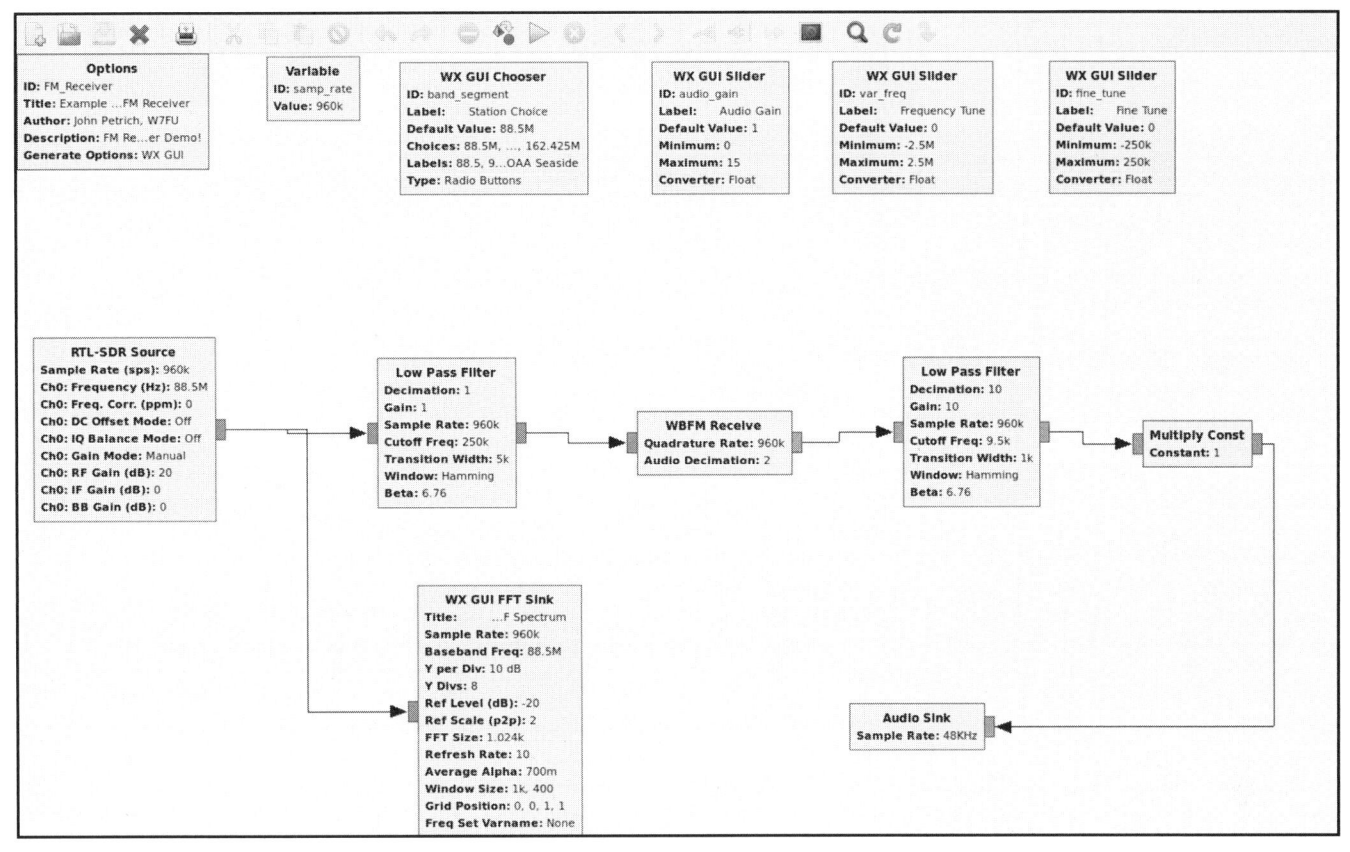

Figure 14.15 — Flow graph for a broadcast FM receiver showing the various function blocks involved.

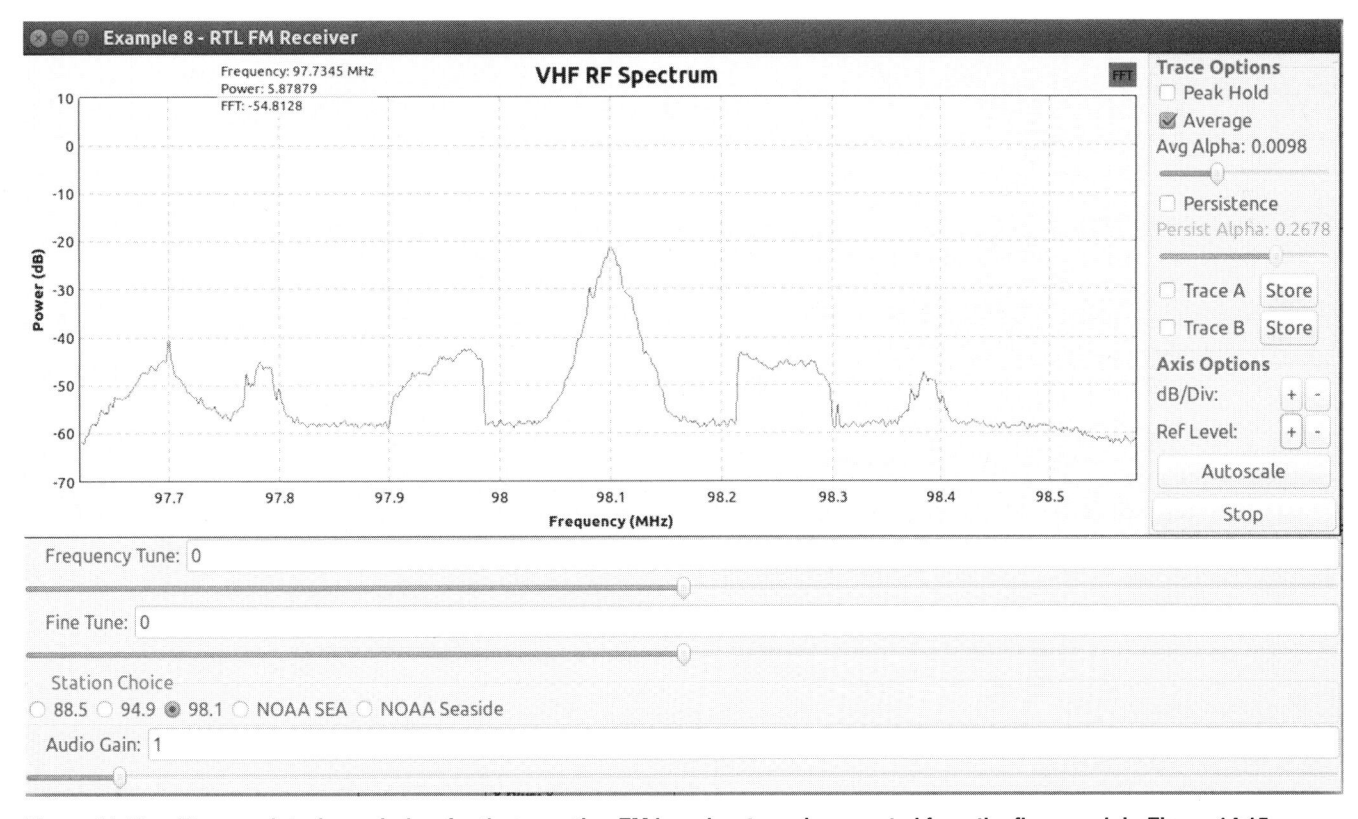

Figure 14.16 — The user interface window for the operating FM broadcast receiver created from the flow graph in Figure 14.15.

can be substituted easily as explained in the section *GNU Radio*, **Radio Hardware, and UHD**.

The RTL-SDR is represented by the *RTL-SDR Source* block on the left. The *Audio Sink* on the right outputs the audio sound. The *WX GUI FFT Sink* in the center generates a panadapter display. The chain of DSP blocks in the center of the work screen perform the filtering and signal demodulation functions for this radio. Compare this flow graph with a block diagram for a simple analog FM receiver to appreciate the fundamental similarity. **Figure 14.16** illustrates the operating receiver GUI that appears when the flow graph is executed. Shown are the radio tuning controls for frequency and audio output, and the FFT panadapter display.

SUCCESS WITH *GNU RADIO* TOOLS

Just as success at woodworking comes from competency with woodworking tools, success with *GNU Radio* comes from learning and using its tools. Viewing a flow graph is the first step is learning the tools. Success with *GNU Radio* inevitably proceeds to DSP competency, as well.

An important part of success with *GNU Radio* comes from an organized and disciplined authoring approach. Lacking organization and discipline, flow graph construction can easily become a chaotic non-functional mess. This section describes one general disciplined approach. Following a description of the general approach, a detailed example flow graph creates entry level DSP competency through flow graphs construction.

DSP competency for new users is not necessary for initial success. Many of the automatic default settings in *GRC* are adequate for entry level flow graphs. Ultimately, DSP competency comes from incrementally constructing more advanced DSPs with simple flow graphs.

GENERAL APPROACH: THE FOUR STEPS TO FLOW GRAPH SUCCESS

The disciplined approach involves following a pattern of four basic steps. These basic steps are useful at getting started the first time with DSP flow graph construction and as an efficient approach to construct more advanced and complex flow graphs.

How does one begin a DSP flow graph using the *GNU Radio GRC* graphical interface? Four steps are required to construct any flow graph: the "block" step, the "parameter" step, the "logical interconnection" step, and the "DSP" step. Each step is explained below.

Step 1 — the Blocks: Arrange the appropriate DSP blocks from the *GRC* library to form a diagram of the desired circuit in the work area. See how the functional blocks are arranged in the example flow graph in the work area of **Figure 14.17**.

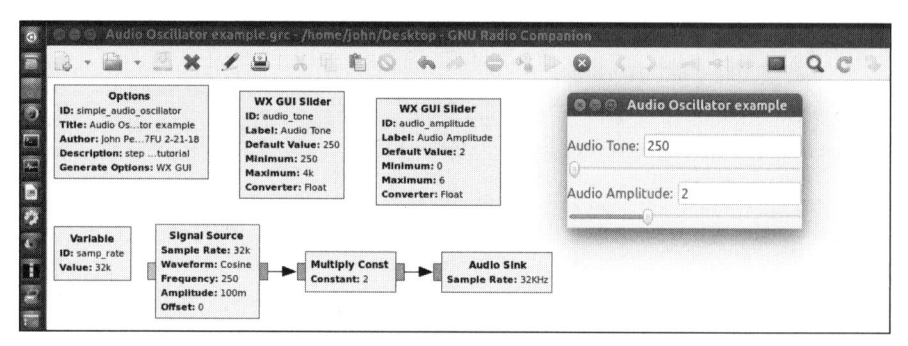

Figure 14.17 — The flow graph for the audio oscillator.

Step 2 — the Parameters: To perform the desired DSP function, each DSP block requires user-specified parameters. In the parameter step, right-click each block, select *Properties*, and enter the parameter values in the available fields. Each block in the flow graph diagram is opened in turn and the desired parameters are entered in each block. Typical parameters are familiar values such as gain, frequency, bandwidth, and so on, as well as some less familiar values such as *Sample Rate* and *Output Type*. The *Sample Rate* and *Output Type* parameter values are unique to DSP as discussed below. These DSP parameters are set by default in many flow graphs and automatically propagated into every DSP block. For one to meaningfully change these default parameters, a basic understanding of DSP theory is required as described in Step 4.

Step 3 — the Logical Interconnections: Each DSP block must be connected to the other blocks by a data link arrow in a logical manner. The data links begin with the "input" or *Source* location in the flow graph end with the "output" or *Sink* in the flow graph.

Step 4 — DSP Parameters: It is in this fourth, and final step, that authoring a flow graph involves DSP issues. Let's begin with the special *Variable* block located in the left-hand corner of the work area. That block is automatically present whenever *GRC* is opened for programming. The *Variable* block is the location for the base line *Sample Rate* parameter for each block in the DSP. The default parameter is 32,000 samples per second (SPS). That default parameter is automatically propagated to the *Sample Rate* field in each DSP block in the flow graph work area. The default *Sample Rate* value is a good starting place for many DSP flow graphs and can be used as a default for many designs. Advanced DSP designs may require different sample rates and may require adjustments to the sample rate parameter in the DSP blocks.

Another default DSP parameter is the *Output Type* parameter for each DSP block. The default parameter is termed *Complex* or I and Q. This default parameter is useful for many, but not all radio-related DSPs. The flow graph example described below illustrates a flow graph where the default *Output Type* must be changed for the simple flow graph to function. (See the **Modulation** chapter for more information about complex signals and modulation.)

FLOW GRAPH EXECUTION

In practice, the above outlined flow graph is created in the *work area* of the *GRC*. To operationalize the flow graph, select the *Execute flow graph* control (a green arrow on the screen) from the tool bar above the *work area*. After the software compiles, the DSP will spring to life. The operational GUI appears on the screen with the control functions displayed as displayed on the right side of the screen in Figure 14.17.

SPECIFIC FLOW GRAPH EXAMPLE: SIMPLE SINGLE-TONE AUDIO OSCILLATOR

Step 1 — the Blocks: Figure 14.17 is a screen capture of the audio oscillator flow graph. The operating GUI is superimposed on the right side of the figure. The operating GUI only appears only after the *Execute flow graph* is selected from the tool bar.

The flow graph blocks are selected from the library off the right-hand edge depicted in Figure 14.12 (not Figure 14.17) and placed in the work area. At a glance, the flow graph block diagram is constructed to look essentially the same as a traditional analog radio block diagram with the same components. The diagram and component content reflect standard signal processing practice. A traditional circuit block diagram for a simple sine wave oscillator with audio output would consist of series of blocks linked by lines; an oscillator block, a frequency control, an audio amplifier, an audio volume control, all connected one after the other, to an audio output block.

In this audio oscillator example, the signal processing pattern is the same for the traditional analog and the *GNU Radio* digital implementation. With a DSP, the interconnections between blocks are no longer signal links (wires in traditional circuits) but digital data links as we will see in Step 3 below.

Step 2 — the Parameters: Most of the parameters for each DSP block are visible in Figure 14.17. Examine the parameters of each block with a right-click on the block and select *Properties*. Right-click the *QT GUI Range* control block with the *ID audio_tone* located at the top of the work space. This block is the control block for the oscillator frequency or audio tone. Note the block ID, *audio_tone*, and the tone's tuning range from 250 Hz to 4 kHz in 1 Hz steps. This block connects to and controls the *Signal Source* DSP block output frequency which is the audio oscillator tone in this example.

The *ID audio_tone* comprises the software link between the control block and the *Signal Source* DSP block. The term *audio_tone* is entered into both the *Signal Source frequency* parameter field and the *QT GUI Range ID* field thereby connecting the two blocks in software.

In the same manner, the audio volume control is linked via software to the audio amplifier. Select *Properties* in the *QT GUI Range* control block with the *ID audio_amplitude*. The multiplication values range from 0 to 10. These numbers are factors that tell the *Multiply Const* DSP block to multiply the digital data stream amplitude for audio volume control. The ID *audio_amplitude*, denotes the software link to the *Multiply Const* DSP block. That ID is entered in the *constant* parameter field in the *Multiply Const* DSP block. The two blocks are linked in the same way as the audio tone frequency is linked to the audio oscillator. The *Sample Rate* value from the *Variable* block, 32k, is automatically propagated to the other DSP blocks but not to the two control blocks

Step 3 — the Logical Interconnections: To complete the basic DSP flow graph, each block is logically interconnected to the others. Additional attention to details are important in this step. Not appreciated in the screen capture is how the *Multiply Const* DSP block became configured to have only single input and single output ports. This block and many other blocks from the DSP library are pre-configured for multiple input and output ports. When placed in the *GRC* work area, pre-configured blocks from the library are reconfigured for the desired number of ports to fit the flow graph. To reconfigure the number of ports, right-click the block, select *Properties,* and enter a value for the number of desired ports in the appropriate port parameter field. In this example, a value of 1 was entered in the *Input Port* field of the *Multiply Const* DSP block. Select OK, the window closes, and the block appears on screen ready to use with a single input and single output port.

Once the block ports are configured, the DSP blocks must be linked with the data stream. To form these data stream links, left-click on the output port of the *Signal Source* DSP block, followed by a left-click on the input port of the *Multiply Const* DSP block. A data link arrow appears, and those two blocks are digitally connected. The output of the *Multiply Const* DSP block connects in a similar manner to the input port of the *Audio Sink* DSP block.

The flow graph is almost complete. The two control blocks have no visible data link arrows. They are automatically connected via the software *ID* parameters described above. Next, we consider the DSP parameter step.

Step 4 — DSP parameters: The audio oscillator flow graph functions fine with the default *Sample Rate* parameter in conjunction with modern computer sound cards. No change is required for the *Sample Rate* parameter. The *Output Type* parameter is different and must be changed from the default setting for this flow graph to function.

The *Output Type* parameter for each DSP block is displayed in a drop-down menu, found by selecting *Properties* for that DSP block. The *Output Type* is also visually displayed in the flow graph by the color of the input and output port tabs on the blocks. (This color code is a useful bug fix hint with advanced DSP programing and not central for this description. The change in color is only visible when viewing the screen capture or flow graph on a computer screen.) The desired *Output Type* for this flow graph is "Float" (digital data using floating-point values). The *Output Type* parameter for each DSP block in this example must be the same: "Float." Right-click and select *Properties* for each DSP block in the flow graph, navigate to the *Output Type* parameter, and select "Float" from the drop-down menu. The two control blocks don't require any DSP parameters.

Once all steps are completed, the flow graph is ready to be executed. Upon execution, a new GUI appears on the screen with the controls displayed. That GUI screen is superimposed in the upper right-hand corner of the screen capture in Figure 14.17. Listen for the 250 Hz audio tone in the speaker. Adjust the audio volume and audio frequency with the GUI controls. You can also experiment with adjusting the sample rate in the *Variable* block, or parameter values in any block and observe the effect these changes have on the operation of the flow graph. (The GRC flow graph for this example is included in the downloadable supplemental package for this book. The file, Chapter 14 - Audio Oscillator example.grc, can be executed in the *GNU Radio* application.)

THE REST OF THE STORY: BASIC DSP THEORY APPLIED TO A FLOW GRAPH

To better understand this DSP flow graph example and to aid authoring more advanced DSP flowgraphs, basic information about the relationship of sample rate, data stream output type, and DSP is important. (See the **DSP and SDR Fundamentals** chapter for a detailed discussion of the analog/digital conversion process.)

Sampling is a foundational aspect of DSP. DSP comes into action in the A/D converter where an analog signal is converted to a digital data stream. The DSP acts to manipulate the series of data points which form a replica of the sinusoid signal as stream of digital data. The greater the number of samples, the more closely the replicated digital data corresponds to the original sinusoid signal. After digital processing, the digital data stream can be reconstructed to generate the familiar analog sound or radio signals with a D/A converter.

Connecting the sampling concept to a functioning flow graph, each DSP block in the flow graph must function with a compatible sample rate parameter. *GRC* automatically enters the default sample rate for each DSP block which is fine for many DSP processes. Advanced DSP techniques using *GNU Radio and* GRC call for a wide range of sample rate parameters beyond the default value. The sample rate parameters can also be individually adjusted for each DSP block in the flow graph. These sample rate changes are accomplished using *Resampler* DSP blocks. Sample rate adjustments within a single flow graph are termed "multi-rate" sampling and a common practice with advanced DSPs such as those for SDR applications.

Another foundational concept regarding DSP is to understand that the sole purpose of each DSP block is to mathematically manipulate the digital data stream. Fortunately, with *GNU Radio* and the *GRC* graphical approach to programming, the user is not required to understand or program the underlying mathematics. The DSP functions in *GNU Radio* DSP library are preloaded with the necessary mathematical algorithms to perform their intended DSP function.

The data stream math algorithms are unique in each DSP block. The operation can be single purpose, such as for the *Multiply Constant* DSP block which functions as an amplifier or attenuator by simple multiplication of the digital data stream amplitude. Other DSP blocks provide filtering or mixing functions and frequently combinations of these functions. All operations are performed mathematically based on algorithms programed by the developers into each DSP block.

Not only is the data stream manipulated in a mathematically determined manner, but the mathematical structure of the digital data stream has an impact on how a flow graph can function. Return to the flow graph in Figure 14.17 where the *Output Type* DSP parameter reflects the structure of the digital data stream that communicates among the DSP blocks. The mathematically processed digital data stream *Output Type* can be customized as necessary for advanced DSP processes.

As a practical matter, the default *Output Type* digital data structure for most *GNU Radio* DSP blocks are set by default to "Complex" or I and Q data. The default setting, "Complex," is the preferred data type for many, if not most, ordinary radio related DSP applications. Some DSP flow graphs, such as those employing phasing techniques and the audio oscillator example in this case, require an *Output Type* that is different from the default "Complex." (Some SDR hardware digital data output types are derived from different math conversions and require a non-default data stream structure conversion in the flow graph, as well.) In other words, one type of digital data stream doesn't fit all. The *Output Type* data stream parameter can be quite specific for the some SDR hardware and quite specific for some DSP process. Mastering the details of *Output Type* for your flow graph constructions will come with more in-depth understanding of DSP fundamentals. For further information on sampling rate choices and *Output Type* digital data streams, review the information on the GNU Radio website.

LEARNING RESOURCES: DSP COMPETENCY AND *GNU RADIO*

This introduction to *GNU Radio*, *GRC* and flow graph construction presents DSP at the high-level of blocks and parameters, consistent with *GNU Radio*s high-level graphical environment. But that is only the beginning of a journey into the world of DSP. The **DSP and SDR Fundamentals** and the **Receiving** chapters contain much useful information about understanding DSP. That information offers important background and context to more in-depth understanding of DSP to apply to *GNU Radio* although not specific to *GNU Radio*.

DSP competency is readily learned using *GNU Radio* as a tool for experiments and simulation. The online educational resources specific to *GNU Radio* are great learning resources. Detailed examples of DSP applications and parameter selection, awkward and sometimes confusing in a text format, are much more easily understood via online video tutorials. The Ettus Corporation-sponsored series of DSP tutorials (**files.ettus.com/tutorials/labs/Lab_1-5.pdf**) and the related video series (**www.youtube.com/playlist?list=PL618122BD66C8B3C4**) are highly recommended for this learning format.

For a more academic treatment of DSP consider both the **DSP and SDR Fundamentals** in this *Handbook* and the DSP texts by Richard Lyons. The Lyons texts provide a particularly "ham friendly," intuitive, approach to understanding DSP. (See the *GNU Radio* **References** section.)

INSTALLING *GNU RADIO*

The very first step for a new user is to review the *GNU Radio* web portal for authoritative information (**gnuradio.org/redmine/projects/gnuradio/wiki**). The *GNU Radio* developers have published a rich source of detailed information to help the new user to get started using *GNU Radio*. From that portal page one can link to installation instructions, tutorials, latest news, and in-depth information about the software development process. Refer to it frequently, since the content changes with the ongoing software development.

To get started with *GNU Radio*, a particularly appealing option is to use the *GNU Radio Live SDR Environment* (**wiki.gnuradio.org/index.php/GNU_Radio_Live_SDR_Environment**). The *Live Environment* allows the user to implement *GNU Radio* without installing *GNU Radio* on the computer hard drive. The latest versions of the *Ubuntu* operating system and *GNU Radio* software are downloaded from the Internet to a storage medium (for example, DVD or USB memory stick) as an executable file. Upon executing from the medium, the *Live Environment* opens in a complete *Ubuntu* operating system with *GNU Radio* application pre-installed. *GNU Radio* and *GRC* can be immediately executed to run at essentially full capability.

To install *GNU Radio* directly to a computer hard drive, installation from the official Source with the "*build-gnuradio script*" is far and away the most dependable and highly recommended approach (**wiki.gnuradio.org/index.php/InstallingGRFromSource**). Installing *GNU Radio* from the Source with the *build-gnuradio* script automatically installs the most recent *GNU Radio* version, all add ons, and the latest driver for compatible SDR hardware, the *Universal Hardware Driver* (*UHD*). The *build-gnuradio* script is a preferred method for initial installation and subsequent updates of *GNU Radio* and UHD as needed. Step by step "ham friendly" help with the installation process is also available at **www.w7fu.com**

GETTING THE MOST OUT OF *GNU RADIO*

Support for *GNU Radio* is available on-line via the "discuss-gnuradio" message reflector. (**lists.gnu.org/mailman/listinfo/discuss-gnuradio**) Questions can be posted on the reflector and the *GNU Radio* developers respond via email. The reflector is very active and a rich source of information.

The most efficient and user-friendly approach to get full benefit of what *GNU* Radio has to offer is to implement *GNU Radio* in the Linux *Ubuntu* operating system. The *GNU Radio* developers develop and maintain *GNU Radio* in *Ubuntu*. Potential cross-platform bugs and incompatibilities are avoided by adopting the same *Ubuntu* operating system that the developers use. *GNU Radio* is reported to operate on Windows and Mac OSX, but there are challenges with full implementation with these operating systems which make them best avoided by beginners.

Computer users unfamiliar with Linux operating systems shouldn't be intimidated by using the *Linux Ubuntu* operating system. *Ubuntu* has the look and feel and straight forward ease of use as MS Windows. The *Ubuntu* operating system is open source, downloadable via the internet, and can easily be installed in a separate hard drive partition if necessary. Installing *Ubuntu* via the internet is straight forward and quick. The official *Ubuntu* website provides the latest downloadable *Ubuntu* versions and instructions for using *Ubuntu*. (**www.ubuntu.com/download/desktop**)

GNU Radio is a dynamic application with version updates on an irregular but frequent basis. It is important to keep abreast of the changes via the web portal and learn to update the application re-using the *build-gnuradio* script as necessary. Follow the "Latest news" for updates and other information (**gnuradio.org/redmine/projects/gnuradio/wiki**).

For serious DSP authoring and most SDR projects, avoid installing the Linux "distribution" versions of *GNU Radio*. The "distribution" versions of *GNU Radio* are built into the *Ubuntu* operating version at the time of that operating system release. These "distribution" versions can be installed easily from within the *Ubuntu* version. Because *GNU Radio* is built into the *Ubuntu* version at the time of initial release, these *GNU Radio* versions are typically out of date, have outdated *UHD* drivers, and are installed differently within the file system from the versions downloaded from the official Source. The UHD might not work with newer SDR hardware. Updating and adding DSP blocks to, distribution, versions is not possible. For all of these reasons it is best to avoid installing a "distribution" version of *GNU Radio* instead install a full installation of the current *GNU* Radio version.

A capable computer is necessary to use *GNU Radio* to its full real-time DSP potential. The developers recommend a dual-core CPU at the i3 level or above to users. Single-core and early dual-core CPUs lack the speed and capacity for many ham DSP designs.

GNU RADIO, RADIO HARDWARE, AND UHD

To implement real-time SDR radio projects with *GNU Radio*, it is necessary to use compatible SDR hardware. The *Universal Hardware Driver* (*UHD*) is a dedicated software package to interface *GNU Radio* and compatible SDR hardware. Of late, there have appeared a new generation of SDRs that interface with a multi-layered PPA system of *GNU Radio* packages or a suite of applications. The documentation for compatible hardware will refer to the *GNU Radio UHD* capability or to a PPA *GNU Radio* package. Given the popularity of *GNU Radio* with the DSP developer community, *UHD* or the *GNU Radio* PPA is commonly specified for modern SDR hardware.

The latest version of *UHD* is installed automatically whenever *GNU Radio* is installed via the *build-gnuradio* script from Source. The *GNU Radio* PPA requires a separate and additional installation. The ever-expanding list of compatible hardware is published at **wiki.gnuradio.org/index.php/Hardware.** Searches of the internet and close reading of the specifications can sometimes find *UHD*-compatible SDR hardware that hasn't yet reached the official list.

GNU RADIO REFERENCE MATERIAL

J. Petrich, W7FU, "Digital Signal Processing and GNU Radio Companion," Jul/Aug 2017, *QEX*, pp. 41-46.

J. Petrich, W7FU, T. McDermott, N5EG, "Digital Signal Processing (DSP) Projects: Examples of GNU Radio and GRC Functionality," Sep/Oct 2014, *QEX*, pp. 25-30.

R. G. Lyons, "Understanding Digital Signal Processing" ISBN 0-201-63467-8

www.w7fu.com — step by step information on installing and maintaining *GNU Radio*, with examples of ham radio oriented SDR flow graphs.

www.reddit.com/r/GNURadio — a very active *GNU Radio* development community.

Suggested reading: **wiki.gnuradio.org/index.php/SuggestedReading**

14.4.2 FPGA Data Engines

What actually implements the DSP functional blocks referenced in the previous chapters? In the early days of amateur SDR and DSP, the only suitable hardware platform with a reasonable cost was a high-end PC or specialized DSP or graphics processing microprocessors (microcontroller units – MCU). These are still used today but after some years in transition, amateur SDR is largely implemented by FPGAs — Field-Programmable Gate Arrays.

An MCU executes instructions from a predefined instruction set in sequential order; the hardware is fixed, but the sequence of instructions is programmable. An FPGA, on the other hand, has no fixed instruction set or sequence of instructions, operates on data in parallel and has programmable logic and interconnections. Software defined radio (SDR) implementations benefit greatly from the FPGA parallel hardware architecture since they can be configured to implement the required math operations directly in hardware, at very high speed. FPGA ICs are now available inexpensively and with a sufficient number of gates (in the 10s of 1000s) to implement high-performance SDR functions.

The FPGA as typically used by non-professional developers is part of a general-purpose computing unit, also known as a *data engine*. Support ICs are included in the package to allow the developer to interact with the FPGA

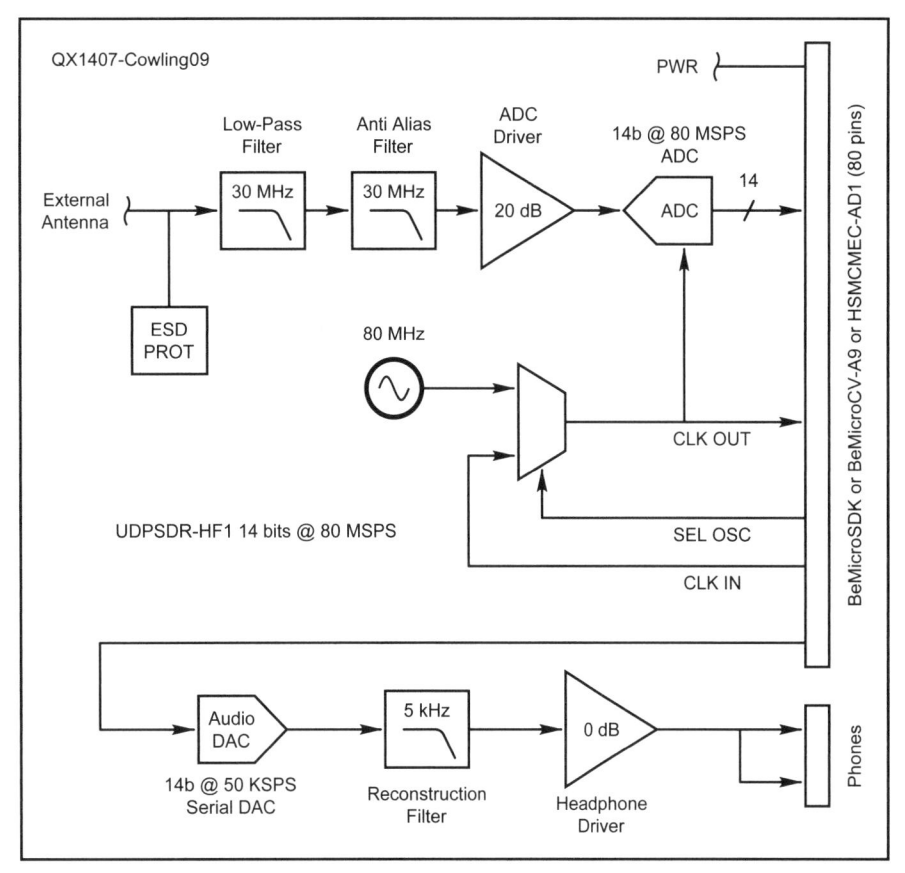

Figure 14.18 — An SDR development system based on the BEMICROCV-A9 data engine and separate SDRStick receive and transmit modules.

and program it. Other data ports are available, depending on what applications the data engine is designed to handle. When combined with external RF hardware and either an on-board user interface or the ability to stream data to an external user interface, the result is an effective SDR development environment. An example is shown in **Figure 14.18** which combines the SDRStick receiver and transmitter with a BEMICROCV-A9 data engine. An Ethernet port provides enough bandwidth to implement the user interface and display on a PC. This is a thin-client implementation as described in the previous section on User Interfaces.

In a series of Hands-On SDR columns in *QEX* magazine beginning in 2014, Scotty Cowling, WA2DFI, described several data engines and the software development environment needed to program the FPGAs. Several of the key columns dealing with FPGA development are included with the online supplemental information for this book.

Contents

15.1 Digital "Modes"
    15.1.1 Symbols, Baud, Bits and Bandwidth
    15.1.2 Error Detection and Correction
    15.1.3 Data Representations
    15.1.4 Compression Techniques
    15.1.5 Compression vs. Encryption

15.2 Unstructured Digital Modes
    15.2.1 Radioteletype (RTTY)
    15.2.2 PSK31 and Variants
    15.2.3 MFSK16
    15.2.4 DominoEX
    15.2.5 THROB
    15.2.6 MT63
    15.2.7 Olivia

15.3 Fuzzy Modes
    15.3.1 Facsimile (fax)
    15.3.2 Slow-Scan TV (SSTV)
    15.3.3 Hellschreiber, Feld-Hell or Hell

15.4 Structured Digital Modes
    15.4.1 WSJT-X Modes
    15.4.2 Message Compression
    15.4.3 Slow Modes
    15.4.4 Fast Modes
    15.4.5 HF Digital Voice
    15.4.6 ALE

15.5 Networking Modes
    15.5.1 OSI Networking Model
    15.5.2 Connected and Connectionless Protocols
    15.5.3 The Terminal Node Controller (TNC)
    15.5.4 PACTOR-I
    15.5.5 PACTOR-II
    15.5.6 PACTOR-III
    15.5.7 G-TOR
    15.5.8 CLOVER-II
    15.5.9 CLOVER-2000
    15.5.10 WINMOR
    15.5.11 Packet Radio
    15.5.12 APRS
    15.5.13 Winlink
    15.5.14 D-STAR
    15.5.15 P25
    15.5.16 Yaesu System Fusion
    15.5.17 DMR
    15.5.18 High-Speed Multimedia (HSMM)

15.6 Digital Mode Table

15.7 Glossary

15.8 References and Bibliography

**Chapter 15 —
Downloadable Supplemental Content**

Supplemental Files
- Table of digital mode characteristics (section 15.6)
- ASCII and ITA2 code tables
- Varicode tables for PSK31, MFSK16 and DominoEX
- Tips for using *FreeDV* HF digital voice software by Mel Whitten, KØPFX
- Digital Modes - Lowest Permitted Amateur Frequency
- "High-Speed Wireless Networking in the UHF and Microwave Bands," by David Bern, W2LNX, and Keith Elkin, KB3TCB

Chapter 15

Digital Protocols and Modes

Amateur Radio operators are creating new digital modes to communicate both as "chat-style" keyboard-to-keyboard operation or using packetized network-compatible protocols. Many new protocols can be entirely implemented using software and a computer sound card, making tools for experimentation and implementation available worldwide via the Internet. New SDR technology will allow digital protocols and modes to be implemented directly without an intervening audio modulation/demodulation step. It is an exciting period for Amateur Radio with frequent innovations and improvements.

This chapter will focus on the protocols for transferring various data types, focusing on the processes by which data is encoded, compressed and error checked, packaged and exchanged. Joe Taylor, K1JT, rewrote the sections on *WSJT-X* modes for this edition. Modulation methods are covered in the **Modulation** chapter, and the **Digital Communications** chapter available with the online supplemental material discusses the practical considerations of operating using these modes.

There is a broad array of digital modes to service various needs with more coming. The most basic modes simply encode text data for transmission in a keyboard-to-keyboard chat-type environment. These modes may or may not include any mechanism for error detection or correction. The second class of modes are generally more robust and support more sophisticated data types by structuring the data sent and including additional error-correction information to properly reconstruct the data at the receiving end. The third class of modes discussed will be networking modes with protocols often the same or similar to versions used on the Internet and computer networks.

15.1 Digital "Modes"

The ITU uses *Emission Designators* to define a "mode" as demonstrated in the **Modulation** chapter. These designators include the bandwidth, modulation type and information being sent. This system works well to describe the physical characteristics of the modulation, but digital modes create some ambiguity because the type of information sent could be text, image or even the audio of a CW session. As an example, an FM data transmission of 20K0F3D could transmit spoken audio (like FM 20K0F3E or 2K5J3E) or a CW signal (like 150H0A1A). These designators don't help identify the type of data supported by a particular mode, the speed that data can be sent, if it's error-corrected, or how well it might perform in hostile band conditions. Digital modes have more characteristics that define them and there are often many variations on a single mode that are optimized for different conditions. We'll need to look at the specifics of these unique characteristics to be able to determine which digital modes offer the best combination of features for any given application.

15.1.1 Symbols, Baud, Bits and Bandwidth

The basic performance measure of a digital mode is the *data rate*. This can be measured a number of ways and is often confused. Each change of state on a transmission medium defines a *symbol* and the *symbol rate* is also known as *baud*. (While commonly used, "baud rate" is redundant because "baud" is already defined as the rate of symbols/second.) Modulating a carrier increases the frequency range, or bandwidth, it occupies. The FCC currently limits digital modes by symbol rate on the various bands as an indirect (but easily measurable) means of controlling bandwidth.

The *bit rate* is the product of the *symbol rate* and the number of bits encoded in each symbol. In a simple two-state system like an RS-232 interface, the bit rate will be the same as baud. More complex waveforms can represent more than two states with a single symbol so the bit rate will be higher than the baud. For each additional bit encoded in a symbol, the number of states of the carrier doubles. This makes each state less distinct from the others, which in turn makes it more difficult for the receiver to detect each symbol correctly in the presence of noise. A V.34 modem may transmit symbols at a baud rate of 3420 baud and each symbol can represent up to 10 discrete states or bits, resulting in a *gross* (or *raw*) *bit rate* of 3420 baud × 10 or 34,200 bits per second (bit/s). Framing bits and other overhead reduce the *net bit rate* to 33,800 bit/s.

Bits per second is abbreviated here as *bit/s* for clarity but is also often seen as *bps*. Bits per second is useful when looking at the protocol but is less helpful determining how long it

Table 15.1
Data Rate Symbols and Multipliers

Name	Symbol	Multiplier
kilobit per second	kbit/s or kbps	1000 or 10^3
Megabit per second	Mbit/s or Mbps	1,000,000 or 10^6
Gigabit per second	Gbit/s or Gbps	1,000,000,000 or 10^9

takes to transmit a specific size file because the number of bits consumed by overhead is often unknown. A more useful measure for calculating transmission times is *bytes per second* or *Bps* (note the capitalization). Although there are only eight bits per byte, with the addition of start and stop bits, the difference between bps and Bps is often tenfold. Since the net bit rate takes the fixed overhead into account, Bytes per second can be calculated as $bps_{net}/8$. Higher data rates can be expressed with their metric multipliers as shown in **Table 15.1**.

Digital modes constantly balance the relationship between symbol rate, bit rate, bandwidth and the effect of noise. The Shannon-Hartley theorem demonstrates the maximum channel capacity in the presence of Gaussian white noise and was discussed in the **Modulation** chapter in the Channel Capacity section. This theorem describes how an increased symbol rate will require an increase in bandwidth and how a reduced signal-to-noise ratio (SNR) will reduce the potential *throughput* of the channel.

15.1.2 Error Detection and Correction

Voice modes require the operator to manually request a repeat of any information required but not understood. Using proper phonetics makes the information more easily understood but takes longer to transmit. If 100% accuracy is required, it may be necessary for the receiver to repeat the entire message back to the sender for verification. Computers can't necessarily distinguish between valuable and unnecessary data or identify likely errors but they offer other options to detect and correct errors.

ERROR DETECTION

The first requirement of any accurate system is to be able to detect when an error has occurred. The simplest method is *parity*. With 7-bit ASCII data, it was common to transmit an additional 8th parity bit to each character. The parity bit was added to make the total number of 1 bits odd or even. The binary representation for an ASCII letter Z is 1011010. Sent as seven bits with even parity, the parity bit would be 0 because there are already an even number of 1 bits and the result would be 01011010. The limitation of parity is that it only works with an odd number of bit inversions. If the last two bits were flipped to 01011001 (the ASCII letter Y), it would still pass the parity check because it still has an even number of bits. Parity is also rarely used on 8-bit data so it cannot be used when transferring binary data files.

Checksum is a method similar to the "check" value in an NTS message. It is generally a single byte (8-bit) value appended to the end of a packet or frame of data. It is calculated by adding all the values in the packet and taking the least significant (most unique) byte. This is a simple operation for even basic processors to perform quickly but can also be easily mislead. If two errors occur in the packet of equal amounts in the opposite direction (A becomes B and Z becomes Y), the checksum value will still be accurate and the packet will be accepted as error-free.

Cyclic redundancy check (CRC) is similar to checksum but uses a more sophisticated formula for calculating the check value of a packet. The formula most closely resembles long division, where the quotient is thrown away and the remainder is used. It is also common for CRC values to be more than a single byte, making the value more unique and likely to identify an error. Although other error detection systems are currently in use, CRC is the most common.

ERROR CORRECTION

There are two basic ways to design a protocol for an error correcting system: *automatic repeat request (ARQ)* and *forward error correction (FEC)*. With ARQ the transmitter sends the data packet with an error detection code, which the receiver uses to check for errors. The receiver will request retransmission of packets with errors or sends an acknowledgement (ACK) of correctly received data, and the transmitter re-sends anything not acknowledged within a reasonable period of time.

With forward error correction (FEC), the transmitter encodes the data with an *error-correcting code (ECC)* and sends the encoded message. The receiver is not required to send any messages back to the transmitter. The receiver decodes what it receives into the "most likely" data. The codes are designed so that it would take an "unreasonable" amount of noise to trick the receiver into misinterpreting the data. It is possible to combine the two, so that minor errors are corrected without retransmission, and major errors are detected and a retransmission requested. The combination is called *hybrid automatic repeat request* (*hybrid ARQ*).

There are many error correcting code (ECC) algorithms available. Extended Golay coding is used on blocks of ALE data, for example, as described in the section below on G-TOR. In addition to the ability to detect and correct errors in the data packets, the modulation scheme allows sending multiple data streams and interleaving the data in such a way that a noise burst will disrupt the data at different points.

15.1.3 Data Representations

When comparing digital modes, it is important to understand how the data is conveyed. There are inherent limitations in any method chosen. PSK31 might seem a good choice for sending data over HF links because it performs well, but it was only designed for text (not 8-bit data) and has no inherent error correction. It is certainly possible to use this modulation scheme to send 8-bit data and add error correction to create a new mode. This would maintain the weak signal performance but the speed will suffer from the increased overhead. Similarly, a digital photo sent via analog SSTV software may only take two minutes to send, but over VHF packet it could take 10 minutes, despite the higher speed of a packet system. This doesn't mean SSTV is more efficient. Analog SSTV systems generally transmit lower resolution images with no error correction. Over good local links, the VHF packet system will be able to deliver perfect images faster or of higher quality.

TEXT REPRESENTATIONS

Morse code is well known as an early code used to send text data over a wire, then over the air. Each letter/number or symbol is represented with a varying length code with the more common letters having shorter codes. This early *varicode* system is very efficient and minimizes the number of state changes required to send a message.

The Baudot code (pronounced "bawd-OH") was invented by Émile Baudot and is the predecessor to the character set currently known more accurately as International Telegraph Alphabet No 2 (ITA2). This code is used for radioteletype communications and contains five bits with start and stop pulses. This only allows for 2^5 or 32 possible characters to be sent, which is not enough for all 26 letters plus numbers and characters. To resolve this, ITA2 uses a LTRS code to select a table of upper case (only) letters and a FIGS code to select a table of numbers, punctuation and special symbols. The code is defined in the ITA2 codes table with the downloadable supplemental content.

Early computers used a wide variety of alphabetic codes until the early 1960s until the advent of the American Standard Code for Information Interchange or ASCII (pronounced "ESS-key"). At that point many computers standardized on this character set to allow simple transfer of data between machines. ASCII is a 7-bit code which allows for 2^7 or 128 characters. It was designed without the *control characters* used by Baudot for more reliable transmissions and the letters appear in English alphabetical order for easy sorting. The code can be reduced to only six bits and still carry numbers and uppercase letters. Current FCC regulations provide that amateur use of ASCII conform to ASCII as defined in ANSI standard X3.4-1977. The international counterparts are ISO 646-1983 and International Alphabet No. 5 (IA5) as published in ITU-T Recommendation V.3. A table of ASCII characters is presented as "ASCII Character Set" with the downloadable supplemental content.

ASCII has been modified and initially expanded to eight bits, allowing the addition of foreign characters or line segments. The different extended versions were often referred to as *code pages*. The IBM PC supported code page 437 which offers line segments, and English *Windows* natively supports code page 1252 with additional foreign characters and symbols. All of these extended code pages include the same first 128 ASCII characters for backward compatibility. In the early 1990s efforts were made to support more languages directly and *Unicode* was created. Unicode generally requires 16 bits per character and can represent nearly any language.

More recent schemes use varicode, where the most common characters are given shorter codes (see **en.wikipedia.org/wiki/Prefix_code**). Varicode is used in PSK31 and MFSK to reduce the number of bits in a message. Although the PSK31 varicode contains all 128 ASCII characters, lower-case letters contain fewer bits and can be sent more quickly. Tables of PSK and MFSK varicode characters are included with the downloadable supplemental content.

IMAGE DATA REPRESENTATIONS

Images are generally broken into two basic types, *raster* and *vector*. Raster or *bitmap* images are simply rows of colored points known as *pixels* (picture elements). Vector images are a set of drawing primitives or instructions. These instructions define shapes, placement, size and color. Similar coding is used with plotters to command the pens to create the desired image.

Bitmap images can be stored at various *color depths* or bits per pixel indicating how many colors can be represented. Common color depths are 1-bit (2 colors), 4-bit (16 colors), 8-bit (256 colors), 16-bit (65,536 colors also called *high color*) and 24-bit (16

Table 15.2
Typical Audio Formats

Audio Format	Bits per Sample	Dynamic Range	Maximum Frequency	kbytes per Minute
44.1 kHz stereo	16	98	22.050 kHz	10,584
22 kHz mono	16	98	11 kHz	2,640
8 kHz mono	8	50	4 kHz	960

million also called *true color*). True color is most commonly used with digital cameras and conveniently provides eight bits of resolution each for the red, green and blue colors. Newer scanners and other systems will often generate 30-bit (2^{30} colors) and 36-bit (2^{36} colors). Images with 4- and 8-bit color can store more accurate images than might be obvious because they include a *palette* where each of their 16 or 256 colors respectively are chosen from a palette of 16 million. This palette is stored in the file which works well for simple images. The GIF format only supports 256 colors (8-bit) with a palette and lossless compression.

Digital photographs are raster images at a specific resolution and color depth. A typical low resolution digital camera image would be 640×480 pixels with 24-bit color. The 24-bit color indicated for each pixel requires three bytes to store (24 bits / 8 bits per byte) and can represent one of a possible 2^{24} or 16,777,216 colors with eight bits each for red, green and blue intensities. The raw (uncompressed) storage requirement for this image would be 640×480×3 or 921,600 bytes. This relatively low resolution image would require significant time to transmit over a slow link.

Vector images are generally created with drawing or CAD packages and can offer significant detail while remaining quite small. Because vector files are simply drawn at the desired resolution, there is no degradation of the image if the size is changed and the storage requirements remain the same at any resolution. Typical drawing primitives include lines and polylines, polygons, circles and ellipses, Bézier curves and text. Even computer font technologies such as TrueType create each letter from Bézier curves allowing for flawless scaling to any size and resolution on a screen or printer.

Raster images can be resized by dropping or adding pixels or changing the color depth. The 640×480×24-bit color image mentioned above could be reduced to 320×240×16-bit color with a raw size of 153,600 bytes — a significant saving over the 921,600 byte original. If the image is intended for screen display and doesn't require significant detail, that size may be appropriate. If the image is printed full sized on a typical 300 dpi (dots per inch) printer, each pixel in the photo will explode to nearly 100 dots on the printer and appear very blocky or pixilated.

AUDIO DATA REPRESENTATIONS

Like images, audio can be stored as a sampled waveform or in some type of primitive format. Storing a sampled waveform is the most versatile but can also require substantial storage capacity. MIDI (musical instrument digital interface, pronounced "MID-ee") is a common music format that stores instrument, note, tempo and intensity information as a musical score. There are also voice coding techniques that store speech as *allophones* (basic human speech sounds).

As with images, storage of primitives can save storage space (and transmission times) but they are not as rich as a high quality sampled waveform. Unfortunately, the 44,100 Hz 16-bit sample rate of an audio compact disc (CD) requires 176,400 bytes to store each second and 10,584,000 bytes for each minute of stereo audio.

The Nyquist-Shannon sampling theorem states that perfect reconstruction of a signal is possible when the sampling frequency is at least twice the maximum frequency of the signal being sampled. With its 44,100 Hz sample rate, CD audio is limited to a maximum frequency response of 22,050 Hz. If only voice-quality is desired, the sample rate can easily be dropped to 8000 Hz providing a maximum 4000 Hz frequency response. (See the **DSP and SDR Fundamentals** chapter for more information on sampling.)

The *bit depth* (number of bits used to represent each sample) of an audio signal will determine the theoretical dynamic range or signal-to-noise ratio (SNR). This is expressed with the formula SNR = (1.761 + 6.0206 × bits) dB. A dynamic range of 40 dB is adequate for the perception of human speech. **Table 15.2** compares the audio quality of various formats with the storage (or transmission) requirements.

VIDEO DATA REPRESENTATIONS

The most basic video format simply stores a series of images for playback. Video can place huge demand on storage and bandwidth because 30 frames per second is a common rate for smooth-appearing video. Rates as low as 15 frames per second can still be considered "full-motion" but will appear jerky and even this rate requires substantial storage. Primitive formats are less common for video but animation systems like Adobe *Flash* are often found on the web.

15.1.4 Compression Techniques

There are a large variety of compression algorithms available to reduce the size of data stored or sent over a transmission medium. Many techniques are targeted at specific types of data (text, audio, images or video). These compression techniques can be broken into two major categories: *lossless compression* and *lossy compression*. Lossless algorithms are important for compressing data that must arrive perfectly intact but offer a smaller compression ratio than lossy techniques. Programs, documents, databases, spreadsheets would all be corrupted and made worthless if a lossy compression technique were used.

Images, audio and video are good candidates for lossy compression schemes with their substantially higher compression rates. As the name implies, a lossy compression scheme deliberately omits or simplifies that data to be able to represent it efficiently. The human eye and ear can easily interpolate missing information and it simply appears to be of lower quality.

Compression of a real-time stream of data such as audio or video is performed by software or firmware *codecs* (from *co*der-*dec*oder). Codecs provide the real-time encoding or decoding of the audio or video stream. Many codecs are proprietary and have licensing requirements. Codecs can be implemented as operating system or application plug-ins or even as digital ICs, as with the P25 IMBE and D-STAR AMBE codecs.

There are also specifically designed low bit-rate codecs for voice that are more accurately called *vocoders*. Vocoders are optimized for voice characteristics and can encode it extremely efficiently. Conversely, they cannot effectively process non-voice signals. This is easily demonstrated with a mobile phone by listening to music through a voice connection, such as when a call is placed on hold. Mobile phones use highly efficient vocoders to minimize the bandwidth of each voice channel which allows more channels per tower. This also means that non-voice sounds such as music or mechanical sounds are not well reproduced.

Good vocoders are extremely valuable and vigorously guarded by their patent holders. This has made it difficult for amateurs to experiment with digital voice techniques. David Rowe, VK5DGR, worked for several years on a project called CODEC2. This is a very effective open source vocoder made available at the end of 2012. It has been incorporated into the *FDMDV* software and there has been extensive testing and tuning made on the HF bands. More information about the project can be found at **www.rowatel.com**. Digital voice is discussed elsewhere in this chapter.

LOSSLESS COMPRESSION TECHNIQUES

One of the earliest lossless compression schemes is known as *Huffman coding*. Huffman coding creates a tree of commonly used data values and gives the most common values a lower bit count. Varicode is based on this mechanism. In 1984, Terry Welch released code with improvements to a scheme from Abraham Lempel and Jacob Ziv, commonly referred to as *LZW* (Lempel-Ziv-Welch). The Lempel-Ziv algorithm and variants are the basis for most current compression programs and is used in the GIF and optionally TIFF graphic formats. *LZW* operates similarly to Huffman coding but with greater efficiency.

The actual amount of compression achieved will depend on how redundant the data is and the size of the data being compressed. Large files will achieve greater compression rates because the common data combinations will be seen more frequently. Simple text and documents can often see 25% compression rates. Spreadsheets and databases generally consist of many empty cells and can often achieve nearly 50% compression. Graphic and video compression will vary greatly depending on the complexity of the image. Simple images with solid backgrounds will compress well where complex images with little recurring data will see little benefit. Similarly, music will compress poorly but spoken audio with little background noise may see reasonable compression rates.

Run length encoding (*RLE*) is a very simple scheme supported on bitmap graphics (*Windows* BMP files). Each value in the file is a color value and "run length" specifying how many of the next pixels will be that color. It works well on simple files but can make a file larger if the image is too complex.

It is important to note that compressing a previously compressed file will often yield a larger file because it simply creates more overhead in the file. There is occasionally some minor benefit if two different compression algorithms are used. It is not possible to compress the same file repeatedly and expect any significant benefit. Modern compression software does offer the additional benefit of being able to compress groups of files or even whole directory structures into a single file for transmission.

The compression mechanisms mentioned above allow files to be compressed prior to transmission but there are also mechanisms that allow near real-time compression of the transmitted data. V.92 modems implement a LZJH adaptive compression scheme called V.44 that can average 15% better throughput over the wire. Winlink uses a compression scheme called B2F and sees an average 44% improvement in performance since most Winlink data is uncompressed previously. Many online services offer "Web Accelerators" that also compress data going over the wire to achieve better performance. There is a slight delay (latency) as a result of this compression but over a slow link, the additional latency is minimal compared to the performance gain.

LOSSY COMPRESSION SCHEMES

Lossy compression schemes depend on the human brain to "recover" or simply ignore the missing data. Since audio, image and video data have unique characteristics as perceived by the brain, each of these data types have unique compression algorithms. New compression schemes are developed constantly to achieve high compression rates while maintaining the highest quality. Often a particular file format actually supports multiple compression schemes or is available in different versions as better methods are developed. In-depth discussion of each of these algorithms is beyond the scope of this book but there are some important issues to consider when looking at these compression methods.

Lossy Audio Compression

Audio compression is based on the psychoacoustic model that describes which parts of a digital audio signal can be removed or substantially reduced without affecting the perceived quality of the sound. Lossy audio compression schemes can typically reduce the size of the file 10- or 12-fold with little loss in quality. The most common formats currently are MP3, WMA, AAC, Ogg Vorbis and ATRAC.

Lossy Image Compression

The Joint Photographic Experts Group developed the JPEG format (pronounced "JAY-peg") in 1992 and it has become the primary format used for lossy compression of digital images. It is a scalable compression scheme allowing the user to determine the level of compression/quality of the image. Compression rates of 10-fold are common with good quality and can be over 100-fold at substantially reduced quality. The JPEG format tends to enhance edges and substantially compress fields of similar color. It is not well suited when multiple edits will be required because each copy will have generational loss and therefore reduced quality.

Lossy Video Compression

Because of the massive amount of data required for video compression it is almost always distributed with a lossy compression scheme. Lossless compression is only used when editing to eliminate generational loss. Video support on a computer is generally implemented with a codec that allows encoding and decoding the video stream. Video files are containers that can often support more than one video format and the specific format information is contained in the file. When the file is opened, this format information is read and the appropriate codec is activated and fed into the data stream to be decoded.

The most common current codecs are H.261 (video conferencing), MPEG-1 (used in video CDs), MPEG-2 (DVD Video), H.263 (video conferencing), MPEG-4, DivX, Xvid, H.264, Sorenson 3 (used by *QuickTime*), WMV (Microsoft), VC-1, RealVideo (RealNetworks) and Cinepak.

The basic mechanism of video compression is to encode a high quality "key-frame" that could be a JPEG image as a starting image. Successive video frames or "inter-

---

FLDIGI

By Ken Humbertson, WØKAH, and Jeff Coval, ACØSC

You may have heard of the free digital mode software *fldigi* by David H. Freese Jr., W1HKJ. It is very popular for use in emergency communications, for example, because of its multimode capabilities and its ability to work with a companion program *flmsg* that generates standard message forms to be transmitted using *fldigi*. The software supports more than 34 modes (as of early 2013) as well as variations of tones, bandwidth, baud rates, number of bits, and other variations for many modes. Versions of *fldigi* are available for Linux/Free-BSD, *Windows* XP/W2K/NT/Vista/Win7, and OS X. See **www.w1hkj.com** for information on downloading the files.

If you have a computer with a sound card and microphone, you can begin using *fldigi* to receive with no additional hardware. A quick example would be to tune to 14.070 MHz or 21.070 MHz USB during the day. Set the radio speaker volume to a normal listening level. Start *fldigi* on the computer with sound card and microphone connected and you should see a waterfall display similar to **Figure 15.A** (left).

If your rig has computer control capability, *fldigi* can likely interface with it to display frequency and mode, as well as control the radio from the program. In Figure 15.A, an ICOM IC-7000 is controlled by *fldigi* and thus shows the current operating frequency and mode of 21.070 MHz USB, the QSO frequency of 21071.511 (kHz) (in the windows at the upper left corner), and the current mode of BPSK31 (lower left corner).

When you see multiple signals in the waterfall, *fldigi* will decode whichever one you choose when you place the mouse cursor over a signal of interest and line up the two vertical red lines on your screen with the sides of the signal, as shown near 1500 Hz. When you change modes or bandwidths within a mode, the spacing of the red lines will adjust to the new bandwidth. **Figure 15.B** (right) shows that by selecting RTTY-45 under the OP MODE tab, you will notice that the red line spacing increases to match the familiar RTTY tone shift of 170 Hz. Simply place the two red lines over the signal you wish to decode and the program does the rest.

Figure 15.B shows a decoded ARRL digital bulletin from January 2, 2013. While the examples show BPSK31 and RTTY, there are many operating modes to choose from, including CW.

Actions in *fldigi* are performed by action buttons that invoke *macros* — text scripts that control the program. For example, to call CQ use the mouse to click on an unoccupied spot in the waterfall display. This shifts the modulating tones of the signal to that offset within your receive bandwidth. Click the CQ action button on the *fldigi* display. The transmitted text is displayed in red above the waterfall display. When the text is finished, *fldigi* will return to receive mode. The tutorial "Beginner's Guide to Fldigi" at **www.w1hkj.com/beginners.html** is recommended and the program has an extensive Help file.

The program can be used with an internal sound card or external sound card adapter such as the Tigertronics Signalink USB (**www.tigertronics.com**) or West Mountain Radio Rigblaster series (**www.westmountainradio.com**). Setting up a sound card to use *fldigi* may require manipulation of the audio device configuration for your computer's operating system. Follow the instructions in the *fldigi* manuals and the manufacturer's manuals if you are using an external adapter. A digital data interface that allows you to connect the sound card to your rig's microphone input is recommended. (See the **Assembling a Station** chapter and the **Digital Communications** chapter with the online supplemental content.

Fldigi is frequently updated to include new modes that are being developed. The program is a user-friendly way to become active on the digital modes, a rapidly expanding aspect of Amateur Radio.

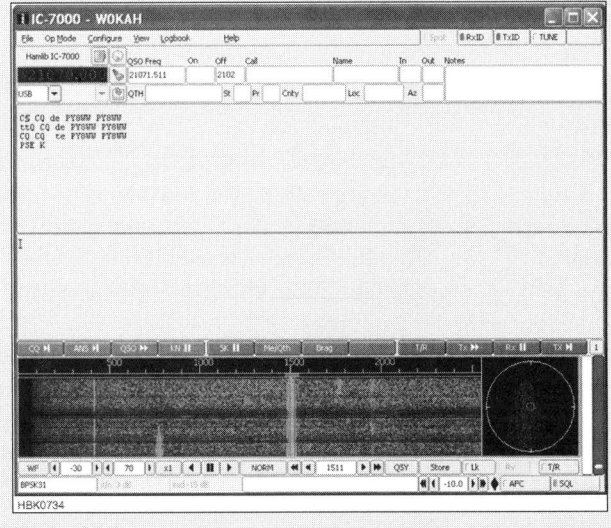

Figure 15.A

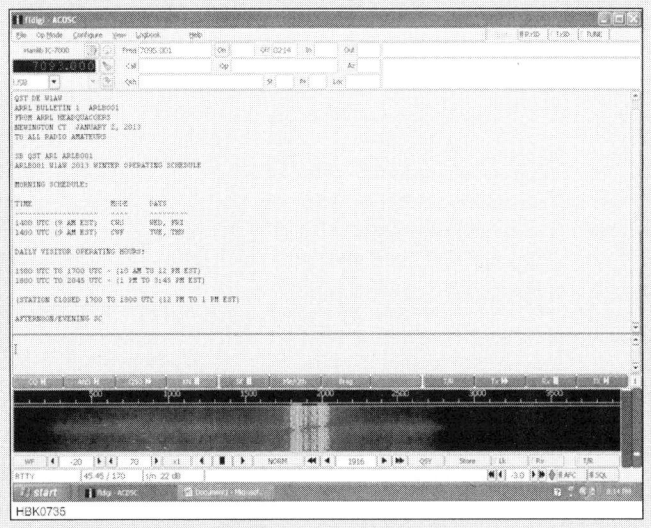

Figure 15.B

frames" contain only changes to the previous frame. After some number of frames, it is necessary to use another key-frame and start over with inter-frames. The resolution of the images, frame rate and compression quality determine the size of the video file.

BIT RATE COMPARISON

Table 15.3 provides an indication of minimum bit rates required to transmit audio and video such that the average listener would not perceive them significantly worse than the standard shown.

Table 15.3
Audio and Video Bit Rates

Audio
8 kbit/s	Telephone quality audio (using speech codecs)
32 kbit/s	AM broadcast quality (using MP3)
96 kbit/s	FM broadcast quality (using MP3)
224-320 kbit/s	Near-CD quality, indistinguishable to the average listener (using MP3)

Video
16 kbit/s	Videophone quality (minimum for "talking head")
128-384 kbit/s	Business videoconference system quality
1.25 Mbit/s	VCD (video compact disk) quality
5 Mbit/s	DVD quality
10.5 Mbit/s	Actual DVD video bit rate

15.1.5 Compression vs. Encryption

There is some confusion about compression being a form of encryption. It is true that a text file after compression can no longer be read unless uncompressed with the appropriate algorithm. In the United States the FCC defines encryption in part 97.113 as "messages encoded for the purpose of obscuring their meaning." Compressing a file with ZIP or RAR (common file compression methods) and transmitting it over the air is simply an efficient use of spectrum and time and is not intended to "obscure its meaning."

As amateur digital modes interact more with Internet-based services, the issue arises because many of these services utilize encryption of various types. Banks and other retailers may encrypt their entire transactions to insure confidentiality of personal data. Other systems as benign as e-mail may simply encrypt passwords to properly authenticate users. The FCC has offered no additional guidance on these issues.

15.2 Unstructured Digital Modes

The first group of modes we'll examine are generally considered "sound card modes" for keyboard-to-keyboard communications. Because each of these modes is optimized for a specific purpose by blending multiple features, they often defy simple categorization.

15.2.1 Radioteletype (RTTY)

Radioteletype (*RTTY*) consists of a *frequency shift keyed* (*FSK*) signal that is modulated between two carrier frequencies, called the *mark* frequency and the *space* frequency. The protocol for amateur RTTY calls for the mark carrier frequency to be the higher of the two in the RF spectrum. The difference between the mark and space frequencies is called the *FSK shift*, usually 170 Hz for an amateur RTTY signal.

At the conventional data speed of 60 WPM, binary information modulates the FSK signal at 22 ms per bit, or equivalent to 45.45 baud. Characters are encoded into binary 5-bit Baudot coded data. Each character is individually synchronized by adding a start bit before the 5-bit code and by appending the code with a stop bit. The start bit has the same duration as the data bits, but the stop bit can be anywhere between 22 to 44 ms in duration. The stop bit is transmitted as a mark carrier, and the RTTY signal "rests" at this state until a new character comes along. If the number of stop bits is set to two, the RTTY signal will send a minimum of 44 ms of mark carrier before the next start bit is sent. A start bit is sent as a space carrier. A zero in the Baudot code is sent as a space signal and a one is sent as a mark signal. **Figure 15.1** shows the character D sent by RTTY.

BAUDOT CODE

The Baudot code (see the downloadable supplemental content) is a 5-bit code; thus, it is capable of encoding only 32 unique characters. Since the combination of alphabets, decimal numbers and common punctuations exceeds 32, the Baudot code is created as two sets of tables. One table is called the LTRS Shift, and consists mainly of alphabetic characters. The second table is called the FIGS Shift, and consists mainly of decimal numerals and punctuation marks. Two unique Baudot characters called LTRS and FIGS are used by the sender to command the decoder to switch between these two tables.

Mechanical teletypewriter keyboards have two keys to send the LTRS and FIGS characters. The two keys behave much like the caps lock key on a modern typewriter keyboard. Instead of locking the keyboard of a typewriter to upper case shift or lower case shift, the two teletypewriter keys lock the state of the teletypewriter into the LTRS table or the FIGS table. LTRS and FIGS, among some other characters such as the space character, appear in both LTRS and FIGS tables so that you can send LTRS, FIGS and shift no matter which table the encoder is using.

To send the letter Q, you need to first make sure that the decoder is currently using the LTRS table, and then send the Baudot codeword for Q, 17 (hexadecimal or "hex" value). If the same hex 17 is received when the decoder is in the FIGS shift, the number 1 will be decoded instead of the Q. Modern software does away with the need for the operator to manually send the LTRS and FIGS codes.

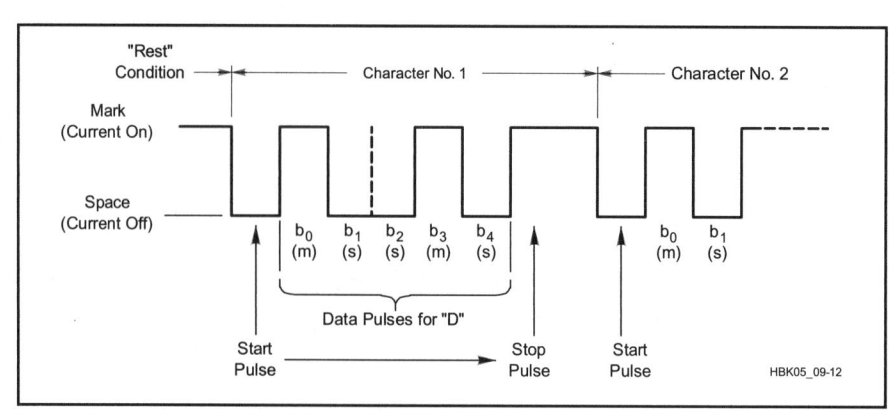

Figure 15.1 — The character "D" sent via RTTY.

When the operator sends a character from the LTRS table, the software first checks to make sure that the previous character had also used a character from the LTRS table; if not, the software will first send a LTRS character.

Noise can often cause the LTRS or FIGS character to be incorrectly received. This will cause subsequent characters to decode into the wrong Baudot character, until a correct LTRS or FIGS is received (see also USOS below). Instead of asking that the message be repeated by the sender, a trick that many RTTY operators use is to observe that on a standard QWERTY keyboard, the Q key is below the 1 key in the row above it, the W key is below the 2 key, and so on. Q and 1 happen to share the same Baudot code; W and 2 share the same Baudot code, and so forth. Given this visual aid, a printed UE can easily be interpreted by context to 73 and TOO interpreted as 599.

If the sender uses one stop bit, an RTTY character consists of a total of seven bits after adding the start and stop bits. If the sender uses 1.5 stop bits, each RTTY character has a total length of 7.5 bits. The least significant bit of the Baudot code follows the start bit of a character.

INVERTED SIGNALS

There are times when the sender does not comply with the RTTY standard and reverses the mark and space order in the spectrum. This is often called an "inverted" signal or "reverse shift." Most RTTY modulators and demodulators have a provision to reverse the shift of an inverted signal.

DEMODULATION AND DECODING

The most common way to decode an RTTY signal is to use a single sideband (SSB) receiver to first translate the two FSK carriers into two audio tones. If the carriers are 170 Hz apart, the two audio tones (called the *tone pair*) will also be 170 Hz apart. The RTTY demodulator, in the form of a terminal unit (TU) or a software modem (modulator-demodulator), then works to discriminate between the two audio tones. Some packet TNCs (terminal node controllers) can be made to function as RTTY demodulators, but often they do not work as well under poor signal-to-noise conditions because their filters are matched to packet radio FSK shifts and baud rate instead of to RTTY shift and baud rate.

As long as the tone pair separation is 170 Hz, the frequencies of the two audio tones can be quite arbitrary. Many TUs and modems are constructed to handle a range of tone pairs. If reception uses a lower sideband (LSB) receiver, the higher mark carrier will become the lower of the two audio tones. If upper sideband (USB) is used, the mark carrier will remain the higher of the tone pair. It is common to use 2125 Hz as the mark tone and 2295 Hz as a space tone. Since the mark tone (2125 Hz) is lower in frequency, the receiver will be set to LSB. In general, modem tone pairs can be "reversed" (see the Inverted Signals section), so either an LSB or a USB receiver can be used. Moreover, the tone pairs of many modems, especially software modems, can be moved to place them where narrowband filters are available on the receiver.

In the past, audio FSK demodulators were built using high-Q audio filters followed by a "slicer" to determine if the signal from the mark filter is stronger or weaker than the signal that comes out of the space filter. To counter selective fading, where ionospheric propagation can cause the mark carrier to become stronger or weaker than the space carrier, the slicer's threshold can be designed to adapt to the imbalance. Once "sliced" into a bi-level signal, the binary stream is passed to the decoder where start bit detection circuitry determines where to extract the 5-bit character data. That data is then passed to the Baudot decoder, which uses the current LTRS or FIGS state to determine the decoded character. The mark and space transmitted carriers do not overlap, although this can occur after they pass through certain HF propagation conditions. Sophisticated demodulators can account for this distortion.

A software modem performs the same functions as a hardware terminal unit, except that the software modems can apply more sophisticated mathematics that would be too expensive to implement in hardware. Modern desktop computers have more than enough processing speed to implement an RTTY demodulator. Software modems first convert the audio signal into a sequence of binary numbers using an analog-to-digital converter which is usually part of an audio chip set either on the motherboard or sound card. Everything from that point on uses numerical algorithms to implement the demodulation processes.

FSK VS AFSK MODULATION

An RTTY signal is usually generated as an F1B or F2B emission. F1B is implemented by directly shifting an RF carrier between the two (mark and space) frequencies. This method of generating FSK is often called *direct FSK*, or *true FSK*, or simply FSK. F2B is implemented by shifting between two audio tones, instead of two RF carriers. The resultant audio is then sent to an SSB transmitter to become two RF carriers. This method of first generating an audio FSK signal and then modulating an SSB transmitter to achieve the same FSK spectrum is usually called AFSK (audio frequency shift keying).

AFSK can be generated by using either an upper sideband (USB) transmitter or a lower sideband (LSB) transmitter. With a USB transmitter, the mark tone must be the *higher* of the two audio tones in the audio FSK signal. The USB modulator will then place the corresponding mark carrier at the higher of the two FSK carrier frequencies. When LSB transmission is used, the mark tone must be the *lower* of the two audio tones in the audio FSK signal. The LSB modulator will then place the corresponding mark carrier at the higher of the two FSK carrier frequencies. As when receiving, the actual audio tones are of no importance. The important part of AFSK is to have the two audio tones separated by 170 Hz, and have the pair properly flipped to match the choice of USB or LSB transmission. (See the **Modulation** chapter for more information on USB and LSB modulation and the relationship between modulating frequency and transmitted signal frequency.)

When using AFSK with older transceivers, it is wise to choose a high tone pair so that harmonic by-products fall outside the passband of the transmitter. Because of this, a popular tone pair is 2125 Hz/2295 Hz. Most transceivers will pass both tones and also have good suppression of the harmonics of the two tones. Not all transceivers that have an FSK input are FSK transmitters. Some transceivers will take the FSK keying input and modulate an internal AFSK generator, which is then used to modulate an SSB transmitter. In this case, the transmitter is really operating as an F2B emitter. This mode of operation is often called "keyed AFSK."

"SPOTTING" AN RTTY SIGNAL

By convention, RTTY signals are identified by the frequency of the mark carrier on the RF spectrum. "Spotting" the suppressed carrier frequency dial of an SSB receiver is useless for someone else unless they also know whether the spotter is using upper or lower sideband and what tone pair the spotter's demodulator is using. The mark and space carriers are the only two constants, so the amateur RTTY standard is to spot the frequency of the mark carrier.

DIDDLE CHARACTERS

In between the stop bit of a preceding character and the start bit of the next character, the RTTY signal stays at the mark frequency. When the RTTY decoder is in this "rest" state, a mark-to-space transition tells a decoder that the start of a new character has arrived. Noise that causes a start bit to be misidentified can cause the RTTY decoder to fall out of sync. After losing sync, the decoder will use subsequent data bits to help it identify the location of the next potential start bit.

Since all mark-to-space transitions are potential locations of the leading edge of a start bit, this can cause multiple characters to be incorrectly decoded until proper synchronization is again achieved. This "character slippage" can be minimized somewhat by not allowing the RTTY signal to rest for longer than its stop bit duration. An idle or *diddle character* (so called because of the sound of the demodulated audio from an idle RTTY signal sending the idle characters) is inserted immediately after a stop bit when the operator is not actively typing. The idle character is a non-printing character from the Baudot set and most often the LTRS character is used. Baudot encodes a LTRS as five bits of all ones making it particularly useful when the decoder is recovering from a misidentified start bit.

An RTTY diddle is also useful when there is selective fading. Good RTTY demodulators counter selective fading by measuring the amplitudes of the mark and space signals and automatically adjusting the decoding threshold when making the decision of whether a mark or a space is being received. If a station does not transmit diddles and has been idle for a period of time, the receiver will have no idea if selective fading has affected the space frequency. By transmitting a diddle, the RTTY demodulator is ensured of a measurement of the strength of the space carrier during each character period.

UNSHIFT-ON-SPACE (USOS)

Since the Baudot code aliases characters (for example, Q is encoded to the same 5-bit code as 1) using the LTRS and FIGS Baudot shift to steer the decoder, decoding could turn into gibberish if the Baudot shift characters are altered by noise. For this reason, many amateurs use a protocol called *unshift-on-space* (USOS). Under this protocol, both the sender and the receiver agree that the Baudot character set is always shifted to the LTRS state after a space character is received. In a stream of text that includes space characters, this provides additional, implicit, Baudot shifts.

Not everyone uses USOS. When used with messages that have mostly numbers and spaces, the use of USOS causes extra FIGS characters to be sent. A decoder that complies with USOS will not properly decode an RTTY stream that does not have USOS set. Likewise, a decoder that has USOS turned off will not properly decode an RTTY stream that has USOS turned on.

OTHER FSK SHIFTS AND RTTY BAUD RATE

The most commonly used FSK shift in amateur RTTY is 170 Hz. However, on rare occasions stations can be found using 425 and 850 Hz shifts. The wider FSK shifts are especially useful in the presence of selective fading since they provide better frequency diversity than 170 Hz.

Because HF packet radio uses 200 Hz shifts, some TNCs use 200 Hz as the FSK shift for RTTY. Although they are mostly compatible with the 170 Hz shift protocol, under poor signal to noise ratio conditions these demodulators will produce more error hits than a demodulator that is designed for 170 Hz shift. Likewise, a signal that is transmitted using 170 Hz shift will not be optimally copied by a demodulator that is designed for a 200 Hz shift.

To conserve spectrum space, amateurs have experimented with narrower FSK shifts, down to 22.5 Hz. At 22.5 Hz, optimal demodulators are designed as *minimal shift keyed* (*MSK*) instead of frequency shift keyed (FSK) demodulators.

SOME PRACTICAL CHARACTERISTICS

When the demodulator is properly implemented, RTTY can be very resilient against certain HF fading conditions, namely when selective fading causes only one of the two FSK carriers to fade while the other carrier remains strong. However, RTTY is still susceptible to "flat fading" (where the mark and space channels both fade at the same instant). There is neither an error correction scheme nor an interleaver (a method of rearranging — interleaving — the distribution of bits to make errors easier to correct) that can make an RTTY decoder print through a flat and deep fade. The lack of a data interleaver, however, also makes RTTY a very interactive mode. There is practically no latency when compared to a mode such as MFSK16, where the interleaver causes a latency of over 120 bit durations before incoming data can even be decoded. This makes RTTY attractive to operating styles that have short exchanges with rapid turnarounds, such as in contests.

Although RTTY is not as "sensitive" as PSK31 (when there is no multipath, PSK31 has a lower error rate than RTTY when the same amount of power is used) it is not affected by phase distortion that can render even a strong PSK31 signal from being copied. When HF propagation conditions deteriorate, RTTY can often function as long as sufficient power is used. Tuning is also moderately uncritical with RTTY. When the signal-to-noise ratio is good, RTTY tuning can be off by 50 Hz and still print well.

15.2.2 PSK31 and Variants

PSK31 is a family of modes that uses differentially encoded varicode (see the next section), envelope-shaped phase shift keying. BPSK31, or binary PSK31, operates at 31.25 bit/s (one bit every 32 ms). QPSK31, or quadrature PSK31, operates at 31.25 baud. Each symbol consists of four possible quadrature phase change (or *dibits*) at the signaling rate of one dibit every 32 ms. QPSK31 sends a phase change symbol of 0°, 90°, 180° or 270° every 32 ms.

Characters that are typed from the keyboard are first encoded into variable-length varicode binary digits. With BPSK31, the varicode bits directly modulate the PSK31 modulator, causing a 180° phase change if the varicode bit is a 0 and keeping a constant phase if the varicode bit is a 1. With QPSK31, the varicode bits first pass through two convolution encoders to create a sequence of bit pairs (dibits). Each dibit is then used to shift the QPSK31 modulator into one of four different phase changes.

PSK63 is a double-clock-rate version of a PSK31 signal, operating at the rate of one symbol every 16 ms (62.5 symbols per second). PSK125 is a PSK31 signal clocked at four times the rate, with one symbol every 8 ms (125 symbols per second). Although PSK63 and PSK125 are both in use, including the binary and quadrature forms, the most popular PSK31 variant remains BPSK31.

Most implementations of PSK31 first generate an audio PSK31 signal. The audio signal is then used to modulate an SSB transmitter. Since BPSK31 is based upon phase reversals, it can be used with either upper sideband (USB) or lower sideband (LSB) systems. With QPSK31 however, the 90° and 270° phase shifts have to be swapped when using LSB transmitters or receivers.

PSK31 VARICODE

Characters that are sent in PSK31 are encoded as varicode, a variable length prefix code as varicode. As described earlier, characters that occur more frequently in English text, such as spaces and the lower-case e, are encoded into a fewer number of bits than characters that are less frequent in English, such as the character q and the upper case E.

PSK31 varicode characters always end with two bits of zeros. A space character is sent as a one followed by the two zeros (100); a lower case e is sent as two ones, again terminated by the two bits of zero (1100). None of the varicode code words contain two consecutive zero bits. Because of this, the PSK31 decoder can uniquely identify the boundary between characters. A special "character" in PSK31 is the idle code, which consists of nothing but the two prefix bits. A long pause at the keyboard is encoded into a string of even numbers of zeros. The start of a new character is signaled by the first non-zero bit received after at least two consecutive zeros.

CONVOLUTION CODE

As described earlier, QPSK31 encodes the varicode stream with two convolution encoders to form the dibits that are used to modulate the QPSK31 generator. Both convolution encoders are fourth-order polynomials, shown in **Figure 15.2**.

The varicode data is first inverted before the bits are given to the convolution encoders. The first polynomial generates the most significant bit and the second polynomial generates the least significant bit of the dibit. Since we are

$G_1(x) = x^4 + x^3 + 1$

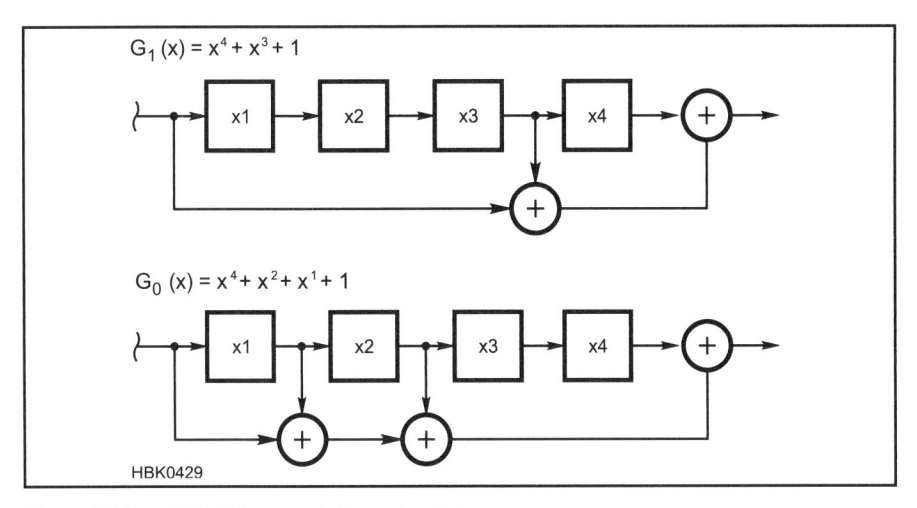

$G_0(x) = x^4 + x^2 + x^1 + 1$

Figure 15.2 — QPSK31 convolution encoders.

Table 15.4
QPSK31 Modulation

Dibit	Phase Change
00	0°
01	90°
10	180°
11	270°

working with binary numbers, the GF(2) sums shown in the above figure are exclusive-OR functions and the delay elements x1, x2, x3 and x4 are stages of binary shift registers. As each inverted varicode bit is available, it is clocked into the shift register and the two bits of the dibit are computed from the shift register taps.

MODULATION

PSK31 uses both differential phase shift modulation and envelope modulation to maintain its narrow-band characteristics. The most common way to generate an envelope-shaped PSK31 signal is to start with baseband in-phase (I) and quadrature (Q) signals. Both I and Q signals settle at either a value of +1 or a value of −1. When no phase transition is needed between symbols, the I and Q signals remain constant (at their original +1 or −1 values). See the **Modulation** chapter for information on creating I and Q signals.

To encode a 180° transition between symbols, both I and Q signals are slewed with a cosinusoidal envelope. If the in-phase signal had a value of +1 during the previous symbol, it is slewed to −1 cosinusoidally. If the in-phase signal had a value of −1 in the previous symbols, it is slewed cosinusoidally to +1. The quadrature signal behaves in a likewise manner. To encode a 90° phase shift in QPSK31, only the in-phase signal is slewed between the two symbols, the quadrature signal remains constant between the two symbols. To encode a 270° phase shift in QPSK31, only the quadrature signal is slewed between the two symbols; the in-phase signal remains constant between the two symbols.

The envelope of the real signal remains constant if there is no phase change. When the signal makes a 180° phase transition, the amplitude of a PSK31 signal will drop to zero in between the two symbols. The actual phase reversal occurs when the signal amplitude is zero, when there is no signal energy. During the 90° and 270° phase shifts between symbols of QPSK31, the amplitude of the signal does not reach zero. It dips to only half the peak power in between the two symbols.

To provide a changing envelope when the operator is idle at the keyboard, a zero in the varicode (remember that an idle varicode consists of two 0 bits) is encoded as a 180° phase change between two BPSK31 symbols. A 1 in the varicode is encoded as no phase change from one BPSK31 symbol to the next symbol. This changing envelope allows the receiver to extract bit timing information even when the sender is idle. Bit clock recovery is implemented by using a comb filter on the envelope of the PSK31 signal.

The convolution code that is used by QPSK31 converts a constant idle stream of zeros into a stream of repeated 10 dibits. To produce the same constant phase change during idle periods as BPSK31, the QPSK31 10 dibit is chosen to represent the 180° phase shift modulating term. **Table 15.4** shows the QPSK31 modulation.

To produce bit clocks during idle, combined with the particular convolution code that was chosen for QPSK31, results in a slightly sub-optimal (non-Gray code) encoding of the four dibits. At the end of a transmission, PSK31 stops all modulation for a short period and transmits a short unmodulated carrier. The intended function is as a squelch mechanism.

DEMODULATION AND DECODING

Many techniques are available to decode differential PSK, where a reference phase is not present. Okunev has a good presentation of the methods (reference: Yuri Okunev, *Phase and Phase-difference Modulation in Digital Communications* (1997, Artech House), ISBN 0-89006-937-9).

As mentioned earlier, there is sufficient amplitude information to extract the bit clock from a PSK31 signal. The output of a differential-phase demodulator is an estimate of the phase angle difference between the centers of one symbol and the previous one. With BPSK31, the output can be compared to a threshold to determine if a phase reversal or a non-reversal is more likely. The decoder then looks for two phase reversals in a row, followed by a non-reversal, to determine the beginning of a new character. The bits are gathered until two phase reversals are again seen and the accumulated bits are decoded into one of the characters in the varicode table.

QPSK31 decoding is more involved. As in the BPSK31 case, the phase difference demodulator estimates the phase change from one bit to another. However, one cannot simply invert the convolution function to derive the data dibits. Various techniques exist to decode the measured phase angles into dibits. The *Viterbi algorithm* is a relatively simple algorithm for the convolution polynomials used in QPSK31. The estimated phase angles can first be fixed to one of the four quadrature angles before the angles are submitted to the Viterbi algorithm. This is called a hard-decision *Viterbi decoder*.

A soft-decision Viterbi decoder (that is not that much more complex to construct) usually gives better results. The soft-decision decoder uses arbitrary phase angles and some measure of how "far" an angle is away from one of the four quadrature angles. Error correction occurs within the trellis that implements the Viterbi algorithm. References to convolution code, trellis and the Viterbi algorithm can be found at **en.wikipedia.org/wiki/Convolutional_code**.

15.2.3 MFSK16

MFSK16 uses M-ary FSK modulation with 16 "tones" (also known as 16-FSK modulation), where only a single tone is present at any instant. MFSK16 has a crest factor of 1, with no wave shaping performed on the data bits. The tone centers of MFSK16 are separated by 15.625 Hz. Data switches at a rate of 15.625 baud (one symbol change every 64 ms).

Characters are first encoded into the MFSK16 varicode, creating a constant bit stream whose rate is one bit every 32 ms. This results in a similar, although not identical, character rate as PSK31. The difference is due to the different varicode tables that are used by the two modes.

This bit stream is clocked into a pair of 6th-order convolution encoders. The result

$G_1(x) = x^6 + x^5 + x^3 + x^2 + 1$

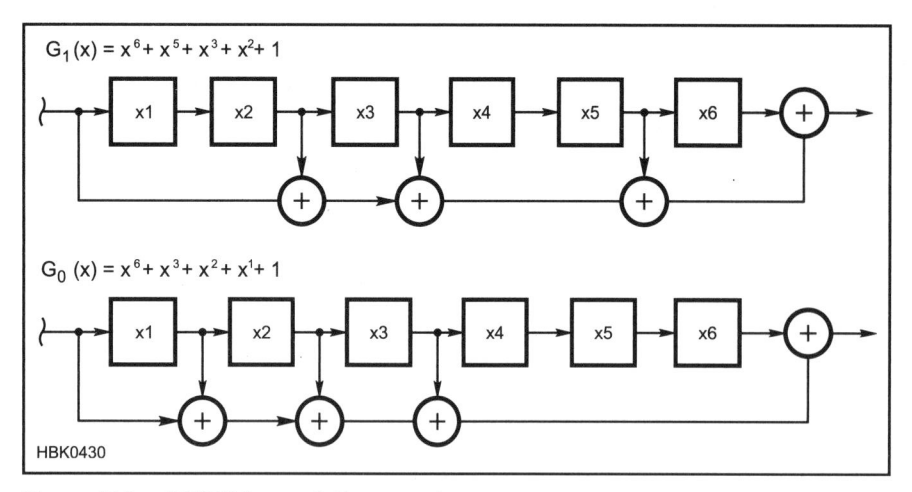

$G_0(x) = x^6 + x^3 + x^2 + x^1 + 1$

Figure 15.3 — MFSK16 convolution encoders.

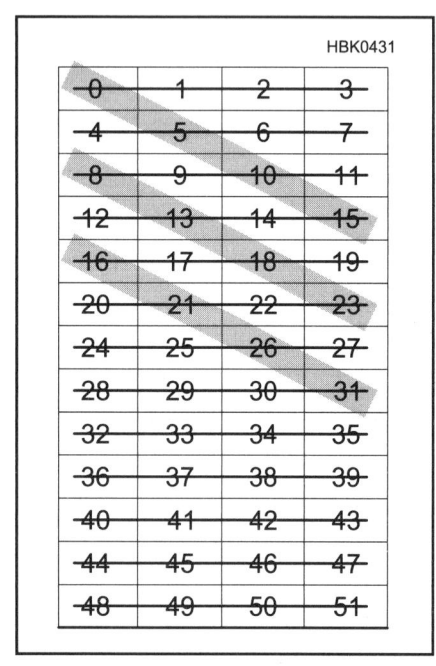

Figure 15.4 — IZ8BLY interleaver.

encodings can contain two or more consecutive zero bits, as long as the consecutive zeros are at the tail of a code word. Character boundaries are determined when two or more consecutive zeros are followed by a one.

CONVOLUTION CODE

As described earlier, MFSK16 encodes the varicode stream with two convolution encoders to form the dibits that are passed on to the interleaver. Both convolution encoders are sixth order polynomial, shown in **Figure 15.3**.

The first polynomial generates the most significant bit and the second polynomial generates the least significant bit of the dibit. Since we are working with binary numbers, the GF(2) sums shown in the above figure are exclusive OR functions and the delay elements x1, x2, x3, x4, x5 and x6 are stages of binary shift registers. As each varicode bit is available, it is clocked into the shift register and the two bits of the dibit are computed from the shift register taps.

INTERLEAVER

HF fading channels tend to generate "burst" errors that are clumped together. An interleaver is used to permute the errors temporally so that they appear as uncorrelated errors to the convolution decoder. MFSK16 uses 10 concatenated stages of an IZ8BLY Diagonal Interleaver. More information on the interleaver can be found at **www.qsl.net/zl1bpu/MFSK/Interleaver.htm**. **Figure 15.4** illustrates how a single IZ8BLY interleaver spreads a sequence of bits.

The bits enter the IZ8BLY interleaver in the order 0, 1, 2, 3, 4,... and are passed to the output in the order 0, 5, 10, 15, 8, 13, ... (shown in the diagonal boxes). In MFSK16, the output of one interleaver is sent to the input of a second interleaver, for a total of 10 such stages. Each stage spreads the bits out over a longer time frame.

is a pair of bits (dibit) for each varicode bit, at a rate of one dibit every 32 ms. Consecutive pairs of dibits are next combined into sets of four bits (*quadbit* or *nibble*). Each nibble, at the rate of one per 64 ms, is then passed through an interleaver. The interleaver produces one nibble for each nibble that is sent to it. Each nibble from the interleaver is then Gray-coded and the resultant 4-bit Gray code is the ordered index of each 16 tones that are separated by 15.625 Hz. The result is a 16-FSK signal with a rate of one symbol per 64 ms. Since the symbol time is the reciprocal of the tone separation, a 16-point fast Fourier transform (FFT) can be conveniently used as an MFSK16 modulator.

MFSK16 VARICODE

Although the varicode table that is used by MFSK16 (see the downloadable supplemental content) is not the same as the one used by PSK31, they share similar characteristics. Please refer to the PSK31 section of this chapter for a more detailed description of varicode. Unlike PSK31 varicode, MSK16 varicode

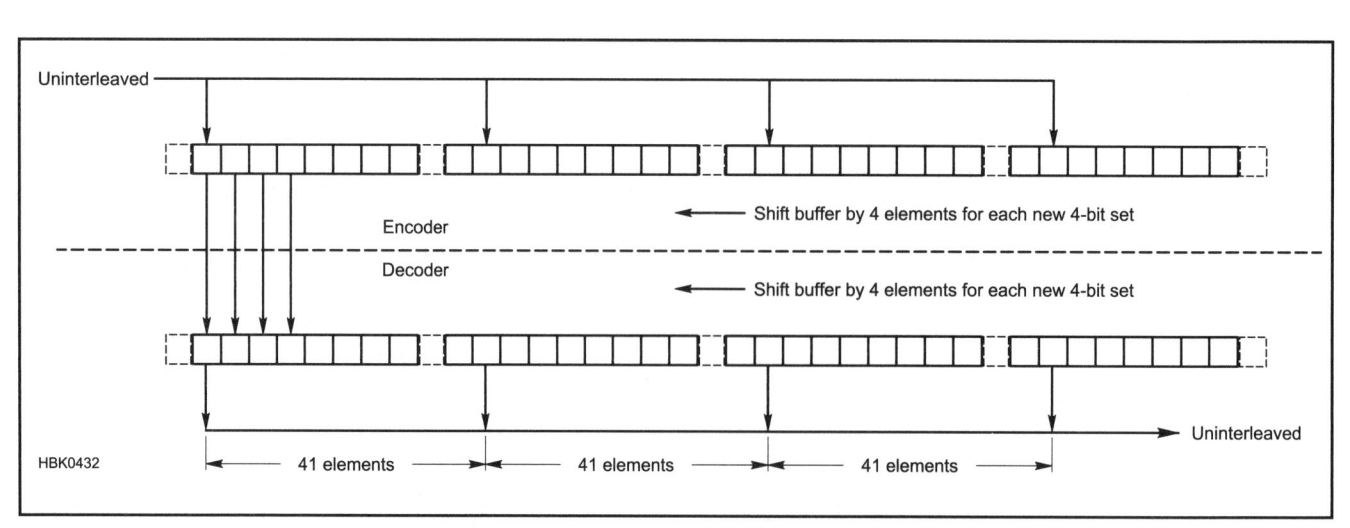

Figure 15.5 — Bit spreading through interpolation.

This concatenated 10-stage interpolator is equivalent to a single interpolator that is 123 bits long. **Figure 15.5** shows the structure of the single interpolator and demonstrates how four consecutive input bits are spread evenly over 123 time periods.

An error burst can be seen to be spread over a duration of almost two seconds. This gives MFSK16 the capability to correct errors over deep and long fades. While it is good for correcting errors, the delay through the long interleaver also causes a long decoding latency.

GRAY CODE

The Gray code creates a condition where tones that are next to one another are also different by a smaller *Hamming* distance. This optimizes the error correction process at the receiver. References to Gray code and Hamming distance can be found at **en.wikipedia.org/wiki/Gray_code** and **en.wikipedia.org/wiki/Hamming_distance** and **en.wikipedia.org/wiki/Hamming_distance**.

DEMODULATION AND DECODING

A 16-point FFT can be used to implement a set of matched filters for demodulating an MFSK16 signal once the input waveform is properly time aligned so that each transform is performed on an integral symbol and the signal is tuned so that the MFSK16 tones are perfectly centered in the FFT bins. A reference to a matched filter can be found at **en.wikipedia.org/wiki/Matched_filter**.

The 16 output bins from an FFT demodulator can first be converted to the "best" 4-bit index of an FFT frequency bin, or they can be converted to a vector of four numerical values representing four "soft" bits. The four bits are then passed through an MFSK16 de-interleaver. In the case of "soft decoding," the de-interleaver would contain numerical values rather than a 0 or 1 bit.

The output of the de-interleaver is passed into a convolution decoder. The Gray code makes sure that adjacent FFT bins also have the lowest Hamming distance; i.e., the most likely error is also associated with the closest FFT bin. The hard or the soft Viterbi Algorithm can be used to decode and correct errors.

15.2.4 DominoEX

DominoEX is a digital mode with MFSK (multi-frequency shift keying) designed for simplex chats on HF by Murray Greenman, ZL1BPU. It was designed to be easier to use and tune than other similar modes, offer low latency for contesting or other quick exchange situations, offer reliable copy down into the noise floor, and work well as an NVIS (near-vertical incidence skywave, see the **Propagation of Radio Signals** chapter) mode for emergency communications.

Generally MFSK requires a high degree of tuning accuracy and frequency stability and can be susceptible to multipath distortion. DominoEX specifically addresses these issues. To avoid tuning issues, IFK (*incremental frequency keying*) is used. With IFK, the data is represented not by the frequency of each tone, but by the frequency difference between one tone and the next. It also uses offset incremental keying to reduce inter-symbol interference caused by multipath reception. These techniques provide a tuning tolerance of 200 Hz and a drift of 200 Hz/minute. DominoEX also features an optional FEC mode that increases latency but provides communications over even more difficult channels. More information can be found online at **www.qsl.net/zl1bpu/MFSK/DEX.htm**.

DominoEX uses M-ary FSK modulation with 18 tones in which only a single tone is present at any instant. Information is sent as a sequence of separate 4-bit ("nibble") symbols. The value of each nibble is represented during transmission as the position of the single tone.

The position of the tone is computed as the difference of the current nibble value from the nibble value of the previously transmitted symbol. In addition, a constant offset of 2 is applied to this difference. Because there are 18 tones, any possible 4-bit value between 0 and 15 can be represented, including the offset of 2.

The additional offset of 2 tone positions ensures that a transmitted tone is separated from the previously transmitted tone by at least two tone positions. It is thus impossible for two sequential symbols to result in the same tone being transmitted for two sequential tone periods. This means sequential tones will always be different by at least two positions, an important consideration in maintaining sync.

This minimum separation of successive tones of incremental frequency keying (IFK) in DominoEX reduces the inter-symbol distortion that results from a pulse being temporally smeared when passing through an HF channel. The double-tone spacing of DominoEX modes (see **Table 15.5**) further reduces inter-symbol distortion caused by frequency smearing.

Incremental frequency keying allows the DominoEX nibbles to immediately decode without having to wait for the absolute tone to be identified. With MFSK16, a tone cannot be uniquely identified until the lowest and highest of the 16 tones have passed through the receiver. This contributes to the decoding latency of MFSK15. There is no such latency with IFK.

Since IFK depends upon frequency differences and not absolute tone frequencies, DominoEX tolerates tuning errors and drifting signals without requiring any additional automatic frequency tracking algorithms.

Like MFSK16, the DominoEX signal is not wave-shaped and has constant output power. The baud rates for DominoEX are shown in Table 15.5. The tone spacings for DominoEX 11, DominoEX 16 and DominoEX 16 have the same values as their baud rates. The tone spacings for DominoEX 8, DominoEX 5 and DominoEX 4 are twice the value of their baud rates.

Unlike PSK31 and MFSK16, characters in DominoEX are encoded into varicode nibbles instead of encoding into varicode bits. The DominoEX varicode table can be found with the downloadable supplemental content.

BEACON MESSAGE

Instead of transmitting an idle varicode symbol when there is no keyboard activity, DominoEX transmits a "beacon" message from an alternate set of varicode (SECVAR columns in the DominoEX varicode table). This user-supplied repeating beacon message is displayed at the receiving station when the sending station is not actively sending the primary message. On average, the character rate of the beacon channel is about half of the character rate of the primary channel.

FORWARD ERROR CORRECTION (FEC)

When FEC is turned off, DominoEX has very low decoding latency, providing an interactive quality that approaches RTTY and PSK31. The first character is decoded virtually instantly by the receiver after it is transmitted. Because of that, FEC is not usually used even though it is available in most software that implements DominoEX.

DominoEX FEC is similar to the FEC that is used in MFSK15. When FEC is on, each 4-bit IFK symbol that is decoded by the receiver is split into two di-bits. The dibits enter

Table 15.5
Comparison of DominoEX Modes

Mode	Baud/(sec)	BW (Hz)	Tones	Speed (WPM)	FEC (WPM)	Tone Spacing
DominoEX 4	3.90625	173	18	~25	~12	Baud rate ×2
DominoEX 5	5.3833	244	18	~31	~16	Baud rate ×2
DominoEX 8	7.8125	346	18	~50	~25	Baud rate ×2
DominoEX 11	10.766	262	18	~70	~35	Baud rate ×1
DominoEX 16	15.625	355	18	~100	~50	Baud rate ×1
DominoEX 22	21.533	524	18	~140	~70	Baud rate ×1

an identical convolution coder to that used by MFSK15. However, instead of a 10-stage IZ8BLY interleaver (see Figure 15.4), only 4 cascaded stages of the basic 4-bit interleaver are present in DominoEX. In the presence of long duration fading, the performance of the shortened interleaver is moderately poor when used with DominoEX 16 and DominoEX 22. However, the interleaver is quite efficient in countering fading when FEC is used with DominoEX 4, DominoEX 5 and DominoEX 8, with their longer symbol periods.

Since DominoEX works in dibit units rather than nibble units when FEC is turned on, it also switches to using the same binary varicode used by MFSK16 instead of using the nibble-based varicode. DominoEX does not implement Gray code as is used by MFSK16 FEC.

Even without FEC, DominoEX works well under many HF propagation conditions, including the ITU NVIS ("Mid-latitude Disturbed") propagation profile. However, there are conditions where DominoEX is not usable unless FEC is switched on, specifically the CCIR Flutter and ITU High Latitude Moderate Conditions profiles. DominoEX modes, especially those with tone spacings that are twice the baud rate, are very robust even under these extreme conditions once FEC is switched on.

DominoEX performance charts (character error rates versus signal-to-noise ratios) are included as the HTML document "DominoEX Performance" with the downloadable supplemental content and online at **www.w7ay.net/site/Technical/DominoEX/Measurements/**.

CHIP64/128

Chip64 and Chip128 modes were released in 2004 by Antonino Porcino, IZ8BLY. The modes were tested on the air by IZ8BLY, Murray Greenman, ZL1BPU, (who also contributed in the design of the system), Chris Gerber, HB9BDM, and Manfred Salzwedel, OH/DK4ZC. According to IZ8BLY, "The design of this new digital mode served to introduce the spread spectrum technology among radio amateurs by providing a communication tool to experiment with. Its purpose was to prove that it's possible to take advantage of the spread spectrum techniques even on the HF channels, making the communication possible under conditions where traditional narrowband modes fail.

"Among the different possible implementations of spread spectrum, Chip64 uses the so-called Direct Sequence Spread Spectrum (DSSS). In a DSSS transmission, the low speed signal containing the data bits to be transmitted is mixed (multiplied) with a greatly higher speed signal called code. The result of this mixing operation, called s*preading*, is a high-speed bit stream which is then transmitted as a normal DBPSK. Indeed, a DSSS signal looks like nothing else than wideband BPSK.

"The system proved to be efficient and we found it comparable to the other modern digital modes. Being totally different in its architecture, it shows better performance during certain circumstances, while in others it shows no actual gain. In particular, it performs better under multipath where normal BPSK can't track arriving symbols, but in quiet environments it doesn't show any improvement over plain BPSK. This is expected because of the losses that occur due to the imperfect autocorrelation of the codes."

Chip64 has a total data rate of 37.5 bit/s and the more robust Chip128 is 21.09 bit/s. Both use the same varicode used by MFSK15. The software can be downloaded from **antoninoporcino.xoom.it/Chip64/index.htm** and more information is available at **www.arrl.org/technical-characteristics**. Spread spectrum is discussed in the **Modulation** chapter, as well.

15.2.5 THROB

Throb is an experimental mode written by Lionel Sear, G3PPT, and gets the name from the "throbbing" sound it makes on the air. It uses either single tones or pairs from a possible nine tones spaced 8 or 16 Hz apart, resulting in a bandwidth of 72 or 144 Hz, respectively. It has three transmission speeds — 1, 2 and 4 throbs/s — resulting in data rates of 10, 20 and 40 WPM, respectively. The 1 and 2 throb/s speeds use a tone spacing of 8 Hz for a 72 Hz bandwidth and the 4-throb/s speed uses a spacing of 16 Hz for a 144 Hz bandwidth. It is implemented as a standalone application or included in a multimode package such as *MixW* (**www.mixw.net**).

15.2.6 MT63

MT63 is a mode developed by Pawel Jalocha, SP9VRC. MT63 is very complex with wide bandwidth, low speed and very high noise immunity. By using 64 different modulated tones, MT63 includes a large amount of extra data in the transmission of each character, so that the receiving equipment can work out, with no ambiguity, which character was sent, even if 25% of the character is obliterated. MT63 also features a secondary channel that operates simultaneously with the main channel that can be used for an ID or beacon.

MT63 likely has the most extensive error correction and can be quite processor intensive. It uses a Walsh function that spreads the data bits of each 7-bit ASCII character across all 64 of the tones of the signal spectrum and simultaneously repeats the information over a period of 64 symbols within any one tone. This coding takes several seconds. The combination of time domain (temporal) and frequency domain (spectral) interleaving results in superb impulse noise rejection. At the same time, in the frequency domain, significant portions of the signal can be masked by unwanted noise or other transmissions without any noticeable effect on successful reception.

On each of the 64 tones, the transmission data rate is fairly slow, which suits the nature of ionospheric disturbances. Despite the low data rate, good text speed is maintained because the text is sent on many tones at once. The system runs at several different speeds, which can be chosen to suit conditions but 100 WPM is typical of the MT63-1K mode. Although the 1 kHz bandwidth mode is typical, MT63 can also run at 500 Hz and 2 kHz bandwidth where the tone spacing and baud rate are halved or doubled and the throughput is halved or doubled, respectively.

Tuning of MT63 modes is not critical. This is because the mode can use FEC techniques to examine different combinations of the 64 tones that calculate the correct location within the spectrum. As an example, MT63-1K will still work if the decoder is off-frequency by as much as 100 Hz. MT63-2K requires even less precision and can tolerate an error of 250 Hz.

The incredible noise immunity comes at a price beyond the large bandwidth required. There is a large latency caused by the error correction and interleaving process. Quick-turnaround QSOs are not possible because there is a several second delay between typing the last character and it being transmitted.

Without confirming each transmission with some type of ARQ mode, there is no more robust digital mode than MT63. The mode was evaluated and recommended for Navy MARS message handling. The evaluation is published on the Navy MARS website (**www.navymars.org**), along with other information on this mode.

15.2.7 Olivia

Olivia is an MFSK-based protocol designed to work in difficult (low signal-to-noise ratio plus multipath propagation) conditions on the HF bands. The signal can still be copied accurately at 10 dB below the noise floor. Olivia was developed in 2003 by Pawel Jalocha, SP9VRC, and performs well for digital data transfer with white noise, fading and multipath, polar path flutter and auroral conditions.

Olivia transmits a stream of 7-bit ASCII characters. The characters are sent in blocks of five with each block requiring two seconds to transmit. This results in an effective data rate of 2.5 characters/second or 150 characters/minute. A transmission bandwidth of 1000 Hz and the baud rate of 31.25 MFSK tones/second, also known as *Olivia 1000/32*, is the most common. To adapt to different propagation conditions, the number of tones and the bandwidth can be changed and the time and frequency parameters are proportionally scaled. The number of tones can be 2, 4, 8, 16, 32, 64, 128 or 256 and the bandwidth can be 125, 250, 500, 1000 or 2000 Hz.

The Olivia is constructed of two layers: the lower, modulation and FEC code layer is a classical MFSK while the higher layer is an FEC code based on Walsh functions. More detail on Walsh functions is available online at **en.wikipedia.org/wiki/Walsh_function**.

Assuming Olivia 1000/32 is being used, in the first layer the orthogonal functions are cosine functions, with 32 different tones. Since only one of those 32 tones is being sent at a time, the demodulator measures the amplitudes of all the 32 possible tones and identifies the tone with the highest amplitude. In the second layer every ASCII character is encoded as one of 64 possible Walsh functions. The receiver again measures the amplitudes for all 64 vectors and selects the greatest as the true value.

To avoid simple transmitted patterns (like a constant tone) and to minimize the chance for a false lock at the synchronizer, the characters encoded into the Walsh function pass through a scrambler and interleaver. The receiver synchronizes automatically by searching through time and frequency offsets for a matching pattern.

More information can be found online at **n1su.com/olivia** and Olivia is supported in a number of digital multimode packages such as *MixW*, *MultiPSK* and *Ham Radio Deluxe*.

15.3 Fuzzy Modes

There is a group of modes referred to as "fuzzy modes" because although they are machine generated and decoded, they are designed to be human-read. These include facsimile (fax), slow-scan TV (SSTV) and Hellschreiber.

15.3.1 Facsimile (fax)

Facsimile was developed as a mechanically transmitted technology where the source material was placed on a spinning drum and scanned line by line into an electrical signal which would be transmitted by wire or over the air. It is important that the receiving station have their drum spinning at the correct speed in order to correctly recreate the image. A value known as the *index of cooperation* (*IOC*) must also be known to decode a transmission. IOC governs the image resolution and is the product of the total line length and the number of lines per unit length divided by π. Most fax transmissions are sent with LPM (RPM) at 120 and an IOC of 576.

Facsimile is generally transmitted in single sideband with a tone of 1500 Hz representing black and 2300 Hz representing white. The *automatic picture transmission* (*APT*) format is used by most terrestrial weather facsimile stations and geostationary weather satellites. It features a start tone that triggers the receiving system, originally used to allow the receiving drum to come up to speed. It also includes a phasing signal with a periodic pulse that synchronizes the receiver so the image appears centered on the page. A stop tone, optionally followed by black, indicates the end of the transmission. The APT format is shown in **Table 15.6**.

Stations with Russian equipment sometimes use RPM 60 or 90 and sometimes an IOC of 288. Photofax transmissions such as those from North Korea use RPM 60 and an IOC 352 with gray tones, and satellite rebroadcast use also RPM 120 IOC 576, with gray tones (4 or more bit depth). For software decoding of weather fax images it is best to decode with Black and White (2-bit depth).

15.3.2 Slow-Scan TV (SSTV)

Slow-Scan TV or SSTV is similar to facsimile where a single image is converted to individual scanned lines and those lines sent as variable tones between 1500 and 2300 Hz. Modern systems use computer software and a sound card to generate and receive the required tones. (Some SSTV communication uses purely digital protocols, in which the picture content is sent as digital data and not directly represented in the modulation scheme.)

There are a number of different SSTV "modes" that define image resolution and color scheme. A color image takes about 2 minutes to transmit, depending on mode. Some black and white modes can transmit an image in under 10 seconds. More information about SSTV may be found in the **Image Communications** chapter with the downloadable supplemental content.

15.3.3 Hellschreiber, Feld-Hell or Hell

Hellschreiber is a facsimile-based mode developed by Rudolph Hell in the 1920s. The name is German and means "bright writer" or "light writer" and is a pun on the inventor's name. In Hellschreiber, text is transmitted by dividing each column into seven pixels and transmitting them sequentially starting at the lowest pixel. Black pixels are transmitted as a signal and white as silence at 122.5 bit/s (about a 35 WPM text rate). Originally the text was printed on continuous rolls of paper so the message could be any length.

Even though each pixel is only transmitted once, they are printed twice, one below the other. This compensates for slight timing errors in the equipment that causes the text to slant. If properly in sync, the text will appear as two identical rows, one below the other or a line of text in the middle with chopped lines top and bottom. Regardless of the slant, it is always possible to read one copy of the text. Since the text is read visually, it can be sent in nearly any language and tends to look like an old dot matrix printer. More information can be found online at **www.qsl.net/zl1bpu/ HELL/Feld.htm** and Randy, K7AGE, has a great introduction to Hellschreiber available on YouTube at **www.youtube.com/ watch?v=yR-EmyEBVqA**.

Table 15.6
Facsimile Automatic Picture Format

Signal	Duration	IOC576	IOC288	Remarks
Start Tone	5 s	300 Hz	675 Hz	200Hz for color fax modes
Phasing Signal	30 s			White line interrupted by black pulse
Image	Variable	1200 lines	600 lines	At 120 LPM
Stop Tone	5 s	450 Hz	450 Hz	
Black	10 s			

15.4 Structured Digital Modes

This group of digital modes has more structured data. This provides more robust data connections and better weak signal performance or more sophisticated data. Each of these modes bundles data into packets or blocks that can be transmitted and error checked at the receive end.

15.4.1 *WSJT-X* Modes

All modes described in Sections 15.4.1 through 15.4.4 are available in a multi-author, open-source software package called *WSJT-X*. Some are also available in other programs derived from *WSJT-X*. These modes are designed around structured messages that optimize the exchange of minimal contact information including call signs, signal reports, Maidenhead grid locators, and acknowledgments, even at very low signal-to-noise ratios. These modes were pioneered by Joe Taylor, K1JT, starting in 2001 when home computers were first widely equipped with sound cards and fast enough to do significant signal processing. The first modes were optimized for use over especially difficult paths such as meteor scatter and Earth-Moon-Earth (EME, or "moonbounce") on VHF and higher bands. More recently, several of the modes have become very popular for HF DXing, as well.

The *WSJT-X* structured modes divide naturally into two groups, *slow* and *fast*. Slow modes send each message frame once per transmission interval, while fast modes send the message frame repeatedly, as many times as will fit into the transmission interval. All but one share a common message format based on compressed, fixed-length packets of 72 information bits; the mode called WSPR uses 50-bit packets. As outlined in this chapter's section "Error Detection and Correction," a number of additional bits are added to the message frames to effect error detection and correction. Details of the mathematical encoding schemes and modulation types differ from mode to mode. In all cases the forward error correction (FEC) algorithm is strong enough that false decodes are very rare: a receiving operator nearly always sees exactly the message that was transmitted, or nothing at all. Transmissions have a fixed duration, for example one minute or 15 seconds, and their start times are synchronized with Coordinated Universal Time (UTC) as maintained by the computer's operating system.

15.4.2 Message Compression

The 72-bit information packets normally consist of two 28-bit call signs and a 15-bit field for a grid locator, signal report, acknowledgment, or "73". One additional bit flags messages containing arbitrary text, up to 13 characters. Special cases allow other information such as add-on call sign prefixes or suffixes (for example, EA8/G4XYZ, K1ABC/4) to be encoded. The basic aim is to compress the most common message formats used for minimal contacts into fixed-length packets.

A standard amateur call sign consists of a one- or two-character prefix, at least one of which must be a letter, followed by a digit and a suffix of one to three letters. Within these rules, the number of possible call signs is equal to 37×36×10×27×27×27, or somewhat over 262 million. (The numbers 27 and 37 arise because in the first and last three positions a character may be absent, or a letter, or perhaps a digit.) Since 2^{28} is more than 268 million, 28 bits are enough to encode any standard call sign uniquely. Similarly, the number of 4-digit Maidenhead grid locators on Earth is 180×180 = 32,400, which is less than 2^{15} = 32,768; thus, a grid locator requires 15 bits. Some otherwise unused values in the 28-bit fields are used for special message components such as CQ, DE, and QRZ, and some values of the 15-bit field not needed for grid locators are used for signal reports, acknowledgments, and the like. Structured messages using these 28-bit and 15-bit fields underlie the efficient, reliable exchange of basic and essential information for minimal station-to-station contacts.

15.4.3 Slow Modes

The slow modes in *WSJT-X* are called FT8, JT4, JT9, JT65, QRA64, and WSPR. Each mode uses continuous-phase frequency-shift keying (FSK), with waveforms normally generated at audio frequency and transmitted as upper sideband by a standard SSB transceiver. Numbers in the mode names indicate the number of distinct tone frequencies used. JT4, JT65, and QRA64 were originally designed for EME on VHF and higher UHF bands; JT9 was intended for the LF, MF, and lower HF bands, FT8 for multi-hop sporadic E at 50 MHz, and WSPR for probing potential propagation paths using low-power transmissions. Not surprisingly, amateurs have discovered many other ways in which each mode can be used. On the HF bands, worldwide contacts are possible with any of these modes using power levels of a few watts (or even milliwatts) and compromise antennas. Reliable two-way contacts can be made with signal levels far too weak to be heard, 10 to 15 dB below the levels required for Morse-coded CW when received and decoded by ear.

Table 15.7A provides a brief summary of essential parameters for the *WSJT-X* slow modes. Column 1 gives the mode name,

Table 15.7
Parameters of Structured Modes

A — Structured Slow Modes

Mode	FEC Type	(n, k)	Q	Modulation Type	Keying Rate	Bandwidth (Hz)	Sync Energy	Transmit Duration (s)	S/N Threshold (dB)
FT8	LDPC, r=1/2	(174,87)	8	8-FSK	6.25	50.0	0.27	12.6	-21
JT4	Convolutional	(206,72)	2	4-FSK	4.375	17.5	0.50	47.1	-23
JT9	Convolutional	(206,72)	8	9-FSK	1.736	15.6	0.19	49.0	-27
JT65	Reed Solomon	(63,12)	64	65-FSK	2.692	177.6	0.50	46.8	-25
QRA64	Q-ary Repeat Accumulate	(63,12)	64	64-FSK	1.736	111.1	0.25	48.4	-26
WSPR	Convolutional	(162,50)	2	4-FSK	1.465	5.9	0.50	110.6	-31

B — Structured Fast Modes

Mode	FEC Type	(n, k)	Q	Modulation Type	Keying Rate	Bandwidth (Hz)	Sync Energy	Transmit Duration (s)
JT9E	Convolutional	(206,72)	8	9-FSK	25	225	0.19	3.4
JT9F	Convolutional	(206,72)	8	9-FSK	50	450	0.19	1.7
JT9G	Convolutional	(206,72)	8	9-FSK	100	900	0.19	0.85
JT9H	Convolutional	(206,72)	8	9-FSK	200	1800	0.19	0.425
MSK144	LDPC	(128,80)	2	OQPSK	2000	2400	0.11	0.072

and column 2 gives the type of forward error correction (FEC) used. Each code maps a sequence of k information symbols into a longer sequence of n transmitted symbols. The results are called (n, k) *block codes*. After encoding, digital message information is modulated onto a carrier so that transfer can take place over a radio channel. The basic unit of transmitted data is called a *channel symbol*. Parameter Q (column 4 in the table) is the *alphabet size*, the number of different symbols used. Q is also the number of distinct waveforms used for conveying information. For frequency-shift keying the waveforms are sinusoids at different frequencies. Additional columns in Table 15.7 specify the keying rate, occupied bandwidth, fraction of transmitted energy devoted to synchronization, duration of transmitted waveform, and threshold signal-to-noise ratio for reliable decoding of each mode. Here and elsewhere in this section, signal-to-noise ratios are assumed measured in a standard reference bandwidth of 2500 Hz.

Figure 15.6 illustrates the appearance of each of the *WSJT-X* slow modes in a typical waterfall-type spectral display. For comparison, this collection of simulated signals also includes an unmodulated carrier and a 25 WPM CW signal. The signals were generated with a key-down signal-to-noise ratio –10 dB, thus simulating typical over-the-air reception of very weak, barely audible signals. WSPR has the narrowest occupied bandwidth of the *WSJT-X* modes, 5.9 Hz, while JT65 is the widest at 177.6 Hz. As described further below, some of the modes offer several submodes with wider tone spacings, which can be useful under certain propagation conditions. JT4, JT9, JT65, and QRA64 use one-minute timed sequences of transmission and reception, synchronized with UTC. FT8 uses 15-second sequences, and WSPR uses two minutes. The following paragraphs give further details for each of the slow modes and describe their typical uses.

FT8

The FT8 protocol was developed by Steven Franke, K9AN, and K1JT. The mode became popular soon after its introduction in early summer, 2017, and a year later is one of the most widely used modes of any type in Amateur Radio. FT8 was designed for circumstances where signals may be weak and fading, so that quick completion of reliable, confirmable QSOs is especially desirable. The terse message exchanges of call signs, locators, signal reports, and acknowledgments serve well for those engaged in country-counting, award-chasing, and the like. The short, 15 second timed sequences for transmission and reception mean that basic sensitivity for steady signals is several dB worse than the other slow modes. Message packets include three extra bits — 75 information bits in all — and a 12-bit cyclic redundancy check (CRC) that helps to ensure a very low false decode rate. A special submode, *FT8 DXpedition Mode*, enables a much-sought-after station to make QSOs at very high rates. One of the extra bits is used to flag a special message type used only in this submode. In DXpedition Mode, *WSJT-X* allows the sought-after station to transmit up to five FT8 signals simultaneously, thereby conducting as many as five minimal contacts at once. FT8 modulation uses 8-tone FSK at 6.25 baud and accomplishes frame synchronization with three 7 × 7 Costas arrays.

JT4

In JT4 mode, each channel symbol carries one information bit (the most significant bit) and one synchronizing bit. The sync bits are determined by a pseudo-random sequence known to the software at both transmitting and receiving ends. After the sync pattern is recognized and removed by the receiving software, the remaining signal amounts to a 2-tone FSK signal. Submodes JT4A through JT4G have tone spacings at increasing multiples 1, 2, 4, 9, 18, 36, and 72 times the basic keying rate, 4.375 baud. The wider submodes have proven very useful on propagation paths with large Doppler spread. For example, JT4F is frequently used for Earth-Moon-Earth (EME) communication on the 10 GHz band.

JT9

The JT9 mode uses eight tone frequencies to convey message information, and one additional tone is used for synchronization. Submodes JT9A-H have tone spacings at multiples 1, 2, 4, 8, 16, 32, and 64 times the 1.736-baud keying rate. JT9A (often called simply JT9) uses less than 10% of the bandwidth of JT65, and for steady, undistorted signals is about 2 dB more sensitive. These characteristics have made JT9 very popular on the 630 meter band.

JT65

The JT65 protocol is the oldest of the weak-signal structured modes; a detailed description was published in *QEX* in 2005 (see References and Bibliography). The protocol uses a (63,12) Reed Solomon code with alphabet size $Q = 64$. Modulation uses one synchronizing tone and 64 data tones, with data and sync information interspersed according to a pseudo-random sync pattern. In *WSJT-X* decoding is accomplished using the Franke-Taylor algorithm (see References and Bibliography) Special features (used only for EME) can be used to convey an EME-style "OOO" signal report and short messages interpreted as RO, RRR, and 73. Submodes JT65B and JT65C, also used only for EME, use tone spacings 2 and 4 times larger than JT65A. JT65 is widely used for low-power DXing at MF and HF, as well as for EME on VHF and higher bands.

QRA64

QRA64 is intended for EME and other extreme weak-signal paths. Its internal code was designed by Nico Palermo, IV3NWV (see References and Bibliography). Synchronization is accomplished by using three 7 × 7 Costas arrays. Submodes QRA64A-E use tone spacings 1, 2, 4, 8, and 16 times the 1.736 baud keying rate. QRA64 is very effective for EME on the VHF and UHF bands. The wider submodes QRA64C-E work extremely well for EME on microwave bands up to 24 GHz.

WSPR

The WSPR mode was designed as a propagation probe rather than for making two-way contacts. It differs from the other structured modes in *WSJT-X* by using message lengths bits and two-minute T/R sequences. Message packets normally include a 28-bit call sign, a 15-bit grid locator, and 7 bits to convey transmitter power in dBm (decibels above one milliwatt). Alternative formats can convey a compound call sign and/or a 6-digit grid locator, using a two-transmission sequence. Typical WSPR usage was described in *QST* in 2010 (see References and Bibliography).

15.4.4 Fast Modes

The fast modes in *WSJT-X* aim to take ad-

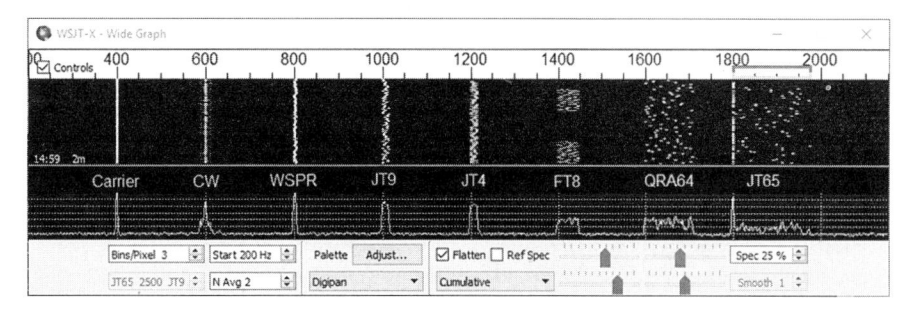

Figure 15.6 — Spectrograms of simulated signals for an unmodulated carrier, a 25 WPM CW signal, and the *WSJT-X* slow modes WSPR, JT9, JT4, FT8, QRA64, and JT65. All signals have S/N = –10 dB in a 2500 Hz reference bandwidth. Horizontal scale is frequency in Hz; vertical axis represents time over the displayed interval of about 50 seconds. Two successive FT8 transmissions are shown, each lasting 15 seconds.

vantage of brief propagation enhancements that bring a signal up to useful levels for a very short time. Keying rates and occupied bandwidths are much larger than for the slow modes, because full messages must be conveyed in a very short time, perhaps less than 100 ms. Table 15.7B lists essential parameter values for the *WSJT-X* fast modes. The last column gives the time required to transmit a message once at the specified keying rate. In these modes the transmitted information is repeated for the full duration of a T/R sequence.

JT9 Fast

Fast submodes JT9E-H differ from their slow JT9 counterparts by using much higher keying rates and wider tone spacings. Otherwise the coding, modulation, and synchronization schemes are the same as for the slow JT9 modes. JT9 fast modes have proven useful for such propagation types as ionospheric scatter and weak multi-hop sporadic E on the 6 meter band.

MSK144

Forward error correction is implemented in the MSK144 mode by augmenting the 72 message bits with an 8-bit cyclic redundancy check (CRC) calculated from the message bits. The resulting 80-bit message is mapped to a 128-bit codeword using a (128, 80) low-density-parity-check (LDPC) code designed by Steven Franke, K9AN, specifically for this purpose. Two 8-bit synchronizing sequences are added to make a message frame 144 bits long. Modulation uses offset quadrature phase-shift keying (OQPSK) at 2000 baud, so the frame duration is 72 ms. Compared to FSK441, the mode widely used for digital meteor-scatter since its introduction in 2001, MSK144 has the advantages strong error correction, an effective character transmission rate about 1.7 times faster, and significantly better sensitivity. (See References and Bibliography for both articles.) MSK144 has become the dominant mode for amateur meteor-scatter contacts.

15.4.5 HF Digital Voice

AOR

In 2004, AOR Corporation introduced its HF digital voice and data modem, the AR9800. Digital voice offers a quality similar to FM with no background noise or fading as long as the signal can be properly decoded. The AR9800 can alternatively transmit binary files and images. AOR later released the AR9000 which is compatible with the AR9800 but less expensive and only supports the HF digital voice mode.

The AR9800 uses a protocol developed by Charles Brain, G4GUO. The protocol uses the AMBE (Advanced Multi-Band Excitation) codec from DVSI Inc. to carry voice. It uses 2400 bit/s for voice data with an additional 1200 bit/s for Forward Error Correction for a total 3600 bit/s data stream. The protocol is detailed below:
- Bandwidth: 300-2500 Hz, 36 carriers
- Symbol Rate: 20 ms (50 baud)
- Guard interval: 4 ms
- Tone steps: 62.5 Hz
- Modulation method: 36 carriers: DQPSK (3.6K)
- AFC: ±125 Hz
- Error correction: Voice: Golay and Hamming
- Video/Data: Convolution and Reed-Solomon
- Header: 1 s; 3 tones plus BPSK training pattern for synchronization
- Digital voice: DVSI AMBE2020 coder, decoder
- Signal detection: Automatic Digital detect, Automatic switching between analog mode and digital mode
- Video Compression: AOR original adaptive JPEG

AOR has more information online at **www.aorusa.com/others/ard9800.html**.

FreeDV

FreeDV is available for *Windows*, *Linux*, and *MacOS* clients, and allows any SSB radio to be used for low-bit-rate digital voice. Speech and call sign data is compressed down to 1400 bit/s, which then modulates an 1125 Hz-wide QPSK signal, which is then applied to the microphone input of an SSB transceiver. On receive, the signal is received as SSB, demodulated to audio, then further demodulated and decoded by *FreeDV* running on a PC.

FreeDV is entirely open source — even the voice codec. This makes it unique among Amateur Radio digital voice systems which typically rely on a proprietary voice codec that is not available to ham experimentation.

FreeDV was coded from scratch by David Witten, KD0EAG (GUI, architecture), and David Rowe, VK5DGR (*Codec2*, modem implementation, integration). The *FreeDV* design and user interface is based on *FDMDV*, which was developed by Francesco Lanza, HB9TLK. The large team of reviewers and beta testers who have supported the development of *FreeDV* are credited on the **freedv.org** home page.

Key *FreeDV* Features

- Waterfall, spectrum, scatter and audio oscilloscope displays
- Adjustable squelch
- Fast/slow SNR estimation
- Microphone and speaker signal audio equalizer
- Control of transmitter PTT via RS-232 levels
- Works with one (receive only) or two (transmit and receive) sound cards (for example, a built-in sound card and USB headphones)

FreeDV Overview

There are three implementations of *FreeDV*:

FreeDV 1600:

- *Codec2* voice codec and *FDMDV* modem
- 1.25 kHz spectrum bandwidth (half SSB) with 75 Hz carrier spacing
- 1275 bit/s voice coding, 25 bit/s text for call sign ID, 300 bit/s FEC,
- 16×50 baud DQPSK carriers, Differential QPSK demodulation
- 1 center BPSK carrier with 2× power for fast and robust synchronization
- 44.1 or 48 kHz sample rate, sound card compatible

FreeDV 700(C):

- 700 bit/s voice coding; no FEC, uses frequency diversity to combat fading, 14×75 baud QPSK carriers, pilot-symbol assisted coherent QPSK demodulation

FreeDV 2400A (for VHF/UHF):

- Bit rate: 2400 bit/s
- RF bandwidth: 5 kHz
- Suggested channel spacing: 6.25 kHz
- Modulation: 4FSK with non-coherent demodulation
- Symbol rate: 1200 symbols/s
- Tone spacing: 1200 Hz
- Frame period: 40 ms
- Bits/frame: 96
- Unique word: 16 bits/frame
- *Codec2 1300*: 52 bits/frame
- Spare bits: 28 bits/frame

FreeDV is composed of two primary software components:

1) The *FreeDV* GUI (see **Figure 15.7A**): A FreeDV Windows/Linux/OSX GUI application. The FreeDV GUI software runs on any PC and requires two sound cards, for example a USB rig interface and a USB headset.

2) The FreeDV API: An open source, C-callable software library, that has interfaces for audio and modem samples. The API can be linked into third-party SDR programs that wish to support *FreeDV*.

A standalone hardware implementation of *FreeDV* (SM1000) is also available that does not require a PC host. (See **freedv.org** for more information about *FreeDV* software and accessories.)

FreeDV Architecture

Figure 15.7B shows a typical *FreeDV* system. Voice signals from a microphone are sampled by the ADC, typically at 8 kHz with 16-bit resolution. A speech encoder (*Codec2*) then compresses the speech to a low bit rate, for example 1300 bit/s. FEC bits are then added to protect against errors encountered

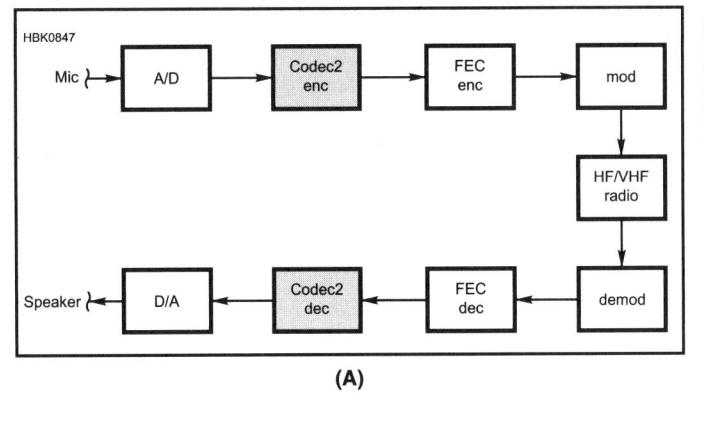

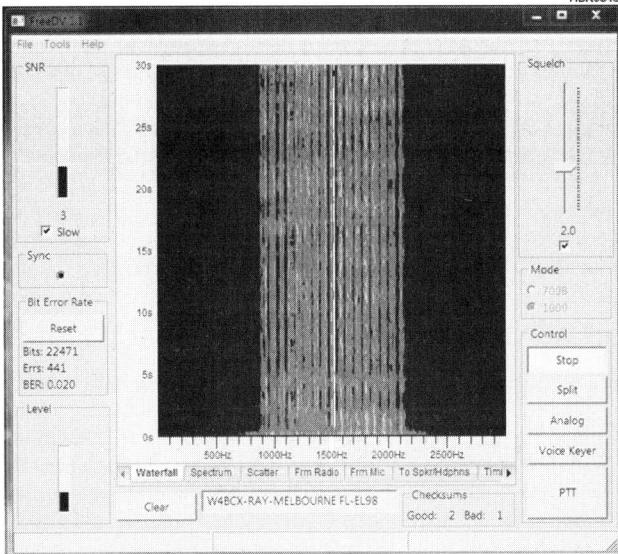

Figure 15.7 — Typical *FreeDV* system architecture (A) and *FreeDV* 1.1 screen shot during reception (B).

in the channel. This may increase the bit rate to 1600 bit/s. A modulator (labeled "mod") then converts the bit stream to tones that can be passed via a radio channel. Over the channel the digital speech signal will encounter noise and other impairments such as fading and frequency offsets.

On the receive side, the demodulator (labeled "demod") then converts the tones back into a bit stream. The FEC decoder attempts to correct channel errors before passing the payload compressed voice information to the voice decoder (labeled "codec 2 dec"). The output of the voice decoder is an 8 kHz, 16-bit/sample sequence that is converted back into analog speech by the DAC and played through a speaker or headphones.

More details and the software can be found at **freedv.org** as well as written and video setup guides. A coordinating website for *FreeDV* QSOs is available at **qso.k7ve.org**.

15.4.6 ALE

Automatic link establishment (*ALE*) was created as a series of protocols for government users to simplify HF communications. The protocol provides a mechanism to analyze signal quality on various channels/bands and choose the best option. The purpose is to provide a reliable rapid method of calling and connecting during constantly changing HF ionospheric propagation, reception interference and shared spectrum use of busy or congested HF channels. It also supports text messages with a very robust protocol that can get through even if no voice-quality channel can be found.

Each radio ALE station uses a call sign or address in the ALE controller. When not actively in communication with another station, each HF SSB transceiver constantly scans through a list of frequencies, listening for its call sign. It decodes calls and soundings sent by other stations, using the bit error rate to store a quality score for that frequency and sender call sign.

To reach a specific station, the caller simply enters the call sign, just like dialing a phone number. The ALE controller selects the best available frequency and sends out brief digital selective calling signals containing the call signs. When the distant scanning station detects the first few characters of its call sign, it stops scanning and stays on that frequency. The two stations' ALE controllers automatically handshake to confirm that a link of sufficient quality is established and they are ready to communicate.

When successfully linked, the receiving station which was muted will typically emit an audible alarm and visual alert for the receiving operator of the incoming call. It also indicates the call sign of the linked station. The operators then can talk in a regular conversation. At the conclusion of the QSO, one of the stations sends a disconnect signal to the other station, and they each return their ALE stations to the scanning mode. Some military / commercial HF transceivers are available with ALE available internally. Amateur Radio operators commonly use the PCALE soundcard software ALE controller, interfaced to a ham transceiver via rig control cable and multi-frequency antenna.

The ALE waveform is designed to be compatible with the audio passband of a standard SSB radio. It has a robust waveform for reliability during poor path conditions. It consists of 8-ary frequency-shift keying (FSK) modulation with eight orthogonal tones, a single tone for a symbol. These tones represent three bits of data, with least significant bit to the right, as shown in **Table 15.8**.

**Table 15.8
ALE Tones**

Frequency	Data
750 Hz	000
1000 Hz	001
1250 Hz	011
1500 Hz	010
1750 Hz	110
2000 Hz	111
2250 Hz	101
2500 Hz	100

The tones are transmitted at a rate of 125 tones per second, 8 ms per tone. The resultant transmitted bit rate is 375 bit/s. The basic ALE word consists of 24 bits of information. Details can be found in Federal Standard 1045, Detailed Requirements at **www.its.bldrdoc.gov/fs-1054a/ 45-detr.htm**.

It would require a lot of time for the radio to go through the sequence of calling a station on every possible frequency to establish a link. Time can be decreased by using a "smarter" way of predictive or synchronized linking. With *Link Quality Analysis* (LQA), an ALE system uses periodic sounding and linking signals between other stations in the network to stay in touch and to predict which channel is likely to support a connection to the desired station at any given time. Various stations may be operating on different channels, and this enables the stations to find and use a common open channel.

The *PCALE* software developed by Charles Brain, G4GUO, is available for download at **hflink.com/software**. Much more ALE information and real-time data is available online at **hflink.com**.

Digital Protocols and Modes 15.17

15.5 Networking Modes

The modes described in this section operate using features and functions associated with computer-to-computer networking. Even though communication using these modes may not involve the creation of a network, the modes are referred to as "networking modes" because of their structure. In cases such as Winlink and D-STAR, the most common use is to implement a networked system and those features are described along with the modes and protocols used to implement communications within the network.

15.5.1 OSI Networking Model

The Open Systems Interconnection Model or *OSI Model* is an abstract description for computer network protocol design. It defines seven different *layers* or functions performed by a *protocol stack*. In the OSI model, the highest level is closest to the user and the lowest is closest to the hardware required to transport the data (network card and wire or radio). The seven layers are described in **Table 15.9**. The modes examined previously implemented the protocols as a *monolithic stack* where all the functions are performed inside a single piece of code. The modes described in this section implement networking features in a more modular fashion. This allows greater flexibility (and complexity) when mixing features.

As a data packet moves through these layers the header or preamble is removed and any required action performed before the data is passed to the next layer, much like peeling away layers of an onion until just the basic clean data is left. The OSI model does not define any interfaces between layers; it is just a conceptual model of the functions required. Real-world protocols rarely implement each layer individually and often span multiple layers.

This description is by no means exhaustive and more information can be found online and in every networking textbook. **Table 15.10** shows the placement of commonly recognized protocols within the OSI layered structure.

15.5.2 Connected and Connectionless Protocols

The protocols discussed to this point have been *connectionless* meaning they don't establish a connection with a specific machine for the purpose of transferring data. Even with packetized modes like FSK441 with a destination call sign specified, the packet is transmitted and it's up to the user to identify they are the intended recipient. In a packet-switched network, connectionless mode transmission is a transmission in which each packet is prepended with a header containing a destination address to allow delivery of the packet without the aid of additional instructions. A packet transmitted in a connectionless mode is frequently called a *datagram*.

In *connection-oriented protocols*, the stations about to exchange data need to first declare to each other they want to "establish a connection". A connection is sometimes defined as a logical relationship between the peers exchanging data. Connected protocols can use a method called *automatic repeat request* (*ARQ*) to insure accurate delivery of packets using *acknowledgements* and *timeouts*. This allows the detection and correction of corrupted packets, misdelivery, duplication, or out-of-sequence delivery of the packets.

Connectionless modes can have error correction and detection included by a higher layer of the protocol but they have no mechanism to request a correction. An advantage of connectionless mode over connection-oriented mode is that it has a low data overhead. It also allows for *multicast* and *broadcast* (net-type) operations, which may save even more network resources when the same data needs to be transmitted to several recipients. In contrast, a connected mode is always *unicast* (point-to-point).

Another drawback of the connectionless mode is that no optimizations are possible when sending several frames between the same two peers. By establishing a connection at the beginning of such a data exchange the components (routers, bridges) along the network path would be able to pre-compute (and hence cache) routing-related information, avoiding re-computation for every packet.

Many network modes incorporate both types of protocol for different purposes. In the Internet TCP/IP protocol, TCP is a connection-oriented transport protocol where UDP is connectionless.

15.5.3 The Terminal Node Controller (TNC)

While a *terminal node controller* (*TNC*) is nominally an OSI Physical layer device, the internal firmware often implements a protocol such as PACTOR that handles all the routing, and error correction through the transport layer. This greatly simplifies the coding of any protocol or application that uses these devices.

A TNC is actually a computer that contains the protocols implemented in firmware and a *modem* (modulator/demodulator). The

---

Table 15.9
OSI Seven Layer Networking Model

7 —	Application Layer	End-user program or "application" that uses the network
6 —	Presentation Layer	The format of data after transfer (code conversion, encryption)
5 —	Session Layer	Manages the transfer process
4 —	Transport Layer	Provides reliable data transfer to the upper layers
3 —	Network Layer	Controls data routing
2 —	Data Link Layer	Provides error detection and flow control
1 —	Physical Layer	Signal used on the medium—voltage, current, frequency, etc.

Table 15.10
Networking Protocols in the OSI Model

Layer	Examples	IP Protocol Suite
7 — Application		NNTP, DNS, FTP, Gopher, HTTP, DHCP, SMTP, SNMP, TELNET
6 — Presentation	ASCII, EBCDIC, MIDI, MPEG	MIME, SSL
5 — Session	Named Pipes, NetBIOS, Half Duplex, Full Duplex, Simplex	Sockets, Session establishment in TCP
4 — Transport		TCP, UDP
3 — Network	AX.25	IP, IPsec, ICMP, IGMP
2 — Data Link	802.3 (Ethernet), 802.11a/b/g/n MAC/LLC, ATM, FDDI, Frame Relay, HDLC, Token Ring, ARP (maps layer 3 to layer 2 address)	PPP, SLIP, PPTP, L2TP
1 — Physical	RS-232, T1, 10BASE-T, 100BASE-TX, POTS, DSL, 802.11a/b/g/n, Soundcard, TNC, Radio	

TNC generally connects to a PC as a serial or USB device on one side and to the radio with appropriate audio and PTT cables on the other. Most of the newer rigs have dedicated data connections available that feature audio lines with fixed levels that are unaffected by settings in the radio. These jacks make swapping mike cables unnecessary when switching between voice and digital modes. Bypassing internal audio processing circuitry eliminates a number of issues that can cause problems with digital modes and makes the use of digital modes more reproducible/reliable by eliminating a number of variables when configuring equipment. These same data jacks are recommended when using a computer sound card.

Although many of the modes discussed can use a computer sound card to generate the required modulation and a separate mechanism to support push-to-talk (PTT), a TNC offers some advantages:

• TNC hardware can be used with any computer platform.

• A computer of nearly any vintage/performance level can be used.

• Data transmission/reception is unaffected by computer interruptions from virus checkers or other "inits."

• Initialization settings are held internal to the TNC and can easily be reset as needed — once working, they stay working.

• Virtually eliminates the computer as a problem/failure point.

• Offers features independent of the computer (digipeat, BBS, APRS beacon, telemetry, weather beacon, and so forth).

The majority of TNCs are designed for 300 or 1200-bit/s packet and implement the Bell 103 or Bell 202 modulation respectively. A *multimode communications processor* (*MCP*) or *multi-protocol controller* (*MPC*) may offer the capability to operate RTTY, CW, AMTOR, PACTOR, G-TOR, Clover, fax, SSTV and other modes in addition to packet. Some of these modes are only available in TNC hardware because the real-time operating system in the TNC provides a more reliable platform to implement the mode and it also helps protect proprietary intellectual property.

KISS-Mode TNCs have become popular. These devices simply provide the modem and filters to implement the baseband signals for a type of digital modulation. They rely on the computer software to generate the appropriate packet protocol and complete the mode. This means the software must be written specifically to support these TNCs by creating the entire AX.25 packet with the data embedded, rather than simply sending the data to the TNC expecting the TNC to frame the packet. By leaving the TNC to handle only the baseband signal generation and data recovery, much simpler, smaller and less expensive designs are possible while still retaining the platform independence and robustness of a separate TNC. The TNC-X from Coastal Chipworks at **tnc-x.com** is a good example of a KISS-mode TNC.

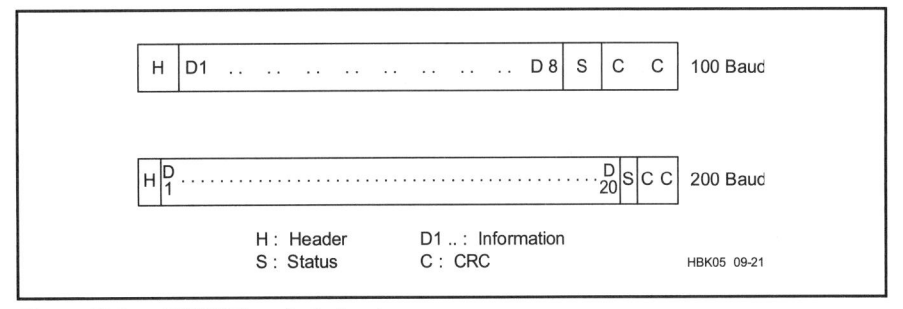

Figure 15.8 — PACTOR packet structure.

Table 15.11
PACTOR Timing

Object	Length (seconds)
Packet	0.96 (200 baud: 192 bits; 100 baud: 96 bits)
CS receive time	0.29
Control signals	0.12 (12 bits at 10 ms each)
Propagation delay	0.17
Cycle	1.25

15.5.4 PACTOR-I

PACTOR, now often referred to as PACTOR-I, is an HF radio transmission system developed by German amateurs Hans-Peter Helfert, DL6MAA, and Ulrich Strate, DF4KV. It was designed to overcome the shortcomings of AMTOR and packet radio. It performs well under both weak-signal and high-noise conditions. PACTOR-I has been overtaken by PACTOR-II and PACTOR-III but remains in use.

TRANSMISSION FORMATS

All packets have the basic structure shown in **Figure 15.8**, and their timing is as shown in **Table 15.11**.

• Header: Contains a fixed bit pattern to simplify repeat requests, synchronization and monitoring. The header is also important for the Memory ARQ function. In each packet that carries new information, the bit pattern is inverted.

• Data: Any binary information. The format is specified in the status word. Current choices are 8-bit ASCII or 7-bit ASCII (with Huffman encoding). Characters are not broken across packets. ASCII RS (hex 1E) is used as an IDLE character in both formats.

• Status word: See Table 15.11

• CRC: The CRC is calculated according to the CCITT standard, for the data, status and CRC.

The PACTOR acknowledgment signals are shown in **Table 15.12**. Each of the signals is 12-bits long. The characters differ in pairs in eight bits (Hamming offset) so that the chance of confusion is reduced. If the CS is not correctly received, the TX reacts by repeating the last packet. The request status can be uniquely recognized by the 2-bit packet number so that wasteful transmissions of pure RQ blocks are unnecessary.

The receiver pause between two blocks is 0.29 s. After deducting the CS lengths, 0.17 s remains for switching and propagation delays so that there is adequate reserve for DX operation.

CONTACT FLOW

In the listen mode, the receiver scans any received packets for a CRC match. This method uses a lot of computer processing resources, but it's flexible.

A station seeking contacts transmits CQ packets in an FEC mode, without pauses for acknowledgment between packets. The transmit time length, number of repetitions and speed are the transmit operator's choice. (This mode is also suitable for bulletins and other group traffic.) Once a listening station has copied the call, the listener assumes the TX station role and initiates a contact. Thus, the station sending CQ initially takes the RX station role. The contact begins as shown in **Table 15.13**.

With good conditions, PACTOR's normal signaling rate is 200 baud, but the system automatically changes from 200 to 100 baud and back, as conditions demand. In addition, Huffman coding can further increase the throughput by a factor of 1.7. There is no loss of synchronization speed changes; only one packet is repeated.

Table 15.12
PACTOR Control Signals

Code	Chars (hex)	Function
CS1	4D5	Normal acknowledge
CS2	AB2	Normal acknowledge
CS3	34B	Break-in (forms header of first packet from RX to TX)
CS4	D2C	Speed change request

All control signals are sent only from RX to TX

Table 15.13
PACTOR Initial Contact

Master Initiating Contact

Size (bytes)	1	8	6
Content	/Header	/SLAVECAL	/SLAVECAL/
Speed (baud)	100	100	200

Slave Response
The receiving station detects a call, determines mark/space polarity, and decodes 100 baud and 200-bd call signs. It uses the two call signs to determine if it is being called and the quality of the communication path. The possible responses are:

First call sign does not match slave's call sign (Master not calling this slave)	none
Only first call sign matches slave's call sign (Master calling this slave, poor communications)	CS1
First and second call signs both match the slaves (good circuit, request speed change to 200 baud)	CS4

When the RX receives a bad 200-baud packet, it can acknowledge with CS4. TX immediately assembles the previous packet in 100-baud format and sends it. Thus, one packet is repeated in a change from 200 to 100 baud.

The RX can acknowledge a good 100-baud packet with CS4. TX immediately switches to 200 baud and sends the next packet. There is no packet repeat in an upward speed change.

The RX station can become the TX station by sending a special change-over packet in response to a valid packet. RX sends CS3 as the first section of the changeover packet. This immediately changes the TX station to RX mode to read the data in that packet and responds with CS1 and CS3 (acknowledge) or CS2 (reject).

PACTOR provides a sure end-of-contact procedure. TX initiates the end of contact by sending a special packet with the QRT bit set in the status word and the call of the RX station in byte-reverse order at 100 baud. The RX station responds with a final CS.

15.5.5 PACTOR-II

This is a significant improvement over PACTOR-I, yet it is fully compatible with the older mode. PACTOR-II uses 16PSK to transfer up to 800 bit/s at a 100 baud rate. This keeps the bandwidth less than 500 Hz.

PACTOR-II uses digital signal processing (DSP) with Nyquist waveforms, Huffman and Markov compression and powerful Viterbi decoding to increase transfer rate and sensitivity into the noise level. The effective transfer rate of text is over 1200 bit/s. Features of PACTOR II include:

• Frequency agility — it can automatically adjust or lock two signals together over a ±100 Hz window.
• Powerful data reconstruction based upon computer power — with over 2 Mbyte of available memory.
• Cross correlation — applies analog Memory ARQ to acknowledgment frames and headers.
• Soft decision making — Uses artificial intelligence (AI), as well as digital information received to determine frame validity.
• Extended data block length — when transferring large files under good conditions, the data length is doubled to increase the transfer rate.
• Automatic recognition of PACTOR-I, PACTOR-II and so on, with automatic mode switching.
• Intermodulation products are canceled by the coding system.
• Two long-path modes extend frame timing for long-path terrestrial and satellite propagation paths.

This is a fast, robust mode that has excellent coding gain as well. PACTOR-II stations acknowledge each received transmission block. PACTOR-II employs computer logic as well as received data to reassemble defective data blocks into good frames. This reduces the number of transmissions and increases the throughput of the data.

15.5.6 PACTOR-III

PACTOR-III is a software upgrade for existing PACTOR-II modems that provides a data transmission mode for improved speed and robustness. Both the transmitting and receiving stations must support PACTOR-III for end-to-end communications using this mode.

PACTOR-III's maximum uncompressed speed is 2722 bit/s. Using online compression, up to 5.2 kbit/s is achievable. This requires an audio passband from 400 Hz to 2600 Hz (for PACTOR-III speed level 6). On an average channel, PACTOR-III is more than three times faster than PACTOR-II. On good channels, the effective throughput ratio between PACTOR-III and PACTOR-II can exceed five. PACTOR-III is also slightly more robust than PACTOR-II at their lower SNR edges.

The ITU emission designator for PACTOR-III is 2K20J2D. Because PACTOR-III builds on PACTOR-II, most specifications like frame length and frame structure are adopted from PACTOR-II. The only significant difference is PACTOR III's multitone waveform that uses up to 18 carriers while PACTOR-II uses only two carriers. PACTOR-III's carriers are located in a 120 Hz grid and modulated with 100 symbols per second DBPSK or DQPSK. Channel coding is also adopted from PACTOR-II's Punctured Convolutional Coding.

PACTOR-III Link Establishment

The calling modem uses the PACTOR-I FSK connect frame for compatibility. When the called modem answers, the modems negotiate to the highest level of which both modems are capable. If one modem is only capable of PACTOR-II, then the 500 Hz PACTOR-II mode is used for the session. With the MYLevel (MYL) command a user may limit a modem's highest mode. For example, a user may set MYL to 1 and only a PACTOR-I connection will be made, set to 2 and PACTOR-I and II connections are available, set to 3 and PACTOR-I through III connections are enabled. The default MYL is set to 2 with the current firmware and with PACTOR-III firmware it will be set to 3. If a user is only allowed to occupy a 500 Hz channel, MYL can be set to 2 and the modem will stay in its PACTOR-II mode.

The PACTOR-III Protocol Specification is available online at **www.scs-ptc.com/pactor.html**. More information can also be found online at **www.arrl.org/technical-characteristics** or in *ARRL's HF Digital Handbook* by Steve Ford, WB8IMY.

The protocol specifications and equipment for PACTOR-IV have been released, but the mode is not yet legal for US amateurs. The symbol rate for PACTOR-IV is 1800 baud, but FCC rules limit US amateurs to 300 baud below the upper end of 10 meters. PACTOR-IV is being used outside the US by individual amateurs and by Winlink stations that are not subject to FCC rules. It is not known if or when this restriction will be lifted.

15.5.7 G-TOR

This brief description has been adapted from "A Hybrid ARQ Protocol for Narrow Bandwidth HF Data Communication" by Glenn Prescott, WBØSKX, Phil Anderson, WØXI, Mike Huslig, KBØNYK, and Karl Medcalf, WK5M (May 1994 *QEX*).

G-TOR is short for Golay-TOR, an innovation of Kantronics. It was inspired by HF automatic link establishment (ALE) concepts and is structured to be compatible with ALE. The purpose of the G-TOR protocol is to provide an improved digital radio communication capability for the HF bands. The key features of G-TOR are:
• Standard FSK tone pairs (mark and space)
• Link-quality-based signaling rate: 300, 200 or 100 baud
• 2.4-s transmission cycle
• Low overhead within data frames
• Huffman data compression — two types, on demand
• Embedded run-length data compression
• Golay forward-error-correction coding
• Full-frame data interleaving
• CRC error detection with hybrid ARQ
• Error-tolerant "Fuzzy" acknowledgments.

Since one of the objectives of this protocol is ease of implementation in existing TNCs, the modulation format consists of standard tone pairs (FSK), operating at 300, 200 or 100 baud, depending upon channel conditions. G-TOR initiates contacts and sends ACKs only at 100 baud. The G-TOR waveform consists of two phase-continuous tones (BFSK), spaced 200 Hz apart (mark = 1600 Hz, space = 1800 Hz); however, the system can still operate at the familiar 170 Hz shift (mark = 2125 Hz, space = 2295 Hz), or with any other convenient tone pairs. The optimum spacing for 300-baud transmission is 300 Hz, but you trade some performance for a narrower bandwidth.

Each transmission consists of a synchronous ARQ 1.92-s frame and a 0.48-s interval for propagation and ACK transmissions (2.4 s cycles). All advanced protocol features are implemented in the signal-processing software.

Data compression is used to remove redundancy from source data. Therefore, fewer bits are needed to convey any given message. This increases data throughput and decreases transmission time — valuable features for HF. G-TOR uses run-length encoding and two types of Huffman coding during normal text transmissions. Run-length encoding is used when more than two repetitions of an 8-bit character are sent. It provides an especially large savings in total transmission time when repeated characters are being transferred.

The Huffman code works best when the statistics of the data are known. G-TOR applies Huffman A coding with the upper- and lower-case character set, and Huffman B coding with upper-case-only text. Either type of Huffman code reduces the average number of bits sent per character. In some situations, however, there is no benefit from Huffman coding. The encoding process is then disabled. This decision is made on a frame-by-frame basis by the information sending station.

The real power of G-TOR resides in the properties of the (24, 12) extended Golay error-correcting code, which permits correction of up to three random errors in three received bytes. The (24, 12) extended Golay code is a half-rate error-correcting code: Each 12 data bits are translated into an additional 12 parity bits (24 bits total). Further, the code can be implemented to produce separate input-data and parity-bit frames.

The extended Golay code is used for G-TOR because the encoder and decoder are simple to implement in software. Also, Golay code has mathematical properties that make it an ideal choice for short-cycle synchronous communication. More information can also be found online at **www.arrl.org/technical-characteristics** or in *ARRL's HF Digital Handbook* by Steve Ford, WB8IMY.

15.5.8 CLOVER-II

The desire to send data via HF radio at high data rates and the problem encountered when using AX.25 packet radio on HF radio led Ray Petit, W7GHM, to develop a unique modulation waveform and data transfer protocol that is now called CLOVER-II. Bill Henry, K9GWT, supplied this description of the CLOVER-II system.

CLOVER modulation is characterized by the following key parameters:
• Very low base symbol rate: 31.25 symbols/second (all modes).
• Time-sequence of amplitude-shaped pulses in a very narrow frequency spectrum.
• Occupied bandwidth = 500 Hz at 50 dB below peak output level.
• Differential modulation between pulses.
• Multilevel modulation.

The low base symbol rate is very resistant to multipath distortion because the time between modulation transitions is much longer than even the worst-case time-smearing caused by summing of multipath signals. By using a time-sequence of tone pulses, Dolph-Chebychev "windowing" of the modulating signal and differential modulation, the total occupied bandwidth of a CLOVER-II signal is held to 500 Hz.

Multilevel tone, phase and amplitude modulation gives CLOVER a large selection of data modes that may be used (see **Table 15.14**). The adaptive ARQ mode of CLOVER senses current ionospheric conditions and automatically adjusts the modulation mode to produce maximum data throughput. When using the Fast bias setting, ARQ throughput automatically varies from 11.6 byte/s to 70 byte/s.

The CLOVER-II waveform uses four tone pulses that are spaced in frequency by 125 Hz. The time and frequency domain characteristics of CLOVER modulation are shown in **Figures 15.9, 15.10** and **15.11**. The time-domain shape of each tone pulse is intentionally shaped to produce a very compact frequency spectrum. The four tone pulses are spaced in time and then combined to produce the composite output shown. Unlike other modulation schemes, the CLOVER modulation spectrum is the same for all modulation modes.

Table 15.14
CLOVER-II Modulation Modes
As presently implemented, CLOVER-II supports a total of seven different modulation formats: five using PSM and two using a combination of PSM and ASM (Amplitude Shift Modulation).

Name Rate	Description	In-Block Data
16P4A	16 PSM, 4-ASM	750 bps
16PSM	16 PSM	500 bps
8P2A	8 PSM, 2-ASM	500 bps
8PSM	8 PSM	375 bps
QPSM	4 PSM	250 bps
BPSM	Binary PSM	125 bps
2DPSM	2-Channel Diversity BPSM	62.5 bps

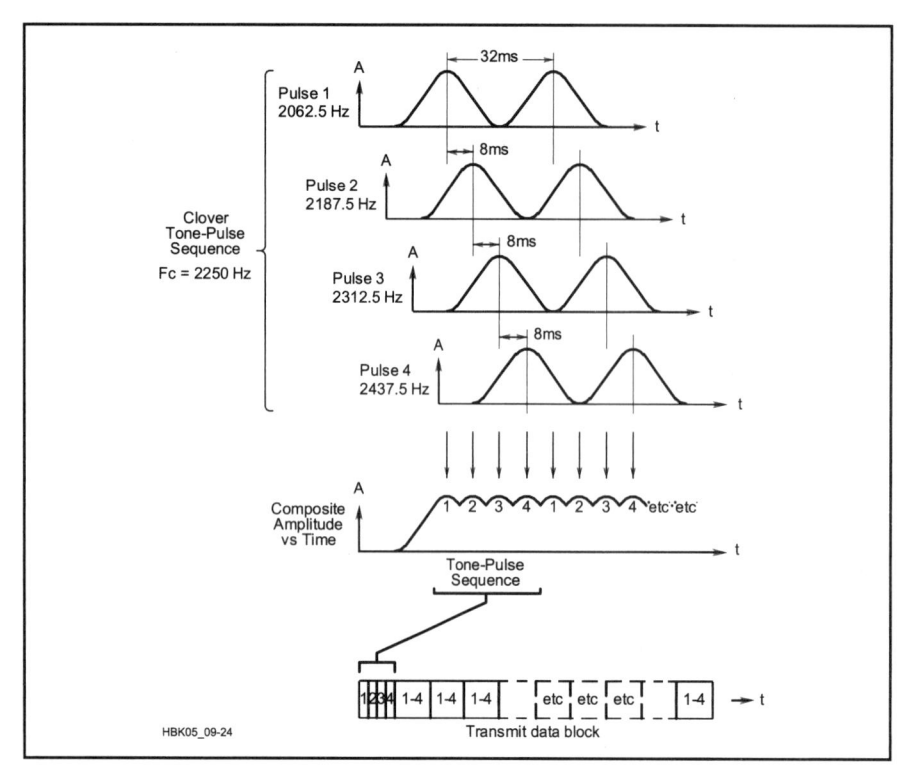

Figure 15.9 — Amplitude vs time plots for CLOVER-II's four-tone waveform.

Table 15.15
Data Bytes Transmitted Per Block

Block	Reed-Solomon Encoder Efficiency			
Size	60%	75%	90%	100%
17	8	10	12	14
51	28	36	42	48
85	48	60	74	82
255	150	188	226	252

Table 15.16
Correctable Byte Errors Per Block

Block	Reed-Solomon Encoder Efficiency			
Size	60%	75%	90%	100%
17	1	1	0	0
51	9	5	2	0
85	16	10	3	0
255	50	31	12	0

Data is modulated on a CLOVER-II signal by varying the phase and/or amplitude of the tone pulses. Further, all data modulation is differential on the same tone pulse — data is represented by the phase (or amplitude) difference from one pulse to the next. For example, when binary phase modulation is used, a data change from 0 to 1 may be represented by a change in the phase of tone pulse one by 180° between the first and second occurrence of that pulse. Further, the phase state is changed only while the pulse amplitude is zero. Therefore, the wide frequency spectra normally associated with PSK of a continuous carrier is avoided. This is true for all CLOVER-II modulation formats. The term *phase-shift modulation* (PSM) is used when describing CLOVER modes to emphasize this distinction.

CLOVER-II has four "coder efficiency" options: 60%, 75%, 90% and 100% ("efficiency" being the approximate ratio of real data bytes to total bytes sent). 60% efficiency corrects the most errors but has the lowest net data throughput. 100% efficiency turns the encoder off and has the highest throughput but fixes no errors. There is therefore a tradeoff between raw data throughput versus the number of errors that can be corrected without resorting to retransmission of the entire data block.

Note that while the In Block Data Rate numbers listed in the table go as high as 750 bit/s, overhead reduces the net throughput or overall efficiency of a CLOVER transmission. The FEC coder efficiency setting and protocol requirements of FEC and ARQ modes add overhead and reduce the net ef-

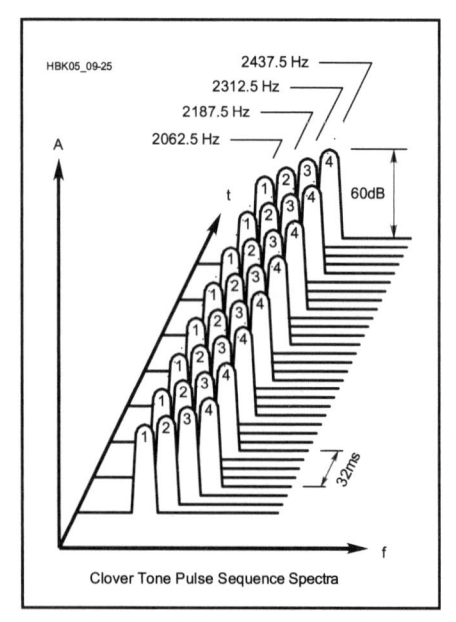

Figure 15.10 — A frequency-domain plot of a CLOVER-II waveform.

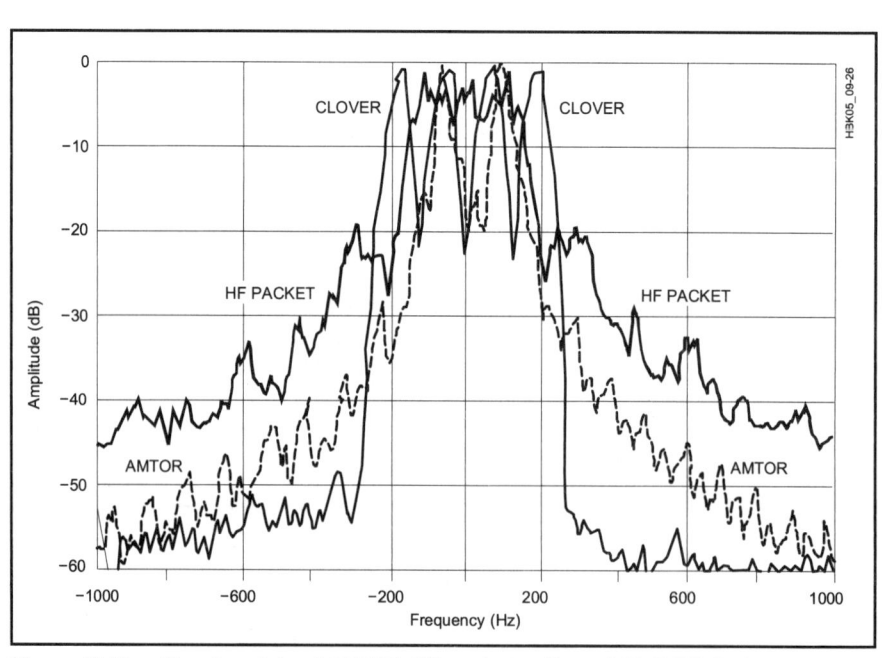

Figure 15.11 — Spectra plots of AMTOR, HF packet-radio and CLOVER-II signals.

15.22 Chapter 15

ficiency. **Tables 15.15** and **15.16** detail the relationships between block size, coder efficiency, data bytes per block and correctable byte errors per block.

With seven different modulation formats, four data-block lengths (17, 51, 85 or 255 bytes) and four Reed-Solomon coder efficiencies (60%, 75%, 90% and 100%), there are 112 (7 × 4 × 4) different waveform modes that could be used to send data via CLOVER. Once all of the determining factors are considered, however, there are eight different waveform combinations that are actually used for FEC and/or ARQ modes.

15.5.9 CLOVER-2000

CLOVER-2000 is a faster version of CLOVER (about four times faster) that uses eight tone pulses, each of which is 250 Hz wide, spaced at 250 Hz centers, contained within the 2 kHz bandwidth between 500 and 2500 Hz. The eight tone pulses are sequential, with only one tone being present at any instant and each tone lasting 2 ms. Each frame consists of eight tone pulses lasting a total of 16 ms, so the base modulation rate of a CLOVER-2000 signal is always 62.5 symbols per second (regardless of the type of modulation being used). CLOVER-2000's maximum raw data rate is 3000 bit/s.

Allowing for overhead, CLOVER-2000 can deliver error-corrected data over a standard HF SSB radio channel at up to 1994 bit/s, or 249 characters (8-bit bytes) per second. These are the uncompressed data rates; the maximum throughput is typically doubled for plain text if compression is used. The effective data throughput rate of CLOVER-2000 can be even higher when binary file transfer mode is used with data compression.

The binary file transfer protocol used by HAL Communications operates with a terminal program explained in the HAL E2004 engineering document. Data compression algorithms tend to be context sensitive — compression that works well for one mode (say, text), may not work well for other data forms (graphics, for example). The HAL terminal program uses the PK-WARE compression algorithm, which has proved to be a good general-purpose compressor for most computer files and programs. Other algorithms may be more efficient for some data formats, particularly for compression of graphic image files and digitized voice data. The HAL Communications CLOVER-2000 modems can be operated with other data compression algorithms in the users' computers.

CLOVER-2000 is similar to the previous version of CLOVER, including the transmission protocols and Reed-Solomon error detection and correction algorithm. The original descriptions of the CLOVER Control Block (CCB) and Error Correction Block (ECB) still apply for CLOVER-2000, except for the higher data rates inherent to CLOVER-2000. Just like CLOVER, all data sent via CLOVER-2000 is encoded as 8-bit data bytes and the error-correction coding and modulation formatting processes are transparent to the data stream — every bit of source data is delivered to the receiving terminal without modification.

Control characters and special "escape sequences" are not required or used by CLOVER-2000. Compressed or encrypted data may therefore be sent without the need to insert (and filter) additional control characters and without concern for data integrity. Five different types of modulation may be used in the ARQ mode — BPSM (Binary Phase Shift Modulation), QPSM (Quadrature PSM), 8PSM (8-level PSM), 8P2A (8PSM + 2-level Amplitude-Shift Modulation) and 16P4A (16 PSM plus 4 ASM).

The same five types of modulation used in ARQ mode are also available in Broadcast (FEC) mode, with the addition of 2-Channel Diversity BPSM (2DPSM). Each CCB is sent using 2DPSM modulation, 17-byte block size and 60% bias. The maximum ARQ data throughput varies from 336 bit/s for BPSM to 1992 bit/s for 16P4A modulation. BPSM is most useful for weak and badly distorted data signals, while the highest format (16P4A) needs extremely good channels, with high SNRs and almost no multipath.

Most ARQ protocols designed for use with HF radio systems can send data in only one direction at a time. CLOVER-2000 does not need an OVER command; data may flow in either direction at any time. The CLOVER ARQ time frame automatically adjusts to match the data volume sent in either or both directions. When first linked, both sides of the ARQ link exchange information using six bytes of the CCB. When one station has a large volume of data buffered and ready to send, ARQ mode automatically shifts to an expanded time frame during which one or more 255 byte data blocks are sent.

If the second station also has a large volume of data buffered and ready to send, its half of the ARQ frame is also expanded. Either or both stations will shift back to CCB level when all buffered data has been sent. This feature provides the benefit of full-duplex data transfer but requires use of only simplex frequencies and half-duplex radio equipment. This two-way feature of CLOVER can also provide a back-channel "order-wire" capability. Communications may be maintained in this chat mode at 55 WPM, which is more than adequate for real-time keyboard-to-keyboard communications.

More information can also be found at **www.arrl.org/technical-characteristics** or in *ARRL's HF Digital Handbook* by Steve Ford, WB8IMY.

15.5.10 WINMOR

While the various PACTOR modes currently dominate and generally represent the best available performance HF ARQ protocols suitable for digital messaging, PC sound cards with appropriate DSP software can now begin to approach PACTOR performance. The WINMOR (Winlink Message Over Radio) protocol is an outgrowth of the work SCAMP (Sound Card Amateur Message Protocol) by Rick Muething, KN6KB. SCAMP put an ARQ "wrapper" around Barry Sanderson's RDFT (Redundant Digital File Transfer) then integrated SCAMP into a Client and Server for access to the Winlink message system. (More on Winlink in a later section.) SCAMP worked well on good channels but suffered from the following issues:

• The RDFT batch-oriented DLLs were slow and required frame pipelining, increasing complexity and overhead.

• RDFT only changed the RS encoding on its 8PSK multi carrier waveform to achieve a 3:1 range in speed/robustness which is not enough.

• RDFT was inefficient in Partial Frame recovery (no memory ARQ).

• RDFT was a 2.4 kHz mode and limited to narrow HF sub bands.

• SCAMP's simple multi-tone ACK/NAK did not carry session ID info, increasing chances of fatal cross session contamination.

WINMOR is an ARQ mode generated from the ground up to address the limitations of SCAMP/RDFT and leverage what was learned. Today, a viable message system (with the need for compression and binary attachments) requires true "error-free" delivery of binary data. To achieve this there must be some "back channel" or ARQ so the receiving station can notify the sender of lost or damaged data and request retransmission or repair. **Table 15.17** outlines the guidelines used in the development of WINMOR.

Perhaps the most challenging of these requirements are:

• The ability to quickly tune, lock and acquire the signal which is necessary for practical length ARQ cycles in the 2-6 s range.

• The ability to automatically adapt the modulation scheme to changing channel conditions. An excellent example of this is Pactor III's extremely wide range of speed/robustness (18:1) and is one reason it is such an effective mode in both good and poor channel conditions.

The most recent development effort has focused on 62.5 baud BPSK, QPSK and 16QAM and 31.25-baud 4FSK using 1 (200 Hz), 3 (500 Hz) and 15 (2000 Hz). With carriers spaced at twice the symbol rate. These appear to offer high throughput and

Table 15.17
WINMOR Development Guidelines

Absolute Requirements	Desirable Requirements
Work with standard HF (SSB) radios	Modest CPU & OS demands
Accommodate Automatic Connections	Bandwidth options (200, 500, 3000 Hz)
Error-free transmission and confirmation	Work with most sound cards/interfaces
Fast Lock for practical length ARQ cycles	Good bit/s/Hz performance ~ P2 goal
Auto adapt to a wide range of changing channel conditions	Efficient modulation and demodulation for acceptable ARQ latency
Must support true transparent binary to allow attachments and compression	Selective ARQ & memory ARQ to maximize throughput and robustness.
Must use loosely synchronous ARQ timing to accommodate OS and DSP demands	Near Pactor ARQ efficiency (~70% of raw theoretical throughput)

robustness especially when combined with multi-level FEC coding.

WINMOR uses several mechanisms for error recovery and redundancy.

1) FEC data encoding currently using:
• 4,8 Extended Hamming Dmin = 4 (used in ACK and Frame ID)
• 16-bit CRC for data verification
Two-level Reed-Solomon (RS) FEC for data:
• First level Weak FEC, for example RS 140,116 (corrects 12 errors)
• Second level Strong FEC, for example RS 254,116 (corrects 69 errors)

2) Selective ARQ. Each carrier's data contains a Packet Sequence Number (PSN). The ACK independently acknowledges each PSN so only carriers with failed PSNs get repeated. The software manages all the PSN accounting and re-sequencing.

3) Memory ARQ. The analog phase and amplitude of each demodulated symbol is saved for summation (phasor averaging) over multiple frames. Summation is cleared and restarted if max count reached. Reed-Solomon FEC error decoding done after summation.

4) Multiple Carrier Assignment (MCA). The same PSN can be assigned to multiple carriers (allows tradeoff of throughput for robustness). Provides an automatic mechanism for frequency redundancy and protection from interference on some carriers.

5) Dynamic threshold adjustment (used on QAM modes) helps compensate for fading which would render QAM modes poor in fading channels.

In trying to anticipate how WINMOR might be integrated into applications they came up with a "Virtual TNC" concept. This essentially allows an application to integrate the WINMOR protocol by simply treating the WINMOR code as just another TNC and writing a driver for that TNC. Like all TNCs there are some (<10) parameters to set up: call sign, timing info, sound card, keying mechanism, etc. A sample image of the virtual TNC appears in **Figure 15.12**.

The WINMOR software DLL can even be made to appear as a physical TNC by "wrapping" the DLL with code that accesses it through a virtual serial port or a TCP/IP port. Like a physical TNC WINMOR has a "front panel" with flashing lights. But since operation is automatic with no front panel user interaction required the WINMOR TNC can be visible or hidden.

WINMOR looks promising and the testing to date confirms:
• Sound card ARQ is possible with a modern CPU and OS while making acceptable CPU processing demands. (CPU Loading of < 20% on a 1.5 GHz Celeron/Win XP)
• Throughput and robustness can be adjusted automatically to cover a wide range of bandwidth needs and channel conditions. (10:1 bandwidth range, 57:1 throughput range)
• ARQ throughput in excess of 0.5 bit/s/Hz is possible in fair to good channels (0.68 - 0.82 bit/s/Hz measured)
• Good ARQ efficiency — 70-75%
• Throughput is currently competitive with P2 and P3 and significantly better than P1

More information about WINMOR is available at **www.winlink.org/Winlink Express**.

15.5.11 Packet Radio

Amateur packet radio began in Canada after the Canadian Department of Communications permitted amateurs to use the mode in 1978. The FCC permitted amateur packet radio in the US in 1980. In the first half of the 1980s, packet radio was the habitat of a small group of experimenters who did not mind communicating with a limited number of potential fellow packet communicators. In the second half of the decade, packet radio took off as the experimenters built a network that increased the potential number of packet stations that could intercommunicate and thus attracted tens of thousands of communicators who wanted to take advantage of this potential.

Packet radio provides error-free data transfer via the AX.25 protocol. The receiving station receives information exactly as the transmitting station sends it, so you do not waste time deciphering communication errors caused by interference or changes in propagation. This simplifies the effort required to build other protocols or applications on top of packet technology since much of the data transfer work is handled seamlessly by the TNC in the lower layers. There are a number of other advantages to the packet radio design:

• Packet uses time efficiently, since packet bulletin-board systems (PBBSs) permit packet operators to store information for later retrieval by other amateurs.

• Packet uses the radio spectrum efficiently, since one radio channel may be used for multiple communications simultaneously, or one radio channel may be used to interconnect a number of packet stations to form a "cluster" that provides for the distribution of informa-

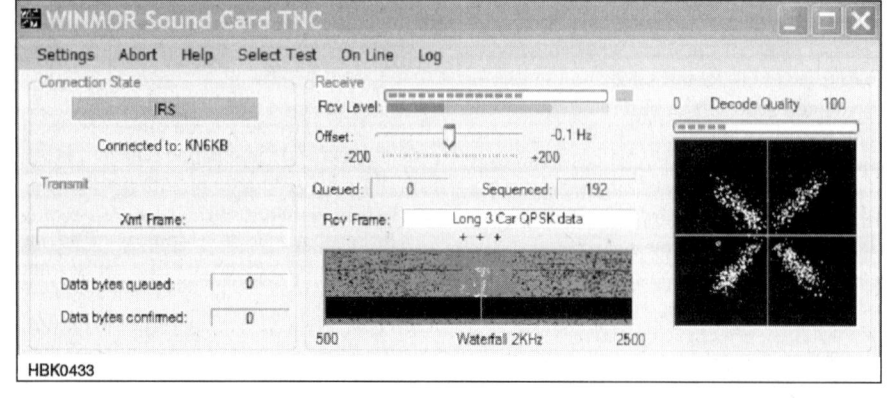

Figure 15.12 — WINMOR sound card TNC screen.

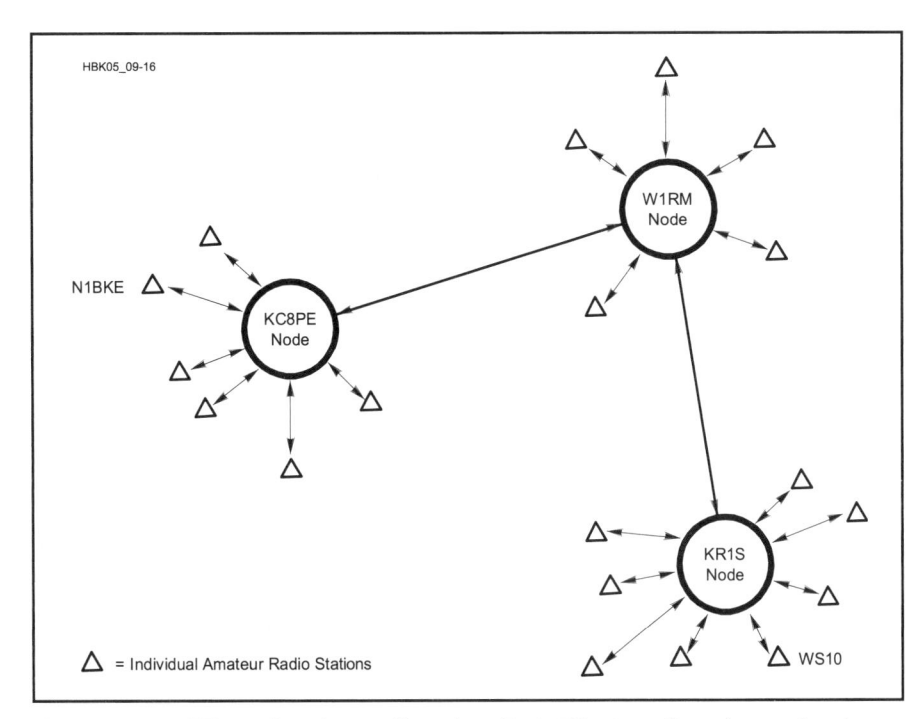

Figure 15.13 — DX spotting clusters (based on *PacketCluster* software) are networks comprised of individual nodes and stations with an interest in DXing and contesting. In this example, N1BKE is connected to the KC8PE node. If he finds a DX station on the air, he'll post a notice — otherwise known as a spot — which the KC8PE node distributes to all its local stations. In addition, KC8PE passes the information along to the W1RM node. W1RM distributes the information and then passes it to the KR1S node, which does the same. Eventually, WS1O — who is connected to the KR1S node — sees the spot on his screen. Depending on the size of the network, WS1O will receive the information within minutes after it was posted by N1BKE. Many such networks can also be found on the web or are accessible by the use of *TELNET* software.

tion to all of the clustered stations. The DX PacketCluster nodes are typical examples (see **Figure 15.13**). Each local channel may be connected to other local channels to form a network that affords interstate and international data communications. This network can be used by interlinked packet bulletin-board systems to transfer information, messages and third party traffic via HF, VHF, UHF, satellite and the Internet.

• Packet uses other stations efficiently, since any packet-radio station can use one or more other packet-radio stations to relay data to its intended destination.

• Packet uses current station transmitting and receiving equipment efficiently, since the same equipment used for voice communications may be used for packet communications. The outlay for the additional equipment necessary to add packet capability to a voice station may be less than $100.

DIGIPEATERS

A *digipeater* is a packet-radio station capable of recognizing and selectively repeating packet frames. An equivalent term used in the network industry is *bridge*. Virtually any TNC can be used as a single-port digipeater, because the digipeater function is included in the AX.25 Level 2 protocol firmware. The digipeater function is handy when you need a relay and no node is available, or for on-the-air testing. Digipeaters are used extensively with APRS (Automatic Packet Reporting System) covered below.

TCP/IP

Despite its name, TCP/IP (Transmission Control Protocol/Internet Protocol) is more than two protocols; it's actually a set of several protocols. TCP/IP provides a standardized set of protocols familiar to many and compatible with existing network technologies and applications. TCP/IP has a unique solution for busy networks. Rather than transmitting packets at randomly determined intervals, TCP/IP stations automatically adapt to network delays as they occur. As network throughput slows down, active TCP/IP stations sense the change and lengthen their transmission delays accordingly. As the network speeds up, the TCP/IP stations shorten their delays to match the pace. This kind of intelligent network sharing virtually guarantees that all packets will reach their destinations with the greatest efficiency the network can provide.

With TCP/IP's adaptive networking scheme, you can chat using the TELNET protocol with a ham in a distant city and rest assured that you're not overburdening the system. Your packets simply join the constantly moving "freeway" of data. They might slow down in heavy traffic, but they will reach their destination eventually. This adaptive system is used for all TCP/IP packets, no matter what they contain.

TCP/IP excels when it comes to transferring files from one station to another. By using the TCP/IP File Transfer Protocol (FTP), you can connect to another station and transfer computer files — including software. As might be imagined, transferring large files can take time. With TCP/IP, however, you can still send and receive mail (using the SMTP protocol) or talk to another ham while the transfer is taking place.

When you attempt to contact another station using TCP/IP, all network routing is performed automatically according to the TCP/IP address of the station you're trying to reach. In fact, TCP/IP networks are transparent to the average user. To operate TCP/IP, all you need is a computer, a 2 meter FM transceiver and a TNC with KISS (keep it simple, stupid) capability. As you might guess, the heart of your TCP/IP setup is software. The TCP/IP software set was written by Phil Karn, KA9Q, and is called NOSNET or just NOS for short. There are dozens of NOS derivatives available today. All are based on the original NOSNET. NOS takes care of all TCP/IP functions, using your "KISSable" TNC to communicate with the outside world. The only other item necessary is your own IP address in Network 44, termed AMPRNet (AMateur Packet Radio Network). Individual IP Address Coordinators assign addresses to new TCP/IP users in the 44.x.x.x subnet based on physical location worldwide. Your local coordinator can be found on AMPR.org on the list at **portal.ampr.org/networks.php**.

More packet information can be found in the annual ARRL/TAPR Digital Communications Conference proceedings and on the TAPR (Tucson Amateur Packet Radio) website at **www.tapr.org**. TAPR also maintains the AX.25 protocol specification at **www.tapr.org/pub_ax25.html**.

15.5.12 APRS

APRS (**aprs.org**) was developed by Bob Bruninga, WB4APR, for tracking and digital communications with mobile GPS equipped stations with two-way radio. APRS is different from regular packet in four ways:

• Integration of maps and other data displays to organize and display data

• By using a one-to-many protocol to update everyone in real time

• By using generic digipeating so that prior knowledge of the network is not required

• Provides worldwide transparent Internet

Digital Protocols and Modes 15.25

backbone, linking everyone worldwide

APRS turns packet radio into a real-time tactical communications and display system for emergencies, public service applications and global communications. Normal packet radio has shown usefulness in passing bulk message traffic (e-mail) from point to point. It has been difficult to apply conventional packet to real time events where information has a very short life time and needs to get to everyone.

The APRS network consists of five types of APRS stations:
- Basic — Full transmit and receive capability
- Tracker — Transmit-only device (portable or weather station)
- RELAY — Provides basic digipeating
- WIDE — Dedicated digipeaters with specific coverage areas
- IGate — Internet gateways to repeat APRS packets to servers on the Internet

APRS stations are generally set to beacon their position and other information at frequent intervals. Fixed stations don't require a GPS and should beacon infrequently to avoid crowding the channel with needless reports. Moving mobile stations can receive their coordinates from a GPS and should report more frequently. More sophisticated APRS devices support "smart beaconing" and "corner pinning" where a station will beacon more frequently when it moves faster or automatically beacon when changing direction more than a predefined angle. An APRS beacon will generally contain a call sign with *Secondary Station ID* (*SSID*), position report (lat/long), heading, speed, altitude, display icon type, status text and routing information. It may also contain antenna/power information, weather data or short message data.

Call signs generally include an SSID that historically provided information about the type of station. For example, a call sign of N7SS-9 would generally indicate a mobile station. Since there are several systems in use, the SSID information is not definitive. Recently a number of dedicated APRS radios have appeared that feature an internal TNC and APRS software. These radios include a method of displaying and entering messages without requiring the use of a computer meaning their user can directly respond to a message sent. There is value in knowing someone can respond and it is recommended they use an SSID of -7. Tactical call signs can also be used if the assigned call sign is included as part of the status text.

The APRS packet includes PATH information that determines how many times it should be digipeated. A local group should be able to offer guidance on how the PATH should be set to not overload the local network. Listening to squawking signals on the national APRS frequency of 144.390 MHz will provide some idea how busy the channel is. In much of the country the APRS network is well developed and a beacon doesn't need more than a couple hops to cover a wide area and find an IGate.

APRS SOFTWARE

There is APRS software available for most any platform with varying levels of support. Some of the most common are DOSAPRS (DOS), WinAPRS / APRS+SA / APRSPoint / UI-View (*Windows*), MacAPRS (Macintosh), PocketAPRS (Palm devices), APRSce (*Windows* CE devices) and Xastir / X-APRS (*Linux*). Because APRS beacons find their way to the Internet via IGates, it is also possible to track station or view the network online. There is a good network view available at **aprs.fi** and individual station information can be found at **map.findu.com/**[call sign to be tracked]. The **Findu.com** site also offers historical weather data, a message display and a large list of other queries.

APRS INTEGRATION WITH OTHER TECHNOLOGIES

APRS is very similar to the *AIS* (*Automatic Identification System*) used to track ships in coastal waters. The AIS transponder equipment is becoming more common in commercial ships and private vessels. The AIS information can be displayed simultaneously with APRS data on the aprs.fi website. More information about AIS can be found at **en.wikipedia.org/wiki/Automatic_Identification_System**.

APRS RF networks worldwide are interconnected via APRS-IS. APRS-IS is an ad hoc network of Amateur Radio servers, gateways (IGates), and clients (display software). APRS-IS facilitates world-wide messaging without having to define special paths. Because all clients have access to all gated packets, databases such as **aprs.fi** and **findu.com** can store and parse the packets for later retrieval from browsers and other clients. APRS-IS messaging support allows many interfaces for the RF ham running an APRS client such as call sign lookups, e-mail, and calling CQ world-wide. More information on many of these features can be found at **www.aprs-is.net**.

APRS position reports are also available from GPS-equipped D-STAR radios via DPRS gateways (more on D-STAR in a later section). The DPRS specification defines how to translate the continuous stream of GPS position reports in the D-STAR DV stream to individual APRS packets. This definition restricts the number of APRS packets generated to prevent overrunning a local RF network because the D-STAR radios continuously stream new position reports while the user is talking. Most D-STAR repeaters have DPRS IGates running on the gateway providing the D-STAR radio positions to APRS-IS. Those positions can be gated to local RF by APRS IGates if the APRS IGate sysop enables this feature.

Keith Sproul, WU2Z, operates an e-mail gateway that allows APRS messages to be converted to short e-mail or text messages. When entering a message, E-MAIL is used for the destination address. The message body must then contain the actual e-mail address followed by a space and very short message. If the message is picked up by an IGate it will be sent to the WU2Z mail server and out to the recipient, with a confirmation APRS message. For dozens of other messaging options, check online at **aprs.org/aprs-messaging.html**.

There is connectivity between APRS and the Winlink system via APRSLink. APRSLink monitors all APRS traffic gated to the Internet, worldwide, and watches for special commands that allow APRS users to:
- Read short e-mail messages sent to their call sign@winlink.org
- Send short e-mail messages to any valid e-mail address or Winlink 2000 user
- Perform e-mail related maintenance (see commands below)
- Be notified of pending Winlink e-mail via APRS message
- Query APRSLink for information on the closest Winlink RMS packet station

Attention must be paid to the APRS traffic generated when using these features but they can be very handy. Details on the APRSLink system are available at **www.winlink.org/aprslink**.

15.5.13 Winlink 2000

Winlink is a worldwide radio messaging system that takes advantage of the Internet where possible. It does this in order to allow the end-user more radio spectrum on the crowded spectrum. The system provides radio interconnection services including: e-mail with attachments, position reporting, graphic and text weather bulletins, emergency / disaster relief communications, and message relay. The PACTOR-I, II, and III protocols are used on HF, and AX.25 Packet, D-STAR and 802.11 are used on VHF/UHF.

Winlink has been assisting the maritime and RV community around the clock for many years. More recently there has been an increasing interest in emergency communications (emcomm), and the Winlink development team has responded by adding features and functions that make the system more reliable, flexible and redundant. The role of Winlink in emergency communications is to supplement existing methodologies to add another tool in the toolkit of the volunteer services deploying emergency communications in their communities.

The Winlink system is a "star" based network containing five mirror-image, redundant Common Message Servers (CMS) located in San Diego (USA), Washington DC (USA), Vienna (Austria), Halifax (Canada) and Perth (Australia). These ensure that the system will remain in operation should any piece of the Internet become inoperative. Each Radio Message Server node (RMS) is tied together as would be the ends of a spoke on a wheel with the hub function performed by the Common Message Servers. Traffic goes in and out between the CMS and the Internet e-mail recipient, and between the end users and the Radio Message Server (RMS) gateways. Multiple radio-to-radio addresses may be mixed with radio-to-Internet e-mail addresses, allowing complete flexibility.

Because each Radio Message Server gateway is a mirror image of the next, it does not matter which station is used. Each can provide over 700 text-based or graphic weather products, and each can relay the user's position to a web-based view of reporting users and interoperates with the APRS system.

One of the most important objectives in the eyes of the Winlink development team was to reduce the use of the HF spectrum to only that required to exchange messages with a user, and to do that at full "machine" speeds. The HF spectrum is very crowded, and limiting the forwarding of messages between Winlink RMS stations to the Internet, a great deal of radio air time is eliminated, making the time and spectrum available to individual users either for message handling or for other operations. A number of the RMS PACTOR servers found on HF restrict their protocols to PACTOR II (400 to 800 bit/s) and PACTOR III (1400 to 3600 bit/s.) In doing so, these RMS stations typically have a much higher ratio of traffic minutes and message counts to connect times than do the RMS stations that also receive the slower PACTOR I (100 to 200 bps) protocol. In other words, the amount of traffic that is passed with an Express station is much greater for an equivalent amount of connect time with approximately the same number of connections. On average, this translates to a PACTOR I station downloading an 80,000 byte file in approximately 80 minutes while on PACTOR III, the same download takes approximately six minutes. Note that PACTOR IV is not yet legal for US amateurs as discussed earlier in the PACTOR section.

The RMS servers provide endpoint connectivity to users via HF or VHF and can be found worldwide. When connecting via the Internet, users can connect directly to the CMS server operational closest to them via TELNET. Formerly, the full-featured messsage servers on HF were known as PMBOs (Participating Mail Box Offices) and there was a packet radio to TELNET bridge component for VHF/UHF called Telpac. These have been replaced with the newer RMS PACTOR (HF) and RMS Packet (VHF/UHF) software although the older terms are still in use. Over the air, PACTOR is used on HF, AX.25 packet on VHF/UHF and both employ the B2F compressed binary format to maximize transmission efficiency. A diagram of the Winlink architecture is shown in **Figure 15.14**.

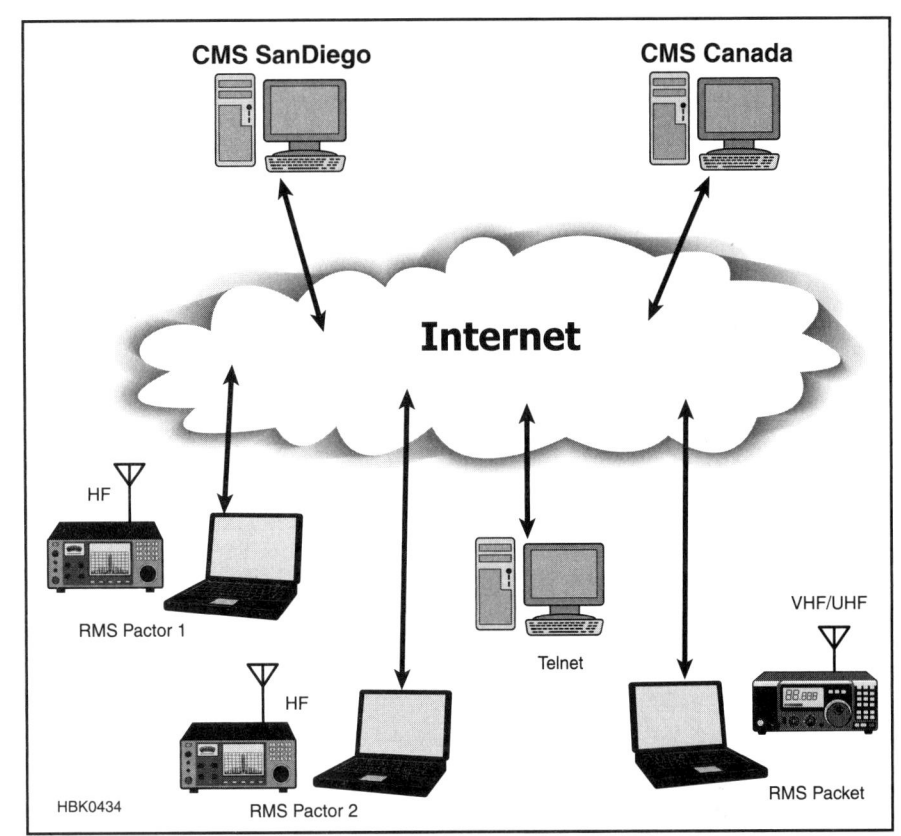

Figure 15.14 — Winlink system.

CLIENT ACCESS TO WINLINK

The primary purpose of the Winlink network system is to assist the mobile or remotely located user and to provide emergency e-mail capabilities to community agencies. Because of this, Winlink supports a clean, simple interface to the Internet SMTP e-mail system. Any message sent or received may include multiple recipients and multiple binary attachments. The radio user's e-mail address, however, must be known to the system as a radio user or the message will be rejected. This simple Internet interface protocol has an added benefit in case of an emergency where local services are interrupted and the system must be used by non-Amateur groups as an alternative to normal SMTP e-mail.

Connecting to any one of the Winlink publicly-used RMS Packet stations via HF or the specialized non-public emcomm RMS stations, can immediately and automatically connect a local amateur station to the Internet for emergency traffic. Using a standard SMTP e-mail client, the *Paclink* mini-e-mail server can replace a network of computers (behind a router) as a transparent substitute for normal SMTP mail. Winlink uses no external source for sending or receiving Internet e-mail. It is a stand-alone function which interacts directly with the Internet rather than through any external Internet service provider.

Airmail is independently developed, distributed and supported by Jim Corenman, KE6RK. It is the oldest and most widely used program for sending and receiving messages using the Winlink system. Airmail may be used for HF Pactor, VHF/UHF Packet, and for TELNET connections over any TCP/IP medium including the Internet and high-speed radio media, such as D-STAR and HSMM. Once connected to a Winlink station, message transfer is completely automatic. On the ham bands, Airmail can transfer messages automatically with any station supporting the BBS or F6FBB protocols, such as Winlink, F6FBB, MSYS and other Airmail stations. When used with Winlink, Airmail also contains position reporting capabilities, and a propagation prediction program to determine which of the participating Winlink stations will work from anywhere on Earth. Airmail also contains a limited mail server that allows it to host e-mail

Digital Protocols and Modes 15.27

independently from the Winlink network.

To obtain a copy of Airmail, including the installation and operating instructions, download the program from the Airmail web page at **www.siriuscyber.net/ham**.

When an RF connection is not available (or necessary) but web access is available, Winlink messages can be retrieved or sent via a web interface. The web browser access is limited to text-based messages without the use of bulletins or file attachments. Password-protected access to the Winlink mailbox is available through the Winlink page at **www.winlink.org/webmail**. There is also a terminal mode for interactive keyboard commands, allowing a terminal rather than computer-based software to connect to an RMS via RF. Because of the inefficient use of airtime, this method is discouraged but may be used for the listing and deletion of messages only.

Airmail provides a super-fast replica of Winlink radio operations while directly connected through the Internet to one of the CMS servers. This method of obtaining messages over the Internet allows multiple attachments, catalog bulletins, and all other Winlink services normally available over radio channels, but at Internet speeds. In order to use this service, a user must currently be listed as a radio user, and obtain the connection information for the closest CMS server. Both Paclink and Airmail support the TELNET client service. This operation allows regular use of the system with the same software configuration at high speed, without using RF bandwidth and provides a full-featured mechanism to access the system where no RF connection is available. An Emergency Operations Center with Internet access can use the TELNET path with RF as a fallback with just a minor change in the software. Similarly, an RV or marine user can use the software from an Internet café or home via TELNET and switch the software back to the TNC when mobile, with no change in functionality.

WINLINK FEATURES

To address the needs of mobile users for near real-time data, Winlinik uses an "on-demand" bulletin distribution mechanism. (Note that such bulletins are not the same as traditional AX.25 Packet Bulletins.) Users must first select requested bulletins from an available "catalog" list managed in Airmail. When bulletin requests are received by an RMS station, a fresh locally cached copy of the requested bulletin is delivered. If no fresh locally-cached version is available, the RMS accesses the Internet and finds the bulletin which is then downloaded to the RMS and then sent to the user. The global catalog currently includes over 700 available weather, propagation, and information bulletins, including, instructions for using the system, World news, and piracy reports. All Winlink RMS stations support a single global catalog which ensures users can access any bulletin from any RMS. Bulletins can contain basic text, graphic fax or satellite images, binary or encoded files like GRIB or WMO weather reports. Local processing is used to re-process images to sizes suitable for HF Pactor transmission. The system prevents bulletin duplication and automatically purges obsolete time-sensitive weather bulletins and replaces them with the current version.

The system also has the ability to contain bulletins with attachment information which is local to each RMS. This is especially useful for the non-public emcomm RMS which may house valuable procedural information pertinent to complex information or instruction needed by specific agencies in any community emergency.

Multiple binary or text-based file attachments of any type or number may be attached to a message by simply selecting the file to be sent from a *Windows* selection dialog in the user's HF AirMail or the Winlink VHF/UHF Paclink server with a standard SMTP e-mail client. E-mail message attachments sent through the Winlink system must be limited in size. Users are provided an option to allow this limit to be determined. When using the default B2F format, the protocol chosen by the user usually determines the file size of an attachment. A user may also turn off the ability to receive file attachments. Certain file attachment types are blocked from the system for the protection of the user from virus attacks.

The Winlink network administrator may post notices that are delivered to all individual Winlink users as a private message. This is a valuable tool for notifying users of system changes, outages, software upgrades, emergencies, etc.

The integrated nature of the system makes possible other services beyond just simple messaging. The bulletin services mentioned above is beyond normal messaging, but Winlink also provides rapid position reporting from anywhere in the world. This facility is interconnected with the APRS, ShipTrak, and YotReps networks. It supports weather reporting from cruising yachts at sea and an interconnection with the YotReps network which is used by government forecasters for weather observations in parts of the world where no others are available. It also allows the maritime user to participate in the National Weather Service's NOAA MAROB a voluntary marine observation reporting program.

To ensure equitable access to the system individual users are assigned daily time limits on HF frequencies by RMS sysops. The default time per any 24-hour period is 30 minutes, however, the user may request more time from the RMS sysop should it be needed. The time limit is individual to each RMS station. Utilization of the PACTOR-II and PACTOR-III protocols are a great timesaver, allowing the user up to 18 times the volume of messages over that of PACTOR-I for the same period of time.

The system has a number of other secondary features to help keep it healthy. Extensive traffic reports are collected, the state of individual RMS stations are monitored and reported if it becomes inactive and daily backups are performed automatically at all RMS stations as well as the Common Message Servers to ensure the system integrity. Security is ensured through the vigorous updating of virus definitions and automatic virus screening for all Internet mail and files. The system has the ability to block any user by both radio (by frequency band) and Internet (by e-mail address) to prevent abuse of the system. Spam is controlled through the use of a secure "acceptance list" or "white list" methodology. More information about the Winlink system is available on the Winlink website at **www.winlink.org**.

15.5.14 D-STAR

D-STAR (Digital Smart Technologies for Amateur Radio) is a digital voice and data protocol specification developed as the result of research by the Japan Amateur Radio League (JARL) to investigate digital technologies for Amateur Radio in 2001. While there are other digital on-air technologies being used by amateurs that were developed for other services, D-STAR is one of the first on-air protocols to be widely deployed and sold by a major radio manufacturer that is designed specifically for amateur service use. D-STAR transfers both voice and data via a data stream over the 2 meter (VHF), 70 cm (UHF) and 23 cm (1.2 GHz) Amateur Radio bands either simplex or via repeater.

One of the interesting features about the D-STAR protocol is the fact the system uses Amateur Radio call signs not only as an identifier, but also for signal routing. In the most common configuration, the most vital part of a D-STAR system is the gateway server, which networks a single system into a D-STAR network via a *trust server*. The trust server provides a central, master database to look up users and their associated system. This allows Amateur Radio operators to respond to calls made to them, regardless of their location on the D-STAR network. While almost all documentation references the Internet as the connection point for a network, any IP network connectivity will work, depending on signal latency. Currently, the global D-STAR trust server is maintained by a group of dedicated D-STAR enthusiasts from Dallas, Texas — the Texas Interconnect Team.

The D-STAR protocol specifies two modes; Digital Voice (DV) and Digital Data (DD). In the protocol, the DV mode provides both voice and low speed data channel on 2 meters, 70 cm and 23 cm over a 4800-bit/s data stream. In the protocol, the DV mode uses a data rate of 4800 bit/s. This data stream is broken down to three main packages: voice, forward error correction (FEC) and data. The largest portion of the data stream is the voice package, which is a total of 3600 bits/s with 1200 bit/s dedicated to forward error correction, leaving 1200 bit/s for data. This additional data contains various data flags as well as the data header, leaving about 950 bit/s available for either GPS or serial data. This portion of the data stream does not provide any type of error correction, which has been overcome by implementing error correction in the application software.

While there are various techniques of encoding and transporting a DV signal, the focus of D-STAR's design was the most efficient way to conserve RF spectrum. While D-STAR's "advertised" occupied bandwidth is 6.25 kHz, tests reveal a band plan of 10 kHz spacing is adequate to incorporate the D-STAR signal as well as provide space for channel guards.

In addition to DV mode, the D-STAR protocol outlines the high speed Digital Data (DD) mode. This higher speed data, 128 kbit/s, is available only on the 23 cm band because it requires an advertised 130 kHz bandwidth, only available at 23 cm in world-wide band plans. Unlike the DV mode repeaters, the DD mode module operates as an "access point" operating in half duplex, switching quickly on a single channel.

As with the DV mode, there is a portion of the data stream used for signal identification with the data header as well as various system flags and other D-STAR related items. Once this portion of the data stream is taken into consideration, the 128 kbit/s is reduced to approximately 100 kbit/s — still more than double a dial-up connection speed with significant range. Another consideration is the data rate specified at 128 kbit/s is the gross data rate. Therefore, the system developers are challenged by the area coverage/potential user issue. This means the higher the elevation of the system, the more potential users and the slower the system will become as all the users split the data bandwidth. Finally, there is an issue from the days of packet radio. While technically, the opportunity for "hidden transmitter" issues does exist and collisions do occur, the TR switching is very fast and this effect is handled by TCP/IP as it is for WiFi access points.

The simplex channel eliminates the need for duplexers at a repeater site if only the DD mode system is installed. It is still recommended to have filtering, such as a band-pass filter,

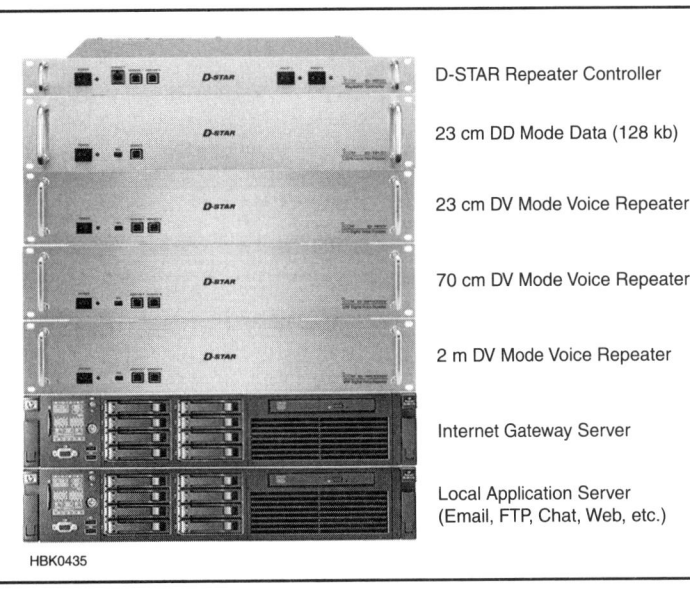

Figure 15.15 — Full D-STAR system.

in place to reduce possible interference from other digital sources close to the 23 cm band as well as to reduce RF overload from nearby RF sources. While some DD mode system owners would like more sensitivity or more output power (10 W), at the time of print, no manufacturer has developed pre-amps or RF power amplifiers with an adequate TR switching time to boost the signals.

Radios currently providing DV mode data service use a serial port for low-speed data (1200 bit/s), while the DD mode radio offers a standard Ethernet connection for high-speed (128 kbit/s) connections, to allow easy interfacing with computer equipment. The DD mode Ethernet jack allows two radios to act as an Ethernet bridge without any special software support required. This allows standard file sharing, FTP, TELNET, HTTP/web browsing, IRC chat or even remote desktop connections to function as if connected by wire.

In a Gateway configuration, *all* users must be registered in the network. This provides the DD mode sysop a layer of authorization, meaning that if someone wants to use a DD mode system, and they have not received authorization to use the gateway, their DD mode access will be denied. Any gateway registered user, on the common network, can use any DD mode system, even if the registration was not made on that system. While we are not able to use encryption in the Amateur Radio service, security can be implemented in standard software or consumer routers and firewalls.

A D-STAR repeater system consists of at least one RF module and a controller. While any combination of RF modules can be installed, typically a full system includes the three voice modules (2 meters, 70 cm and 23 cm) and the 23 cm DD mode module shown in **Figure 15.15**. A computer with dual Ethernet ports, running the Gateway software, is required for Internet access to the global network. An additional server, as shown in the diagram, can be incorporated for local hosting of e-mail, chat, FTP, web and other services. In a D-STAR system installation, the standard repeater components (cavities, isolators, antennas and so forth) are not shown but are required as with any analog system. Some groups have removed analog gear and replaced it with D-STAR components on the same frequency with no additional work beyond connecting the power and feed lines. More information about D-STAR systems may be found in the **Repeaters** chapter and in the **Digital Communications** chapter with the downloadable supplemental content.

USER-CREATED FEATURES AND TOOLS

D-STAR has already benefitted from a strong user community that has been developing applications, products and upgrades at a rapid pace. The *DPlus* gateway add-on provides a number of new features, such as an echo test, voicemail, simulcast to all modules, a linking feature, playback of voice or text messages and more. There are also a number of "D-STAR Reflectors" around the world that act like conference bridges for connecting multiple repeater systems.

One of the other projects that came from the Open D-STAR project is the DV Dongle by Robin Cutshaw, AA4RC. The DV Dongle contains the DSVI AMBE codec chip and a USB interface to allow a computer user to talk with other D-STAR voice users much the way

EchoLink users can connect to the system with a PC. The DV Tool software is written in Java to provide cross-platform support. The DV Dongle is available at ham radio dealers and the latest software and manual can be downloaded from **www.opendstar.org/tools**.

Pete Loveall, AE5PL, created a DPRS-to-APRS gateway that moves D-STAR GPS data to the APRS-IS network. Although it doesn't natively appear on the APRS RF network (unless IGated specifically), it does appear in all the online APRS tools. DPRS has been implemented in software with *DStarMonitor* running on many D-STAR gateways and *DPRS Interface* available for most computers at **www.aprs-is.net/dprs**. DPRS has been implemented in hardware with the µSmartDigi manufactured by Rich Painter, AB0VO. The µSmartDigi offers a compact, portable TNC designed to act as a gateway for position packets between a D-STAR digital network and a conventional analog APRS RF network via a D-STAR radio and a conventional FM radio. More DPRS and µSmartDigi information is available at **www.aprs-is.net/dprs** and **www.usmartdigi.com** respectively.

Satoshi Yasuda, 7M3TJZ/AD6GZ, created a D-STAR node adapter or "hot spot" that connects to a standard simplex FM radio and allows a D-STAR radio user to access the D-STAR network. The system requires the FM rig be accurately configured for a clean signal and loses the D-STAR benefit of only consuming 6.25 kHz of bandwidth. It does allow D-STAR users access to the network via RF where there is Internet access and no repeater infrastructure available. More information can be found online at **d-star.dyndns.org/rig.html.en**.

Dan Smith, KK7DS developed D-RATS with public service users in mind. In addition to chat, D-RATS supports file/photo downloads bulletins, forms, email and a sophisticated mapping capability. It also has a "repeater" functionality that allows sharing a D-STAR radio data stream over a LAN. The repeater feature is interesting in an environment where the radio would be physically separated from the software user, like in an emergency operations center. Dan has current developments and downloads available at **www.d-rats.com/wiki**.

This is just a sample of the development taking place and there will undoubtedly be more applications coming as the user base increases. The two websites with the most current D-STAR information are **www.dstarinfo.com** and **www.dstarusers.org**.

15.5.15 APCO Project 25 (P25)

Project 25 (P25) or APCO-25 is a suite of standards for digital radio communications for use by public safety agencies in North America. P25 was established by Association of Public-Safety Communications Officials (APCO) to address the need for common digital public safety radio communications standards for first responders and Homeland Security/Emergency Response professionals. In this regard, P25 fills the same role as the European Tetra protocol, although not interoperable with it.

P25 has been developed in phases with Phase 1 completed in 1995. P25 Phase 1 radio systems operate in 12.5 kHz analog, digital or mixed mode. Phase 1 radios use Continuous 4-level FM (C4FM) modulation for digital transmissions at 4800 baud and two bits per symbol, yielding 9600 bit/s total channel throughput. In the case of data transmission, data packets basically consist of a header, containing overhead information, followed by data. In the case of digitized voice transmission, after the transmission of a header containing error protected overhead information, 2400 bit/s is devoted to periodically repeating the overhead information needed to allow for late entry (or the missed reception of the header).

After evaluating several candidates, Project 25 selected the IMBE (Improved MultiBand Excitation) vocoder from DVSI for phase 1, operating at 4400 bit/s. An additional 2800 bit/s of forward error correction is added for error correction of the digitized voice. An 88.9-bit/s low-speed data channel is provided in the digitized voice frame structure and several forms of encryption are supported.

P25 Phase 2 requires a further effective bandwidth reduction to 6.25 kHz by operating as two-slot TDMA (Time Division Multiple Access) with support for trunking systems. This provides two channels from the same 12.5 kHz spectrum when working through a repeater to provide time synchronization. The TDMA timing requirements does limit range to a published 35 km but this is plenty for public safety users. It uses the newer AMBE (Advanced MultiBand Excitation) codec from DVSI to accommodate the bit rate reduction to 4800 bit/s. Phase 2 radios will still offer backward compatibility with Phase 1. Phase 3 work has started and will support access to the new 700 MHz band in the US.

P25 radios offer a number of features of interest to public service agencies such as an emergency mode, optional text messaging, over the air programming/deactivation. More P25 information can be found at **www.apcointl.org/spectrum-management/resources/interoperability/p25.html**.

15.5.16 Yaesu System Fusion

Yaesu released a specification for System Fusion in 2013, becoming the most recent DV methodology. System Fusion supports digital voice and data in a 12.5 kHz narrow-band channel at 9600 bps, using C4FM modulation over VHF (144-148 MHz) and UHF (440-450 MHz). System Fusion supports three modes of operation: voice full rate (Voice FR) mode, data full rate (Data FR) mode, or voice/data (V/D) mode. Voice FR mode is typically displayed on System Fusion transceivers as "VW," with voice/data mode appearing as "DN." The two full rate modes use the entire 9600 bps channel for their respective voice or data payloads, whereas the V/D mode splits the channel into two 4800 bps payloads, with voice information on one and data on the other.

The voice modes also include robust forward error correction (FEC) and utilize the AMBE+2 (Advanced MultiBand Excitation) CODEC from DVSI. In V/D mode, the voice and FEC data use the AMBE+2 "Enhanced Half-Rate" mode where voice and FEC payloads consume individual 3600 bps totals, with header, synchronization, and routing data consuming much of the remainder of the 4800 bps available. The data component of the V/D mode can be used for features like GPS information, in order to provide APRS-like functionality. The Voice FR mode encodes using the AMBE+2 "Enhanced Full-Rate" mode, where voice information and FEC consume 7200 bps. The Voice FR mode provides the highest quality voice exchange.

Each transmission comprises 960 byte (100 ms) packets. Each transmission begins with a header packet (HC), followed by communication channel packets (CC), and ends with a terminator packet (TC). The HC and TC packets synchronization information, source, and destination call signs, plus uplink and downlink call signs, as used for routing. In the V/D mode, each of the CC packets contain 40 bytes of frame sync, then 200 bytes of frame information, followed by 72 bytes of interleaved voice and data frames, for a total of 960 bytes. In the Voice FR mode, the first CC packet contains some overflow call sign information, but is generally segmented into 144 byte frames with voice information.

Yaesu repeaters offer the System Fusion environment with an "Automatic Mode Select" (AMS), operating in both FM analog and System Fusion digital modes. The repeaters can be configured in a combination of modes. While the repeaters are capable of operation in a purely analog mode, this prevents digitally equipped users from taking advantage of the enhancements that digital operation offers. With a similar discouragement toward digital enhancements, the repeaters can be configured in such a way as to allow analog or digital reception, but forcing the output to analog only. While this configuration allows both analog and digital users to coexist, it does so in a constrained fashion, negating the digital advantages of a white noise and hiss free experience, plus strips away GPS and call sign information. Operating in purely digital mode is also possible, offering enhancements for digital users, but effectively "locking out" analog FM operations, as with other DV methodologies. This is typically implemented when there is more than one System Fusion repeater operating in a given area.

More interesting (and common) is the hybrid AMS configuration, allowing analog FM in to analog FM out and digital in to digital out. In this configuration, analog users are not suddenly "disconnected" from a repeater and other analog-only capable operators. Also, digital users are free to take full advantage of the enhancements available with their transceivers. With the users' System Fusion transceivers configured in AMS, digital users can hear an analog call placed on the repeater, in between transmission exchanges. The transceivers will switch to analog, automatically allowing them to communicate with the analog station. This furthers an environment of inclusion for both "camps" to enjoy and allows analog users to upgrade to System Fusion digital at a time of their choosing, rather than forcing a transition, all at once.

In order for analog FM transceivers to remain quiet during digital transmissions on the selected receive frequency, enabling the tone squelch feature to match the repeater's transmitted continuous tone coded subaudible squelch (CTCSS) or digital coded squelch (DCS) signal, is required. Watching for a visual "channel busy" indicator on the analog users' transceivers or enabling a Busy Channel Lockout feature will prevent accidental interference, when digital communications are taking place.

15.5.17 Digital Mobile Radio — DMR

Digital Mobile Radio (DMR) is a worldwide standard defined by the European Telecommunications Standards Institute (ETSI) based on Motorola MOTOTRBO and is used in commercial products from a number of manufacturers. Although the transmission fits in a standard 12.5 kHz-wide narrowband channel, it is structured as a two-time-slot Time Division Multiple Access (TDMA) so two channels fit in same the narrowband spectrum. This makes DMR ultra-narrowband compliant by providing the equivalent of two 6.25 kHz channels.

DMR uses C4FM modulation and the DVSI AMBE+2 codec to encode and decode the voice audio. Each TDMA time slot is 30 ms long with a 108-bit payload and 2.5 ms of guard time between the time slots. Since a user radio would only be transmitting using a single time slot, it has to be good quality for the transmitter to turn on and insure that its frequency settles during the guard time. It also means that the transmitter is only operating at 50% duty cycle, unlike an FM or FDMA-based digital mode transmitter. This translates to longer battery life on handheld units.

The timing is also critical and requires a time source. During simplex communications, the first transmitter becomes the time source and the repeater acts as a time source when the signal is retransmitted. The critical nature of this timing also limits the practical range of the system to about 50 miles. This is entirely acceptable for commercial communications where there is significant infrastructure but may be an issue for long-range amateur use.

The original specification for DMR covered conventional simplex or repeater operation. In 2013 the specification for trunked operation was approved. It also features the ability to link repeater sites over the Internet using IP (Internet Protocol), IP-addressable radios, and a beaconing capability to allow radios to scan and acquire new sites.

Like many digital modes, the DMR specification only covers the air interface to allow radios to interoperate over the air. It does not cover the network linking protocols so these are manufacturer-specific. Motorola's IP SiteConnect system has been expanded by the use of a product called a c-Bridge by Rayfield Communications to allow many more linked systems and many more users. The ultimate limit may be more a practical one than physical. This has allowed the creation of two major Amateur Radio networks; DCI (**www.trbo.org**) and MARC (**www.dmr-marc.net**) which are bridged.

The DMR networks generally reserve one time slot for local communications and the other is used for linked operations within a region, nationally or international. The trunked talk groups programmed into the radios determine which connections are used. This requires locating local programming information for the radio or a pre-existing programming template and each radio must be registered and authorized by the system. Details and the latest information are available online at the DCI and MARC websites. (See also the **Repeaters** chapter for information about DMR.)

15.5.18 High-Speed Multimedia (HSMM)

The following material is excerpted from High-Speed Multimedia for Amateur Radio by Glen Popiel, KW5GP, and from the 2014 ARRL-TAPR Digital Communications Conference presentation "High-Speed Wireless Networking in the UHF and Microwave Bands" by David Bern, W2LNX, and Keith Elkin, KB3TCB. This section identifies certain key elements of the rapidly expanding Broadband-Hamnet family of network technologies. For detailed information, see the book by KW5GP.

Currently, three primary technologies are used to implement Amateur Radio HSMM networks. HSMM is *high-speed multimedia* and covers a wide range of software and hardware components. Broadband-Hamnet (BBHN — **www.broadband-hamnet.org**) and Amateur Radio Emergency Data Network (AREDN) technologies are used to create a peer-to-peer mesh topology, while HamWAN is used to implement a star topology. The GGHN and AREDN technologies use the 802.11g modulation method, while HamWAN uses the 802.11n-based MikroTik Nv2 modulation method. Both are TCP/IP-based, and you can provide the same applications and services regardless of which networking technology you choose to implement. Both also provide a means of connecting your HSMM network to the public Internet. The systems use commercial systems operating in the amateur allocations of microwave frequency bands as shown in **Table 15.18**.

Originally known as HSMM-Mesh, BBHN uses inexpensive, commercial off-the-shelf (COTS) Linksys and Ubiquiti wireless routers. The firmware in the routers is replaced to become a fully functional node in a peer-to-peer mesh topology network. The

Table 15.18
Wireless Networking Frequencies

airMAX	Ubiquiti	ISM	Amateur
M900 900 MHz	902-928	902-928	902-928
M2 2.4 GHz	2402-2462	2400-2500	2390-2459
M3 3 GHz[1]	3370-3730		3300-3500[3]
M5 5 GHz	5725-5850	5725-5875[2]	5650-5925

[1]For export from USA
[2]U-NII: 5150-5350, 5470-5825 MHz
[3]ARRL Band Plan

Table 15.19
Digital Modulation Modes and Formats Used in Amateur Radio

See the text of this chapter for definitions and abbreviations

Lowest Permitted Frequency is the lowest amateur frequency at which this emission may be used according to Part 97.307 limits on symbol rate and bandwidth

See also the supplemental PDF file "Digital Modes - Lowest Permitted Amateur Frequency" in the online supplemental material accompanying this book.

Mode or Format Name	Developer	Principal Freq	Principal Application	Lowest Permitted Frequency	Data Rate (bits/sec)
ALE	MIL-STD-188-141, FED-STD-1045	HF	Data		<375
AMTOR-A	G3PLX	HF	Data		53
AMTOR-B	G3PLX	HF	Data		57
AOR AMBE	AOR Corp	HF	Voice, Data		2400
APCO P25	APCO	VHF	Voice	50 MHz	6800
Chip64	IZ8BLY	HF	Keyboarding		21.1/37.5
CLOVER-II	Hal Comm.	HF	Data		< 37.5-750
CLOVER-2000	Hal Comm.	HF	Data		108-1994
DMR	Motorola	VHF	Voice	50 MHz	
Domino	ZL2AFP	HF	Keyboarding		31/44/62?
DominoEX	ZL1BPU	HF	Keyboarding		(<15.63)-86.13
D-Star (DV)	JARL	VHF	Voice & data	28 MHz	D:960 V:2400
D-Star (DD)	JARL	UHF	Data	902 MHz	72k-124k
Facsimile		HF	Image		
FDMDV	G3PLX/HB9TLK	HF	Voice		1450
FSK441	K1JT	VHF	Meteor scatter	28 MHz	882
G-TOR	Kantronics	HF	Data		35/75/115
Hellschreiber (Feld)	Rudolf Hell	HF	Keyboarding		2.5 char/s
JT6M	K1JT	50 MHz	Meteor scatter		77.9
JT65	K1JT	V/UHF	Moonbounce		1.54
MFSK16	ZL1BPU/IZ8BLY	HF	Keyboarding, Data		31.25
MT63	SP9VRC	HF	Keyboarding		35/70/140
Olivia	SP9VRC	HF	Keyboarding		8.75/17.5
Packet (Bell202)		VHF	Data	28 MHz	<1200
PACTOR-I	DL6MAA/DF4KV	HF	Data, Winlink email		51.2/128
PACTOR-II	Spec. Comm. Sys.	HF	Data, Winlink email		100-700
PACTOR-III	Spec. Comm. Sys.	HF	Data, Winlink email		85-2722
PSK31	G3PLX	HF	Keyboarding		31.25
QPSK31	G3PLX	HF	Keyboarding		31.25
PSK63/125		HF	Keyboarding		62.5/125
QPSK62/126		HF	Keyboarding		62.5/125
Q15X25	SP9VRC	HF	Data		300/1200/2400
RTTY (Baudot)		HF	Keyboarding, contests		30.3
SSTV (traditional)	WØORX	HF	Image		8 s/frame
SSTV Martin M1	Martin Emmerson	HF	Image		114 s/frame
SSTV Scottie S1	Eddie Murphy	HF	Image		110 s/frame
System Fusion	Yaesu	VHF	Voice, data	50 MHz	
Throb	G3PPT	HF	Keyboarding		10/20/40 wpm
WINMOR	KN6KB	HF	Winlink email		
WSPR (MEPT-JT)	K1JT	HF-VHF	Weak signal beacon		0.45

Bit rate (bits/sec)	Symbol rate (baud)	Modulation ("N-" means multi-carrier)	Error handling
375	125	8FSK	FEC
114	114	FSK	ARQ
114	114	FSK	FEC
3600	50	36-QPSK	FEC
9600	4,800	4FSK/QPSK	FEC
300	300	DBPSK-DSSS	FEC
62.5-750	31.25	4-(2-16)DPSK/(2-4)DASK	FEC/FEC+ARQ
500-3000	62.5	8-(2-16)DPSK/(2-4)DASK	FEC/FEC+ARQ
9600	4800	4FSK/QPSK/C4FM	FEC
31/44/62	7.8/11/15.6	16FSK	None
15.63-86.13	3.9-21.5	18FSK	None/FEC
4800	4800	0.5 GMSK/QPSK/4PSK	FEC
128000	128000	0.5 GMSK/QPSK/4PSK	FEC
	120 lpm	FM, 1500-2300 Hz	None
1450	50	15-QPSK	None
882	441	4FSK	None
80/160/240	100/200/300	FSK, 170/200 Hz shift	FEC + ARQ
122.5	122.5	ASK	None
116.8	21.53	44FSK	None
16.1	2.7	65FSK	FEC
62.5	15.625	16FSK	FEC
320/640/1280	5/10/20	64-DPSK	FEC
78.13/156.25	15.63/31.25	32-FSK	FEC
1200	1200	FSK	ARQ
100/200	100/200	FSK, 200 Hz shift	ARQ
200-800	100	2-DBPSK/PI-4DQPSK/8,16DPSK	FEC + ARQ
200-3600	100	(2-18)-DBPSK/DQPSK	FEC + ARQ
31.25	31.25	BPSK	None
62.5	31.25	QPSK	FEC
62.5/125	62.5/125	BPSK	None
125/250	62.5/125	QPSK	FEC
2500	83.33	15-QPSK	FEC + ARQ
45.45	45.45	FSK, 170 Hz shift	None
	120-line B/W	FM, 1200-2300 Hz	None
	240-line RGB	FM, 1200-2300 Hz	None
	240-line RGB	FM, 1200-2300 Hz	None
9600	4800	4FSK/QPSK/C4FM	FEC
	1/2/4	9FSK/2-9FSK	None
62.5-3750	31.25/62.5	(1-15)-QPSK/16QAM/4FSK	FEC + ARQ
2.93	1.46	4FSK	FEC

router is configured to only connect to other BBHN devices using the same firmware. Non-amateur devices such as smartphones, tablets, and laptops can detect and display the BBHN network, they cannot connect to it. The system uses the Domain Name Server (DNS) system and also includes the station call sign in beacon packets to satisfy the FCC Part 97 requirements.

The AREDN development group is focused on developing software for the Ubiquiti series of wireless routes in HSMM networks. The current firmware includes Virtual Private Network (VPN) tunneling capability. AREDN is implemented based on the BBHN firmware and is self-discovering, self-configuring, and self-advertising with the same peer-to-peer mesh technology as BBHN. Both BBHN and AREDN are based on carrier-sense, multiple-access (CSMA) technology.

HamWAN is based on a star network topology, in which all of the user nodes (also known as client nodes) connect directly to a central node, also known as a cell site or distribution node. The cell sites typically have a point-to-point link between other cell sites. The cell sites are linked together, forming the HamWAN network's backbone. HamWAN cell sites communicate over a dedicated link at 3.4 or 5 GHz. HamWAN client nodes use MicroTik Nv2 command protocols, which allows time division multiple access (TDMA) technology. HamWAN also uses digital certificates to authenticate users.

Additional information on amateur high-speed multimedia networking is available in the referenced book and article (see the book's online supplemental information) and at the following websites:
www.aredn.org
www.broadband-hamnet.org
www.HamWAN.org
www.memHamWAN

15.6 Digital Mode Table

Table 15.19 is a summary of common digital modes used by amateurs as of early 2013 and their primary characteristics. The following text is intended to make high-level comparisons. For more information on these modes see the earlier sections of this chapter. This table and a detailed listing showing the lowest permitted frequency for a number of digital mode variants are also available as a PDF file with the downloadable supplemental content.

Many modes have a number of variants, with the most common shown in the table. High reliability, low data rate modes are more common on HF. Higher data rates are available on VHF/UHF, where the bands have less noise and require less effort to make them reliable. Some modes have very specific intended uses like the meteor scatter, moonbounce and beaconing modes created by Joe Taylor, K1JT as *WSJT* (see the section Structured Digital Modes).

There can be a significant difference between data rate and bit rate in high reliability modes. The data rate is the amount of user data transmitted where the bit rate includes the packet and error correction overhead. Some of these rates are approximate and can vary based on conditions and the variant of the mode used. The symbol rate is a function of the modulation scheme and how many simultaneous carriers are used to transmit the data.

The error handling mechanism is critical to note when sending data. Some modes include no error handling which means errors are not detected and must be addressed in a higher protocol layer (as in AX.25 packet). Forward error correction (FEC) makes a best effort to address errors in real time as part of the data sent in each packet. FEC can add substantial overhead to each packet and does not guarantee error-free delivery but does make the mode robust in high noise environments. Automatic Retry Request (ARQ) can guarantee error-free delivery of data but has no ability to actually correct received data. The combination of FEC and ARQ allows minor errors to be corrected in real time with major errors generating a retry request.

15.7 Glossary

ACK — Acknowledgment, the control signal sent to indicate the correct receipt of a transmission block.
Address — A character or group of characters that identifies a source or destination.
AFSK — Audio frequency-shift keying.
ALE — Automatic link establishment.
Algorithm — Numerical method or process.
APCO — Association of Public Safety Communications Officials.
ARQ — Automatic Repeat reQuest, an error-sending station, after transmitting a data block, awaits a reply (ACK or NAK) to determine whether to repeat the last block or proceed to the next.
ASCII — American National Standard Code for Information Interchange, a code consisting of seven information bits.
AX.25 — Amateur packet-radio link-layer protocol.
Baud — A unit of signaling speed equal to the number of discrete conditions or events per second. (If the duration of a pulse is 20 ms, the signaling rate is 50 baud or the reciprocal of 0.02, abbreviated Bd).
Baudot code — A coded character set in which five bits represent one character. Used in the US to refer to ITA2.
Bell 103 — A 300-baud full-duplex modem using 200-Hz-shift FSK of tones centered at 1170 and 2125 Hz.
Bell 202 — A 1200-baud modem standard with 1200-Hz mark, 2200-Hz space, used for VHF FM packet radio.
BER — Bit error rate.
BERT — Bit-error-rate test.
Bit stuffing — Insertion and deletion of 0s in a frame to preclude accidental occurrences of flags other than at the beginning and end of frames.
Bit — Binary digit, a single symbol, in binary terms either a one or zero.
Bit/s or *bps* — Bits per second.
Bitmap — See **raster.**
Bit rate — Rate at which bits are transmitted in bit/s or bps. **Gross**

(or **raw**) **bit rate** includes all bits transmitted, regardless of purpose. **Net bit rate** (also called **throughput**) only includes bits that represent data.

BLER — Block error rate.

BLERT — Block-error-rate test.

BPSK — Binary phase-shift keying in which there are two combinations of phase used to represent data symbols.

Byte — A group of bits, usually eight.

Cache — To store data or packets in anticipation of future use, thus improving routing or delivery performance.

Channel — Medium through which data is transmitted.

Checksum — Data representing the sum of all character values in a packet or message.

CLOVER — Trade name of digital communications system developed by Hal Communications.

COFDM — Coded Orthogonal Frequency Division Multiplex, OFDM plus coding to provide error correction and noise immunity.

Code — Method of representing data.

Codec — Algorithm for compressing and decompressing data.

Collision — A condition that occurs when two or more transmissions occur at the same time and cause interference to the intended receivers.

Compression — Method of reducing the amount of data required to represent a signal or data set. **Decompression** is the method of reversing the compression process.

Constellation — A set of points that represent the various combinations of phase and amplitude in a QAM or other complex modulation scheme.

Contention — A condition on a communications channel that occurs when two or more stations try to transmit at the same time.

Control characters — Data values with special meanings in a protocol, used to cause specific functions to be performed.

Control field — An 8-bit pattern in an HDLC frame containing commands or responses, and sequence numbers.

Convolution — The process of combining or comparing signals based on their behavior over time.

Cyclic Redundancy Check (CRC) — The result of a calculation representing all character values in a packet or message. The result of the CRC is sent with a transmission block. The receiving station uses the received CRC to check transmitted data integrity.

Datagram — A data packet in a connectionless protocol.

Data stream — Flow of information, either over the air or in a network.

DBPSK — Differential binary phase-shift keying.

Dibit — A two-bit combination.

DQPSK — Differential quadrature phase-shift keying.

Domino — A conversational HF digital mode similar in some respects to MFSK15.

DRM — Digital Radio Mondiale. A consortium of broadcasters, manufacturers, research and governmental organizations which developed a system for digital sound broadcasting in bands between 100 kHz and 30 MHz.

DV — Digital voice.

Emission — A signal transmitted over the air.

Encoding — Changing data into a form represented by a particular code.

Encryption — Process of using codes and encoding in an effort to obscure the meaning of a transmitted message. **Decryption** reverses the encryption process to recover the original data.

Error Correcting Code (ECC) — Code used to repair transmission errors.

Eye pattern — An oscilloscope display in the shape of one or more eyes for observing the shape of a serial digital stream and any impairments.

Fast Fourier Transform (FFT) — An algorithm that produces the spectrum of a signal from the set of sampled value of the waveform.

FEC — Forward error correction.

Frame — Data set transmitted as one package or set.

Facsimile (fax) — A form of telegraphy for the transmission of fixed images, with or without half-tones, with a view to their reproduction in a permanent form.

FCS — Frame check sequence. (see also **CRC**)

FDM — Frequency division multiplexing.

FDMA — Frequency division multiple access.

FEC — Forward error correction, an error-control technique in which the transmitted data is sufficiently redundant to permit the receiving station to correct some errors.

FSK — Frequency-shift keying.

Gray code — A code that minimizes the number of bits that change between sequential numeric values.

G-TOR — A digital communications system developed by Kantronics.

HDLC — High-level data link control procedures as specified in ISO 3309.

Hellschreiber — A facsimile system for transmitting text.

Host — As used in packet radio, a computer with applications programs accessible by remote stations.

IA5 — International Alphabet, designating a specific set of characters as an ITU standard.

Information field — Any sequence of bits containing the intelligence to be conveyed.

Interleave — Combine more than one data stream into a single stream or alter the data stream in such a way as to optimize it for the modulation and channel characteristics being used.

IP — Internet Protocol, a network protocol used to route information between addresses on the Internet.

ISO — International Organization for Standardization.

ITU — International Telecommunication Union, a specialized agency of the United Nations. (See www.itu.int.)

ITU-T — Telecommunication Standardization Sector of the ITU, formerly CCITT.

Jitter — Unwanted variations in timing or phase in a digital signal.

Layer — In communications protocols, one of the strata or levels in a reference model.

Least significant bit (LSB) — The bit in a byte or word that represents the smallest value.

Level 1 — Physical layer of the OSI reference model.

Level 2 — Link layer of the OSI reference model.

Level 3 — Network layer of the OSI reference model.

Level 4 — Transport layer of the OSI reference model.

Level 5 — Session layer of the OSI reference model.

Level 6 — Presentation layer of the OSI reference model.

Level 7 — Application layer of the OSI reference model.

Lossless (compression) — Method of compression that results in an exact copy of the original data

Lossy (compression) — Method of compression in which some of the original data is lost

MFSK16 — A multi-frequency shift communications system

Modem — Modulator-demodulator, a device that connects between a data terminal and communication line (or radio). Also called **data set**.

Most significant bit (MSB) — The bit in a byte or word that represents the greatest value.

Multicast — A protocol designed to distribute packets of data to many users without communications between the user and data source.

MSK — Frequency-shift keying where the shift in Hz is equal to half the signaling rate in bit/s.

Digital Protocols and Modes   15.35

MT63 — A keyboard-to-keyboard mode similar to PSK31 and RTTY.

Nibble — A four-bit quantity. Half a byte.

Node — A point within a network, usually where two or more links come together, performing switching, routine and concentrating functions.

OFDM — Orthogonal Frequency Division Multiplex. A method of using spaced subcarriers that are phased in such a way as to reduce the interference between them.

OSI-RM — Open Systems Interconnection Reference Model specified in ISO 7498 and ITU-T Recommendation X.200.

PACTOR — Trade name of digital communications protocols offered by Special Communications Systems GmbH & Co KG (SCS).

Packet — 1) Radio: communication using the AX.25 protocol. 2) Data: transmitted data structure for a particular protocol (see also **frame**.)

Parity (parity check) — Number of bits with a particular value in a specific data element, such as a byte or word or packet. Parity can be odd or even. A **parity bit** contains the information about the element parity.

Pixel — Abbreviation for "picture element."

Primitive — An instruction for creating a signal or data set, such as in a drawing or for speech.

Project 25 — Digital voice system developed for APCO, also known as P25.

Protocol — A formal set of rules and procedures for the exchange of information.

PSK — Phase-shift keying.

PSK31 — A narrow-band digital communications system developed by Peter Martinez, G3PLX.

QAM — Quadrature Amplitude Modulation. A method of simultaneous phase and amplitude modulation. The number that precedes it, for example, 64QAM, indicates the number of discrete stages in each symbol.

QPSK — Quadrature phase-shift keying in which there are four different combinations of signal phase that represent symbols.

Raster (image) — Images represented as individual data elements, called pixels.

Router — A network packet switch. In packet radio, a network level relay station capable of routing packets.

RTTY — Radioteletype.

Sample — Convert an analog signal to a set of digital values.

Shift — 1) The difference between mark and space frequencies in an FSK or AFSK signal. 2) To change between character sets, such as between LTRS and FIGS in RTTY.

SSID — Secondary station identifier. In AX.25 link-layer protocol, a multipurpose octet to identify several packet radio stations operating under the same call sign.

State — Particular combination of signal attributes used to represent data, such as amplitude or phase.

Start (stop) bit — Symbol used to synchronize receiving equipment at the beginning (end) of a data byte.

Symbol — Specific state or change in state of a transmission representing a particular signaling event. **Symbol rate** is the number of symbols transmitted per unit of time (see also **baud**).

TAPR — Tucson Amateur Packet Radio Corporation, a nonprofit organization involved in digital mode development.

TDM — Time division multiplexing.

TDMA — Time division multiple access.

Throb — A multi-frequency shift mode like MFSK15.

TNC — Terminal node controller, a device that assembles and disassembles packets (frames).

Trellis — The set of allowed combination of signal states that represent data. (see also **Viterbi coding** and **constellation**.)

Turnaround time — The time required to reverse the direction of a half-duplex circuit, required by propagation, modem reversal and transmit-receive switching time of transceiver.

Unicast — A protocol in which information is exchanged between a single pair of points on a network.

Varicode — A code in which the different data values are represented by codes with different lengths.

Vector — Image represented as a collection of drawing instructions.

Word — Set of bits larger than a byte.

15.8 References and Bibliography

D. Bern, W2LNX, and K. Elkin, KB3TCB, "High-Speed Wireless Networking in the UHF and Microwave Bands," *QST*, Nov. 2015, pp. 33-37

D. Bern, W2LNX, and K. Elkin, KB3TCB, "High-Speed Wireless Networking in the UHF and Microwave Bands," available from **tapr.org/pdf/DCC2014-High-Speed-Wireless-Networking-UHF-Microwave-Bands-W2LNXpresentation.pdf**

A. Bombardiere, K2MO, "A Quick-Start Guide to ALE400 ARQ FAE," *QST*, Jun. 2010, pp. 34-36.

S. Ford, WB8IMY, *Get on the Air with HF Digital Handbook*, 2nd edition, ARRL, 2018.

S. Ford, WB8IMY, *HF Digital Handbook*, 4th edition, ARRL, 2007.

S. Ford, WB8IMY, *VHF Digital Handbook*, ARRL, 2008.

S. Franke, K9AN, and J. Taylor, K1JT, "Open Source Soft-Decision Decoder for the JT65 (63,12) Reed-Solomon Code," *QEX*, May/Jun. 2016, pp. 8 – 17.

S. Franke, K9AN, and J. Taylor, K1JT, "The MSK144 Protocol for Meteor-Scatter Communication," *QEX*, Sep./Oct. 2018, pp. 30 – 36.

B.P. Lathi, *Modern Digital and Analog Communication Systems*, Oxford University Press, 1998.

"Manual of Transmission Methods – Reference Document," Rohde & Schwarz, 2014, available at **resources.rohde-schwarz-usa.com/c/manual-of-transmissi-2**

N. Palermo, IV3NWV, "Q-ary Repeat-Accumulate Codes for Weak Signals Communications," **microtelecom.it/qracodes/ QRACodes-Rev10.pdf**.

G. Popiel, KW5GP, *High-Speed Multimedia for Amateur Radio*, ARRL, 2016

B. Sklar, *Digital Communications, Fundamentals and Applications*, Prentice Hall, 1988.

Yaesu System Fusion Standard, "Amateur Radio Digital Standards" v1.0 January 15, 2013, rev 1.01 April 18, 2013," available for download from **www.yaesu.com.**

J. Taylor, K1JT, "The JT65 Communications Protocol," *QEX*, Sep./Oct. 2005, p. 3.

J. Taylor, K1JT, and B. Walker, W1BW, "WSPRing Around the World," *QST*, Nov. 2010, p. 30.

J. Taylor, K1JT, "*WSJT*: New Software for VHF Meteor-Scatter Communication," *QST*, Dec. 2001, pp. 36-41.

Contents

16.1 Platform Overview
    16.1.1 Platform Structure
    16.1.2 Types of Platforms

16.2 Sensors
    16.2.1 Resistance-Based Sensors
    16.2.2 Current-Based Sensors
    16.2.3 Voltage-Based Sensors
    16.2.4 Capacitance-Based Sensors
    16.2.5 Sensor Calibration
    16.2.6 Digital Sensor Protocols
    16.2.7 Powering Sensors

16.3 Navigation Data and Telemetry
    16.3.1 Dead Reckoning
    16.3.2 GPS Data
    16.3.3 Automatic Packet Reporting System (APRS)
    16.3.4 Satellite Telemetry
    16.3.5 Non-Licensed Telemetry Transmissions
    16.3.6 Other Telemetry Digital Modes
    16.3.7 Receiving and Relaying Telemetry

16.4 Payloads
    16.4.1 VHF/UHF/Microwave Payloads
    16.4.2 HF Payloads

16.5 High Altitude Balloon Platforms
    16.5.1 FAA Requirements
    16.5.2 Balloon Platform Environment
    16.5.3 Balloon Platform Physical Design

16.6 Unmanned Aerial Vehicles (UAVs)
    16.6.1 General UAV Platform Requirements
    16.6.2 UAV Data and Navigation Subsystems
    16.6.3 UAV Platform Configuration
    16.6.4 UAV Electronic Subsystems
    16.6.5 Powering the UAV

16.7 Rockets
    16.7.1 General Rocket Platform Requirements
    16.7.2 Suitable Rocket Data and Navigation Subsystems
    16.7.3 Rocket Platform Configuration

16.8 Robotics
    16.8.1 General Robotics Platform Requirements
    16.8.2 Suitable Robotics Data and Navigation Subsystems
    16.8.3 Robotics Platform Configuration

16.9 Fixed Stations
    16.9.1 General Fixed Station Platform Requirements
    16.9.2 Suitable Fixed Station Data and Navigation Subsystems
    16.9.3 Fixed Station Platform Configuration
    16.9.4 Powering the Fixed Station Platform

16.10 References and Bibliography

Chapter 16 — Downloadable Supplemental Content

Supplemental Files

- "A Simple Sensor Package for High Altitude Ballooning" by John Post, KA5GSQ
- "Touching Near Space on a Budget" by Paul Verhage, KD4STH
- Collection of *Powerpoint* presentations and PDF articles by KD4STH on high-altitude platforms, including BalloonSat construction and testing
- "APRS Unveiled" by Bob Simmons, WB6EYV
- "APRS with a Smartphone" by Pat Cain, KØPC
- "ARRL Education and Technology Program Space/Sea Buoy" by Mark Spencer, WA8SME
- "Fox-1 Satellite Telemetry – Part 1: On the Satellite," by Burns Fisher, W2BFJ
- "Fox-1 Satellite Telemetry – Part 2: *FoxTelem*," by Chris Thompson, AC2CZ

Chapter 16

Amateur Radio Data Platforms

This chapter addresses the increasing use of amateur communication as a key element of scientific experimentation. The use of amateur means to collect and track data focuses on high-altitude balloons which are the most popular platform used for this purpose today. Other types of platforms, such as drones and rockets, are also used for experimenting and enjoying operating them. Amateur Radio plays an important role in supporting their use.

The chapter begins with a discussion of what types of sensors and transducers are used to collect data on these platforms. Navigation and telemetry streams are also fundamental to collecting data and operating the platform. Several types of telemetry and location data are covered here along with a review of how the information is transmitted from the platform. (See the **Digital Protocols and Modes** for descriptions of the modes themselves.)

Future editions will continue to expand coverage to additional technologies, platforms and applications. Material in this edition was updated by Paul Verhage, KD4STH and Bill Brown, WB8ELK.

Amateurs conducting science experiments and operating mobile craft frequently use Amateur Radio for their data links and control signals, even as they cross continents and entire oceans! Such *platforms* include balloons and multi-rotor copters. Others are land-based (such as weather stations, animal tracking, or robots) or marine (ocean or river buoys or rovers). CubeSats (**www.cubesat.org**) also use Amateur Radio control and data links.

Building these platforms combines several technical fields: using sensors and data acquisition systems to measure events and phenomena, mechanical and electrical engineering to construct the platform, 3-dimensional navigation, and the data link and associated radio technologies. These hybrids are attracting the experimentalists and scientists to Amateur Radio, just as they were attracted at the dawn of the wireless age.

Support of scientific experimentation is hardly a new aspect of Amateur Radio — amateurs have supported science almost since the beginning when Tom Mix, 1TS, accompanied the explorer MacMillan to the Arctic aboard the *Bowdoin* in 1923. Amateurs assisted the Naval Laboratory in listening tests that helped establish the existence of the ionosphere. The story continued with Grote Reber, W9GFZ, and radio astronomy in the 1930s, broad participation by hams during the International Geophysical Year of 1957-1958, wildlife tracking, propagation reporting, satellite construction, and numerous other instances. Recently, hundreds of amateurs participated in the Solar Eclipse QSO Party (**hamsci.org**) to observe the effect of a total solar eclipse on HF propagation. There is no doubt that fulfillment of FCC Part 97.1 is thriving as hams continue to "improve the radio art" by adapting technology to new uses.

This chapter is organized in four parts: platform overview, sensors, telemetry and navigation, and platform design. The goal is to cover the engineering necessary to assemble an effective platform. In recognition of the rapid innovation in these activities, this chapter will change in future editions. Expect to see new digital protocols and miniature telemetry and audio-image transmitters. Improvements will be forthcoming in portable-mobile power sources and antennas.

Although the *ARRL Handbook* strives to be complete, covering all aspects of these efforts is beyond the scope of this book. The referenced magazines and websites in the References and Bibliography section at the end of this chapter provide additional material and the latest updates on platforms and technology.

16.1 Platform Overview

Automated platforms are found in many locations carrying out a multitude of functions. They are often the solution to data collection in locations where it's not practical for humans to operate data collection devices for reasons such as safety or extensive time commitment requirements. Aside from data collection, automated platforms are also pressed into service as transponders, repeaters, and beacons. In instances such as these, automated platforms are well served by Amateur Radio because of the wireless communication requirements these platforms need to telemeter the data they generate, report their location and status, or forward analog and digital radio communications.

Although the primary platforms used today involve high-altitude balloon-borne experiments, similar considerations apply to other fixed and mobile terrestrial and marine experiment platforms.

16.1.1 Platform Structure

The generic structure of a remote sensing platform is shown in **Figure 16.1**. Along with the power source, there are five separate functions:

1) Sensor data or image acquisition — conversion of analog data into digital format and acquisition of still images or video

2) GPS or navigation data — acquisition of location data in digital form

3) Integration of sensor and location data — collection of all data to be stored and/or transmitted to the ground station

4) Protocol engine — packaging and encoding of data for transmission

5) Amateur transmitter — generates the digitally modulated RF signal

These functions can be implemented by separate modules, or everything can be performed by a single microcontroller-based module such as one of the APRS trackers. The choice is completely up to the platform designer and varies with the requirements for the particular mission. For example, **Figure 16.2** shows a two-module solution in which everything except GPS location is provided by the single MMT module. The ATV payload described later uses a separate controller to integrate the video and GPS data for transmission as part of the overall audio-video signal. The combinations are endless! The websites listed in the following section on High-Altitude Platforms (balloons) are good places to begin looking for the right subsystems for your mission.

DATALOGGERS

Dataloggers are standalone microprocessor-based devices that acquire or "log" digital and analog data on a pre-determined schedule or when prompted by a pre-determined event. They can also acquire digital data from avionics and navigation equipment. The data is stored or transmitted for later analysis. Dataloggers are available as commercial products or they can be home-built. Commercial dataloggers have the advantage of being durable and standardized. On the other hand, they may not be customizable to the extent desired for a science flight into the stratosphere. Popular microcontrollers such as the BASIC Stamp (Parallax), PICAXE, Arduino, and Raspberry Pi have made it much easier to create custom dataloggers that are also capable of operating experiments as well as just recording data.

TEMPERATURE RANGES AND HUMIDITY

The platforms discussed in this chapter are often used outdoors or in unprotected environments. As a result, the electronics and other sub-systems can be subjected to extreme temperatures for long periods of time. When selecting components, modules, or other equipment, make sure they are properly rated for the intended use.

The four most common temperature specifications for electronics and electro-mechanical systems are as follows:

Commercial: 0 °C to   85 °C
Industrial: –40 °C to 100 °C
Automotive: –40 °C to 125 °C
MIL-SPEC (or MIL-STD):
          –55 °C to 125 °C

Components meeting Commercial Specifications will work well for fixed stations residing indoors. However, when designing outdoor fixed stations, the amateur must consider using components that at least meet Industrial Specifications.

A closely related specification is for relative humidity (RH) which is specified in percent and condensing or non-condensing. RH can range from 0% in the desert or upper atmosphere to 100% from rain or fog or in water-borne environments. "Condensing" means that liquid water forms on surfaces of the device or component directly from the air. If your platform will be subjected to condensing humidity or direct water spray or splash, consult the equipment manufacturer for the best methods of protecting the platform components.

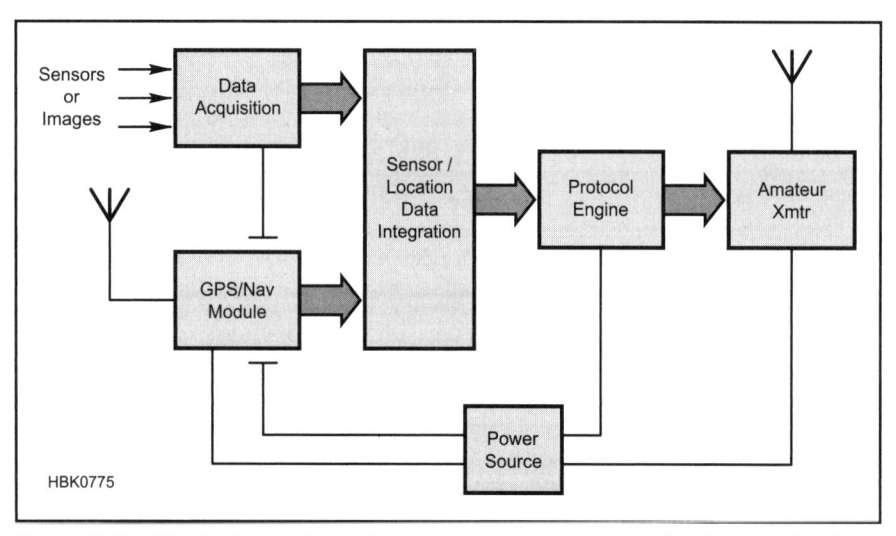

Figure 16.1 — The basic structure of a remote sensing platform using Amateur Radio for the telemetry link.

Figure 16.2 — A two-module payload consisting of a GPS receiver module (right) and WB8ELK's MMT (Multi-Mode Transmitter) on the left.

16.1.2 Types of Platforms

HIGH ALTITUDE BALLOONS

High altitude balloons are most frequently latex (mixed with neoprene) weather balloons designed to carry automated platforms weighing up to 12 pounds (heavier weights are possible) into near space. Altitudes above 60,000 feet (flight level 600) and below 328,000 feet are often referred to as *near space*. This region of the atmosphere has conditions that are closer to those found in Earth orbit than to Earth's surface.

Altitudes in excess of 100,000 feet are accessible using large weather balloons and lightweight platforms. Heavier platforms rely on polyethylene skinned balloons called *zero pressure balloons*. These balloons are vented to the atmosphere and do not develop an internal pressure above that of the surrounding atmosphere at any height. (**www.eoss.org/faq/zero_pressure**)

The need for long duration flights across continents, oceans, and even circumnavigating the planet has necessitated the development of *super-pressure balloons*. These balloons have skins of high-tech plastics and are sealed airtight. This prevents their lifting gas from escaping and shortening their flight times. While zero pressure and super pressure balloons are traditionally in the realm of professionals, amateurs have been making use of sealed Mylar foil party balloons as well as larger custom-built super-pressure envelopes using a special plastic film.

To be successful, the total weight of the payload should be a half-ounce or less. A handful of amateurs have developed incredibly lightweight payloads and most are totally solar-powered. In one instance, a UK-launched Mylar party balloon remained aloft for months and circled the globe nine times. More recently, a balloon launched from Atlanta, Georgia has stayed aloft over a year and has circled the globe more than 20 times.

A number of conditions are commonly measured or monitored, with a microprocessor-based datalogging system to acquire the data and convert it to digital form. The data is stored in onboard memory for recovery or transmitted to ground stations as a telemetry stream. The sensor data can also be integrated with the GPS data for transmission via APRS. Some APRS trackers can acquire analog and digital sensor data and integrate it into the APRS data messages.

Standalone experiments can also be attached to the balloon then located and recovered after landing. Data collected by sensors carried by the weather balloon can then be analyzed and correlated to the balloon's altitude. Thus, it is extremely important that the payload be able to transmit or store position and altitude data during the flight while collecting data.

You can find a considerable amount of information about balloons and experimental platforms suitable for balloons at **arhab.org**, **wb8elk.com**, **eoss.org**, **ansr.org**, and **near-sys.com**. See also the References and Bibliography section at the end of this chapter.

BalloonSats

BalloonSats are packages with standalone high-altitude experiments. They do not include a tracker since it is assumed they will be carried by operational platforms that include trackers. BalloonSats are an excellent way to introduce school students to near space exploration. They are simple systems that permit students to perform experiments in the space-like environment of near space.

UNMANNED AERIAL VEHICLES (UAV)

UAV development goes back centuries. However, it was the development of lightweight electronic autopilots that turned the UAV into the practical and affordable platform of today. With the commercial marketing of the four-bladed quadcopter and the six-bladed hexacopter with rechargeable lithium-polymer batteries, amateurs gained access to practical UAVs. The UAV has severe altitude and weight limits that balloons do not. However, the UAV provides a platform for imaging and datalogging at higher resolutions, over more restricted regions, with higher data immediacy, and quicker turn-around time. The popularity of this platform and the potential risks posed to conventional aviation have resulted in registration requirements and flight restrictions.

AMATEUR ROCKETRY

Experiments with amateur rocketry began in the late 1920s in Germany. By the 1950s, amateur rocketry had become a growing hobby for post-war America, especially after the launch of Sputnik 1 in 1957.

With the introduction of modern composite propellants and lightweight digital electronics, serious data collection is now possible. Unlike balloons and UAVs, rocket-based platforms must account for the rapid accelerations and tight dimensions inherent in rocketry. Because of their high accelerations, the rocket makes data collection possible at high altitudes but only over very short time frames.

ROBOTICS

Robots can be described as either *autonomous* or *semiautonomous*, depending on the amount of human input they require. Among the most famous robots are the series of rovers NASA has sent to explore the surface of Mars. Inexpensive microcontrollers, which are a form of programmable logic, have brought robotics to the amateur level. Robots often have fewer weight limits than balloons, rockets, or UAVs. They are also capable carrying platforms to desired locations and remaining on site while their platform performs its mission. Finally, robots usually place fewer power limits to their platforms than balloons, rockets, and UAVs. However, robots tend to cover the ground at slow speeds and limit their platforms to recording data from the ground level.

FIXED AND FLOATING PLATFORMS

Fixed platforms are any data collection stations that remain in one location. This can be due to their being mounted to a pole like a weather station or anchored to the seabed like a buoy. Typically, fixed platforms remain in place for long duration data collecting or imaging. As such, they require protection from the elements. They also require occasional maintenance from a human who goes onsite to service the fixed platform.

Some are floating buoys that may or may not be anchored. Anchored buoys can be treated as a fixed station. Free-floating buoys or marine rover-style platforms travel on the body of water either under self-contained power or by following the winds and currents.

16.2 Sensors

Inexpensive sensors and microcontrollers combined with Amateur Radio create opportunities for the amateur to perform experiments in environments that are otherwise inaccessible for one reason or another. Many interesting regions of the Earth, including extremely high altitudes in the atmosphere or the distant ocean, fall into this category. Hams can be instrumental in helping both amateurs and professionals explore these environments.

These platforms enable *remote sensing* — observing or measuring an object or event without a human being actually being in contact with the condition being measured. Data from the measurement is then stored on the platform for eventual collection after recovery or transmitted to a ground station for recording and analysis (telemetry). Examples of parameters that are measured by amateur remote sensing platforms include temperature, pressure (air and water/fluid), humidity, ozone and other gasses, acceleration, and light.

A sensor is a device that reacts to a specific condition of interest, such as temperature or pressure, and produces a predictable output in response. The first step is to select the appropriate sensor or sensors for the parameter of interest and a means of converting sensor outputs to digital data, usually by connecting the outputs to a microcontroller or analog to digital converter IC. Sensors and their associated *signal conditioning* circuits are the "front end" of remote sensing. Analogous to the speech and video circuits of traditional amateur transmitters, the same care in their design is required if quality results are to be obtained.

This section divides sensors into the following four types of outputs: *resistance-based, current-based, voltage-based,* and *digital*. In addition, four common types of sensor outputs are discussed here. Not all of these outputs are directly readable by a microcontroller. However, methods exist to convert the output of these sensors into a form that can be interfaced to a microcontroller. (See the Analog/Digital Conversion section of the **DSP and SDR Fundamentals** chapter.)

16.2.1 Resistance-Based Sensors

Resistance-based sensors change an internal resistance in response to the environmental variable they measure. An example includes the photocell, which is constructed of the chemical cadmium sulfide (CdS), a semiconductor that produces electrons and holes when irradiated by light. The production of free electrons and holes reduces the resistance of CdS when it is exposed to light.

In many cases, the change in resistance in response to changes in the measured condition is small. Therefore, sensor manufacturers often incorporate additional circuitry with the sensing element to convert this changing resistance into a more easily measured change in voltage. However, resistive-type sensors (without signal conditioning) are still available and quite useable.

Resistance-based sensors do not create a signal that a microcontroller can measure directly. Instead, the resistance of the sensor is used to vary the voltage from a regulated voltage source. A simple and popular circuit capable of converting a changing resistance into a changing voltage is the voltage divider as described in the **Electrical Fundamentals** chapter.

The voltage divider circuit of two resistors as shown in **Figure 16.3**. One resistor is fixed in resistance (R_F) and the other is the sensor and therefore variable in resistance (R_V). The current through the voltage divider circuit is variable. It increases as the resistance of the variable sensing element decreases and vice-versa. However, the sum of the two voltage drops is always equal to the supply voltage. The preferred arrangement of the two resistors depends on the response of the sensing resistor to the condition to which it responds — temperature, humidity, illumination, and so on.

A microcontroller connected to the voltage divider circuit digitizes the voltage across the resistor connected to ground. This permits the design of resistance-based sensors into circuits that produce changing voltages which follow the change in the condition. For example, the resistance of photocells decreases as the light intensity increases. A microcontroller digitizing the voltage across a photocell connected as R_V in Figure 16.3A will observe V_{OUT} increasing as light intensity *decreases*. If however, the photocell is connected as R_V in Figure 16.3B, V_{OUT} *increases* as the light intensity *increases*. The latter case is easier to understand and work with than having output voltage and the sensed condition varying in opposite directions (or inversely proportional).

There are two equations that describe the output of the voltage divider circuit. The first describes the voltage drop across the variable resistor and the second describes the voltage drop across the fixed resistor.

For Figure 16.3A:

$$V_{OUT} = +V (R_V/(R_F + R_V))$$

For Figure 16.3B:

$$V_{OUT} = +V (R_F/(R_F + R_V))$$

OPTIMIZING R_F

The equations above show that the value selected for R_F has a large impact on the range of output voltages created by the voltage divider circuit. The precision of the sensor output is greatest when the voltage range of V_{OUT} is maximized. The value of R_F that generates the maximum range is the geometric mean of the sensor's highest expected resistance (R_H) and lowest expected resistance (R_L). The equation for calculating the best fixed resistor value (R_F) in a voltage divider circuit is:

$$R_f = \sqrt{R_H R_L}$$

The maximum range for V_{OUT} of the voltage divider circuit is thus equal to 1/3 of the supply voltage, V_{DD}. Furthermore, the voltage range is centered at the midpoint of the

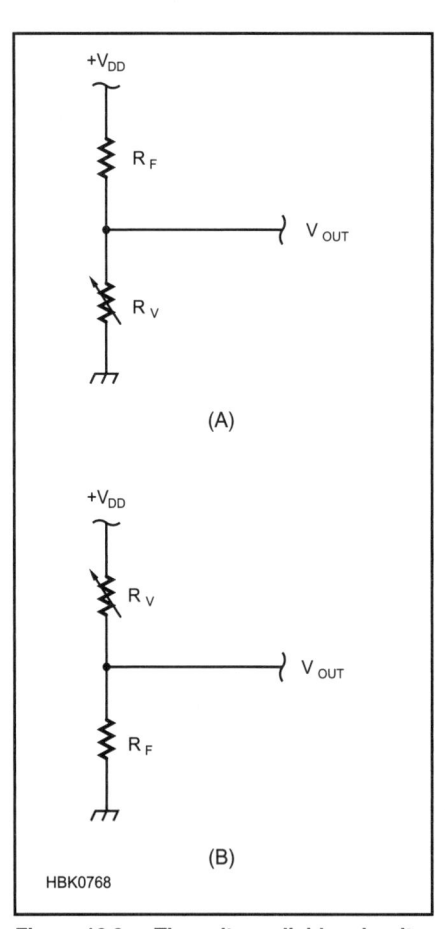

Figure 16.3 — The voltage divider circuit, a series circuit of two resistors. The orientation of resistors in A is preferable when the sensing resistor increases resistance in response to an increasing condition. Use B when the sensing resistor decreases resistance in response to an increasing condition. This results in the output voltage increasing with the increasing condition.

supply voltage. The following three equations calculate the minimum voltage, maximum voltage, and voltage range of an optimized voltage divider.

$$V_{MIN} = V_{DD}/3$$

$$V_{MAX} = 2V_{DD}/3$$

$$Range = V_{MIN} - V_{MAX} = V_{DD}/3$$

16.2.2 Current-Based Sensors

Some types of sensors generate or change output current in response to the environmental condition they are measuring. Examples include the photodiode, solar cell and light-emitting diode (LED). All three of these devices are similar, although not used in similar ways. When a photon of light is absorbed, its energy gives an electron in the device enough energy to jump across the PN junction. The electron creates a measurable current from the sensor.

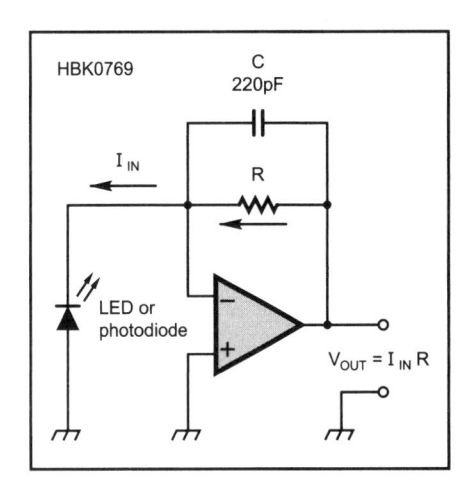

The LED is one of the most surprising current-based sensors. While the photodiode is sensitive to a wide range of frequencies, the LED is most sensitive to light at the wavelength it emits when forward biased. This makes the LED a very inexpensive spectrally sensitive photometer. (See the References and Bibliography section entry for Mims for a description of the LED responses.)

A current-based sensor can provide useful data when connected to a digital multimeter (DMM) set to measure milliamps of current. However, this is not a suitable configuration for a microcontroller with the capability to digitize voltage. Therefore, it is necessary to find a way to convert changing current into a changing voltage. Two popular ways to accomplish this are to use a transimpedance amplifier or by measuring the charging time of a capacitor.

THE TRANSIMPEDANCE AMPLIFIER

The transimpedance amplifier in **Figure 16.4** is a popular op amp circuit that converts input current into an output voltage. The feedback resistor, R, sets the gain of the transimpedance amplifier. The output voltage is given by the following equation:

$$V_{OUT} = I_{IN} \times R$$

The capacitor, C, reduces gain at high frequencies above 1/RC, acting as a low-pass filter to reduce noise. A generally useful value is 220 pF with the usual values of R for LED light-sensing. You will have to take the bandwidth of your measurement into account when choosing the value of C.

It is important that the value selected for the feedback resistor does not result in amplifier saturation for high sensor output levels. In those circumstances, data is lost when the sensor output is too high and the amplifier saturates.

USING CAPACITOR CHARGE TIME

A second method to digitize the current from a sensor is to measure the length of time required for a current to charge or discharge a capacitor to a certain voltage. One example can be found in the book *Earth Measurements* by Parallax (**www.parallax.com**, manufacturer of the BASIC Stamp microcontrollers). Here, the BASIC Stamp initially charges a capacitor. The Stamp then measures the length of time required for the capacitor to discharge due to the current entering it from the current-based sensor. The capacitor and resistor values are selected according to the expected current output of the sensor. The book uses the circuit in **Figure 16.5** to measure the current output of a photodiode or LED.

The program shown in **Table 16.1** (*Earth Measurements*, Program 4.2) was written to use the schematic in Figure 16.5. It assumes the circuit connects to the BASIC Stamp via I/O pin 6. Change the I/O reference to another pin as needed by your circuit.

The program reports the light intensity once per second. It begins by charging the capacitor to the same potential as the supply voltage through the use of the HIGH 6 command. Afterward, the reverse current emitted by the LED, due to its exposure to light, discharges the capacitor. The changing potential of the capacitor makes the voltage drop across the LED appear to decrease from its start at +5 V. Any voltage above 1.4 V is treated as a logic high by the BASIC Stamp. Therefore, as reverse current from the LED brings the capacitor voltage lower, the voltage across the LED eventually becomes lower than 1.4 V and a logic low.

The RCTime command counts the time (in units of 2 μs) required for I/O pin 6 to change from a logic high (above 1.4 V) to a logic low (below 1.4 V). The result in units of 2 μs is stored in the variable RCT. The greater the

---

Table 16.1
BASIC Stamp Program

This BASIC Stamp program is used with the circuit of Figure 16.3 for measuring light intensity.

```
RCT VAR Word
Light VAR Word
HIGH 6

Loop:
    RCTIME 6,1,RCT
    HIGH 6
    Light = 65535/RCT
    DEBUG "Light Intensity: ", DEC Light
    PAUSE 1000
    GOTO Loop
```

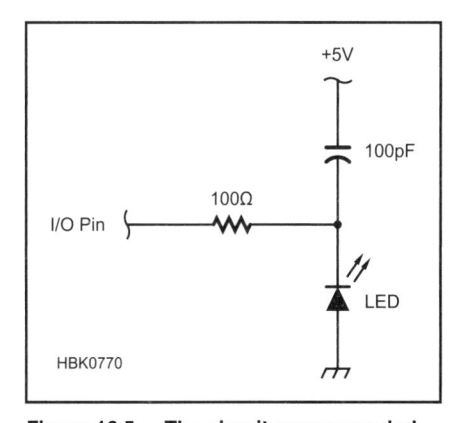

Figure 16.5 — The circuit recommended by Parallax for digitizing the current output of a photodiode or LED. See text for more information about using this circuit for current measurement.

intensity of the light shining on the LED, the faster the capacitor discharges and the smaller the value stored in the variable RCT. The value in RCT is then divided into 65535 to invert the relationship and then stored in the variable Light which then contains a value directly proportional to light intensity.

16.2.3 Voltage-Based Sensors

Some types of sensors change their voltage output in response to the condition they are measuring. Examples include the LM355 temperature sensor, Honeywell's HIH-4000 relative humidity sensor, and Microdyne's MPS-3138 pressure sensor. These devices are typically current or resistance-based sensors along with circuitry to amplify and condition the output into a useable voltage change.

The voltage-based sensors easiest to interface are those that include signal amplification and correction on the chip. The result can be a ratiometric output that is linear and proportional to the supply voltage. The conversion factor for the sensor needed to convert its voltage into the environmental condition being measured is documented in the device's datasheet.

Pressure sensors can be used as altitude sensors for an airborne platform if a digital solution, such as GPS, is not available. Absolute pressure is preferred although it must be calibrated against ground barometric pressure before launch and, if the flight covers long distance, requires additional corrections based on local pressure data.

16.2.4 Capacitance-Based Sensors

Capacitance-based sensors use changes in capacitance as their primary means of measurement. Capacitance between two electrodes of known area depends on the distance between the electrodes and the dielectric constant of the insulating material separating them. Any process that changes either separation or dielectric constant can be then be sensed as a change in the capacitance. Parameters that are sensed in this manner include motion, moisture, fluid and material level, chemical composition, and acceleration.

Sensors based on capacitance are rarely supplied without signal conditioning and linearization. Many have digital outputs that supply the measurement as a digital value. Another option is to have the sensor's capacitance control the frequency of an oscillator, which can then be read by a digital circuit. For more information on capacitive sensing, the excellent overview at **www.capsense.com/capsense-wp.pdf** is recommended.

16.2.5 Sensor Calibration

Sensors come in two basic configurations: *sensing elements* and *conditioned sensors*. The voltage divider discussed earlier is an example of a sensing element. There are no electronics associated with the divider — the package contains only the two resistors and the necessary connecting wires or terminals. Conditioned sensors contain electronic circuitry that operates on the signal from the sensing element before it is made available externally. The circuits usually regulate power applied to the sensor and also *linearize* the data so that a linear range of measurements are represented by a linear change in output voltage.

All sensing elements and some conditioned sensors require a calibration equation to convert the output signal into the parameter value the sensor is measuring. In some cases, the equation is simple and linear as in the LM335 temperature sensor. In other cases, the equation may be complicated, such as for the thermistor and photocell when used in a voltage divider circuit.

It is important to understand the range over which a sensor will be measuring a condition before attempting to calibrate it. The calibration equation is usually more accurate when based on the interpolation of measurements than when based on the extrapolation of measurements. There are exceptions to this rule. For example, the calibration equations of linear sensors can be just as accurate when extrapolated, as long as the maximum operating conditions of the sensor are not exceeded. Otherwise, is it best to expose the sensor to the entire range of expected environmental conditions while collecting measurements of its output to create the calibration equation.

The ham can easily create some of these conditions, such as temperature, on the bench top. High temperatures can be created with the use of heat lamps and low temperatures created with the use of dry ice packed in Styrofoam coolers. Other conditions might need to be simulated. For example, light intensity is easily changed by changing the distance between the sensor and a fixed light source. Recall however that light intensity decreases by a factor of $1/r^2$ when using this method to create the calibration curve of a sensor.

The spreadsheet is a powerful tool for creating calibration equations. To create the calibration equation, carefully measure the output of the sensor as the environmental condition is varied. Enter the readings and distance into a spreadsheet. In the next column, calculate the intensity of the source, based solely on its distance from the sensor. Graph the results so that the independent variable (X axis) is the distance and the dependent variable (Y axis) is the intensity. Then select the function to create a regression line from the data in the chart.

16.2.6 Digital Sensor Protocols

Some types of sensor outputs are in digital form. These sensors communicate their data as a serial protocol in which data is exchanged as a series of bits over one or more circuits. Data can be transmitted synchronized to an external timing signal (*synchronous protocol*) or synchronized to special signals embedded within the data being transmitted (*asynchronous protocol*).

Examples of synchronous serial data protocols include 1-Wire, Inter-Integrated Circuit (I2C), and Serial Peripheral Interface (SPI). Examples of asynchronous serial data transmission include USB and the RS-232 (COM) ports on PCs. These serial protocols can transfer measured data to a microprocessor without additional conditioning.

Another type of digital sensor is one in which an event's detection is signaled as a voltage pulse or as a switch closure. For example, the detection of ionizing radiation by Geiger counters is signaled by voltage pulses created when ionizing radiation passes through a Geiger-Muller tube. These signals require additional processing, such as by a counter or register circuit that is often implemented by a microprocessor.

SYNCHRONOUS SENSOR DATA PROTOCOLS

The following protocols are by no means the only ones used by sensors, but they are the ones amateurs are most likely to use or encounter. The manufacturer websites mentioned below have numerous resources to support design and development with devices that support these protocols.

1-Wire

1-Wire is a communication system developed by Dallas Semiconductor (now part of Maxim Electronics — **www.maximintegrated.com**) to enable communication between two or more integrated circuits. Devices on a 1-Wire network are daisy-chained together on a single-wire bus, called a *microlan*. (See **Figure 16.6**.) One device acts as the master device, and it controls communication between itself and the slave devices connected to the microlan. Some available 1-Wire devices include:
- Temperature sensor: (MAX51826)
- EEPROM memory (DS24B33)
- Low voltage sensor (DS25LV02)

Since a microlan may not include a separate power wire, many devices attached to the microlan include a small capacitor in their

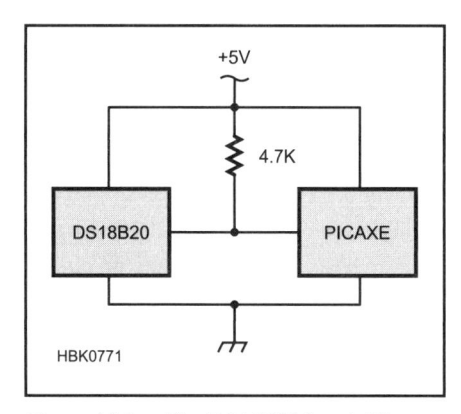

Figure 16.6 — The DS18B20 is a 1-Wire temperature sensor. In this circuit, the device does not use parasitic power and is connected to a 5 V source. A PICAXE microcontroller communicates with this device using the READTEMP or READTEMP12 command.

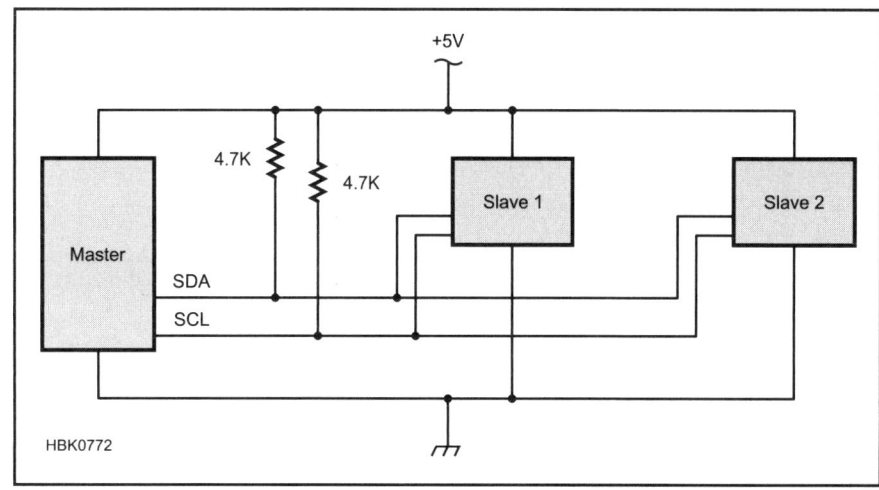

Figure 16.8 — An example of a master and two slave ICs connected via a I2C network.

Figure 16.7 — A comparison between an iButton and a nickel.

design. The capacitor provides *parasitic power* to the device while communications are taking place. The capacitor is necessary because communication requires the voltage on the single wire to alternate between power and ground. Without some temporary power source, devices would lose power during communications.

The master device communicates with each slave device by transmitting the slave address over the microlan prior to other commands. Because multiple devices can be connected to a microlan, each device must have a unique address to avoid confusion. Slave addresses are laser etched into 1-Wire devices. Alternatively, if a single 1-Wire device is attached to a microlan, communication on the network can ignore addressing altogether.

1-Wire is a two-way communication protocol. The master device begins communication by sending the slave device's address and then commands over the network. Only the device with the address in the message will respond to the commands.

iButtons

An iButton is a sealed 1-Wire device resembling a thick watch battery (see **Figure 16.7**). iButtons include memory and a lithium battery. The memory contains the ID of the device and can often be used to store data. The battery permits an iButton to operate independently of a microlan.

iButton devices download their stored data when connected to a microlan. The microlan connection is made by pressing the iButton device against a 1-Wire receptor. 1-Wire receptors are available for integration into microcontroller projects. Some available iButton devices include the following:

• Time and temperature loggers (DS1920 Thermochron)

• Time, temperature and humidity data loggers (DS1923 Hygrochron)

The amateur may be interested in the ongoing development of a 1-Wire weather station. Consult Maxim Integrated (**www.maximintegrated.com**) for the latest information concerning 1-Wire devices, including iButtons.

I2C

Inter-Integrated Circuit or I2C is a communication method developed by Phillips to enable communication between two or more ICs. Devices on an I2C network are daisy-chained together on a two-wire bus as in **Figure 16.8**. One device acts as the master device and it controls communications between itself and the slave devices connected to the network. The I2C network is described in detail at **www.i2c-bus.org** and in the application notes supplied by manufacturers of devices that use it.

The first connection in the I2C network is the serial data (SDA) line. This line carries slave device addresses, data, and instructions between devices. The second line is the serial clock (SCL) line. This connection provides timing pulses to synchronize the data sent from the sending IC (master) to the receiving IC (slave). In an I2C network, the SDA and SCL lines are pulled up to +5 V by pull-up resistors. A value of 4.7 kΩ works well.

The master device communicates with each slave device by transmitting an address over the I2C bus prior to other commands. Because multiple devices can be connected to an I2C network, each device must have a unique address to avoid confusion. Slave addresses may be designed into the IC or may be externally configured for an IC by connecting a combination of address pins to +5 V and ground.

I2C is a two-way communication protocol. The master device begins communication by sending the slave device's address and then commands over the network. Only the device receiving its address in the message will respond to the commands. Serial data can be sent in either in fast (400 kHz) or slow (100 kHz) mode. The master device sends commands and memory addresses in either one byte or one word (two bytes) long commands. Some available I2C devices include the following:

• Memory: the 24LCxxx series of I2C memory.

• Real-time clocks: DS1307

• Analog to digital converters: LTC2903 (12 bit), AD7991 (12 bit), and MCP3421 (18 bit)

SPI and Microwire

Serial Peripheral Interface or SPI is a communication method developed by Motorola (now Freescale) to enable communication between two or more ICs. Devices on a SPI network are daisy-chained together on a two- or three-wire bus. (See **Figure 16.9**.) Like I2C, one device is the master that controls communications between it and the slave devices connected to the network. The Microwire network originally developed by National Semiconductor (now Texas Instruments) is essentially a subset of SPI. Microchip (manufacturer of the PIC processor family) has published an overview and

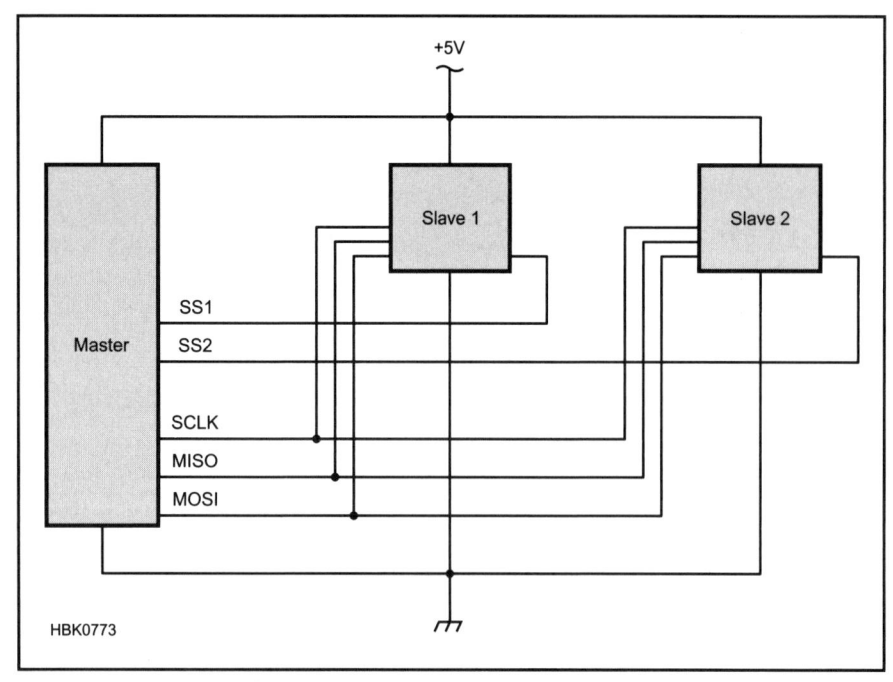

Figure 16.9 — An example of a master and two slave ICs connected via an SPI network.

tutorial about SPI at **ww1.microchip.com/downloads/en/DeviceDoc/spi.pdf**.

Two lines of the SPI bus are used to transmit data and instructions: MOSI (master out/slave in) and MISO (master in/slave out). In some cases, the MISO and MOSI lines can be combined into a single shared line. The third line of the bus is the timing clock line (SCLK) that provides timing pulses to synchronize the data sent between the master device and the slave device. None of these lines requires being pulled high by a resistor.

The master device communicates with the slave devices by activating each slave device's Slave Select (SS) line. To avoid confusion, each slave device must have a unique connection to the master device. This is a major difference between I2C and SPI. An I2C network requires only two communication lines between devices, while an SPI network requires two or three communication lines in addition to an SS line between the master and each slave. A large number of slave devices require a large number of dedicated SS lines between the master and the slave devices.

SPI is also a two-way communication protocol. The master device begins communications by activating the slave device's SS line. Only the device with the activated SS line will respond to the commands. Serial data is sent as fast as the master device pulses the SCLK line. The number of bytes in each transmission between master device and slave device is limited by the design of the slave device rather than to eight or 16 bits. Some available SPI devices include the following:

• Analog to digital converters: MAX186 (12 bit resolution)
• Temperature sensor: LM74
• Hall effect sensor: MLX90363
• Pressure sensor: MPL115A1
• Memory: AT25010B

Note that the popular Dallas Semiconductor DS1620 Temperature Sensor uses a three-wire interface similar to SPI.

ASYNCHRONOUS SENSOR DATA PROTOCOLS

Asynchronous communication is any form of communication that does not use a clock signal to maintain timing between the sender and the receiver. A message begins with a start signal that allows the receiver to synchronize with the transmitter's message. The rest of the communication follows at a predefined rate in bits of data per second or baud. (See the **Digital Protocols and Modes** chapter for a discussion of data rate.) As long as the sender and receiver use equally accurate clocks, they will transmit and receive the same bits of data.

Some sensors supply their output data using RS-232 and USB ports. The data is transmitted as a stream of characters controlled by a protocol developed by the manufacturer. USB devices often conform to certain classes of data objects so that generic device drivers can be used to acquire data from the sensor. Control and configuration protocols that allow the user to interact with the sensor are usually proprietary.

Time-independent serial devices produce a change in output voltage only at the detection of an event. The primary example is the *event counter*. The simplest event counters detect the closure of a switch, which can be

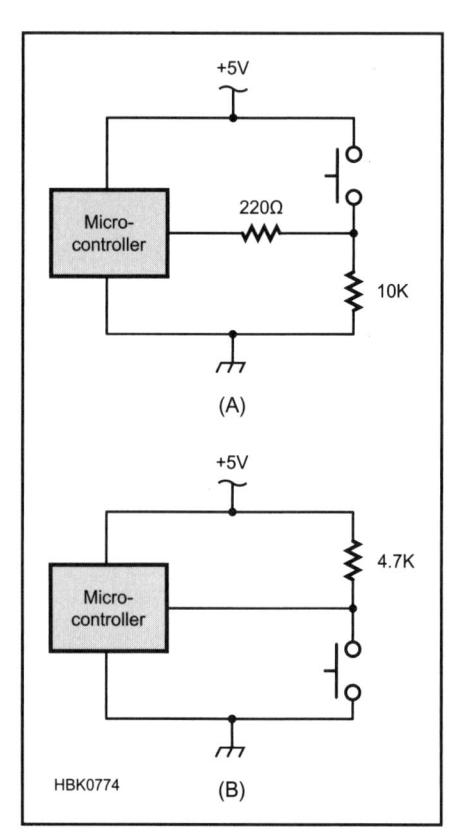

Figure 16.10 — (A) This circuit produces a logic high signal, typically 5 V, when an event is detected, represented as a switch closure. (B) This circuit produces a logic low signal, typically ground or 0 V, when an event is detected.

useful for detecting the presence of wildlife. Game cameras use switches in this way to trigger a camera to record an image of wildlife. Thermostats and thermal switches are another example.

Switches can be used to signal a microcontroller by two different methods. In the first, called *active low*, the switch connects a microcontroller I/O pin to ground at the detection of an event. When the event is not present, the I/O pin is connected to positive voltage or pulled up to a positive voltage by a pull-up resistor. In the second method, called *active high*, the switch connects a microcontroller I/O pin to positive voltage at the detection of an event. When the event is not present, the I/O pin is connected to ground. Schematics for both of these switch circuits are shown in **Figure 16.10**.

An example of a sensor that produces asynchronous output is the Geiger counter. The output of the RM-60 Geiger counter from Aware Electronics' RM-60 (**www.aw-el.com**) maintains a 5 V level until ionizing radiation is detected. Then the output voltage drops to 0 V for 20 µs. The amount of radiation detected by a RM-60 Geiger counter is measured by counting the number of pulses emitted by the sensor over a fixed period.

Other event counters can be modified for microcontroller use if they use an LED indicator or piezoelectric annunciator. When an LED is illuminated, greater than 1.4 V appears across its terminals. Wires soldered to the LED can be connected to ground and one of a microcontroller's I/O pins to permit the microcontroller to count the number of LED flashes. Care in counting the number of flashes is necessary since some inexpensive sensors may output several pulses each time the event is detected or in the case of contact bounce for a switch closure.

16.2.7 Powering Sensors

The output of sensing element sensors is typically very sensitive to power supply voltage and noise. Any changes in power supply voltage on the voltage divider also appear, proportionally reduced, at the output of the voltage divider. This includes noise, transients, slowly dropping battery voltage — any change in the sensing element's supply voltage. The sensing element user must provide clean, filtered, regulated power to the sensor to avoid contaminating the sensor output voltage.

Loading of the sensing element is also an issue for the designer to deal with. A high-impedance sensing element will output erroneous voltages if connected to a load impedance that is too low. Be sure you know what the sensing element's ratings are!

Conditioned sensors are far less sensitive to noise and power supply variations. Some kind of voltage regulator circuit is included to make sure the electronics operate with a "clean" supply. The conditioning electronics, which often include laser-trimmed calibration circuitry, assume clean, well-regulated dc voltage from a power supply. They are much less sensitive to the effects of output loading although there are usually limits as to the amount of capacitance they can tolerate at the output, such as from a long run of wire.

In portable or mobile platforms, power is usually supplied by a battery pack. Make sure you have fresh, fully charged batteries before heading out to launch the platform for the experiment. Take into account the gradual reduction in voltage from the battery pack as its charge is consumed — it's awfully hard to swap out batteries with a balloon that is in flight! In the quest to save weight in these platforms, make sure you still have enough capacity in the battery pack voltage (see the **Power Sources** chapter) so that the experiment won't run out of power during its mission.

16.3 Navigation Data and Telemetry

Navigation data allows the sensor measurements to be combined with geographical data, which is important for correlating data to location (including altitude). A final step involves using Amateur Radio to either transmit the collected data to a ground station as telemetry or to track and recover a remote sensing payload for later data extraction. Since the most common use of this data is for weather balloons and other near-space missions, that context will be used.

It is important to note that transmitting data as ASCII characters (7- or 8-bit) is preferred to more compact binary formats. ASCII characters have the advantage of being human-readable so that even raw data can be inspected and used. At the low data rates of most amateur remote sensing, little overall throughput is lost by using ASCII characters. The ability to read the raw data stream directly is often invaluable during troubleshooting, as well.

16.3.1 Dead Reckoning

If a digital navigation data source such as GPS is not available, it is also possible to estimate platform position, including altitude by the process of dead reckoning. In dead reckoning, navigation (or tracking) depends on determining a known position — called a *fix* — and then calculating subsequent positions from the platform speed and direction.

Direction data can be obtained from compass sensors that output direction as an analog voltage or digitally encoded signal. Altitude can be calculated based on ground barometric pressure and absolute pressure readings from the platform.

Obtaining accurate ground speed data is difficult for mobile platforms such as balloons or water-borne instruments which move with the wind or current. If some other form of position tracking is available, it is possible to infer ground speed although rarely accurately.

16.3.2 GPS Data

As currently practiced, a GPS (Global Positioning System) module is the usual means of acquiring navigation data which is then transmitted as a telemetry stream using the Automatic Packet Reporting System (APRS). Thus, the two are combined in this section.

Depending on the model, GPS receivers produce a number of *navigation sentences*, such as the GPGGA and GPRMC sentences described below. GPS sentences are human-readable text with information in fields separated by commas. Below is a brief description of the two more important GPS sentences (when it comes to high altitude ballooning) and their fields.

THE GPGGA SENTENCE

The GPGGA sentence is the Global Positioning System Fixed Data sentence and a typical GPGGA sentence from a balloon-based GPS looks like this.

$GPGGA,153919.00,4332.2076,N, 11608.6666,W,1,08,1.1,13497.1 ,M,18.3,M,,*78

There are 13 fields in the GPGGA sentence following the sentence identifier, "$GPGGA". The fields from left to right are as follows.

1) Time in UTC (hours, minutes, seconds)
2) Latitude North (degrees and decimal minutes — note that there is no separator between degrees and minutes)
3) N (north)
4) Longitude West (degrees and decimal minutes — note that there is no separator between degrees and minutes)
5) W (west)
6) GPS Quality Indicator (0 = no GPS fix, 1 = GPS fix, and 2 = differential GPS fix)
7) Number of Satellites (number of satellites detected — not all of them may be used in determining the position)
8) Dilution of Horizontal Position (or DOHP, which is an indication of how precise the fix is and the closer to 1.0 the better)
9) Altitude (in meters)
10) M (meters)
11) Geoidal Separation (the difference in the actual height and a mathematic description of the height of an idealized Earth's surface in meters)
12) M (meters)
13) Checksum (result of exclusive ORing the sentence and used to verify that the text is not corrupted)

THE GPRMC SENTENCE

The GPRMC sentence is the Recommended Minimum Specific GPS/Transit Data sentence and a typical GPRMC sentence from a balloon-based GPS looks like this.

$GPRMC,153924.00,A,4332.2317, N,11608.6330,W,24.4,46.3,2310 99,16.1,E*7E

There are 12 fields in the GPRMC sentence following the sentence identifier, "$GPRMC". The fields from left to right are as follows:

1) Time in UTC (hours, minutes, seconds)
2) Navigation warning (A = okay and V = warning)
3) Latitude North (degrees and decimal minutes — note that there is no separator between degrees and minutes)
4) N (north)
5) Longitude West (degrees and decimal minutes — note that there is no separator between degrees and minutes)
6) W (west)
7) Speed (in knots)
8) Heading (in degrees true north)
9) Date (day, month, and year — note that there is no separation between them)
10) Magnetic Variation (number of degrees)
11) Direction of magnetic variation (E = east and W = west)
12) Checksum (result of exclusive ORing the sentence and used to verify that the text is not corrupted)

16.3.3 Automatic Packet Reporting System (APRS)

Most mobile platforms include an APRS station in order to follow the platform's position and altitude throughout a mission to the edge of space. The APRS position reports, usually containing GPS data as described above, can be used directly to locate the position of the platform for recovery or tracking. (For more details about APRS, see the **Digital Protocols and Modes** chapter.)

There is a large network of dedicated ground stations, digipeater and Internet gateway stations operating on the US national APRS frequency of 144.390 MHz (144.800 and other frequencies are used elsewhere in the world). Thanks to this network, the platform's position will be plotted onto a map in near real-time. Two popular websites to view the maps are at **aprs.fi** and **findu.com**. These sites are databases of APRS packets received and routed through APRS Internet gateways.

Chase crews collect a platform's APRS data directly over Amateur Radio or over the Internet using the APRS maps. The platform or payload can then be recovered based on this position data. Later the data is correlated with other sensor data and images that are stored in on-board memory.

There are a number of APRS "trackers" that combine a low-power GPS module with a VHF transmitter and microprocessor that creates the APRS message packets. For example, Byonics (**www.byonics.com**) makes a number of APRS tracking and telemetry products, including the Micro-Trak RTG FA High Altitude Combo that contains an altitude-certified GPS for balloon payloads.

The RPC-Electronics (**www.rpc-electronics.com**) RTrak-HAB - High Altitude APRS Tracker Payload is specially made for high-altitude ballooning, as well.

The tracker combination built by WB8ELK is shown in Figure 16.2. On the right is a GPS module that creates the GPS sentences discussed previously. On the left is the MMT (Multi-Mode Transmitter) that creates and transmits the APRS packets.

APRS POSITION DATA

A simple APRS tracker can generate a stream of useful navigation data for a mission. The data begins at the GPS receiver where two navigation sentences are generated. The sentences are then combined to create a position report in the required APRS format. Like GPS sentences, the raw APRS packets are also readable text that is easily interpreted.

An APRS position report uses a combination of commas and slashes as field delimiters. An example of an APRS report from a balloon mission looks like this:

```
13:37:23 UTC: KD4STH-
8>APT311,WIDE1-2,qAS,KC0QBU,1
33721h3836.39N/09500.
51W>160/031/A=049114
```

There are 12 fields in the APRS report. The fields from left to right are as follows:

1) Time in UTC (hours, minutes, seconds)
2) Call sign and SSID
3) Routing Information
4) GPS Time (time in UTC — note there is no separator between hours, minutes, and seconds)
5) h (hours)
6) Latitude North (degrees and decimal minutes — note that there is no separator between degrees and minutes)
7) N/ (north)
8) Longitude West (degrees and decimal minutes — note that there is no separator between degrees and minutes)
9) W> (west)
10) Heading (in degrees from true north)
11) Speed (in knots)
12) A= (altitude equals)
13) Altitude (feet)

There are other formats and fields that may be present. Additional telemetry fields can be added in a variety of formats following the altitude data. For more information about the APRS reports, see "APRS Formats Used in Edge of Space Sciences," at **www.eoss.org/aprs/aprs_formats_eoss**.

APRS CONFIGURATION

High altitude APRS trackers should be programmed to provide altitude data and not to use Smart Beaconing. Altitude data is a fascinating datum and useful for determining when a platform has landed. Smart Beaconing prevents APRS trackers from transmitting their position while the tracker is not changing its speed or direction. At landing, it's important that the tracker continue to announce its position on a regular schedule. This is particularly important if the tracker was out of range of the chase crew at the time of landing.

The horizon for high altitude balloons and larger rockets can be hundreds of miles away. Therefore, their transmission footprint can cover tens of thousands of square miles. To prevent high altitude APRS trackers from interfering with orderly use of APRS, the high-altitude ballooning community recommends programming an APRS tracker with the following settings if a frequency of 144.390 MHz is used. (Thanks, Jerry Gable, KF7MVY)

1. Path Recommendations: Use no Path or set Path to WIDE2-1. Never use a two-part path such as the common WIDE2-1, WIDE-1 nor use WIDE2-2 or WIDE3-3.

2. Transmit Rate: Limit the transmit rate to once per 60 seconds during ascent and no less than 30 seconds during descent.

If possible or practical, you may want to use a frequency other than 144.390 MHz.

16.3.4 Satellite Telemetry

Amateur satellites use a variety of modulation methods and data encoding to construct and transmit the stream of data coming from the satellite. Bit rates vary from 1200 to 9600 bps and modulation types of CW, PSK, BPSK, FSK, and AFSK are common. Each satellite also uses a custom scheme to encode the data, often using the AX.25 packet radio protocol.

Decoding satellite data would be very challenging except that the team building the satellite usually publishes a description of the telemetry stream and provides software for receiving and decoding the data. In this way, individual amateurs can collect telemetry data for the satellite's operational team.

Information on particular satellites is often available at one of the AMSAT websites such as **www.amsat.org** (AMSAT North America) or **amsat-uk.org/satellites/telemetry/** (AMSAT UK). Satellite status, including whether telemetry decoder software is available, can be found at DK3WN's website (**www.dk3wn.info/p/?page_id=29535**). Additional information for CubeSats launched by universities or other private groups is usually available on a web page provided by the satellite's sponsor.

To decode satellite telemetry reliably at the higher bit rates, particularly 9600 bps, you will need to provide the full bandwidth audio from the receiver or use packet radio TNCs that are rated for 9600 baud operation.

The Fox-1 satellite (AO-85, see **www.amsat.org/status** for the satellite's current status) has both a low-speed 200 bps DUV (data under voice) and a high-performance 9600 bps FSK telemetry stream. *FoxTelem* software is available for decoding the information. As an example of current best practices for satellite data, a two-part article from *AMSAT Journal* on the Fox-1 telemetry system is available as a PDF on the downloadable supplemental information. (See the reference listings for Burns Fisher, W2BFJ and Chris Thompson, AC2CZ.) Numerous other satellites use the same or similar telemetry formats and modulations.

16.3.5 Non-Licensed Telemetry Transmissions

There are many low-power data links operating in the unlicensed 915 MHz and 2.4 GHz bands. Typically, these are intended to be used for short-range applications but with the balloon payload at great altitude, the range of these devices is much longer, particularly if a high-gain Yagi antenna is used to track the payload. (See the **Antennas** chapter for information on VHF and UHF beams.)

Many of the data link modules use a standard two-way protocol such as Zigbee and have direct analog and digital inputs and outputs. Some modules support Ethernet and Bluetooth interfaces, offering even more options for modules that can be assembled into the payload.

It is also important to note that unlicensed transmitters operating under FCC Part 15 rules are also subject to certain restrictions such as field strength. In addition, the type of antenna may be fixed and even required to be attached to the transmitter permanently. These and other restrictions are required in order to limit the range of these devices. Amateurs are used to modifying and adjusting their equipment, and this may not be allowed for some of these devices! Be sure to obtain the full documentation for any unlicensed device you plan on using and be sure you can use it in the way you expect.

16.3.6 Other Telemetry Digital Modes

The usual method of communication from airborne and other remotely located platforms is via the APRS network. APRS messages are packaged in X.25 packets and usually transmitted as FSK or PSK modulation on FM transmissions. This works well and takes advantage of the extensive ground network of APRS digipeaters and servers.

Along with APRS, other subsystems are popular in the amateur balloon community. These include Weak Signal Propagation Reporter (WSPR), Hellschreiber, DominoEX, Contestia, JT9, PSK31, RTTY, CW (especially for fox hunting a lost near space balloon), FM for voice repeaters, and imagery through ATV and SSTV. (All of these digital modes are described in detail in the **Digital Protocols and Modes** chapter.)

WSPR

WSPR, part of the *WSJT-X* software suite (see the **Digital Protocols and Modes** chapter), is a simple location reporting method using HF and therefore, a practical tracking data system for long duration balloon flights. WSPR takes a bit less than two minutes for one transmission.

The format of a WSPR report specified in the protocol definition is limited to: call sign, transmitter location (using the Maidenhead grid locator system), and transmitter power (in dBm). To send telemetry, amateurs have developed a way to encode altitude, voltage, temperature and a six-digit grid locator by sending a second WSPR transmission that uses a call sign beginning with a "0" or a "Q" which are prefixes not used in Amateur Radio. The telemetry is embedded in the call sign field and power levels and one method also uses the grid square. There are several protocols in use and undergoing development as of early 2018. You can find information on them by doing an Internet search for "wspr telemetry".

Figure 16.11 shows the track of WB8ELK's ballon that took six trips around the world in 75 days. The track is based on WSPR.net reports and displayed on the UK High Altitude Society's (UKHAS) **tracker.habhub.org** website which features tracking of many balloons that are flying at any given time.

WSPR has a similar advantage to APRS in that there is a distributed network of ground stations around the world that relay reports to a centralized web server which can be viewed on the **wsprnet.org** website. The data from a long duration balloon can be picked up from many thousands of miles away using a very low power HF transmitter in the 10 to 25-mW range.

JT9

JT9, part of the *WSJT-X* software suite (see the **Digital Protocols and Modes** chapter), is also very effective for low-power HF telemetry and has been used for long duration, high altitude balloon platforms. It takes less than a minute to send a transmission. It does allow a free-form transmission in which telemetry can be embedded, however the amount of information is very limited. There is no distributed world-wide ground station network that exists, as there is for the APRS and WSPR modes.

HELLSCHREIBER

Hellschreiber ("light writer" in German) is an HF transmission method that can send balloon location and other data as a fax image. The characters are formed with an accurately timed sequence of on/off keying that forms an image of the data in a received waterfall-style display. This makes it an ideal mode for poor reception conditions, since human eyes are very good at retrieving information from a noisy image.

ASCII RTTY

ASCII RTTY is very easy to implement with a small microcontroller. It uses two tones and speeds similar to Baudot RTTY but uses the full ASCII character set to send telemetry. Speeds ranging from 45 baud for HF systems. 100 to 300 baud RTTY can be sent via VHF and UHF FM transmitters.

CONTESTIA AND OLIVIA

Contestia and Olivia are MFSK modes with excellent FEC correction. They can be

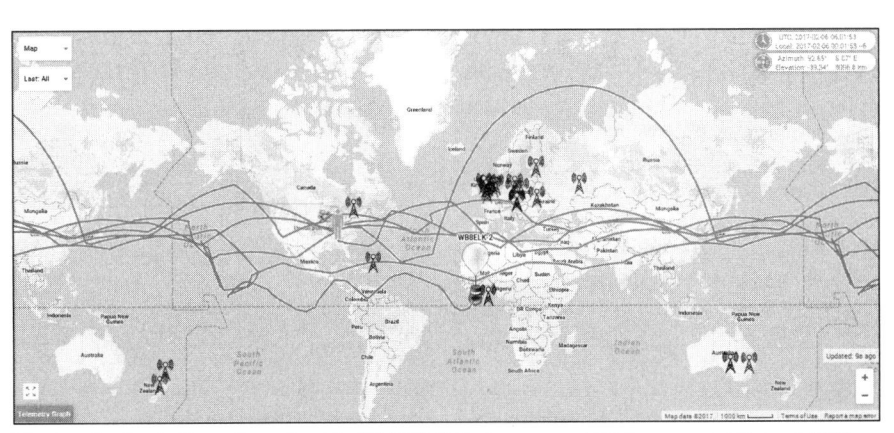

The track of a balloon launched by WB8ELK that managed 6 trips around the world in 75 days. The image was generated from WSPR reports collected by the UKHAS website (tracker.habhub.org).

used for HF, VHF and UHF payloads. Information about these modes and how to encode them in a microcontroller can be found here: **ukhas.org.uk/guides:olivia_and_contestia**

DOMINOEX

DominoEX is designed for very weak signals using an 18-tone sequence that can send balloon data using a low power signal on either HF, VHF or UHF. It uses Offset Incremental Frequency Keying (IFK+) which uses the frequency difference between tones rather than the absolute frequency of each tone. As a result, it is very tolerant of frequency drift.

PSK31

PSK31 is a phased shift keyed mode primarily for HF payloads that requires a stable transmitter and can provide a 31.25 baud data rate.

CW (MORSE CODE)

CW is likely the easiest mode to implement with a small microcontroller performing On/Off Keying or OOK. It is primarily used as a backup transmitter for direction-finding a lost balloon payload. With the addition of a small GPS, some balloon groups actually send the position and altitude via Morse code so that the chase crew can decode the position without using a decoding program on a laptop computer.

SATELLITE COMMUNICATION

Some missions use satellite communications as a backup and telemetry-message system. These are unlicensed communication methods that charge a subscription fee. The two satellite communications services used today are Spot (for position tracking below 20,000 feet altitude — **www.findmespot.com**) and Iridium modems (for sending messages — such as the RockBlock Mk2 modem (**www.sparkfun.com/products/13745**). There are no format standards for data transmitted using satellite or mobile phone systems.

16.3.7 Receiving and Relaying Telemetry

Most digital modes can be readily received by a modified version of the free software package *FLdigi* called *dl-FLdigi* which can be downloaded from **ukhas.org.uk/projects:dl-fldigi**. This software receives and decodes the telemetry, uses a checksum to ensure the accuracy of the received data and sends that data to a server. The position report can then be viewed at: **tracker.habhub.org** which is maintained by the UK High Altitude Society (UKHAS). The site can display telemetry from any platform but has a number of features specifically designed for high altitude balloon platforms, both Amateur Radio and license-free transmitters.

The format for generating telemetry for use with **tracker.habhub.org** is comma-separated values (CSV) of ASCII characters as follows:
$$CALLSIGN,
sentence_id,
time,latitude,
longitude,
altitude,
speed (optional),
bearing (optional),
internal temperature (optional),
*CHECKSUM\n

Although these parameters can be changed with the exception of $$ to start and a checksum at the end. More information on the telemetry formats can be found at **ukhas.org.uk/communication:protocol**.

16.4 Payloads

16.4.1 VHF/UHF/Microwave Payloads

NEAR SPACE TRACKER

A very popular configuration for high-altitude payloads is the Near Space Tracker, consisting of avionics to acquire and record or transmit data, an APRS tracker module coupled with a GPS receiver for position data, and a simple dipole or omnidirectional antenna. **Figure 16.12** shows a typical physical layout for such a package. The APRS tracker module consists of a *terminal node controller* (TNC) and a transceiver module. It is advisable to use a complete APRS tracker for balloons than to use a separate TNC and radio. Using a combined system reduces the complexity, weight, and battery needs of the tracker.

A complete construction article is included in this book's downloadable supplemental content, titled "Touching Near Space on a Budget," by Paul Verhage, KD4STH. The assembled tracker is shown in **Figure 16.13**. It uses an inexpensive insulated lunch cooler to hold the electronics, battery, and antenna.

Tracker packages such as this are excellent experiments not only for hams but for students and other groups when assisted by a licensed amateur to allow the use of the APRS module. Such experiments are a good way to introduce students to Amateur Radio and can often be supported by a local radio club.

Key considerations for trackers are their weight (less is better) and time of operation (or how long will they operate on a fully charged battery). The lighter the tracking system, the more available weight for science

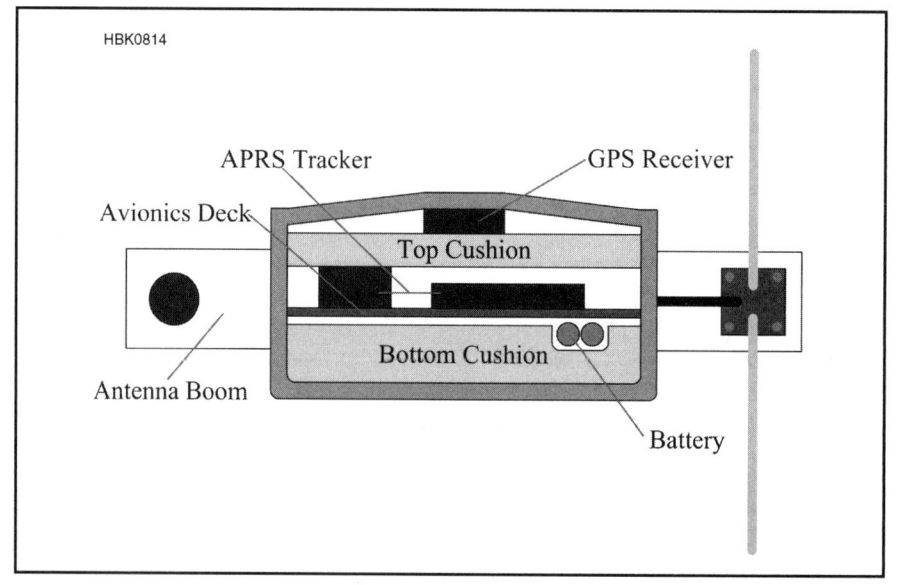

Figure 16.12 — A cut-away graphic showing an idealized Near Space Tracker including an APRS tracker, GPS receiver, an avionics package, batteries, and a dipole antenna.

payloads. It also means a given balloon will reach a higher altitude before bursting (on account of the reduced initial volume of lifting gas). Since it can take an hour to fill a launch a balloon, ninety minutes to reach peak altitude, forty-five minutes to descend, and a few hours to recover, a tracker should

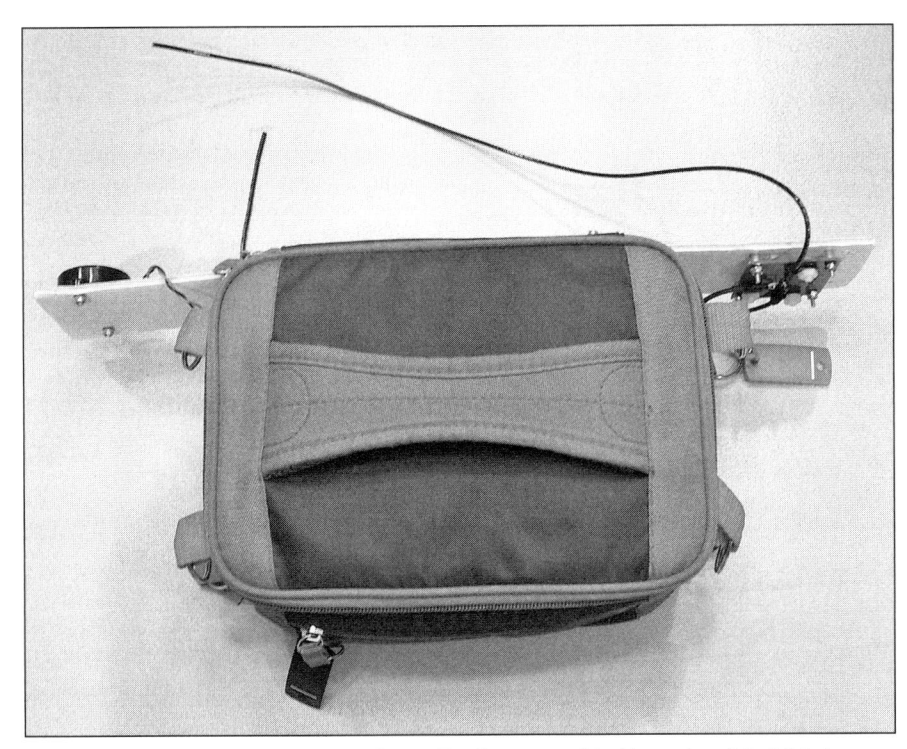

Figure 16.13 — The complete Near Space Tracker assembled in an insulated fabric lunch cooler.

be capable of running for at least six hours on a set of batteries.

APRS trackers such as the Byonic TinyTrak 3, Argent Data Systems Tracker3, Tracksoar, and others are software configurable. This means the tracker's behavior can be pre-programmed using configuration software provided for the tracker. An APRS tracker is configured for settings such as Callsign, SSID, Symbol, Smart Tracking, Transmit Times, Time Slotting, and Status Messages. (See the previous section on APRS.)

A tracker producing a 300 mW signal is adequate for a balloon flight. Even an APRS transmitter producing only 25 mW such as the Skytracker (**wb8elk.com**) can be used as a backup tracker. Even at this low power it is comparable to higher power transmitters down to about 1500 feet AGL (above ground level). This means a battery with a capacity of several hundred mAhrs will be sufficient for most balloon flights (a 2200 mAh is even better since it permits an overnight recovery).

Since a 5-V LM2940T-5 voltage regulator has a drop-out of 0.5 V, a two-cell (2S) rechargeable LiPo battery can provide more than enough power for most avionics on a balloon flight. In addition, these batteries are commonly available from hobby stores where they are sold for RC racing cars.

A vertical dipole is the recommended antenna for near space tracking modules using APRS. They are simple to construct, light weight, and are not direction sensitive with respect to chase vehicle antennas (which tend to be mag-mounted vertical whips).

GPS RECEIVERS

GPS receivers are a vital component for APRS trackers. To prevent their use in guided missiles, the Coordinating Committee for Multilateral Export Controls requires GPS receivers to stop creating position data when they are moving faster than 1,000 knots at an altitude above 59,000 feet. Some companies have taken this as an OR condition and not an AND condition as it was meant. Therefore, amateurs must verify their selected GPS receiver will operate above 59,000 feet. Amateurs can find a list of appropriate receivers through an Internet search.

GPS signals are weak signals. This means it can be easy to block the radio signals that GPS receivers depend upon. Experiments have shown that several inches of Styrofoam will not block a GPS signal, but that a layer of aluminized Mylar will. It's important that amateurs test their APRS tracker prior to launch after they have finished constructing their airframe.

SIMPLEX REPEATER

Readers should be aware that a high-altitude balloon at 100,000 feet has a radio line-of-sight horizon of more than 400 miles. The formula for radio signal line-of-sight in miles can be calculated as follows:

Distance (in miles) $= 1.41 \times \sqrt{\text{height (in feet)}}$

where H is the height in feet.

Since antenna height is so important for operating on VHF and UHF, imagine having an antenna that is 19 miles high. If you could fly a repeater to that altitude, two ground stations 800 miles apart could communicate with each other through the repeater. One simple way to do this is to fly a single hand-held radio operating on 2 meters or the 70 cm band. Connecting a voice recorder and playback device to the handheld radio creates a *simplex repeater*. One such device is the Argent Data ADS-SR1. A discontinued Radio Shack simplex repeater module can be sometimes found online.

It takes some practice and patience to get the hang of a simplex repeater conversation, but this provides a very simple way to make some very exciting contacts over a multi-state region using minimal equipment on the ground.

CROSSBAND REPEATER

If you use two handheld radios, one on 2 meters and one on 70 cm, you can build a crossband repeater payload. (Some handheld radios can also operate as crossband repeaters by themselves.) You'll need to build an audio level control to adjust the audio between the two radios and also provide a PTT control.

Although more complicated, heavier and more expensive than the simplex repeater, this does provide a real-time repeater without having to worry about flying large filters to prevent desense. The input is usually on the 2 meter band with the output on the 70 cm band. Although you can set it up the other way around, the 3rd harmonic of the 2 meter transmit can cause desense issues with the 70 cm receiver.

STILL IMAGES

A great addition to any balloon flight is the ability to actually receive live images during the flight. From 100,000 feet you can clearly see a spectacular view of the blackness of space and the curve of the Earth since the balloon is above 99 percent of the atmosphere. **Figure 16.14** shows a photo taken from by a balloon-launched camera. Suitable lightweight cameras are available in thumb drive (USB) formats and helmet- or bike-cams designed to be used while being worn.

SSTV has been flown since at least 1998 and is still used with 2 meter FM transmitters by using a SSTV module such as SSTVcam by Argent Data (**www.argentdata.com**). The SSTV images are decoded using sound cards and software on a PC. The ability to use software means amateurs are free to use virtually any SSTV mode they prefer. The Argent system is configurable to produce images in the following four modes, Robot 36, Robot 72, Scottie 1, and Scottie 2. Scottie 2 will transmit one image in 71 seconds and Robot

Figure 16.14 — A balloon carrying a camera payload was launched from the Dayton Hamvention in 2010 by Bill Brown, WB8ELK. This picture was obtained a few minutes later from an altitude of about 1000 feet.

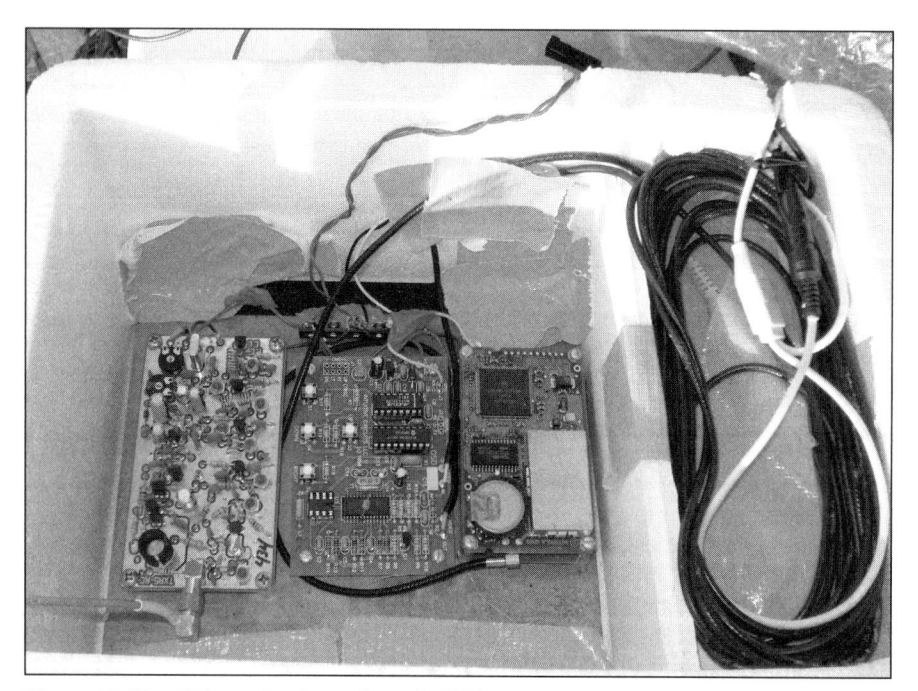

Figure 16.15 — This payload consists of a GPS receiver (right), payload controller (center), and an ATV transmitter (left). Batteries and cables are in the far-right compartment and the entire platform is contained in a Styrofoam enclosure.

36 is somewhat quicker although with some loss of resolution. The Scottie modes are most commonly used for balloon flights. (See the downloadable **Image Communications** chapter)

There are several programs to decode the SSTV audio signal and display the images on a computer screen. *MMSSTV*, *MixW*, *MultiPSK* and *Ham Radio Deluxe* (DM780) are a few programs that can be used to capture and view SSTV images.

VIDEO

There is nothing like watching a live video camera view from a flight to the edge of space. Typically, a 1 W to 3 W AM-modulated ATV transmitter on either 434 or 439.25 MHz is used for best results. You can also use FM ATV transmitters on higher frequencies, such as the 23 cm and 13 cm bands, but the path loss will be much higher on those frequencies and that will limit your maximum downrange reception distance. There are many lightweight video cameras that can be used. (See the **Image Communications** chapter with the downloadable supplemental material for more information about analog and digital ATV.)

Analog and digital methods are used to transmit video. In digital mode, Raspberry Pi computers can produce the video and 5.8 GHz modems are used to transmit the video. UHF can also be used to transmit digital video. By using video overlays, GPS data can be superimposed on images as a backup tracking method.

A variety of transmitters can be found at these websites: **www.hamtv.com**, **www.hamtv.com/videolynx.html#VM70X**, **kh6htv.com** and **www.hides.com.tw/product_eng.html**.

Figure 16.15 shows a typical ATV payload in the insulating Styrofoam box enclosure. On the left is the low-power 70 cm transmitter. In the middle is the microprocessor-based controller. The GPS receiver module is on the right. The batteries and cables are placed in the separate compartment at the far right. Note that the three electronics boards are mounted over a common PCB ground-plane to provide mechanical stability and to minimize RFI from the transmitter. The antenna for the ATV link hangs below the package.

On UHF, Little Wheel or Big Wheel omnidirectional antennas have been a staple of high altitude weather balloons. The balloon group Project Traveler has a webpage on making a Little Wheel antenna for high altitude balloon flights at **www.projecttraveler.org/index.php/how-to-s/6-little-wheel-antenna-for-70cm-atv**. PC Electronics (**www.hamtv.com/wheel.html**) carries the Olde Antenna Labs line of "wheel" antennas for various bands as well as video camera modules, ATV transmitters and receivers.

Analog video will produce P5 (high-quality) signals early in the flight while the balloon's altitude is relative low. At high altitudes, it's not uncommon to receive P1 (low-quality) signals on the ground, even from below the balloon.

Remember that the power requirements for a continually operating 1 W TV transmitter will be much higher than an APRS or audio repeater payload. You'll typically need at least 12 V with an Ah rating sufficient to allow for at least three hours of operating time. High capacity, four-cell, RC racing car batteries are a good option for powering ATV transmitters.

You will need a good antenna on the ground, an ATV downconverter, and an analog TV receiver. If you are flying in an area where horizontal polarization is used for local ATV activity, the Big Wheel antenna is a good option for the payload's ATV antenna. It provides good coverage at the horizon as well as underneath the payload. You can also use a vertical antenna, but there will be a null directly underneath a vertical radiator.

16.4.2 HF Payloads

The RF range of a high-altitude balloon at peak altitude is limited to about 450 miles when using VHF and UHF. Some balloon groups have flown transmitters on the HF bands with reception reports many thousands of miles away. It's a great way to include Amateur Radio operators far outside your local region.

There are several digital modes that can be programmed into a small microcontroller without having to invoke floating point math (see **www.elktronics.com** for an example of a multi-mode HF balloon transmitter). Morse code, RTTY, PSK31, DominoEX, and Hellschreiber have all been successfully flown, as well.

Transmit power levels under 1 W will work well due to the weak signal advantage of some of these digital modes. DominoEX, Hellschreiber, and PSK31 are particularly good for very weak signal reception. WSPR will also provide tracking information.

RESTRICTIONS ON UNATTENDED OPERATION

Note that unattended "beacon" operation and stations making transmission on their own are restricted to the automatic control band segments when located in areas under FCC jurisdiction. There should be a way to turn the HF transmitter on or off under remote control. (Being able to turn the transmitter on and off does not constitute full control via the remote link so the transmitter is still considered to be operating under automatic control.) There are a number of inexpensive and lightweight UHF handheld radios that can be used as a control receiver along with a DTMF decoder board.

Be sure to comply with the requirements of FCC Part 97.221 – Restricted Operation, which reads as follows:

§97.221 *Automatically controlled digital station.*

(a) This rule section does not apply to an auxiliary station, a beacon station, a repeater station, an earth station, a space station, or a space telecommand station.

(b) A station may be automatically controlled while transmitting a RTTY or data emission on the 6 m or shorter wavelength bands, and on the 28.120-28.189 MHz, 24.925-24.930 MHz, 21.090-21.100 MHz, 18.105-18.110 MHz, 14.0950-14.0995 MHz, 14.1005-14.112 MHz, 10.140-10.150 MHz, 7.100-7.105 MHz, or 3.585-3.600 MHz segments.

(c) Except for channels specified in §97.303(h), a station may be automatically controlled while transmitting a RTTY or data emission on any other frequency authorized for such emission types provided that:

(1) The station is responding to interrogation by a station under local or remote control; and

(2) No transmission from the automatically controlled station occupies a bandwidth of more than 500 Hz.

16.5 High Altitude Balloon Platforms

The reader will find plenty of near space information downloadable by using search terms such as "near space," "ARHAB," or "BalloonSats". Persons and organizations planning a near space event will find a series of papers and presentations on the **nearsys.com** website in its "Other People's Helium." section (**www.nearsys.com/arhab/ophe/ophe.htm**). The free e-book *BASIC Stamp Near Space* (see the References section) covers every aspect of high altitude ballooning. It is written for the amateur who wants to begin a near space program from scratch or who is looking for new ideas. Finally, the "Near Space" column in *Nuts and Volts* magazine contains articles on designing and using microcontrollers for high altitude balloon projects.

Here are a few websites with a great deal of information about Amateur Radio high altitude ballooning (ARHAB):
- Amateur Radio High Altitude Ballooning (ARHAB) — **www.arhab.org**
- Near Space — **nearsys.com**
- Edge of Space Sciences — **www.eoss.org**
- WB8ELK Balloons — **www.wb8elk.com**
- UK High Altitude Society — **www.habhub.org**
- Great Plains Super Launch — **www.superlaunch.org**

16.5.1 FAA Requirements

The regulating agency for unmanned free balloons is the Federal Aviation Administration (FAA). The applicable regulation for unmanned free balloons is the Federal Aviation Regulation Part 101 (FAR 101) or Title 14: Aeronautics and Space, 14 CFR 101.

FAR 101 Section 101.1 applies to any unmanned free balloon if it falls under one of these four conditions:

1. The unmanned free balloon carries a payload weighing more than 4 pounds and has a weight/size ratio greater than 3 ounces per square inch (This "surface density" is measured on the side of a payload with the smallest area).

2. The unmanned free balloon carries a single payload weighing more than 6 pounds

3. The unmanned free balloon carries a payload of two or more packages weighing a combined 12 pounds

4. The unmanned free balloon uses a rope or line to connect the payload to the balloon, which requires more than 50 pounds of force to separate the payload form the balloon.

Amateurs are strongly encouraged not to exceed the four limitations outlined above. When any of these limitations are exceeded, the balloon flight must meet additional requirements. These requirements are explained in Subpart D and include the following.

A) Limitations on launch site selection

B) Limitations regarding cloud cover at the time of launch

C) Requirement to add payload cutdown devices

D) Requirement to add balloon termination devices

E) Requirement to add a radar reflector to the balloon train

F) Requirement to increase the visibility of the balloon train

G) Additional pre-launch notification requirements

H) The requirement to regularly report the balloon's position

Section 101.3 states that one can request a waiver for a balloon flight that cannot meet the requirements of FAR 101. Anyone requiring a waiver must complete an FAA Form 7711-2, Application for Certificate of Wavier or Authorization.

Section 101.5 states that an unmanned free balloon cannot be launched from a restricted or prohibited area without permission from the controlling agency, or agency that uses that restricted or prohibited area.

Section 101.7 states that you cannot operate a balloon in a manner that creates a hazard to people or their property. For example, a balloon cannot be launched if during its flight objects will be dropped objects in such a way that can harm or injure people or their property.

The maximum weight per payload is six

pounds for a total of twelve pounds for the platform. Launching additional weight requires getting special permission from the FAA. This doesn't mean that you can fly 6-pound lead weights. You have to make sure that the density of your payload will not inflict damage to others, and it also needs to protect all those expensive electronics that you have packed inside.

16.5.2 Balloon Platform Environment

The near space environment has environmental conditions that are in many ways closer to those found in outer space than Earth's surface as **Table 16.2** illustrates (LEO stands for Low Earth Orbit).

HORIZONTAL DEPRESSION

For an observer at the Earth's surface, the visual horizon forms a horizontal line, 90 degrees from the zenith (the point overhead) for all azimuths (directions). As height increases, the horizon is determined by the point at which a line from the observer's eye is tangent to the Earth's surface. (The radio horizon is a bit more distant as explained in the chapter on **Propagation of Radio Signals**.) As an observer's altitude increases, as shown in **Figure 16.16**, that tangent point becomes more distant due to the curvature of the Earth. The angle from the zenith to the tangent line also increases, therefore the horizon appears lower to the observer. This lowering of the horizon is called *horizontal depression*.

ATMOSPHERIC DENSITY AND PRESSURE

Air pressure, and therefore density, decreases as altitude increases because the weight of air still above that level decreases. The scientific way of specifying changes in atmospheric density is *scale height*. Similar to a capacitor discharging, scale height is the change in height by which the density of the atmosphere decreases by a factor of e (which equals 2.718). Scale height depends on factors such as acceleration of gravity, the average atomic mass of atmospheric gases, and temperature. Scale height is a characteristic of every planet's atmosphere and a useful measurement for astrodynamics and astronomy. The scale height of Earth's atmosphere is 4.9 miles. Therefore, for every 4.9-mile increase in height, Earth's atmosphere is 1/e or 37% as dense. A simple rule of thumb is that air pressure drops by 50% per 18,000-foot increase in altitude.

Air pressure (see **Figure 16.17**) is a concern in near space experiments for keeping organisms alive, high voltage electrical circuits that might arc over without the insulation provided by the air, and where contact with the air is a factor in keeping devices cool.

TEMPERATURE

The atmosphere consists of four layers, two of which are observable in the **Figure 16.18** chart. The lowest layer is the *troposphere* and it includes all our weather. It's heated by its contact with the ground (which is heated by sunlight) and not directly by sunlight. The higher in the troposphere, the farther from the warm ground and therefore the colder the air.

The second atmospheric layer is the *stratosphere* and it grows warmer from energy absorbed by ozone molecules in the layer. As ozone blocks solar ultraviolet from reaching the ground, the energy of the ultraviolet photons warms the ozone molecules. The higher one climbs into the stratosphere, the more ultraviolet there is to block and therefore the warmer the air.

The *tropopause* is the boundary between the troposphere and stratosphere. Sensors often show the air temperature remaining constant within this transition layer. Figure 16.18 shows a typical temperature profile measured during a balloon experiment.

Temperature is a factor in how fast chemical processes operate. Low temperatures are a concern for the voltage and current output of batteries. Low temperature can also increase viscosity to the point that lubricated mechanical systems will seize. Another issue is that some items (such as plastic zip ties) become brittle in the cold and may not perform as expected in near space.

ALTITUDE AND TEMPERATURE RATING

Many GPS receiver modules will not work above 60,000 feet. When choosing a GPS receiver, make sure the datasheet specifies a maximum altitude above the expected maximum altitude of the balloon. Some popular modules known to work at stratospheric altitudes are those made by Trimble, Garmin, u-Blox and Inventek as well as high-altitude modules offered by Byonics and Argent Data.

Instrument modules designed for high altitude experiments should have a sufficient rating for conditions found at high altitude. Modules and other items made for general purpose use may not have an adequate altitude

Table 16.2
Balloon Environment Summary

	Sea Level	Near Space	LEO
Pressure	1013 mb	60 mb to 5 mb	0 mb
Temperature	59 °F	−60 °F to 20 °F	undefined
Gravity	32.2 ft/sec^2	31.09 ft/s^2	28.9 ft/s^2
Distance to Horizon*	3 miles for 6' tall adult	300 miles to 400 miles	1260 miles
Horizontal Depression**	0 degrees	5 degrees	18 deg
Cosmic Rays	8 counts/min	800 counts/min	?
UV Radiation	UV-A, small amount UV-B	UV-A and UV-B	UV-A, B, & C

* Distance to horizon can be calculated by the formula distance (miles) = sqrt(height(feet) * 1.5)
** See text

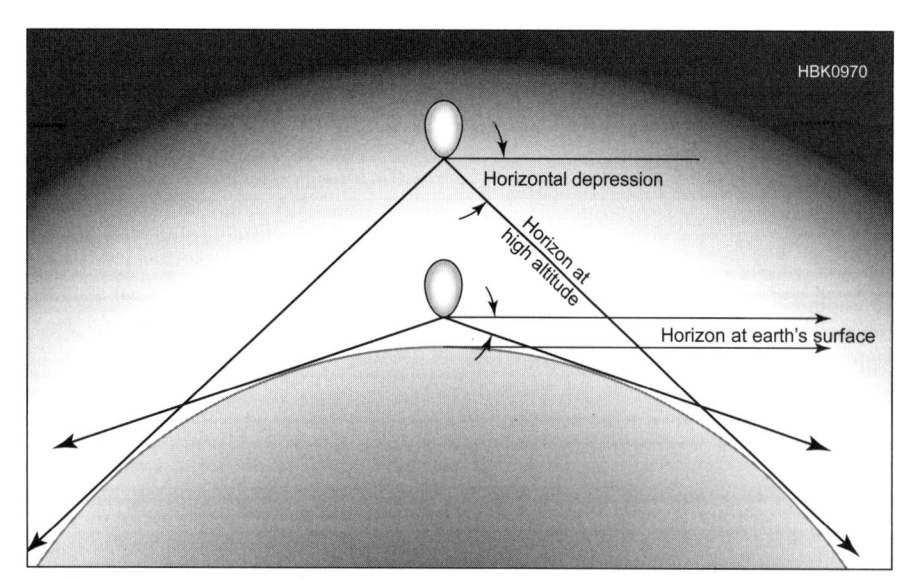

Figure 16.16 — In this highly exaggerated view, the higher balloon has a more distant horizon than at lower altitudes. This depresses the higher altitude balloon's horizon as altitude increases.

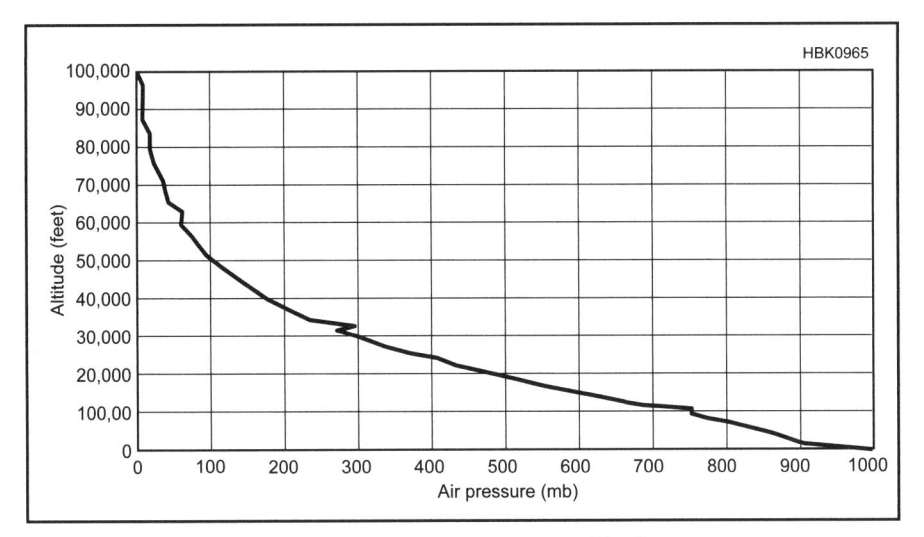

Figure 16.17 — A typical change of air pressure versus altitude.

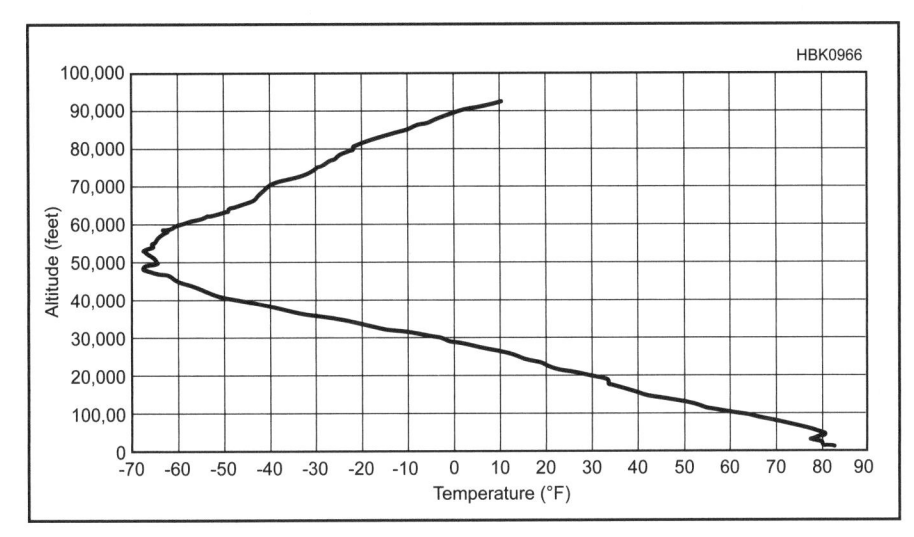

Figure 16.18 — Typical air temperature profile versus altitude, showing the troposphere (up to 50,000 feet) and the stratosphere (above 50,000 feet).

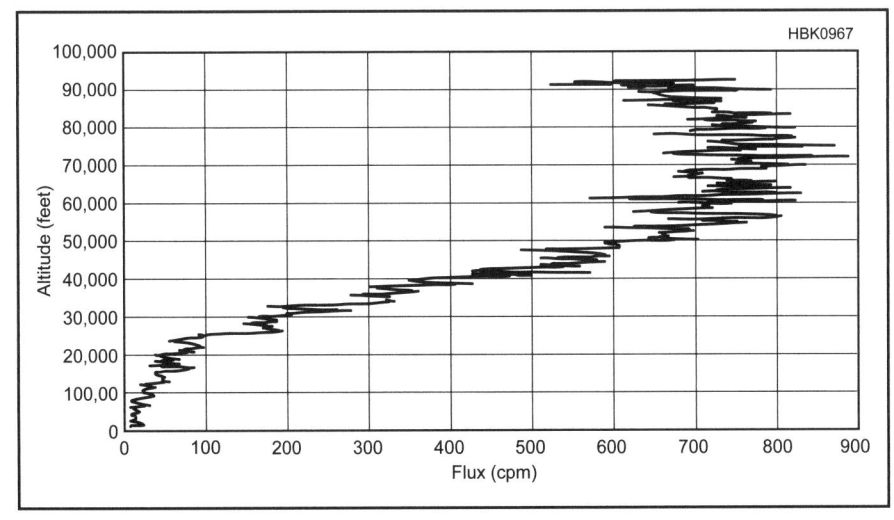

Figure 16.19 — Cosmic rays are encountered more frequently with increasing altitude in this typical balloon experiment.

and temperature rating. That does not mean that will not work when those ratings are exceeded but they may become unreliable or fail to meet their performance specifications.

Since most consumer electronics and integrated circuits are rated for 0 to 70 °C you may want to find devices that are rated for the industrial temperature range (–40 to 100 °C) or the automotive temperature range (–40 to 125 °C) for near space payloads. Forums and user communities involved with high altitude ballooning will often have recommendations for specific models of equipment that perform well in these extreme conditions. (See the preceding section on Temperature and Relative Humidity.)

Cosmic rays are energetic subatomic particles. Most of this population of particles are protons, or the nuclei of hydrogen atoms. A smaller population of heavier nuclei can also be found in cosmic rays. When atomic particles enter the upper atmosphere, they are called *primary cosmic rays*.

When primary cosmic rays collide with molecules of oxygen and nitrogen, they break apart the atoms and create a shower of *secondary cosmic rays*. These secondary cosmic rays contain energetic X-rays and other subatomic particles such as neutrons, pions, and muons. Many of the secondary cosmic rays decay and lose energy though further collisions. The result of the multiple collisions is a peak in cosmic ray flux at around 62,000 feet (called the Pflotz Line). Depending on the type of radiation sensor used, at the Pflotz line, the cosmic ray flux can be one hundred times greater than at sea level. (See **Figure 16.19**.)

Cosmic ray strikes can affect sensitive electronics. However, this should only be a concern in electronic devices with Very Large Scale Integration (VLSI) integrated circuits. This includes memories, processors, and advanced processing units. Smaller scale ICs have larger logic and circuit structures, making it more difficult for a cosmic ray to "flip a bit."

High-speed avionics may be at a slightly greater risk from cosmic-ray induced *single-event upsets* (SEU) during a near space flight. In fact, NASA research has found that avionics at 100,000 feet may experience an SEU once per 2.3 hours on average. Chances are the amateur will not have access to radiation-hardened electronics; in fact, it may raise suspicions if an amateur were to purchase such electronics! Advanced avionics uses software to detect and correct SEUs, but this may not be practical for amateurs either. The amateur's simplest solution is to design their avionics using electronics with large memory cells, and therefore not to use VLSI integrated circuits.

Amateur Radio Data Platforms   16.17

16.5.3 Balloon Platform Physical Design

Figure 16.20 shows a pair of typical balloon platforms. A weather balloon, once filled, is around seven feet tall. It is attached to the parachute and payloads with a *load line*. The load line is cut between 15 and 20 feet long so that the burst balloon's remains don't collapse on top of the parachute. Doing so may prevent the parachute from opening properly and slowing down the payload. Just after burst, the balloon's remains will fall slower than the parachute which places the balloon above the parachute during the early descent.

There is however a risk of entanglement between the burst balloon and the parachute shroud lines or tracking antenna during late descent. This risk rarely is a problem as long as the load line is long enough to suspend the burst balloon below the tracking modules.

The parachute's diameter is chosen based on the payload's total weight. The goal is to provide a low-speed landing no greater than 5 meters/second, 1,000 feet/minute, or 10 miles per hour. A parachute six feet in diameter is usually large enough for a 12-pound payload.

Below the parachute and part of its shroud lines is a plastic ring called the *spreader ring*. The spreader ring is usually a plastic ring one foot in diameter loosely suspended between the parachute's shroud lines. It keeps the shroud lines from touching and wrapping around each other during the ascent. As long as the parachute shroud lines do not twist, the parachute will open properly soon after the balloon bursts (video records indicate this can take as little as one second). If the shroud lines are allowed to twist, the payload's descent is not properly braked. A descent from 70,000 feet can take as little as seven minutes in such cases. Furthermore, an improperly operating parachute can tangle up in payload antennas or even the payload itself.

A *cutdown device* is optional on a balloon flight meeting the strictest limits of FAR 101. The cutdown separates the parachute and payload from the balloon and load line on command or when conditions such as balloon burst or time of flight requirements are met. Most, if not all cutdown systems in use today use a series of DTMF tones sent over VHF or UHF FM channels. Typically, a DTMF decoder chip is connected to a VHF or UHF receiver on the payload and the commands are sent as audio tones from a transmitter on the ground on the command frequency.

DTMF tone control permits the user to transmit a cutdown command followed by its password. Password protection for balloon cutdown ensures no false activation from DTMF tones intended for another purpose or payload. The cutdown is designed to either melt the load line with a coil of nichrome wire or slice the load line with a sharp blade.

Initiating cutdown starts the descent of the payload and allows the balloon to continue rising until it reaches its burst altitude. A cutdown that operates after the balloon bursts separates the balloon remains from the parachute. Separating the balloon fragments and load line from the parachute makes the descent less chaotic and protects the payload from the shock and acceleration of initial descent.

Following cutdown, the release of a near space balloon generates shaking and twisting for the attached platforms; however, the descent after balloon burst is significantly more traumatic. In fact, it's very evident when the balloon burst in the accelerometer chart shown in **Figure 16.21**.

Any object that places mass away from its center (has a lever arm) is subject to damage during balloon burst. Any object that is significantly denser than the rest of the platform can break free during balloon burst and become an impact hazard inside the platform or even escape the platform completely. Mounting methods that become brittle in the cold cannot be used to restrain dense or heavy objects on the platform.

ENCLOSURE AND INSTALLATION

The platform design must take into account the low temperature and low pressure of near space, the shock and vibration of the balloon burst, and to a much lesser extent, increased cosmic radiation.

A Styrofoam box is one of the most common enclosures. The foam is very light, provides insulation against the extreme temperatures encountered during flight for the payload electronics, and helps reduce the impact of landing. Even on the hottest summer day on the ground, it can be approximately –60 °F at 50,000 feet above the Earth. Most battery types do not work well at these temperature extremes which are also outside the specification range of most electronic components. Fortunately, a Styrofoam box will help keep the internal temperatures well above those brutal outside conditions.

Covering the exterior of the Styrofoam housing with black tape (such as black packing tape) creates a passive heating system for the enclosed components. A second heat source is a chemical hand warmer. Hand warmers produce heat from the oxidation of iron and can produce heat for a two-hour flight. Start hand warmers an hour before launch to ensure the items they are heating get thoroughly warm. The ability of hand warmers to produce heat will degrade during the ascent (less oxygen availability) but the initial warmth and gradually decreasing heat output of the hand warmers will keep items about 10 degrees warmer throughout the flight.

Another technique is to mount the electronics and batteries on a foam-core board and wrap everything with three layers of small-cell bubble wrap. The insulation and trapped sunlight will keep the electronics warm.

Components inside the balloon platform can be protected from shock using foam rubber (foamed urethane). In all cases, every component must be mounted to the platform using fasteners that are strong enough to hold several times the weight of the component being immobilized. In addition, the fasteners cannot be constructed of materials that become brittle due to cold. Therefore, do not use plastic zip ties to restrain heavy or dense objects for high altitude balloon flights.

Any instrument requiring high voltage should receive additional electrical insulation, such as a coating of silicone glue. Items that may expand in volume when exposed to low air pressure should be evaluated on the ground (a vacuum chamber is ideal for this purpose) before being sent into near space. Devices requiring air cooling should be replaced with items not requiring air cooling, or perhaps given larger heat sinks.

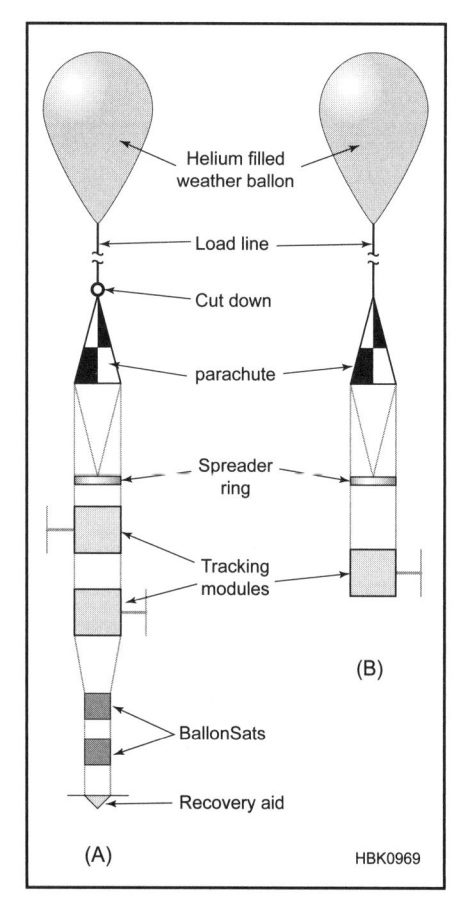

Figure 16.20 — (A) An idealized balloon platform showing the various components. (B) A simplified balloon platform with only the minimum necessary components.

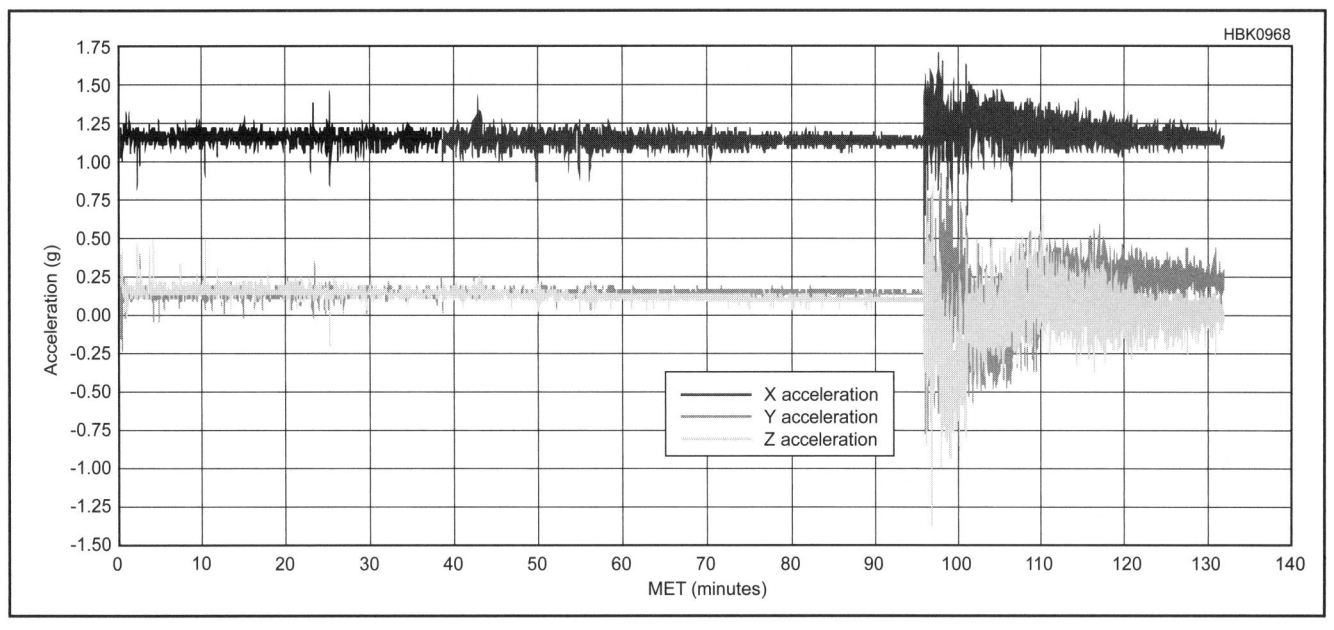

Figure 16.21 — The acceleration profile of a typical balloon experiment clearly shows the balloon bursting very clearly at about 95 minutes.

BATTERIES

Lithium-based batteries are strongly recommended as a high-altitude power source as they tend to handle the cold temperatures without excessive voltage drop. Batteries may be incorporated into the main enclosure or they can be included in a separate container. The weight of a separate battery box below the main enclosure helps to stabilize the entire platform.

A practical source of lithium batteries is an RC hobby shop. Racing car batteries come in several voltages and capacities. Since many APRS trackers are designed to operate on 5 V, select a two- or three-cell battery pack (7.2 V or 11.1 V). If your tracker electronics has a low dropout voltage regulator, then your tracker can operate with a two-cell battery pack. The Eveready L91 AA lithium battery is popular for use with Amateur Radio high-altitude balloon platforms.

Not only do you have a choice of battery voltages with RC racing car batteries, you also have a choice of capacities. Measure the current draw of your APRS tracker and avionics and multiply that value by 24 hours. That will give a rough idea of the minimum battery capacity for your tracker.

Batteries must have sufficient capacity to operate the tracking system for its typical three-hour near-space flight plus additional time spent on the ground prior to launch and awaiting recovery. For example, it's nice to have extra reserve to make sure the tracker produces position reports overnight should it get lost during descent.

PREDICTING FLIGHT PATHS AND TRACKING

When flying a high-altitude balloon, it is a good idea to run a flight prediction a few days before launch. Repeat the prediction the night before a flight. The goal is to be sure the balloon doesn't land in a densely populated area or where making a successful recovery will be difficult. There are two popular downloadable prediction programs that can be accessed at the **www.arhab.org** website.

Amateur Radio is a popular way to monitor the progress of a balloon's flight. The minimum system required to track a weather balloon flight consists of a GPS receiver that is certified to operate above 60,000 feet, an APRS TNC (terminal node controller), and a 2 meter FM transmitter. (A radar reflector is often included to increase the platform's visibility to air traffic control systems.)

The usual APRS configuration is to transmit a position report once a minute with the recommended path set to WIDE2-1. A power level below 1 W is quite sufficient and many systems work quite well with just 200 mW.

Note that time and altitude data can be used to calculate the ascent rate of the weather balloon as a function of altitude. In addition, the same information can be used to calculate the descent rate of the parachute. Since a parachute's descent rate is a function of air drag which is controlled by air density, the parachute's descent speed during descent can be used to estimate air density as a function of altitude. Note also that since a weather balloon is captive to the wind, measurements of altitude, speed, and heading are measurements of wind speed and direction at specific altitudes.

Including a second tracker may be an attractive form of insurance for mobile automated platforms such as weather balloons. If an APRS tracker were to fail at an altitude of 100,000 feet, the weather balloon can still be tracked and recovered using the second tracker. Redundant APRS trackers will need to use different SSIDs. In addition, they need to be time slotted so that their transmissions do not occur at the same time and jam each other. Preferably, redundant trackers will transmit on the same frequency as the primary tracker, which simplifies tracking for the people in search of the automated platform.

Finally, a *recovery aid* is a backup recovery method that's most useful after the parachute and its payload have landed. A recovery aid can include systems such as a loud audio beeper, strobe lights, or a fox-hunting (direction finding) transmitter. These help a chase crew recover a balloon platform after it has landed in trees or brush or tall crops where a GPS position is not enough to locate the platform.

APRS TELEMETRY

APRS is most popular and often used on short duration balloon flights (lasting for only a few hours) and where line of sight communication is possible between the chase crew and digipeaters. The use of IGates permits unlicensed individuals to participate in balloon chases by using a smartphone or tablet.

The simplest APRS telemetry string useful for balloon flights includes an identification, time of message, the balloon's three-dimensional position, the balloon's course and the balloon's speed. Such a string looks like the following as described in the APRS message format specification at **www.eoss.org/aprs/aprs_formats_eoss** and in the APRS-IS.net specification at **www.aprs-is.net/q.aspx**. (See the preceding section on APRS for a sample string.)

16.6 Unmanned Aerial Vehicles (UAVs)

16.6.1 General UAV Platform Requirements

Drones or UAVs and their control systems are grouped in the category of *Unmanned Aerial Systems* (UAS). The regulating agency for UAS is the Federal Aviation Administration (FAA). For the purposes of Part 107, the FAA does not consider UAVs to be the same as model airplanes. One reason is that model airplanes are considered to be simple systems incapable of flying autonomously. Therefore, a model airplane must remain within sight of the pilot to be controlled. The applicable regulation for UAS is Federal Aviation Regulation Part 107 (FAR 107) or Title 14: Small Unmanned Aircraft Systems (14 CFR 107). Part 107 applies to pilots flying UAVs for a business; hobbyists have different requirements. By becoming a licensed remote pilot however, additional privileges become available to the pilot.

This chapter will only focus on the requirement for people flying UAVs as a hobby or for education. For these people, the following stipulations apply:

1) You do not need to be certified as a remote pilot to fly your UAV if you are flying for a hobby or pleasure.

2) You must register your UAV if it weighs between 0.55 and 55 pounds (this requirement has changed several times since it was first implemented).

3) You cannot fly your UAV within five miles of an airport without first contacting the airport and/or *air traffic control* (ATC). Note that some small airports do not have an ATC. In those cases, you'll need to contact the airport manager.

4) Your UAV must always yield right of way to manned aircraft.

5) You must keep your UAV within sight, or in visual line-of-sight.

6) Your UAV must weigh less than 55 pounds.

7) You must follow any community-based safety guidelines.

8) You cannot fly a UAV higher than 400 feet above the ground.

9) You cannot fly a UAV over people or stadiums.

10) You cannot fly a UAV over people who are not a part of the drone operation.

11) You cannot fly a UAV over moving vehicles.

12) You cannot fly a UAV while under the influence of drugs or alcohol.

13) You cannot fly a UAV over or around sensitive property or infrastructure.

14) You cannot use a UAV to spy on or monitor people when they have a reasonable expectation of privacy.

UAV pilots can find additional information at **www.faa.gov/uas** and from the Academy of Model Aeronautics (AMA) at **www.modelaircraft.org**.

UAV pilots are strongly encouraged to download the app *B4UFly* to their mobile phones prior to flying a UAV. The app shows airports and other restricted sites close to your location, or in other words, locations near which you are not allowed to fly a UAV.

16.6.2 UAV Data and Navigation Subsystems

Commercial UAVs require the same digital radio controllers used for traditional radio-controlled airplanes. These controllers can come with the UAV or may be purchased separately. A separate purchase is more common for advanced UAV pilots who are assembling their UAV from parts. Since the radio controller is operating a multirotor aircraft rather than a fixed wing aircraft, the aircraft pilot must configure the radio controller for UAV operation. Otherwise, the operation of the radio controller for a UAV is nearly identical to that of a fixed-wing aircraft.

An outdoor multirotor UAV is so complex that a human pilot cannot directly operate one by controlling each of the UAV's rotors. Instead, many UAVs carry an onboard flight controller that incorporates a GPS receiver and inertial navigation components such as accelerometers, gyroscopes, and a compass (magnetometer). The flight controller makes adjustments to the UAV's rotors based on joystick input and internal conditions. Combining all these elements into a single flight controller makes it so much easier to fly a UAV — the pilot only needs to push joysticks to control the thrust, pitch, roll, and yaw of the UAV.

Many onboard UAV flight controllers permit the pilot to set the UAV's flight characteristics and behaviors by changing the flight computer's settings through RC switch settings or even software. For example, a UAV can be configured to hold altitude (remain at the same altitude when the thrust joystick is left centered), fly in the direction the joysticks are pushed (regardless of the UAV's heading), and even programmed to fly predefined course without further joystick input.

The most popular data transmitted from a UAV is video imagery (called *first person view* or FPV). Some UAVs transmit helpful navigational data such as altitude, heading, and speed. In addition, battery condition is transmitted in some UAVs to help the pilot manage the UAV's flight. Battery condition is frequently indicated by onboard LED colors.

To be a successful platform, UAVs are not usually required to transmit other types of data as a telemetry stream, because of the immediacy of the data collected. In other words, a drone can rapidly reach operational altitude, record data, then return to the launch site in a few minutes or less. Therefore, unlike weather balloons, data from UAVs is rapidly accessible and remains timely when it's downloaded.

However, if a UAV is going to transmit data, the pilot must test for the compatibility between the data transmitter and the radio controller and the onboard GPS. A pilot cannot safely operate a UAV if an onboard data transmitter interferes with the reception of RC commands or if it interferes with the UAV's GPS receiver.

Testing for interference between the data transmitter and the UAV must be performed outdoors and with the UAV propellers removed. The pilot can then safely monitor the UAV's status LEDs or other status transmissions while the data transmitter operates onboard the UAV.

One additional safety test the pilot should perform is a measure of the UAV's center of gravity. UAV flight controllers have expectations about the UAV's center of gravity. Adding a payload to a UAV that changes that center of gravity substantially will make the UAV difficult or even impossible to control. If a payload will be added to a UAV, the pilot must determine the center of gravity before and after the modification.

16.6.3 UAV Platform Configuration

Most pilots purchase their UAV *ready to fly* (RTF) or *almost ready to fly* (ATF). Therefore, in the vast majority of the cases, there is no need to worry about mounting or protecting the UAV's flight subsystems.

If a pilot is purchasing a UAV in parts and assembling it, then follow the assembly directions to construct the UAV. Directions will show the proper way to mount the UAV's flight subsystems. The proper placement is important in order to maintain the UAV's proper *center of gravity* (CG). When the CG is not located as the UAV's flight controller expects, unpredictable flights and even crashes can result.

16.6.4 UAV Electronic Subsystems

Prior to installing a new electronic system on a UAV, the pilot must ensure RFI from the payload cannot interfere with the UAV's GPS receiver. This can be an issue with some digital cameras for example, where the crystal-controlled clock inside the camera can emit enough RF to prevent a GPS from gaining a proper lock or even worse, losing satellite lock during flight. Therefore, the UAV should be left on the ground while its new electronics payload is tested in place on the UAV and then tested around the UAV. Since many commercial UAVs are capable of reporting their GPS status through LEDs and the radio controller, the remote pilot should monitor them for a while to ensure GPS lock remains steady as the new payload electronics is tested.

One useful electronic subsystem for a UAV is a voice or digital repeater. (See the preceding section on VHF/UHF Payloads.) The UAV's ability to climb to an altitude of several hundred feet with a payload makes it a rapid-to-deploy antenna tower. The limitations of a UAV-based antenna tower include some of the following:
- Limited weight — usually no more than one pound
- Limited time aloft — upwards of 30 minutes with new batteries and less as the payload becomes heavier
- Limited authority — poor authority means a UAV cannot prevent it from drifting with the wind, if the wind blows too strongly
- Limited to flying during daylight hours
- Limited antenna orientations — antennas must be placed where they do not interfere with the UAV's propellers
- Limited to only flying above people who are not involved with operation of the UAV

A second useful electronic subsystem is FPV or first person view video. (See the preceding section on Image and Video payloads.) A UAV flown with FPV adds a synergy to search and rescue (SAR). Hams can use the UAV to rapidly scan long distances, fly over steep terrain, and even peer over fences and into steep canyons. These abilities can reduce search times and the risk hams experience climbing into and out of potentially hazardous terrain. A thermal imaging camera is another powerful tool to add to a UAV-enhanced SAR.

Complete FPV systems, containing the video camera and the transmitter are readily available at minimal cost. They use the unlicensed 5.8 GHz radio frequencies and transmit with a power of hundreds of milliwatts. In addition, the systems are designed to be lightweight and not to interfere with the operation of the UAV. However, the remote pilot will need an observer to provide assistance to the pilot who is flying the UAV.

A non-electronic application of UAVs is carrying one end of a lightweight string over a tree or structure so that an antenna can be pulled up afterward. This permits an operator to place an antenna with more precision than is usually possible with a sling shot or "antenna launcher."

16.6.5 Powering the UAV

The motors of a UAV have a very high current demand. Twenty or more amps per motor isn't uncommon. The heavy current demands of motors (four of them on a quadcopter and six on a hexacopter) and requirement for a lightweight quadcopter means a high capacity, high current draw, and lightweight battery is required. These requirements and the ability to recharge the flight battery is best met with lithium polymer (LiPo) batteries. Read the recommendations for your UAV before purchasing new batteries.

16.7 Rockets

16.7.1 General Rocket Platform Requirements

Like Amateur Radio, amateur rocketry is a self-regulated activity. Since model rockets use the national air space, the ultimate regulating agency for model rockets is the Federal Aviation Administration (FAA). The applicable FAA regulation for model rockets is the Federal Aviation Regulation Part 101 (FAR 101) or Title 14: Aeronautics and Space, 14 CFR 101. In addition, the National Fire Protection Association (NFPA) creates safety codes that keep rocket motors safe to transport and use. NFPA 1127 - Code for High Power Rocketry Scope covers the construction, propellant mass, and reliability of rocket motors for amateur use. Rocket motor manufacturers follow these codes and as long as amateurs purchase their motors from reputable dealers, this will not be a concern when flying model rockets. The National Association of Rocketry (NAR) and Tripoli Rocketry Association (TRA) are the self-regulating organizations for model rocketry. Therefore, it's strongly encouraged that you join either one of these organizations prior to launching model or amateur rockets.

16.7.2 Suitable Rocket Data and Navigation Subsystems

Amateur Radio is seldom used with low-power model rocket flights. This is mostly because of the extreme weight limits placed on payloads by small model rockets and their limited range. Amateur Radio does however appear in some high power amateur rockets as an aid to recovering rockets after flight. There are several commercial products available for this purpose.

Radio tracking products for rockets are available in licensed and unlicensed frequencies. They also appear as either APRS (onboard rocket GPS receivers) or radio direction finding (fox hunting) products. The only other tracking system is an audio beacon and therefore does not rely on Amateur Radio.

Amateur Radio is also making an appearance in model rocketry for purposes of telemetry. Data typically includes acceleration, velocity, and altitude. UHF frequencies are preferable for rocket telemetry in order to keep the antenna short and lightweight. The antenna's orientation is necessarily vertical due to the construction of the rocket.

16.7.3 Rocket Platform Configuration

All electronics mounted inside an amateur rocket will experience very high accelerations at lift off, over 10 g of acceleration in some cases. (1 g is equivalent to the force of gravity at the Earth's surface.) Therefore, all electronics must be securely mounted to the rocket's airframe in a way that will prevent them from coming loose. This is especially true for batteries, which can be denser than electronics. In additional to acceleration, rocket payloads can experience mechanical shock and rapid shaking in multiple directions.

Most model rockets can't climb high enough to experience significant changes in temperature and pressure. Therefore, their electronics payloads do not have to be protected from these conditions. However, there are some high power amateur rockets that do climb to over 10,000 feet and can therefore experience rapid changes in air pressure and air temperature. Unlike high altitude weather balloons, the electronics reach high altitudes so fast (compared to a balloon) that the payload does not cold soak long enough to become completely chilled.

Sensors onboard rockets experience rapid changes in the physical conditions they are measuring. This can result in noisy reading from the sensors that must be accounted for. Sensors used to control the operation of the rocket, such as for determining peak altitude for parachute deployment, must have their outputs filtered in real-time to be useful. Other data can be filtered after the rocket is recovered and its data downloaded.

Antennas on rockets must be small and lightweight and they must not interfere with rocket staging or parachute deployment (which involves ejecting the rocket nose cone). These requirements make a UHF dipole a useful antenna. The ends of the antenna must be secured to the rocket body so they don't vibrate in the air flowing over the rocket body. Or the antenna must be secured inside the rocket body. Some radio trackers use flexible antennas and whips. Bird trackers make popular radio trackers for rockets since they have similar requirements.

As with UAVs, any electronic devices included in a rocket's payload should be tested for interference — especially when a GPS receiver is used for the rocket's maximum altitude determination.

Since rocket flights tend to be short, a high capacity battery is not typically required. Form factor (shape and dimensions) and weight are often the important considerations. This means alkaline batteries are often acceptable for rocket electronics.

16.8 Robotics

16.8.1 General Robotics Platform Requirements

Robots are defined as systems capable of acquiring sensory input, making decisions based on that input and the robot's current state, then acting based on the results of that decision. A robot's need to combine sensory data and current status means most robots include some type of programmable microcontroller.

Being able to act doesn't mean a robot must be very mobile. Industrial robots for example, are typically stationary and only able to operate within defined boundaries. A robot's method of acting can be electrical (such as motors and servos), pneumatic (air pressure), or hydraulic (liquid pressure). Each has its own abilities, requirements, and interfacing requirements to a robot controller.

Robots span a range of autonomies. A robot can be completely autonomous and capable of operating without any human intervention for long periods of time or a robot can require regular, predictable human intervention (such as a planetary rover). When a robot requires human input, that communication can be wireless or via a tether containing wire or fiber optics.

The many types of sensors, the many internal states, the many types of control systems, the many levels of limitation of mobility, many mechanical systems, and many ways to communicate between humans and robots makes it impossible to define a general platform for robotics. Each robot is typically as unique as the person or people creating it.

Unless robots interact with the public, there is no regulation controlling the amateur use of robots. This is changing with the advent of self-driving cars and trucks.

16.8.2 Suitable Robotics Data and Navigation Subsystems

Robots confined to traveling in small areas typically use inertia navigation methods or position measurement systems to navigate. Typical sensors include:
- Accelerometers
- Magnetometers
- Encoders
- Range Finders
- Light Detectors
- Line Detectors
- Laser Range Finders
- Limit Switches

Robots traveling over large distances or regions can combine GPS-based navigation systems into onboard inertia and local position measurement systems.

Robots that send navigation or sensory data to a human operator/monitor (such as the Mars Rover) will find APRS a good method for relaying this information wirelessly. In addition, a human operator can send instructions back to the robot via APRS messages.

Robots that transmit imagery can rely on either slow scan (SSTV) or amateur television (ATV). SSTV is a suitable method when conditions are slow to change or when where only low power levels are available to send imagery. ATV is important where the robot is traveling at speeds high enough that human intervention is needed constantly. (See the preceding sections on Image and Video payloads.)

Although robotics projects using Amateur Radio are currently few, one of the more successful as of early 2018 is the HF Voyager project. (**www.jrfarc.org/hf-voyager**) An autonomous "wave glider", HF Voyager operates under automatic control, making contacts with the call sign KH6JF/mm on 20 meters using FT8 and PSK-31 as the primary operating modes. It can also use WSPR in times of poor propagation.

A possible solution to long-range communication between humans and a robot might be through satellites. An Iridium modem would permit the onboard robot controller to send and receive data from virtually anywhere in the world.

Finally, there are unlicensed radio bands, such as ISM, that amateur robotics engineers are using for their short-range robotics projects. These bands permit human-robot communications in both imagery and data.

16.8.3 Robotics Platform Configuration

Small, indoor robots typically have few limitations (other than those imposed for competitions). The roboticist can replace their batteries frequently, the robots don't experience extreme high or low temperatures, no rain falls on them, and small and lightweight motors suffice for making them mobile.

A roboticist designing a large, outdoor robot will need to balance the robot design with the many of the limitations mentioned above. This starts with a strong, but lightweight robot body (often made from aluminum). Weatherproof enclosures are required to protect the onboard electronics. Motors need to be sealed where dust and rain are issues. The motors must be powerful enough to make the robot mobile at reasonable speeds. The robot's battery design must have the capacity to operate the robot's electronics and motors without excessively weighing down the robot. Finally, depending on the speed of the robot, the design might call for physical shock protection.

Most robots use flexible antennas to communicate with human operators. The antenna is typically mounted at a high location on the robot where it can't interfere with cameras and robotic arms.

Robots that operate without direct human contact for long periods of time will need to use solar charging in order to keep their batteries topped off. Solar charging systems need to monitor the battery level and then act to recharge batteries at the appropriate voltage and current. The high power demands of robots means they can never operate solely on solar power and without batteries. This also means robots will need down time at some point in order to recharge their batteries.

Lithium polymer (LiPo) batteries are good batteries for robots since they are light weight, can operate across a large range of temperatures, and are capable of meeting high current demands.

16.9 Fixed Stations

16.9.1 General Fixed Station Platform Requirements

Fixed stations such as weather stations are found in locations where environmental conditions are hostile to humans or where it's not practical or safe to record data. Moored or drifting buoys are included in this classification. Therefore, fixed stations must be constructed to handle extreme weather conditions. And their data subsystems are critically important if they can't be tended on a regular basis.

The FCC is the agency responsible for the telemetry requirements of fixed stations that use radios to communicate. The data transmission requirements for fixed site data collectors and dataloggers (such as moored buoys) are simpler than they are for drifting buoys. This is because a drifting buoy can be carried by ocean currents into international waters or the coastal waters of other countries. Since each country has its own rules governing the use of Amateur Radio, a drifting buoy designer and builder must become acquainted with the communication rules of other countries to insure their drifting buoy doesn't violate Amateur Radio laws.

When the need is to monitor weather conditions continuously on land, a weather station is the preferred solution. An amateur must mount a weather station above the level of obstacles (such as buildings and trees) that will interfere with the flow of wind. This means many weather stations can be found mounted above roofs and on tall masts or radio towers.

When it comes to monitoring conditions in bodies of water, a buoy is used. Buoys can be of two types — those remaining stationary by mooring them to the seabed or those free to drift with the ocean and wind currents. Moored buoys have been used by the National Oceanographic and Atmospheric Administration (NOAA) since 1951 and drifting buoys have been in use since 1979 (Wikipedia). At this time, the editors are unaware of any communication requirements from NOAA.

Anchored or fixed datalogging stations should not be anchored or fixed in locations where people have a reasonable expectation of privacy or their presence will interfere with navigation or right of way.

16.9.2 Suitable Fixed Station Data and Navigation Subsystems

The needs of data and navigation systems for weather stations and buoys are similar to those mentioned in previous sections. The data needs are addressed based on the distance between the station and the amateur recording the data.

For short distances, such as from the roof to the interior of a house, a wire connection between the station and a PC or display often suffices. Where it's not practical to route a communication cable into the house, then an unlicensed radio system will often work and is usually available with the fixed station. Otherwise, where long distance, line-of-sight communication is needed, APRS is one of the best methods available. In fact, there are many weather stations with integrated APRS capability available for purchase.

For fixed stations located long distances from the data user, HF modes are often the best solution. This includes the WSPR, Hellschreiber, RTTY, CW, and JT9 modes.

Satellite communication methods such as Spot (**findmespot.com**) and Iridium modems are a possible solution for long distance fixed and mobile stations. A Spot tracker only reports its position; therefore it is best used for reporting the position of mobile stations such as buoys. An Iridium satellite modem will telemeter data, unlike the Spot. Both of these satellite systems require a subscription. Therefore the amateur must determine whether or not the value of the data justifies the cost of a subscription prior to placing the fixed station into operation.

16.9.3 Fixed Station Platform Configuration

WEATHER STATIONS

Commercial weather stations use components capable of handling hot and cold temperatures and house most of them inside of an enclosure. Weather sensors, on the other hand, must be exposed to the elements in order to collect their data.

Pressure sensors can be left inside the house (if it's close to the weather station) or inside the enclosure since the enclosure is not air tight. Relative humidity sensors must be exposed to the air, while at the same time, protected from rain and condensation. One solution is to house the relative humidity (RH) sensor inside of a housing with vents cut in its sides. Temperature sensors (such as the LM335) must be exposed to the air, but not to sunlight because solar absorption will warm the sensor above ambient air temperature. A sun shield placed over the temperature sensor usually suffices. Alternatively, a temperature sensor can be mounted to the underside of the weather station enclosure.

Two of the more difficult weather sensors are the anemometer and wind vane. They are often made from position sensors that can rotate 360 degrees without needing to unwind (for the wind vane) or with generators (for the anemometer). These are mechanical systems that need protection from moisture while still remaining free to rotate continuously without impediment. Other solutions that are less difficult to protect include the hot wire anemometer and the ultrasonic anemometer and wind vane.

BUOYS

Drifting buoys are used to track ocean currents, water, and weather conditions (temperature, pressure, RH, water temperature, salinity). A moored buoy can report on wind speed and direction while a drifting buoy can't report with the same level of accuracy due to its movement.

Buoys must have an overall density less than the density of water (1.0 grams/cc) if they are to float. A lower density will raise the top of the buoy higher above the water than for a higher density buoy. Be careful — density that is too low can result in an unstable buoy that tips over. Therefore, buoys need ballast so they can maintain an upright configuration in rolling waters and waves. The ballast placed in a buoy must be located below the buoy's desired center of gravity. Any ballast must be securely attached to the buoy so that it can't shift its position when the buoy is tilted by waves. Finally, the ballast attachment cannot compromise the water-tightness of the buoy.

All buoy components must be protected from fresh or salt water. Therefore, buoys must be constructed with water-tight seals.

This can be a challenge for buoy antennas which are often located on top of the buoy. These antennas will be exposed to fresh or salt water on a regular basis. Therefore, buoy antennas require insulation to keep salt water off of their metal components, including connectors. Be careful in the selection of insulating materials, cold water can make some materials stiff or brittle. Select insulating materials that maintain their strength and flexibility when they get cold.

Insulation slows changes in temperature but can't stop those changes. Since buoys can operate for days or weeks in cold conditions, insulation such as Styrofoam is less effective in protecting electronics. Two options are to add heaters to the buoy or to use electronics that are designed to operate in cold conditions.

16.9.4 Powering the Fixed Station Platform

Indoor and some outdoor fixed stations may have access to household or commercial electrical power. If so, there will be no power concerns for these stations. Other outdoor fixed stations require batteries that must function in extreme conditions unless heating and cooling is provided for the batteries. In addition, batteries may be exposed to damp conditions if they can't be hermetically sealed in protective containers. The requirement to seal batteries is critical for buoys since they are exposed to salt water.

If a fixed station must operate for a good part of a year without maintenance, then the amateur should give consideration to using solar power to recharge the station's batteries. The solar cells must be encapsulated to protect them from moisture.

16.10 References and Bibliography

The ARRL Operating Manual, 11th edition, (ARRL, 2016).
The ARRL Antenna Book, 23rd edition, (ARRL, 2015).
Britain, K., WA5VJB, "Cheap Yagis," **www.wa5vjb.com/yagi-pdf/cheapyagi.pdf**
Buchmann, I., *Batteries in a Portable World* (Cadex, 2011).
Cain, P., KØPC, "APRS with a Smartphone," *NCJ*, Sep/Oct 2012, pp 16-17.
Fisher, B., W2BFJ, "Fox-1 Satellite Telemetry – Part 1: On the Satellite," *AMSAT Journal*, Nov/Dec 2015, pp 9-12.
Horzepa, S., WA1LOU, *APRS: Moving Hams on Radio and the Internet*, (ARRL, 2004 — out of print).
Mims, F., "Sun Photometer with Light-emitting Diodes as Spectrally Selective Filters," Applied Optics, Vol. 31, No. 33, 20 Nov 1992, pp. 6965-6967.
Post, J., KA5GSQ, "A Simple Sensor Package for High Altitude Ballooning," *QEX*, May/Jun 2012, pp 10-19.
Simmons, B., WB6EYV, "APRS Unveiled," *QEX*, Nov/Dec 2012, pp 19-23.
Spencer, M., WA8SME, "ARRL Education and Technology Program Space/Sea Buoy," *QST*, May 2012, pp 33-35.
Thompson, C., AC2CZ, "Fox-1 Satellite Telemetry – Part 2: FoxTelem," *AMSAT Journal*, Jan/Feb 2016, pp 7-9.
Verhage, Paul, KD4STH, *BASIC Stamp Near Space* (see the References section), nearsys.com/pubs/book/index.htm.
Williams, D., AJ5W, "APRS and High-Altitude Research Balloons," *QST*, Aug 2007, pp 48-49.

CQ VHF Articles (out of print)

Benton, D., KE5URH, "Tulsa (OK) Technology Center's Innovative Approach to Training Future Engineers," *CQ VHF*, Fall 2008, p 32.
Brown, B., WB8ELK, "Up in the Air: Kentucky Space Balloon-1," *CQ VHF*, Spring 2009, p 57.
Brown, B., WB8ELK, "Up in the Air: HF Balloon Tracking," *CQ VHF*, Winter 2011, p 63.
Dean, T., KB1JIJ, "ATV: W2KGY BalloonSat Payload," *CQ VHF*, Fall 2010, p 68.
Ferguson, D., AI6RE, "Transatlantic Balloon Flight 2012, CNSP-18 K6RPT-12," *CQ VHF*, Winter 2013, p 8.
Helm, M., WC5Z, "A Low Cost 70 cm Tracking Beacon for Rocket or Balloon Payloads," *CQ VHF*, Fall 2010, p 31.
Whitham, R., VE3NSA and Cieszecki, J. VE4CZK, "The WinCube Project," *CQ VHF*, Winter 2009, p 12.
An index to all of the articles in *CQ VHF*, including the "Up In The Air" column on balloons, has been compiled by KB9MWR at **www.qsl.net/kb9mwr/files/ham/cq-vhf.html**.

Nuts and Volts Magazine Articles by Paul Verhage, KD4STH

"Near Space: Approaching the Final Frontier," Mar 2013, p 68.
"Near Space: Using the Nearspace Simple Flight Computer," Jan 2013, p 72.
"Near Space: Approaching the Final Frontier," Nov 2012, p 14.
"Near Space: A New BalloonSat Airframe Design," Jul 2012, p 68.
"Near Space: The NearSpace UltraLight — The Everyman's Flight Computer," Jan 2011, p 67.
"Near Space: Your Own Micro Datalogger," May 2009, p 80.
Verhage continues to write the "Near Space" column as of early 2018.

Contents

17.1 High Power, Who Needs It?

17.2 Types of Power Amplifiers
    17.2.1 Why a "Linear" Amplifier?
    17.2.2 Solid State vs Vacuum Tubes

17.3 Vacuum Tube Basics
    17.3.1 Thermionic Emission
    17.3.2 Components of a Vacuum Tube
    17.3.3 Tube Nomenclature
    17.3.4 Tube Mounting and Cooling Methods
    17.3.5 Vacuum Tube Configurations
    17.3.6 Classes of Operation in Tube Amplifiers
    17.3.7 Understanding Tube Operation

17.4 Tank Circuits
    17.4.1 Tank Circuit Q
    17.4.2 Tank Circuit Efficiency
    17.4.3 Tank Output Circuits

17.5 Transmitting Tube Ratings
    17.5.1 Plate, Screen and Grid Dissipation
    17.5.2 Tank Circuit Components
    17.5.3 Other Components

17.6 Sources of Operating Voltages
    17.6.1 Tube Filament or Heater Voltage
    17.6.2 Vacuum-Tube Plate Voltage
    17.6.3 Grid Bias
    17.6.4 Screen Voltage For Tubes

17.7 Tube Amplifier Cooling
    17.7.1 Blower Specifications
    17.7.2 Cooling Design Example
    17.7.3 Other Considerations

17.8 Vacuum Tube Amplifier Stabilization
    17.8.1 Amplifier Neutralization
    17.8.2 VHF and UHF Parasitic Oscillations
    17.8.3 Reduction of Distortion

17.9 MOSFET Design for RF Amplifiers
    17.9.1 LDMOS versus VDMOS
    17.9.2 Designing Amplifiers with MOSFETs
    17.9.3 The Transistor Data Sheet
    17.9.4 Summary Observations

17.10 Solid State RF Amplifiers
    17.10.1 Solid State vs Vacuum Tubes
    17.10.2 Classes of Operation
    17.10.3 Modeling Transistors
    17.10.4 Impedance Transformation — "Matching Networks"
    17.10.5 Combiners and Splitters
    17.10.6 Amplifier Stabilization
    17.10.7 Amplifier "Pallet" Modules

17.11 Solid State Amplifier Projects
    17.11.1 *Project:* A 250 W Broadband Linear Amplifier
    17.11.2 *Project:* All-Mode, 2 Meter, 80 W Linear Amp
    17.11.3 *Project:* 10 GHz 2 W Amplifier

17.12 Tube Amplifier Projects
    17.12.1 *Project:* The Everyham's Amplifier
    17.12.2 *Project:* 3CX1500D7 RF Linear Amplifier

17.13 References and Bibliography

Chapter 17 — Downloadable Supplemental Content

Supplemental Articles

- Tuned (Resonant) Networks (for use with MATCH.EXE)
- "Amplifier Overshoot — Drive Protection" by Phil Salas, AD5X
- Design Example — RF Amplifier using 8877 Vacuum Tube by John Stanley, K4ERO
- Design Example — MOSFET Thermal Design by Dick Frey, K4XU
- Determining a Transistor's Power Rating (APT Application Note) by Dick Frey, K4XU
- *ARRL RF Amplifier Classics* Table of Contents
- "Designing to Avoid Interactive Tuning and Load Adjustments" (full article) by John Stanley, K4ERO

HF Amplifier Projects

- "The Everyham's Amp" by John Stanley, K4ERO (including files with construction notes, layouts, use of different tubes, etc.)
- "A 3CX1500D7 RF Linear Amplifier" by Jerry Pittenger, K8RA (including PCB layout, Pi-L values spreadsheet, etc.)
- "A 250 W Broadband Solid-State Linear Amplifier" by Dick Frey, K4XU (including files with construction notes and photos, PCB layouts, parts lists, etc.)
- "The Sunnyvale/Saint Petersburg Kilowatt-Plus," a 4CX1600B HF amplifier project by George Daughters, K6GT

VHF Amplifier Projects

- "A 6 Meter Kilowatt Amplifier" by Dick Stevens, W1QWJ
- "144 MHz Amplifier Using the 3CX1200Z7" by Russ Miller, N7ART
- "Build a Linear 2 Meter, 80 W All Mode Amplifier" by James Klitzing, W6PQL
- "Design Notes for 'A Luxury Linear' Amplifier" by Mark Mandelkern, K5AM
- "High-Performance Grounded-Grid 220-MHz Kilowatt Linear" by Robert Sutherland, W6PO

UHF/Microwave Amplifier Projects

- "432 MHz 3CX800A7 Amplifier" by Steve Powlishen, K1FO
- "A High-Power Cavity Amplifier for the New 900-MHz Band" by Robert Sutherland, W6PO
- "A Quarter-Kilowatt 23-cm Amplifier" by Chip Angle, N6CA
- "2 Watt RF Power Amplifier for 10 GHz" by Steven Lampereur, KB9MWR
- "2304 MHz 70 W Rover Amplifier" by Bill Koch, W2RMA, and John Brooks, N9ZL

Chapter 17 Downloadable Software

The following software is available with this book's downloadable supplemental content.

- *TubeCalculator* by Bentley Chan and John Stanley, K4ERO, for analysis of operation of popular high power transmitting tubes.
- *PI-EL* by Jim Tonne, W4ENE, for design and analysis of PI and PI-L networks for transmitter output.
- *SVC Filter* by Jim Tonne, W4ENE, for design and analysis of low-pass and high-pass filters using standard value components.
- *MeterBasic* by Jim Tonne, W4ENE, for design and printing of custom analog meter scales.
- *MATCH.EXE* software (for use with Tuned (Resonant) Networks discussion)

Chapter 17

RF Power Amplifiers

Amateur Radio operators typically use a very wide range of transmitted power — from milliwatts to the full legal power limit of 1.5 kW. This chapter covers RF power amplifiers beyond the 100 – 150 W level of the typical transceiver. The sections on tube-type amplifiers, including a new sidebar on a design method to avoid interactive tuning, were prepared by John Stanley, K4ERO. The sections on solid-state amplifiers were contributed by Richard Frey, K4XU, along with an overview of the new "pallet" amplifier modules. Roger Halstead, K8RI, contributed material on amplifier tuning and the use of surplus components in amplifier construction. This edition includes several amplifier projects using tubes, transistors, and integrated circuits. An overview is provided in print while more complete construction information is included with the downloadable supplemental content.

17.1 High Power, Who Needs It?

There are certain activities where higher power levels are almost always required for the greatest success — contesting and DXing, for example. While there are some outstanding operators who enjoy being competitive in spite of that disadvantage, the high-power stations usually have the biggest scores and get through the pileups first. On the VHF and higher bands, sometimes high power is the only way to overcome path loss and poor propagation.

Another useful and important area where higher power may be needed is in net operations. The net control station needs to be heard by all potential net participants, some of whom may be hindered by a noisy location or limited antenna options or operating mobile. This can be crucial to effective emergency communications. General operation also benefits from the availability of high power when conditions demand it to maintain contact.

How do you decide that you need amplification? As a rule of thumb, if you have a good antenna and hear a lot of stations that don't seem to hear you, you probably need to run more power. If you operate on bands where noise levels are high (160 and 75/80 meters) or at times when signals are weak then you may find that running the legal limit makes operations more enjoyable. On the other hand, many stations will find that they can be heard fine with the standard 100 W transmitter or even with lower power.

Power requirements also depend on the mode being used. Some digital modes, such as PSK31, work very well with surprisingly low power. CW is more power efficient than SSB voice. Least effective is full carrier AM, which is used by vintage equipment lovers. Once you have determined that higher power will enhance your operations, you should study the material in this chapter no matter whether you plan to build or buy your amplifier.

Note that many power amplifiers are capable of exceeding the legal limit, just as most

Safety First!

YOU CAN BE KILLED by coming in contact with the high voltages inside a commercial or homebrew RF amplifier. Please don't take foolish chances. Remember that you cannot go wrong by treating each amplifier as potentially lethal! For a more thorough treatment of this all-important subject, please review the applicable sections of the **Power Sources** and the **Safety** chapters in this *Handbook*.

High-power amplifiers generate strong RF fields, especially near a tube or transistor and around the output circuits. High levels of RF at frequencies of 50 MHz through microwaves are particularly hazardous. Avoid exposing yourself to intense RF fields when adjusting or measuring energized equipment and follow the RF exposure guidelines for yourself and others. See the **Safety** chapter for more information.

automobiles are capable of exceeding posted speed limits. That does not mean that every operator with an amplifier capable of more than 1.5 kW output is a scofflaw. Longer life for the amplifying devices and other amplifier components as well as a cleaner signal result from running an amplifier below its maximum rating. However, just as with automobiles, that extra capability also presents certain temptations. Remember that FCC rules require you to employ an accurate way to determine output power, especially when you are running close to the limit.

17.2 Types of Power Amplifiers

Power amplifiers are categorized by their power level, intended frequencies of operation, device type, class of operation and circuit configuration. Within each of these categories there are almost always two or more options available. Choosing the most appropriate set of options from all those available is the fundamental concept of design.

17.2.1 Why a "Linear" Amplifier?

The amplifiers commonly used by amateurs for increasing their transmitted power are often referred to as "linears" rather than amplifiers or linear amplifiers. What does this mean and why is it important?

The active device in amplifiers, either tube or transistor, is like a switch. In addition to the "on" and "off" states of a true switch, the active device has intermediate conditions where it presents a finite value of resistance, neither zero nor infinity. As discussed in more detail in the **RF Techniques** chapter, active devices may be operated in various *classes of operation*. Class A operation never turns the device fully on or off; it is always somewhere in between. Class B turns the device fully off for about half the time, but never fully on. Class C turns the device off for about 66% of the time, and almost achieves the fully on condition. Class D switches as quickly as possible between the on and off conditions. Other letters have been assigned to various rapid switching methods that try to do what Class D does, only better. Class E and beyond use special techniques to ensure that high voltage and current do not occur during switching.

During the operating cycle, the highest efficiency is achieved when the active device spends most of its time in the on or off condition and the least in the resistive condition. For this reason, efficiency increases as we go from Class A to B to C to D.

A *linear amplifier* is one that produces an output signal that is identical to the input signal, except that it is stronger. Not all amplifiers do this. Linear amplifiers use Class A, AB or B operation. They are used for modes such as SSB where it is critical that the output be a close reproduction of the input.

The Class C amplifiers used for FM trans-

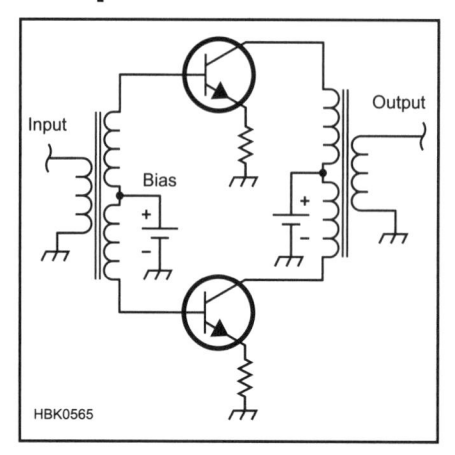

Figure 17.1 — This simple circuit can operate in a linear manner if properly

mitters are *not* linear. A Class C amplifier, properly filtered to remove harmonics, reproduces the frequencies present in the input signal, but the *envelope* of the signal is distorted or even flattened completely. (See the **Modulation** chapter for more information on waveforms, envelopes and other signal characteristics.)

An FM signal has a constant amplitude, so it carries no information in the envelope. A CW signal does carry information in the amplitude variations. Only the on and off states must be preserved, so a Class C amplifier retains the information content of a CW signal. However, modern CW transmitters carefully shape the pulses so that key clicks are reduced to the minimum practical value. A Class C amplifier will distort the pulse shape and make the key clicks worse. Therefore, except for FM, a linear amplifier is recommended for all amateur transmission modes.

Some digital modes, such as RTTY using FSK, are a form of FM and can also use a nonlinear Class C, D or E amplifier. If these signals are not clean, however, a Class C amplifier may make them worse. Also, Class C or even D and E can be used for very slow CW, for very simple low-power CW transmitters or on uncrowded bands where slightly worse key clicks are not so serious. After all, Class C was used for many years with CW operation.

Class of operation as it relates to tube-type

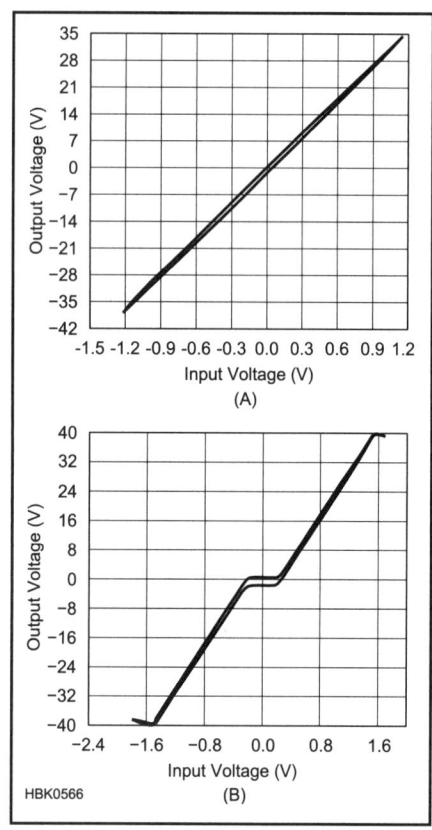

Figure 17.2 — Input versus output signals from an amplifier, as observed with the X-Y display on an oscilloscope. At A, an amplifier with proper bias and input voltage. At B, the same amplifier with improper bias and high input voltage.

amplifier design is discussed in more detail in a later section of this chapter.

ACHIEVING LINEAR AMPLIFICATION

How is linear amplification achieved? Transistors and tubes are capable of being operated in a linear mode by restricting the input signal to values that fall on the linear portion of the curve that relates the input and output power of the device. Improper bias and excessive drive power are the two most common causes of distortion in linear amplifiers. All linear amplifiers can be improperly

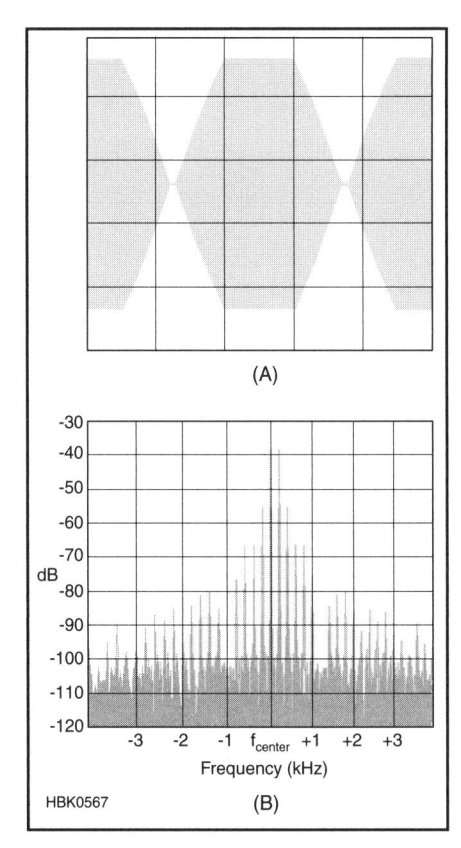

Figure 17.3 — Improper operation of a linear using a two-tone test will show peak clipping on an oscilloscope (A) and the presence of additional frequencies on a spectrum analyzer (B). When these patterns appear, your "linear" has become a "nonlinear" amplifier. Users of adjacent channels will not be happy. More information on transmitter testing may be found in the Test Equipment and Measurements chapter.

biased or overdriven, regardless of the power level or whether transistors or tubes are used.

Figure 17.1 shows a simple circuit capable of operating in a linear manner. For linear operation, the bias on the base of the transistors must be such that the circuit begins to produce an output signal even with very small input signal values. As shown in **Figure 17.2**, when properly adjusted for linear operation, the amplifier's output signal faithfully tracks the input signal. Without proper bias on the transistors, there will be no output signal until the input voltage goes above a threshold. As shown in Figure 17.2B, the improperly adjusted amplifier suddenly switches on and produces output when the input signal reaches 0.5 V.

Some tubes are designed for *zero bias* operation. This means that an optimum bias current is inherent in the design of the tube when it is operated with the correct plate voltage. Other types of tubes and all transistors must have bias applied with circuits made for that purpose.

All amplifiers have a limit to the amount of power they can produce, even if the input power is very large. When the output power runs up against this upper limit (that is, when additional drive power results in no more output power), *flat topping* occurs and the output is distorted, as shown in **Figure 17.3**. Many amplifiers use *automatic level control* (ALC) circuits to provide feedback between the amplifier and the companion transceiver or transmitter. When adjusted properly, ALC will control the transmitter output power, preventing the worst effects of overdriving the amplifier. Even with ALC, however, overdriving can occur.

17.2.2 Solid State vs Vacuum Tubes

With the exception of high-power amplifiers, nearly all items of amateur equipment manufactured commercially today use solid state (semiconductor) devices exclusively. Semiconductor diodes, transistors and integrated circuits (ICs) offer several advantages in designing and fabricating equipment. Solid state equipment is smaller, offers broadband (no-tune-up) operation, and is easily manufactured using PC boards and automated (lower cost) processes.

Based on all these facts, it might seem that there would be no place for vacuum tubes in a solid state world. Transistors and ICs do have significant limitations, however, especially in a practical sense. Individual present-day transistors cannot generally handle the combination of current and voltage needed nor can they safely dispose of the amount of heat dissipated for RF amplification to high power levels. Pairs of transistors, or even pairs of pairs, are usually employed in practical power amplifier designs at the 100 W level and beyond. Sometimes various techniques of power combination from multiple amplifiers must be used.

Tube amplifiers can be more economical to build for a given output power. Vacuum tubes operate satisfactorily at surface temperatures as high as 150-200 °C, so they may be cooled by simply blowing sufficient ambient air past or through their relative large cooling surfaces. The very small cooling surfaces of power transistors should be held to 75-100 °C to avoid drastically shortening their life expectancy. Thus, assuming worst-case 50 °C ambient air temperature, the large cooling surface of a vacuum tube can be allowed to rise 100-150 °C above ambient, while the small surface of a transistor must not be allowed to rise more than about 50 °C.

Furthermore, RF power transistors are much less tolerant of electrical abuse than are most vacuum tubes. An overvoltage spike lasting only microseconds can — and is likely to — destroy RF power transistors. A comparable spike is unlikely to have any effect on a tube. So the important message is this: designing with RF power transistors demands caution to ensure that adequate thermal and electrical protection is provided.

Even if one ignores the challenge of the RF portions of a high-power solid state amplifier, there is the dc power supply to consider. A solid state amplifier capable of delivering 1 kW of RF output might require regulated (and transient-free) 50 V at more than 40 A. Developing that much current can be challenging. A vacuum tube amplifier at the same power level might require 2000 to 3000 V, unregulated, at less than 1 A.

At the kilowatt level, the vacuum tube is still a viable option for amateur constructors because of its cost-effectiveness and ease of equipment design. Because tube amplifiers and solid state amplifiers are quite different in many ways, we shall treat them in different sections of this chapter. Also, the author of the solid state section presents a slightly different perspective on the tube-vs-solid state discussion.

17.3 Vacuum Tube Basics

The term *vacuum tube* describes the physical construction of the devices, which are usually tubular and have a vacuum inside. The British call them electron valves which describes the operation of the devices, since they control the flow of electrons, like a water valve controls the flow of water.

17.3.1 Thermionic Emission

Metals are electrical conductors because the electrons in them readily move from one atom to the next under the influence of an electrical field. It is also possible to cause the electrons to be emitted into space if enough energy is added to them. Heat is one way of adding energy to metal atoms, and the resulting flow of electrons into space is called *thermionic emission*. As each electron leaves the metal surface, it is replaced by another provided there is an electrical connection from outside the tube to the heated metal.

In a vacuum tube, the emitted electrons hover around the surface of the metal unless acted upon by an electric field. If a positively charged conductor is placed nearby, the electrons are drawn through the vacuum and arrive at that conductor, thus providing a continuous flow of current through the vacuum tube.

17.3.2 Components of a Vacuum Tube

A basic vacuum tube contains at least two parts: a *cathode* and a *plate*. The electrons are emitted from the *cathode*. The cathode can be *directly heated* by passing a large dc current through it, or it can be located adjacent to a heating element (*indirectly heated*). Although ac currents can also be used to directly heat cathodes, if any of the ac voltage mixes with the signal, ac hum will be introduced into the output. If the ac heater supply voltage can be obtained from a center tapped transformer, and the center tap is connected to the signal ground, hum can be minimized.

The difficulty of producing thermionic emission varies with the metal used for the cathode, and is called the "work function" of that metal. An ideal cathode would be made of a metal with a low work function that can sustain high temperatures without melting. Pure tungsten was used in early tubes as it could be heated to a very high temperature. Later it was learned that a very thin layer of thorium greatly increased the emission. Oxides of metals with low work functions were also developed. In modern tubes, thoriated-tungsten is used for the higher power tubes and oxide-coated metals are commonly used at lower power levels.

Filament voltage is important to the proper operation of a tube. If too low, the emission will not be sufficient. If too high, the useful life of the tube will be greatly shortened. It is important to know which type of cathode is being used. Oxide-coated cathodes can be run at 5 to 10%. Tube manufacturers specify an allowable range of filament voltages for proper operation and maximum tube life — follow those recommendations. Tubes should never be operated with filament voltages above the allowable value. Reducing filament voltage below the specified range in hopes of extending tube life is definitely not recommended for tubes with oxide-coated cathodes. In addition, low filament voltage can cause distortion and spurious emissions for any type of tube. Tube failures from low filament emission in amateur service are rare. For more information, see the Reference section entry for T. Rauch, W8JI, on filament voltage management.

Every vacuum tube needs a receptor for the emitted electrons. After moving though the vacuum, the electrons are absorbed by the *plate*, also called the *anode*. This two-element tube — anode and cathode — is called a *diode*. The diode tube is similar to a semiconductor diode: it allows current to pass in only one direction. If the plate goes negative relative to the cathode, current cannot flow because electrons are not emitted from the plate. Years ago, in the days before semiconductors, tube diodes were used as rectifiers.

TRIODES

To amplify signals, a vacuum tube must also contain a control *grid*. This name comes from its physical construction. The grid is a mesh of wires located between the cathode and the plate. Electrons from the cathode pass between the grid wires on their way to the plate. The electrical field that is set up by the voltage on these wires affects the electron flow from cathode to plate. A negative grid voltage repels electrons, blocking their flow to the plate. A positive grid voltage enhances the flow of electrons to the plate. Vacuum tubes containing a cathode, a grid and a plate are called *triode* tubes (*tri* for three components). See **Figure 17.4**.

The input impedance of a vacuum tube amplifier is directly related to the grid current. Grid current varies with grid voltage, increasing as the voltage becomes more positive. When the grid voltage is negative, no grid current flows and the input impedance of a tube is nearly infinite. When the grid is driven positive, it draws current and thus presents a lower input impedance, and requires significant drive power. The load placed across the plate of the tube strongly affects its output power and efficiency. An important part of tube design involves determining the optimum load resistance. These parameters are plotted as *characteristic curves* and are used to aid the design process. **Figure 17.5** shows an example.

Since the elements within the vacuum tube are conductors that are separated by an insulating vacuum, the tube is very similar to a capacitor. The capacitance between the cathode and grid, between the grid and plate, and between the cathode and plate can be large enough to affect the operation of the amplifier at high frequencies. These capacitances, which are usually on the order of a few picofarads, can limit the frequency response of an amplifier and can also provide signal feedback paths that may lead to unwanted oscillation. Neutralizing circuits are sometimes used to prevent such oscillations. Techniques for neutralization are presented later in this chapter.

TETRODES

The grid-to-plate capacitance is the chief source of unwanted signal feedback. Therefore tubes were developed with a

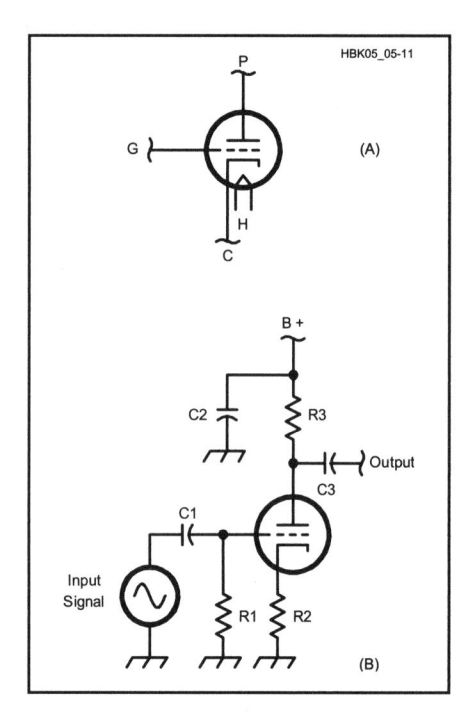

Figure 17.4 — Vacuum tube triode. (A) Schematic symbol detailing heater (H), cathode (C), grid (G) and plate (P). (B) Audio amplifier circuit using a triode. C1 and C3 are dc blocking capacitors for the input and output signals to isolate the grid and plate bias voltages. C2 is a bypass filter capacitor to decrease noise in the plate bias voltage, B+. R1 is the grid bias resistor, R2 is the cathode bias resistor and R3 is the plate bias resistor. Note that although the cathode and grid bias voltages are positive with respect to ground, they are still negative with respect to the plate.

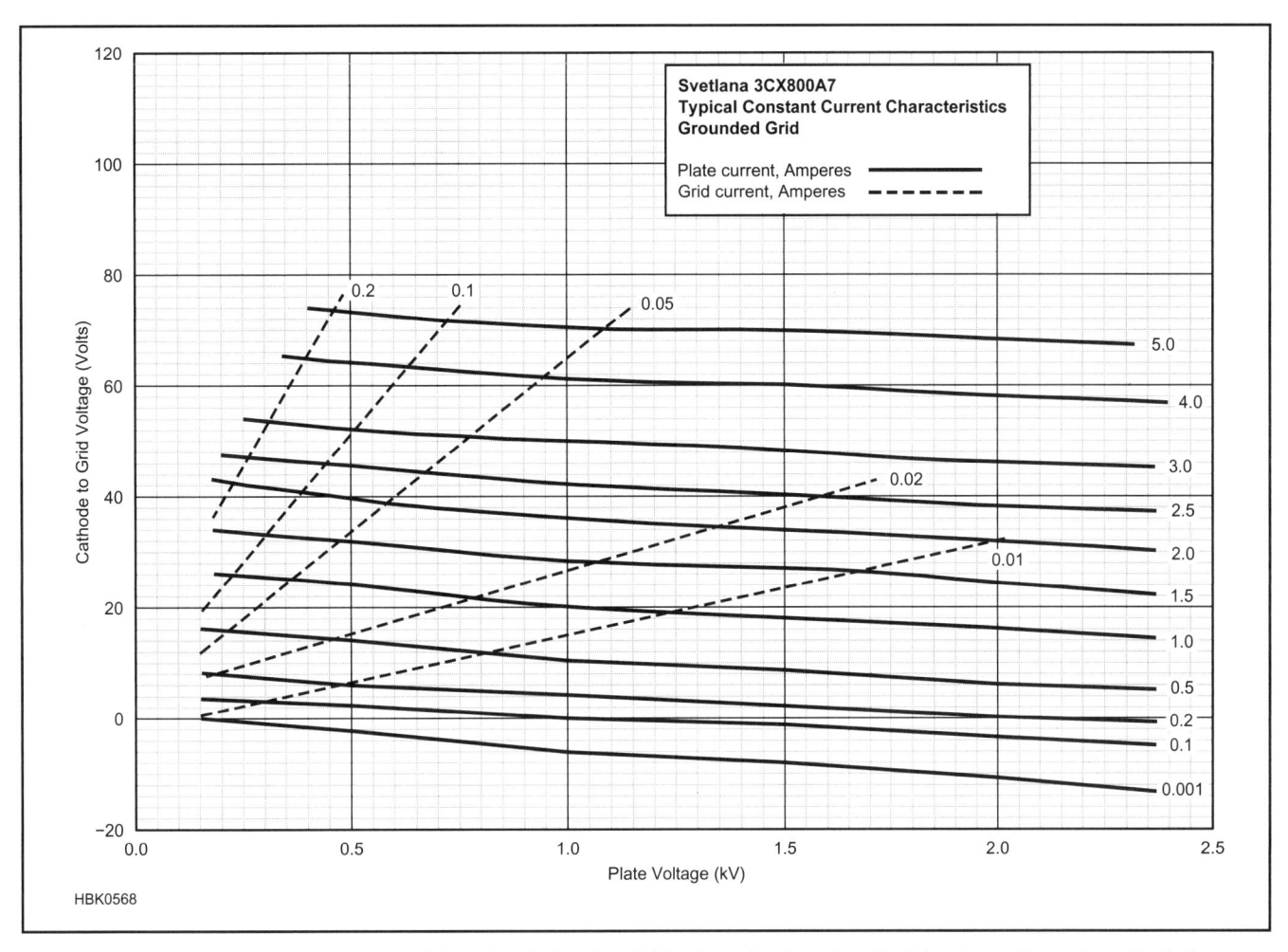

Figure 17.5 — Characteristic curves for a 3CX800A7 triode tube. Grid voltage is plotted on the left, plate voltage along the bottom. The solid lines are plate current, the dashed lines are grid current. This graph is typical of characteristic curves shown in this chapter and used with the *TubeCalculator* program described in the text and available with this book's downloadable supplemental content.

second grid, called a *screen grid*, inserted between the original grid (now called a *control grid*) and the plate. Such tubes are called tetrodes (having four elements). See **Figure 17.6**. This second grid is usually tied to RF ground and acts as a screen between the grid and the plate, thus preventing energy from feeding back, which could cause instability. Like the control grid, the screen grid is made of a wire mesh and electrons pass through the spaces between the wires to get to the plate.

The screen grid carries a high positive voltage with respect to the cathode, and its proximity to the control grid produces a strong electric field that enhances the attraction of electrons from the cathode. The gain of a tetrode increases sharply as the screen voltage is increased. The electrons accelerate toward the screen grid and most of them pass through the spaces and continue to accelerate until they reach the plate. In large tubes this is aided by careful alignment of the screen wires with the grid wires.

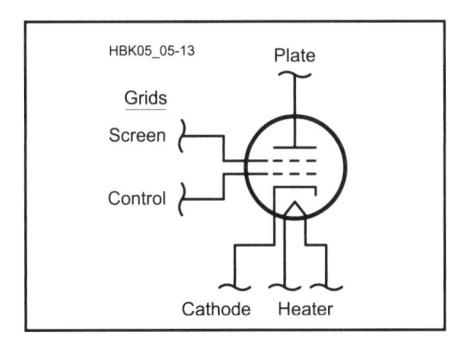

Figure 17.6 — Vacuum tube tetrode. Schematic symbol detailing heater (H), cathode (C), the two grids: control and screen, and the plate (P).

The effect of the screen can also be seen in the flattening of the tube curves. Since the screen shields the grid from the plate, the plate current vs plate voltages becomes almost flat, for a given screen and grid voltage. **Figure 17.7** shows characteristic curves for a typical tetrode, and curves for many more tube types are available with this book's downloadable supplemental content.

A special form of tetrode concentrates the electrons flowing between the cathode and the plate into a tight beam. The decreased electron-beam area increases the efficiency of the tube. *Beam tetrodes* permit higher plate currents with lower plate voltages and large power outputs with smaller grid driving power. The 6146 is an example of a beam power tube.

PENTODES

Another unwanted effect in vacuum tubes is the so-called *secondary emission*. The electrons flowing within the tube can have so much energy that they are capable of dislodging electrons from the metal atoms in the grids and plate. Secondary emission can cause a grid, especially the screen grid, to lose more electrons than it absorbs. Thus while a screen usually draws current from its supply, it occasionally pushes current into the supply. Screen supplies must be able to absorb as well as supply current.

RF Power Amplifiers 17.5

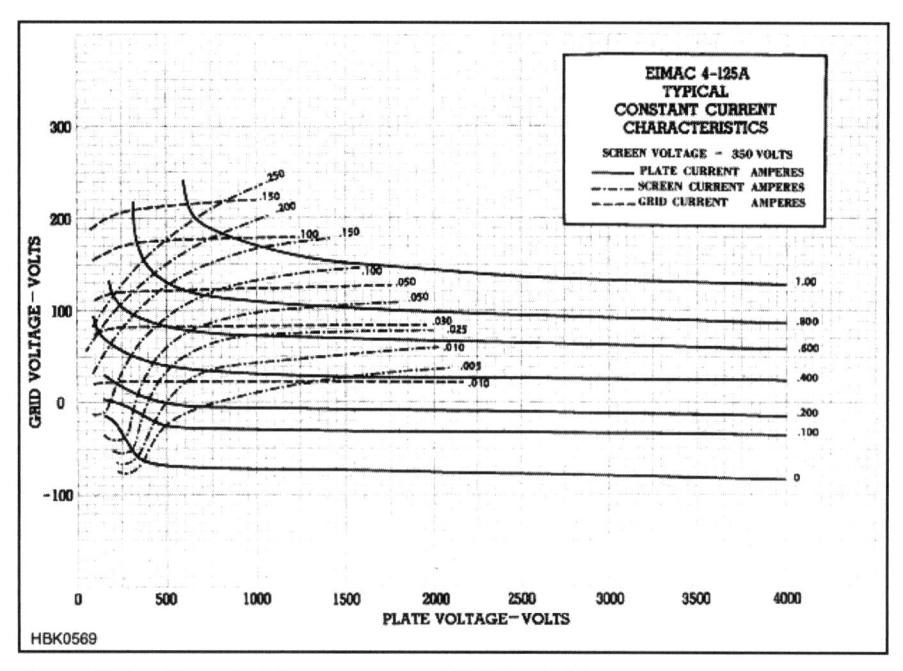

Figure 17.7 — Characteristic curves for a 4-125 tetrode tube.

A third grid, called the *suppressor grid*, can be added between the screen grid and the plate. This overcomes the effects of secondary emission in tetrodes. A vacuum tube with three grids is called a *pentode* (penta- for five elements). The suppressor grid is connected to a low voltage, often to the cathode.

17.3.3 Tube Nomenclature

Vacuum tubes are constructed with their elements (cathode, grid, plate) encased in an envelope to maintain the vacuum. Tubes with glass envelopes, such as the classic transmitting tube shown in **Figure 17.8**, are most familiar. Over time, manufacturers started exploring other, more rugged, methods for making high power transmitting tubes. Modern power tubes tend to be made of metal parts separated by ceramic insulating sections (**Figure 17.9**).

Because of their long history, vacuum tube types do not all follow a single logical system of identification. Many smaller tubes types begin with an indication of the filament voltage, such as the 6AU6 or 12AT7. Other tubes such as the 811 (Figure 17.8) and 6146 were assigned numbers in a more or less chronological order, much as transistors are today. Some glass envelope power tubes follow a numbering system that indicates number of tube elements and plate dissipation — 3-500Z and 4-1000A are two common examples in amateur circles.

Some power tubes follow the 3CX and 4CX numbering system. The first number indicates a triode (3) or tetrode (4) and the C indicates ceramic/metal construction. The X indicates cooling type: X for air, W for water and V for vapor cooling. The cooling type is followed by the plate dissipation. (The tubes that amateurs use typically have three or four numbers indicating plate dissipation; those used in commercial and broadcast service can have much higher numbers.) Thus a 4CX250 is a ceramic, air cooled 250 W tetrode. A 3CX1200 is a ceramic, air cooled, 1200 W triode. Often these tubes have additional characters following the plate dissipation to indicate special features or an upgraded design. For example, a 4CX250R is a special version of the 4CX250 designed for AB1 linear operation. A 4CX1500B is an updated version of the 4CX1500A.

During the heyday of tube technology, some tube types were developed with several tubes in the same glass envelope, such as the 12AX7 (a dual triode). Except for a very few devices used in the specialty audio market, tubes of this type are no longer made.

17.3.4 Tube Mounting and Cooling Methods

Most tubes mount in some kind of socket so that they can be easily replaced when they reach the end of their useful life. Connections to the tube elements are typically made through pins on the base. The pins are arranged or keyed so that the tube can be inserted into the socket only one way and are sized and spaced to handle the operating voltages and currents involved. Tubes generally use a standard base or socket, although a great many different bases developed over the years. Tube data sheets show pinouts for the various tube elements, just like data sheets for ICs and transistors. See the **Component Data and References** chapter for base diagrams of some popular transmitting tubes.

For transmitting tubes, a common arrangement is for filament and grid connections to be made through pins in the main base, while

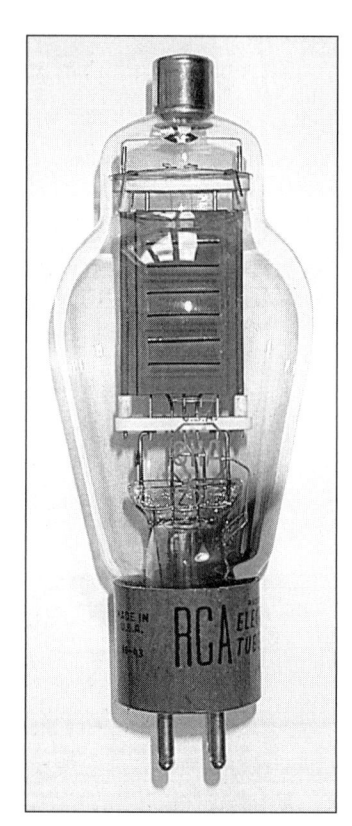

Figure 17.8 — The RCA 811A is an example of a transmitting triode with a glass envelope. [Photo courtesy the Virtual Valve Museum, www.tubecollector.org]

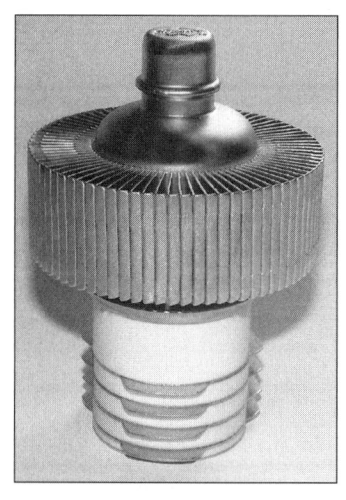

Figure 17.9 — Modern power tubes, such as this 4CX1000A tetrode, tend to use metal and ceramic construction.

the plate connection is made through a large pin or post at the top of the tube for easier connection to the high voltage supply and tank circuit. This construction is evident in the examples shown in Figures 17.8 and 17.9. To reduce stray reactances, in some older glass tubes the grid used a separate connection.

Heat dissipation from the plate is one of the major limiting factors for vacuum tube power amplifiers. Most early vacuum tubes were encased in glass, and heat passed through it as infrared radiation. If more cooling was needed, air was simply blown over the outside of the glass. Modern ceramic tubes suitable for powers up to 5 kW are usually cooled by forcing air directly through an external anode. These tubes require a special socket that allows free flow of air. The large external anode and cooling fins may be seen in the example in Figure 17.9. Conduction through an insulating block and water cooling are other options, though they are not often seen in amateur equipment. Practical amplifier cooling methods are discussed in detail later in this chapter.

17.3.5 Vacuum Tube Configurations

Just as the case with solid state devices described in the **Circuits and Components** chapter, any of the elements of the vacuum tube can be common to both input and output. A common plate connection — called a cathode follower and similar to the emitter follower — was once used to reduce output impedance (current gain) with little loss of voltage. This application is virtually obsolete.

Most modern tube applications use either the common cathode or the common grid connection. Figure 17.4B shows the common cathode connection, which gives both current and voltage gain. The common grid (often called *grounded grid*) connection shown in **Figure 17.10** gives only voltage gain. Thus the common cathode connection is capable of 20 to 30 dB of gain in a single stage, whereas the grounded grid connection typically gives 10 to 15 dB of gain.

The input impedance of a grounded grid stage is low, typically less than a few hundred ohms. The input impedance of a grounded cathode stage is much higher.

17.3.6 Classes of Operation in Tube Amplifiers

Class of operation was discussed briefly in the previous section describing the need for linear operation of RF power amplifiers for most Amateur Radio modes except FM. The class of operation of an amplifier stage is defined by its conduction angle, the angular portion of each RF drive cycle, in degrees, during which plate current flows. The conduction angle is determined by the bias on the device, and to a lesser extent on the drive level. These, in turn, determine the amplifier's efficiency, linearity and operating impedances. Refer to **Figure 17.11** for the following discussion.

Class A is defined as operation where plate current is always flowing. For a sine wave this means during 360° of the wave. Class A has the best linearity, but poor efficiency.

Class B is when the bias is set so that the tube is cut off for negative input signals, but current flows when the input signal is positive. Thus for a sine wave, conduction occurs during 1/2 of the cycle, or 180°. Class B is linear only when two devices operate in push-pull, so as to provide the missing half of the wave, or when a tuned circuit is present to restore the missing half by "flywheel" action (discussed later in this chapter).

Class AB is defined as operation that falls between Class A and Class B. For a sine wave, the conduction angle will be more than 180°, but less than 360°. In practice Class AB amplifiers usually fall within the gray area shown in the center area of the graph. Like Class B, a push pull connection or a tuned circuit are needed for linear operation. Class AB is less efficient that class B, but better than Class A. The linearity is better than class B but worse than class A.

Class AB vacuum tube amplifiers are further defined as class AB1 or AB2. In class AB1, the grid is not driven positive, so no grid current flows. Virtually no drive power is required. In Class AB2, the grid is driven positive at times with respect to the cathode and some grid current flows. Drive power and output both increase as compared to AB1. Most linear amplifiers used in the Amateur service operate Class AB2, although for greater linearity some operate Class AB1 or even Class A.

Class C is when conduction angle is less than 180° — typically 120° to 160° for vacuum

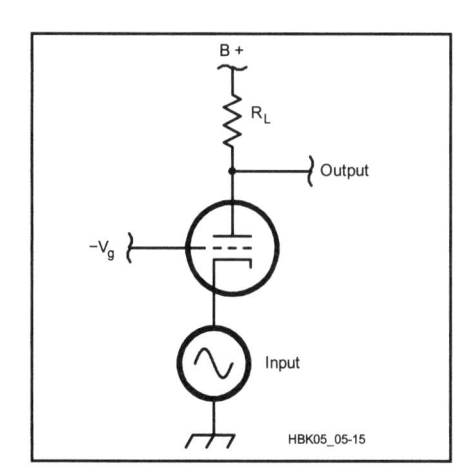

Figure 17.10 — Grounded grid amplifier schematic. The input signal is connected to the cathode, the grid is biased to the appropriate operating point by a dc bias voltage, $-V_G$, and the output voltage is obtained by the voltage drop through R_L that is developed by the plate current, I_P.

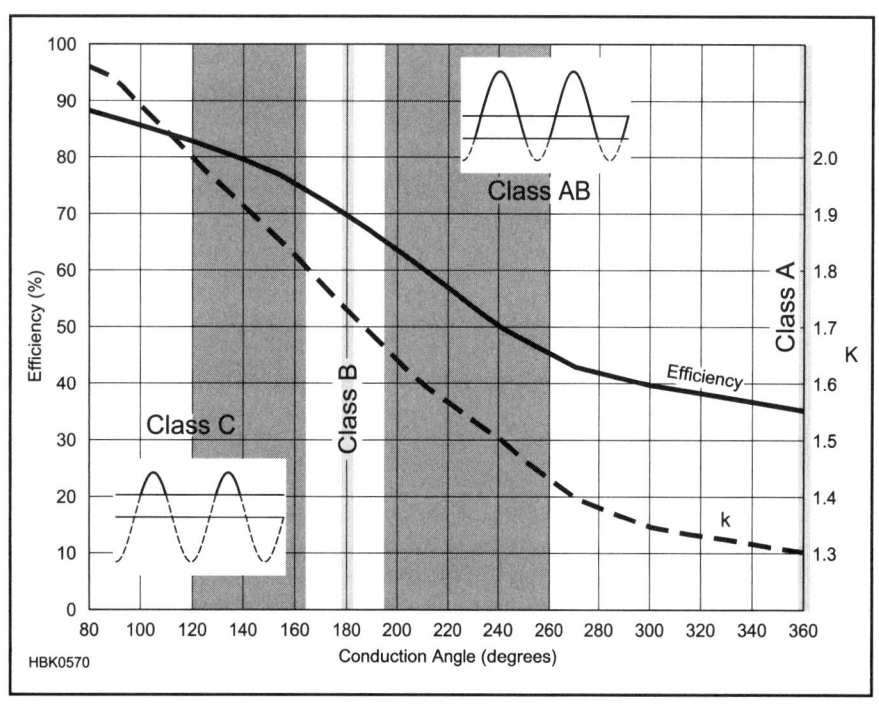

Figure 17.11 — Efficiency and K for various classes of operation. Read the solid line to determine efficiency. Read the dashed line for K, which is a constant used to calculate the plate load required, as explained in the text.

> ## The Flywheel Effect
>
> The operation of a resonant tank circuit (see the **Oscillators and Synthesizers** chapter for a discussion of resonant LC circuits) is sometimes referred to as the "flywheel" effect. A flywheel does illustrate certain functions of a resonant tank, but a flywheel alone is non-resonant; that is, it has no preferred frequency of operation.
>
> A better analogy for a resonant tank — although not exact — is found in the balance wheel used in mechanical watches and clocks in which a weighted wheel rotates back and forth, being returned to its center position by a spiral spring, sometimes called a hairspring. The balance wheel stores energy as inertia and is analogous to an inductor. The hairspring also stores energy and is similar in operation to a capacitor. The spring has an adjustment for the frequency of operation or resonance (1 Hz). An escapement mechanism gives the wheel a small kick with each tick of the watch to keep it going.
>
> A plot of the rotational (or radial) velocity of the balance wheel will give a sine function. It thus converts the pulses from the escapement into smooth sinusoidal motion. In a similar way, pulses of current in the plate of a tube are smoothed into a sine wave in the tank circuit.
>
> The plate (or collector or drain) voltage is a sine wave, even though the plate current is made up of pulses. Just as the escarpment mechanism must apply its kicks at just the right time, the frequency at which current pulses are added to the tank must match the natural resonant frequency of the tank, which is adjusted with the "plate tune" capacitor.
>
> Efficient operation of the tank itself occurs when the losses are small compared to the energy transferred to the output. In a similar manner, lowering the losses in a balance wheel by using jeweled bearings makes the watch more efficient. The amount of energy stored in the balance wheel should also be kept as low as practical since excess "oscillation" of the wheel wastes energy to the air and bearings. Likewise, the "circulating currents" in the tank must be limited to reduce heating from the inevitable losses in the components.
>
> **Figure 17.A1** — A balance wheel and hairspring in a mechanical clock illustrate the flywheel effect in tank circuits.

tube amplifiers or within the gray area to the left in Figure 17.11. The tube is biased well beyond cutoff when no drive signal is applied. Output current flows only during positive crests in the drive cycle, so it con-sists of relatively narrow pulses at the drive frequency. Efficiency is high, but nonlinear operation results. Class C amplifiers always use tuned circuits at the input and output. Attempts to achieve extreme efficiency with very narrow pulses (small conduction angles) require very high drive power, so a point of diminishing returns is eventually reached.

Classes D through H use various switched mode techniques. These are used almost exclusively with solid state circuits.

17.3.7 Understanding Tube Operation

Vacuum tubes have complex current transfer characteristics, and each class of operation produces different RMS values of RF current through the load impedance. As described earlier, tube manufacturers provide characteristic curves that show how the tube behaves as operating parameters (such as plate and grid voltage and current) vary. See Figures 17.5 and 17.7 for examples of characteristic curves for two different transmitting tubes. The use of tube curves provides the best way to gain insight into the characteristics of a given tube. Before designing with a tube, get a set of these curves and study them thoroughly.

Because of the complexity and interaction among the various parameters, computer-aided design (CAD) software is useful in analyzing tube operation. One such program, *TubeCalculator*, is available with this book's downloadable supplemental content, along with curves for many popular transmitting tubes. This software makes it easier to do analysis of a given operation with the tube you have chosen. **Figure 17.12** shows a *TubeCalculator* screen with an example of "constant current" curves for a typical tube used in high power amplifiers and tables showing values for the various operating parameters. The curves shown have grid voltage on the vertical axis and plate voltage on the horizontal axis. Older tubes and some newer ones use a slightly different format in which plate voltage is plotted on the horizontal axis and plate current on the vertical. *TubeCalculator* allows analysis using either type.

The tube is the heart of any amplifier. Using the software to arrive at the desired operating parameters is a major step toward understanding and designing an amplifier. The second most important part of the design is the tuning components. Before they can be designed, the required plate load resistance must be determined and *TubeCalculator* will do that. In addition it will give insight into what happens when a tube is under driven or over driven, when the bias is wrong, or when the load resistance incorrect.

If a tube is to be used other than with nominal voltages and currents, analysis using the tube curves is the only solution short of trial and error. Trial and error is not a good idea because of the high voltages and currents found in high power amplifiers. It's best to conduct your analysis using curves and software, or else stick to operating the tube very close to the voltages, currents, drive levels and load values specified by the manufacturer.

ANALYZING OPERATING PARAMETERS

Characteristic curves allow a detailed look at tube operation as voltages and currents vary. For example, you can quickly see how much negative grid voltage is required to set the plate current to any desired value, depending also on the plate voltage and screen voltages. You can also see how much grid voltage is needed to drive the plate current to the maximum desired value.

With RF power amplifiers, both the grid voltage and the plate voltage will be sinusoidal and will be 180° out of phase. With constant current curves, an operating line can be drawn that will trace out every point of the operating cycle. This will be a straight line connecting two points. One point will be at the intersection of the peak plate voltage and the peak negative grid voltage. The other point will be at the intersection of the peak positive grid voltage and the minimum plate voltage.

If we plot the plate current along this line as a function of time, it will be seen that it changes in a nonlinear fashion; the exact shape of which depends on the class of operation. For class AB2 operation, which is the most commonly used in linear RF power amplifiers, it will look something like the

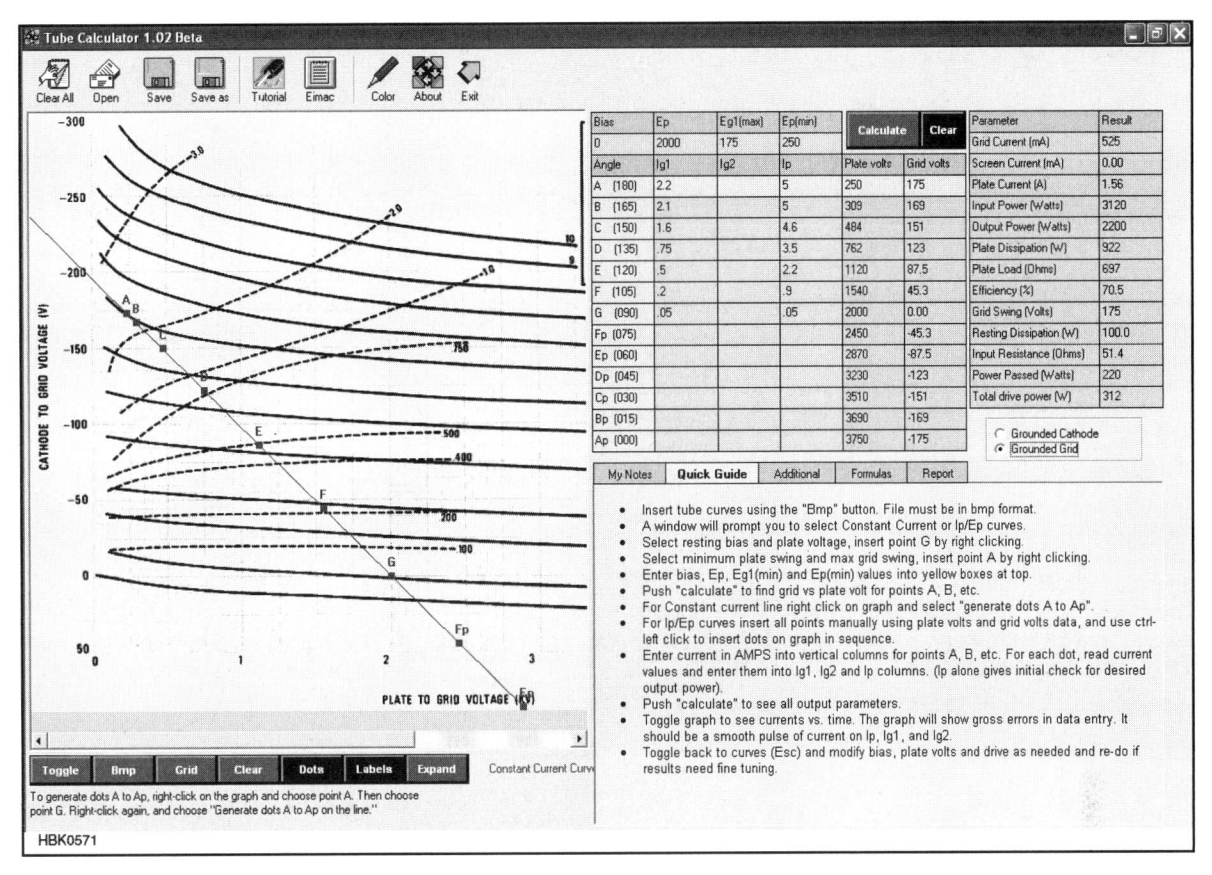

Figure 17.12 — Main screen of *TubeCalculator* program (available with this book's downloadable supplemental content). A characteristic curve plot is loaded in the window on the left side of the screen.

plot shown in **Figure 17.13**. This rather complicated waveform is not easily evaluated using simple formulas, but it can be analyzed by taking the current values vs time and applying averaging techniques. This method was developed by Chaffee in 1936 and popularized by Eimac, the company that developed many of the power tubes used today.

With *TubeCalculator*, data can be extracted from the curves and can be converted into many useful operating parameters such as input power, output power, grid power required, grid and plate dissipation and required load resistance.

MANUAL METHODS FOR TUBE PARAMETER SELECTION

For those not wishing to use a computer for design, most tube manufacturers will supply a table of typical operating values. A summary of some of this information is available in the **Component Data and References** chapter. These values have already been determined both from the tube characteristics and actual operational tests. As long as your proposed operation is close to the typical values in terms of voltages and currents, the typical values can provide you the desired load resistance and expected output power and efficiency. The typical operating parameters may also include a suggested optimum load resistance. If not, we can use well established "rules of thumb."

The optimum load resistance for vacuum-tube amplifiers can be approximated by the ratio of the dc plate voltage to the dc plate current at maximum signal, divided by a constant appropriate to each class of operation. The load resistance, in turn, determines the maximum power output and efficiency the amplifier can provide. The approximate value for tube load resistance is

$$R_L = \frac{V_p}{K \times I_p} \qquad (1)$$

where

R_L = the appropriate load resistance, in ohms
V_P = the dc plate potential, in V
I_P = the dc plate current, in A
K = a constant that approximates the RMS current to dc current ratio appropriate for each class. For the different classes of operation: Class A, K ≈ 1.3; Class AB, K ≈ 1.5-1.7; Class B, K ≈ 1.57-1.8; Class C, K ≈ 2. The way in which K varies for different conduction angles is shown in Figure 17.11 (right scale).

Once we determine the optimum load resistance value for the tube(s) to be used we are ready to design the output networks for the amplifier. After tube selection, this is the most important part of the total design.

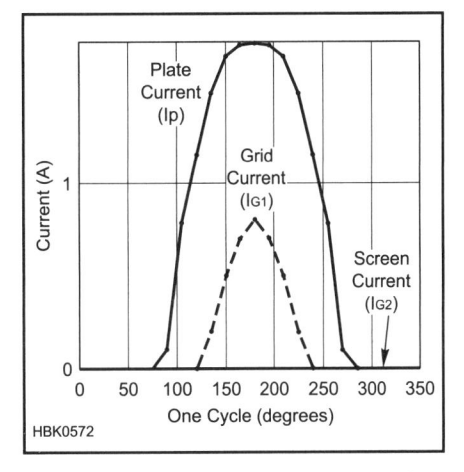

Figure 17.13 — Class AB2 plate and grid current over one cycle as plotted by the *TubeCalculator* program. This plot is for a triode, so there is no curve for screen (G2) current.

RF Power Amplifiers 17.9

17.4 Tank Circuits

Usually we want to drive a transmission line, typically 50 Ω, with the output of our amplifier. An output network is used to transform that 50 Ω impedance to the optimum load resistance for the tube. This transformation is accomplished by resonant output networks which also serve to reduce harmonics to a suitable level. The **Radio Fundamentals** chapter of this *Handbook* gives a detailed analysis of the operation of resonant circuits. We summarize here only the most important points.

Resonant circuits have the ability to store energy. Capacitors store electrical energy in the electric field between their plates; inductors store energy in the magnetic field induced by the coil winding. These circuits are referred to as *tank circuits* since they act as storage "tanks" for RF energy. This energy is continuously passed back and forth between the inductive storage and the capacitive storage. It can be shown mathematically that the "alternating" current and voltage produced by this process are sinusoidal in waveform with a frequency of

$$f = \frac{1}{2\pi\sqrt{LC}} \quad (2)$$

which, of course, is the resonant frequency of the tank circuit.

17.4.1 Tank Circuit Q

In order to quantify the ability of a tank circuit to store energy, a quality factor, Q, is defined. Q is the ratio of energy stored in a system during one complete RF cycle to energy lost.

$$Q = 2\pi \frac{W_S}{W_L} \quad (3)$$

where
W_S = is the energy stored
W_L = the energy lost to heat and the load

A load connected to a tank circuit has exactly the same effect on tank operation as circuit losses. Both consume energy. It just happens that energy consumed by circuit losses becomes heat rather than useful output. When energy is coupled out of the tank circuit into a load, the loaded Q (Q_L) is:

$$Q_L = \frac{X}{R_{Loss} + R_{Load}} \quad (4)$$

where R_{Load} is the load resistance. Energy dissipated in R_{Loss} is wasted as heat. And X represents the reactance of the inductor or the capacitor, assumed to be equal at resonance. Ideally, all the tank circuit energy should be delivered to R_{Load}. This implies that R_{Loss} should be as small as possible.

17.4.2 Tank Circuit Efficiency

The efficiency of a tank circuit is the ratio of power delivered to the load resistance (R_{Load}) to the total power dissipated by losses (R_{Load} and R_{Loss}) in the tank circuit. Within the tank circuit, R_{Load} and R_{Loss} are effectively in series and the circulating current flows through both. The power dissipated by each is proportional to its resistance. The loaded tank efficiency can, therefore, be defined as

$$\text{Tank Efficiency} = \frac{R_{Load}}{R_{Load} + R_{Loss}} \times 100 \quad (5)$$

where efficiency is stated as a percentage. The loaded tank efficiency can also be expressed as

$$\text{Tank Efficiency} = \left(1 - \frac{Q_L}{Q_U}\right) \times 100 \quad (6)$$

where
Q_L = the tank circuit loaded Q, and
Q_U = the unloaded Q of the tank circuit.

For practical circuits, Q_U is very nearly the Q of the coil with switches, capacitors and parasitic suppressors making a smaller contribution. It follows, then, that tank efficiency can be maximized by keeping Q_L low which keeps the circulating current low and the I^2R losses down. Q_U should be maximized for best efficiency; this means keeping the circuit losses low. With a typical Q_L of 10, about 10% of the stored energy is transferred to the load in each cycle. This energy is replaced by energy supplied by the tube. It is interesting to contemplate that in a typical amplifier which uses a Q_L of 10 and passes 1.5 kW from the tube to the output, the plate tank is storing about 15 kW of RF energy. This is why component selection is very important, not only for low loss, but to resist the high voltages and currents.

Resonant circuits are always used in the plate circuit. When the grid is used as the input (common cathode), both matching and a tuned circuit may be used or else a low impedance load is connected from grid to ground with a broad matching transformer or network. The "loaded grid" reduces gain, but improves stability. In grounded grid operation, a tuned circuit may not be needed in the cathode circuit, as the input Z may be close to 50 Ω, but a tuned network may improve the match and usually improves the linearity. These resonant circuits help to ensure that the voltages on grid and plate are sine waves. This wave-shaping effect is the same thing as harmonic rejection. The reinforcing of the fundamental frequency and rejection of the harmonics is a form of filtering or selectivity.

The amount of harmonic suppression is dependent upon circuit loaded Q_L, so a dilemma exists for the amplifier designer. A low Q_L is desirable for best tank efficiency, but yields poorer harmonic suppression. High Q_L keeps amplifier harmonic levels lower at the expense of some tank efficiency. At HF, a compromise value of Q_L can usually be chosen such that tank efficiency remains high and harmonic suppression is also reasonable. At higher frequencies, tank Q_L is not always readily controllable, due to unavoidable stray reactances in the circuit. Unloaded Q_U can always be maximized, however, regardless of frequency, by keeping circuit losses low.

17.4.3 Tank Output Circuits

THE PI NETWORK

The pi network with the capacitors to ground and the inductor in series is commonly used for tube type amplifier matching. This acts like a low pass filter, which is helpful for

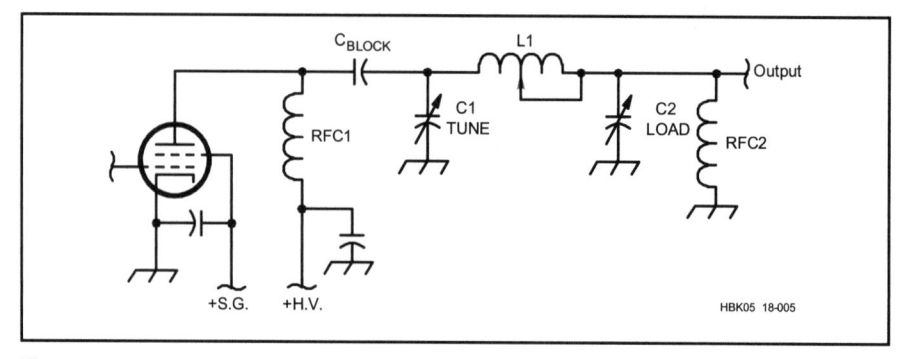

Figure 17.14 — A pi matching network used at the output of a tetrode power amplifier. RFC2 is used for protective purposes in the event C_{BLOCK} fails.

Figure 17.15 — *PI-EL Design* software, available with this book's downloadable supplemental content, may be used to design pi and pi-L networks. A pi network is shown at top right and a pi-L network at

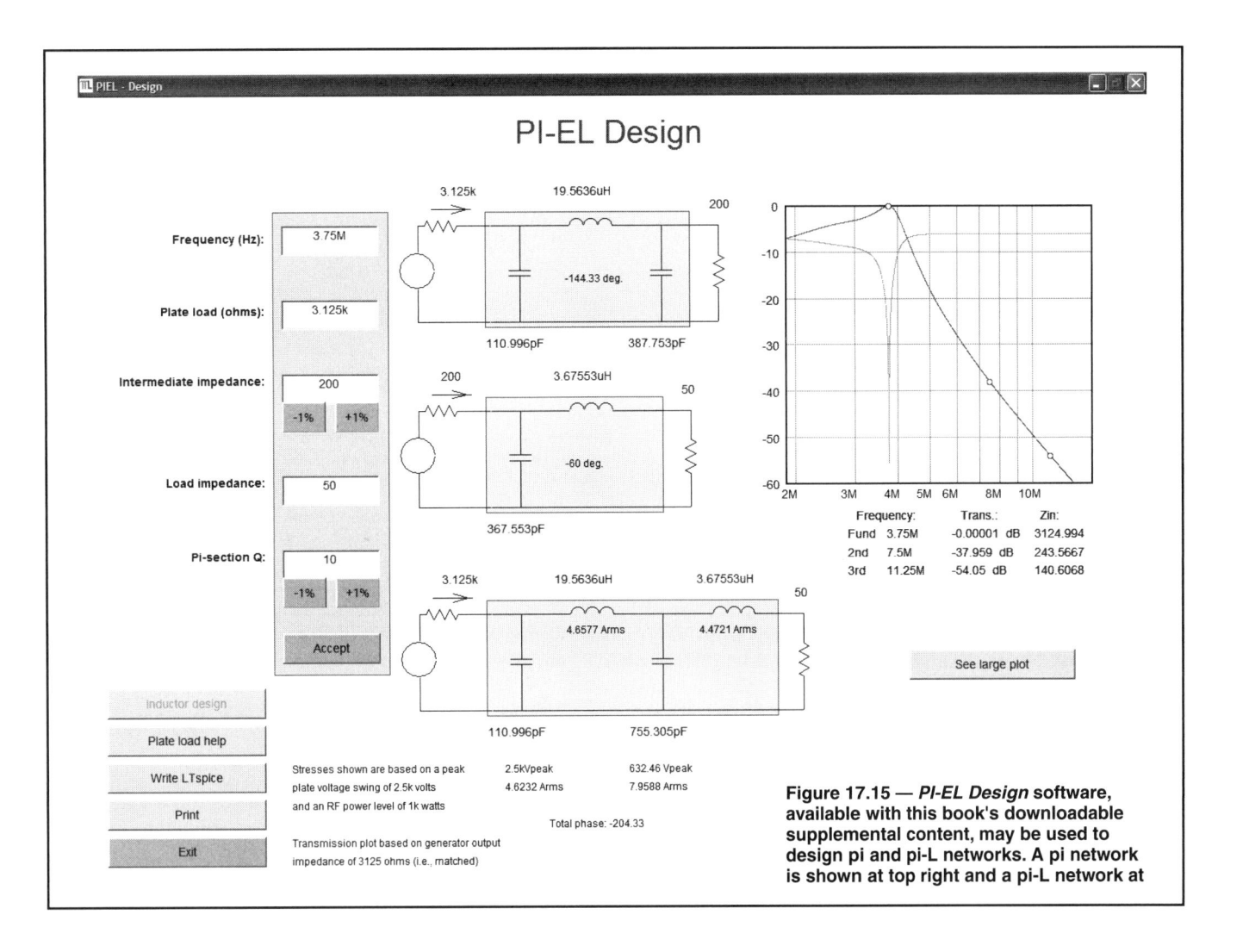

getting rid of harmonics. Harmonic suppression of a pi network is a function of the impedance transformation ratio and the Q_L of the circuit. Second-harmonic attenuation is approximately 35 dB for a load impedance of 2000 Ω in a pi network with a Q_L of 10. In addition to the low pass effect of the pi network, at the tube plate the third harmonic is already typically 10 dB lower and the fourth approximately 7 dB below that. A typical pi network as used in the output circuit of a tube amplifier is shown in **Figure 17.14**. The **Analog and Digital Filtering** chapter describes harmonic filters that can also greatly reduce harmonics. These are typically not switched but left in the circuit at all times. With such a filter, the requirements for reducing the harmonics on the higher bands with the amplifier pi network is greatly reduced.

The formulas for calculating the component values for a pi network, for those who wish to use them, are included with this book's downloadable supplemental content, along with tabular data for finished designs. The input variables are desired plate load resistance, output impedance to be matched (usually 50 Ω), the desired loaded Q (typically 10 or 12) and the frequency. With these inputs one can calculate the values of the components C1, L1 and C2. These components are usually referred to as the plate tune capacitor, the tank inductor and the loading capacitor. In a multi-frequency amplifier, the coil inductance is changed with a band switch

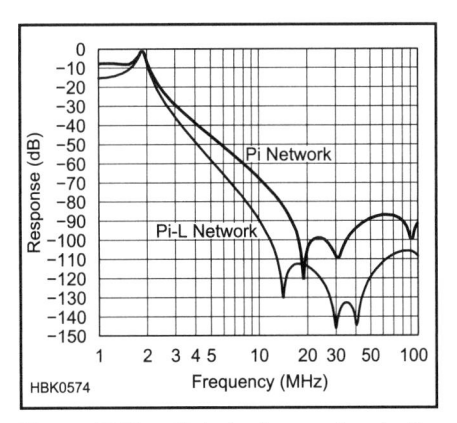

Figure 17.16 — Relative harmonic rejection of pi and pi-L circuits

and the capacitors are adjusted to the correct value for the band in question.

Tank circuit component values are most easily found using computer software. The program *PI-EL Design* by Jim Tonne, W4ENE, is available with this book's downloadable supplemental content and is illustrated here. With this software, all of the components for a pi or pi-L network (described in the next section) can be quickly calculated. Since there are so many possible variables, especially with a pi-L network, it is impractical to publish graphical or tabular data to cover all cases. Therefore, the use of this software is highly recommended for those designing output networks. The software allows many "what-if" possibilities to be quickly checked and an optimum design found.

THE PI-L NETWORK

There are some advantages in using an additional inductor in the output network, effectively changing it from a pi network to a pi-L network as shown in the bottom right corner of **Figure 17.15**. The harmonic rejection is increased, as shown in **Figure 17.16**,

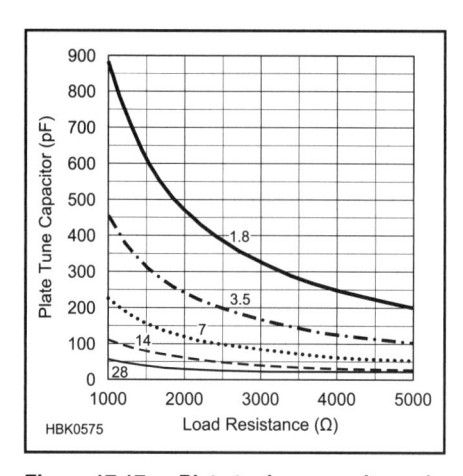

Figure 17.17 — Plate tuning capacitor values for various bands and values of load resistance. Figures 17.17 through 17.19 may be used for manual design of a tank circuit, as explained in the text.

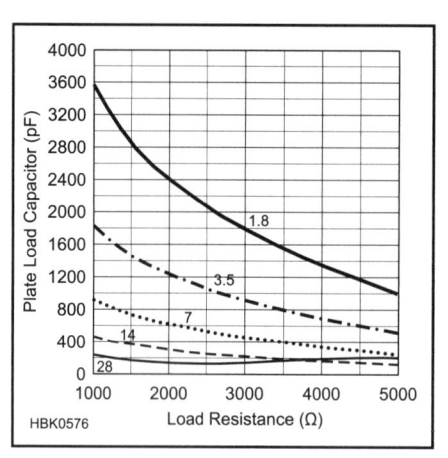

Figure 17.18 — Plate loading capacitor values for various bands and values of load resistance.

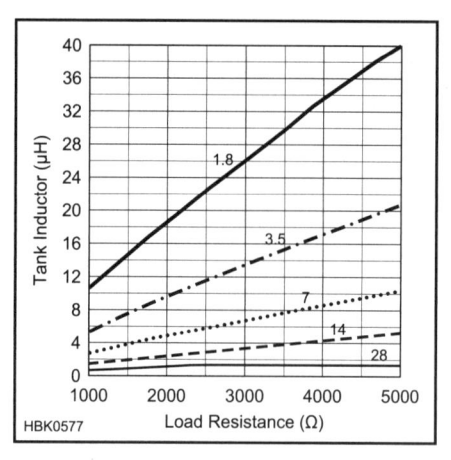

Figure 17.19 — Tank inductor values for various bands and values of load resistance.

and the component values may become more convenient. Alternatively, the Q can be reduced to lower losses while retaining the same harmonic rejection as the simple pi. This can reduce maximum required tuning capacitance to more easily achievable values.

With a pi-L design, there are many more options than with the simple pi network. This is because the intermediate impedance can take on any value we wish to assign between the output impedance (usually 50 Ω) and the desired plate resistance. This intermediate impedance need not be the same for each frequency, providing the possibility of further optimizing the design. For that reason, it is especially desirable that the software be used instead of using the chart values when a pi-L is contemplated. Using this software, one can quickly determine component values for the required load resistance and Q values for any frequency as well as plotting the harmonic rejection values. Even the voltage and current ratings of the components are calculated.

Further analysis can be done using various versions of *SPICE*. A popular *SPICE* version is *LTspice* available from Linear Technologies and downloadable for free on their website, www.linear.com. The *PI-EL Design* software mentioned above generates files for *LTspice* automatically. *PI-EL Design* assumes that the blocking capacitor has negligible reactance and the RF choke has infinite reactance. There are times when these assumptions may not be valid. The effect of these components and changes to compensate for them can easily be evaluated using *LTspice*. It can also evaluate the effects of parasitic and stray effects, which all components have. The deep nulls in the response curves in Figure 17.16 are caused by the stray capacitance in the inductors. These can be used to advantage but, if not understood, can also lead to unexpected results. See the **RF Techniques** chapter for more information.

MANUAL METHODS FOR TANK DESIGN

For those who wish to try designing a pi network without a computer, pi designs in chart form are provided. These charts (**Figure 17.17** to **Figure 17.19**) give typical values for the pi network components for various bands and desired plate load resistance. For each value of load resistance the component values can be read for each band. For bands not shown, an approximate value can be reached by interpolation between the bands shown. It's not necessary to be able to read these values to high precision. In practice, unaccounted-for stray capacitance and inductance will likely make the calculated values only an approximate starting point. For those desiring greater precision, this data is available in tabular form with this book's downloadable supplemental content along with the formulas for calculating them.

Several things become obvious from these charts. The required capacitance is reduced and the required inductance increased when a higher load resistance is used. This means that an amplifier with higher plate voltage and lower plate current will require smaller capacitor values and larger inductors. The capacitors will, of course, also have to withstand higher voltages, so their physical size may or may not be any smaller. The inductors will have less current in them so a smaller size wire may be used. It will be obvious that for an amplifier covering many bands, the most challenging parts of the design are at the frequency extremes. The 1.8 MHz band

Table 17.1
Pi-L Values for 1.8 MHz

Plate Load Resistance (Ω)	Plate Tune Capacitor (pF)	Plate Inductor (µH)	Plate Load Capacitor (pF)	Output Inductor (µH)	Intermediate Resistance (Ω)	Loaded Q (Q_L)	Harmonic Attenuation (3rd/5th, dB)
1000	883	10.5	3550	None (pi)	None (pi)	12	30/42
1000	740	15	2370	7.7	200	12	38/54
1000	499	21.5	1810	7.7	200	8	35/51
2200	376	26.4	1938	7.7	200	12	39/55
2200	255	37.7	1498	7.7	200	8	36/52
5000	180	50.4	1558	7.7	200	12	39/55
5000	124	71	1210	7.7	200	8	36/53
5000	114	83	928	11.7	400	8	39/55

Designing to Avoid Interactive Tune and Load Adjustments

It can be annoying when tuning a tube amplifier if adjusting the loading control requires that we also re-dip the plate current. This happens when the loading capacitor changes the reactance seen by the final tube, rather than just the resistive part of its load. Setting the output power to a chosen value may require numerous readjustments of both controls.

The plate tuning capacitor is directly across the load seen by the tube, hence it only tunes for resonance. The loading capacitor is seen by the tube through the pi network and the network's phase shift will determine how the plate load impedance changes when the loading control is adjusted. For the loading capacitor to change only the resistive part of the tube load, choose a phase shift value for the pi network that is an odd multiple of 45°. Since a pi network with 45° phase shift will have very low Q, the best choice is a network with 135° phase shift.

The Smith chart in **Figure 17.A2** illustrates this effect. The solid line with dots shows the effect of adjusting the plate tuning capacitor. When close to resonance, it does not change the resistive part of the load seen by the tube, but does tune out the reactive part as shown by the fact that it crosses the horizontal resistance axis at a right angle. When the load is purely resistive at resonance, we get a dip in the plate current.

The thick dashed curve shows what happens when we adjust the loading capacitor with a 135° pi network. The resistive part of the tube load changes as shown by the curve moving along the horizontal axis, but the resonance is largely unaffected. The thin dashed line shows an example of what happens when we change the load capacitor with a network with a phase shift that is not 135°. Both the resistive part and the reactive part of the tube load change, making it necessary to retune the plate capacitor to resonance.

The phase shift of a pi network is determined by the Q of the network and the impedance transformation ratio. The value of Q that will give us the "magic" 135° phase shift will thus depend on the plate load to output impedance ratio. For a 50 Ω load at the output of the pi network, the desired Q value can be determined from the upper curve of **Figure 17.A3**. Putting this value of Q into the pi-L design program will generate the pi network component values desired. For example, for 2500 Ω plate load we see that the desired Q of the tank will be 12.4, a reasonable Q to choose that is close to the commonly used value of 10. Thus, with a slight adjustment of the design Q we can get to a "non interactive loading control" design.

As we can see on the upper curve of Figure 17.A3, with very high or low plate load values, the excursion from the normally used Q value of 10 may be excessive and a fully non-interactive tuning solution not practical with the simple pi network. For a plate load of 4000 Ω we see that a Q of 16.4 would be required. This is somewhat high and would lead to excessive losses in the tank. An alternate approach would be to use the pi-L network, and allow the intermediate value to be 100 Ω. The lower curve shows this allows the pi-L network to be designed using a Q value of 11.2, which is more acceptable.

A further discussion of this method, with formulas, a spreadsheet calculator, and more Smith chart graphics illustrating how it works is available with this book's downloadable supplemental content.

Figure 17.A2 — Effect of plate and load capacitors for various phase shift values through the pi network.

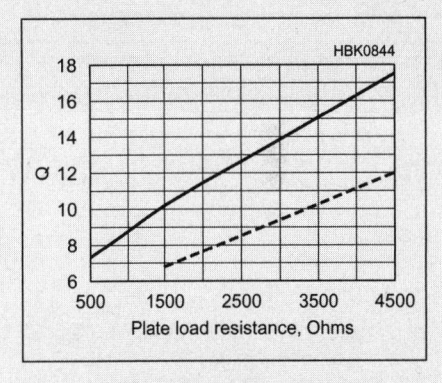

Figure 17.A3 — Pi network Q versus plate load resistance for non-interactive tuning. Use the upper curve for a 50 Ω simple pi network and the lower curve for a pi-L network with a 100 Ω intermediate resistance valu

---

requires the most inductance and capacitance and the 28 MHz band requires the least. Often, the output capacitance of the tube plus the minimum value of the plate capacitor along with assorted stray capacitance will put a lower limit on the effective plate capacitance that can be achieved. These charts assume that value to be 25 pF and the other components are adjusted to account for that minimum value. An inevitable trade-off here is that the Q of the tank will be higher than optimum on the highest bands.

When tuning to the lower frequency bands, the maximum value of the capacitor, especially the loading capacitor, will be a limiting factor. Sometimes, fixed mica or ceramic transmitting rated capacitors will be switched in parallel with the variable capacitor to reach the total value required.

COMPONENT SELECTION FOR THE PI-L NETWORK

For those wishing to use manual methods to design a pi-L network, there are look-up tables with this book's downloadable supplemental content along with the mathematical formulas from which they are derived. **Table 17.1** is an abbreviated version that shows the general trends. Values shown are for 1.8 MHz. Other bands can be approximated by dividing all component values by the frequency ratio. For example, for 18 MHz, divide all component values by 10. For 3.6 MHz, divide values by two, and so on.

For a given Q_L, the pi-L circuit has better harmonic rejection than the pi circuit. This allows the designer to use a lower Q_L, resulting in lower losses and lower capacitor values, which is an advantage on the lower frequencies. However, the inductor values will be higher, and the lower capacitor values may be unachievable at higher frequencies. With the pi-L circuit there are many more variables to work with and, thus, one can try many different possibilities to make the circuit work within the limits of the components that are available.

PROBLEMS AT VHF AND HIGHER FREQUENCIES

As the size of a circuit approaches about 5% of a wavelength, components begin to seriously depart from the pure inductance or capacitance we assume them to be. Inductors begin to act like transmission lines. Capacitors often exhibit values far different from their marked values because of stray internal reactances and lead inductance. Therefore, tuned circuits are frequently fabricated in the form of striplines or other transmission lines in order to circumvent the problem of building "pure" inductances and capacitances. The choice of components is often more significant than the type of network used.

The high impedances encountered in VHF tube-amplifier plate circuits are not easily matched with typical networks. Tube output capacitance is usually so large that most matching networks are unsuitable. The usual practice is to resonate the tube output capacitance with a low-loss inductance connected in series or parallel. The result can be a very high-Q tank circuit. Component losses must be kept to an absolute minimum in order to achieve reasonable tank efficiency. Output impedance transformation is usually performed by a link inductively coupled to the tank circuit or by a parallel transformation of the output resistance using a series capacitor.

Since high values of plate load impedance call for low values of plate tuning capacitance, one might be tempted to add additional tubes in parallel to reduce the required load impedance. This only adds to the stray plate capacitance, and the potential for parasitic oscillations is increased. For these reasons, tubes in parallel are seldom used at VHF. Push-pull circuits offer some advantages, but with modern compact ceramic tube types, most VHF amplifiers use a single tube along with distributed type tuned networks. Other approaches are discussed later in this chapter.

"COLD TUNING" AN AMPLIFIER

Because of the high voltage and current involved, as well as the danger of damaging an expensive tube or other component, it is prudent to "cold tune" an amplifier before applying power to it. This can actually be done early in the construction as soon as tank components and the tube are in place. Cold tuning requires some test equipment, but is not difficult or time consuming. Only if you have a problem in getting the tuning right will it take much time, but that is exactly the case in which you would not want to turn on the power without having discovered that there is a problem. With cold tuning, you can also add and remove additional components, such as the RF choke, and see how much it affects the tuning.

There are always stray capacitances and inductances in larger sized equipment, so there is a good chance that your carefully designed circuits may not be quite right. Even with commercial equipment, you may want to become aware of the limitations of the tuning ranges and the approximate settings for the dials for each band. The equipment manual may provide this information, but what if the amplifier you have is a bit out of calibration? In all of these cases, cold tests provide cheap insurance against damage caused by bad tuning and, at the same time, give you practice in setting up.

The first step is to ensure that the equipment is truly cold by removing the power plug from the wall. Since you will be working around the high voltage circuits, you may want to remove fuses or otherwise ensure that power cannot come on. In a well-designed amplifier there will be interlocks that prevent turn on and, perhaps, also short out the plate voltage. If these are in a place that affects the RF circuits, they may have to be temporarily removed. Just be sure to put them back when done.

The adjustment of the plate circuit components is the most important. The easiest way to check those is to attach a resistor across the tube from plate to ground. The resistor should be the same value as the design load resistance and must be non-inductive. Several

---

Tuning Your Vacuum-Tube Amplifier

Today most hams are used to a wide variety of amplifiers using triodes that are tuned for maximum power output. Unfortunately, not all amplifiers or tubes are rugged enough for this approach. For example, amplifiers that use tetrodes employ a different tuning procedure in which tuning for maximum power may result in a destroyed control grid or screen grid! Procedures vary depending not only on the ratings of the tetrode, but the voltages as well. When tuning any amplifier, monitor grid currents closely and do not exceed the specified maximum current as those are the easiest elements of the tube to damage.

For commercial amplifiers, "Read the Manual" as the following procedures may not be exactly the same as the manufacturer's directions and can be quite different in some cases. In all cases, the last tuning adjustments should be made at full power output, not at reduced power, because the characteristics of the tube change with different power levels. Operating the amplifier at high power after tuning at low power can result in spurious emissions or over-stressing the output network components.

Begin by making sure you have all band-switching controls set properly. If the amplifier TUNE and LOAD controls (sometimes referred to as PLATE TUNE and OUTPUT, respectively) have recommended settings on a particular band, start at those settings. If your amplifier can be set to a TUNE mode, do so. Set the initial amount of drive (input power) from the exciter — read the amplifier manual or check the tube's specifications if a manual is not available. The exciter output should be one-half or more of full power so that the exciter's ALC systems function properly.

Tuning a triode-based, grounded-grid amplifier is the simplest: Tune for maximum output power without exceeding the tube ratings, particularly grid current, or the legal output power limit. The typical procedure is, while monitoring grid current, to increase drive until the plate current equals about one-quarter to one-half of the target current (depending on the tube and grid bias) while monitoring the output on a wattmeter or the internal power meter. Adjust the TUNE control then advance the LOAD control for maximum output. Repeat the sequence of peaking TUNE then increasing LOAD until no more output power can be obtained without exceeding the ratings for the tube or the legal power limit. If necessary, increase drive and re-peak both the TUNE and LOAD controls.

Operating somewhat differently, a grid-driven tetrode (or pentode) amplifier operating near its designed output power uses the TUNE control for peaking output power and the LOAD control for increasing, but not exceeding, the maximum allowable screen current. Generally, the first part of tetrode amplifier tuning is the same as for a triode amplifier with both the TUNE and LOAD controls adjusted for maximum power output while monitoring screen and control grid current. After the initial tuning step, the LOAD control is used to peak the screen current. Maximum power should coincide with maximum screen current. The screen current is just a better indicator. As with the triode amplifier, if drive needs to be increased, readjust the TUNE and LOAD controls.

For both triode and tetrode amplifiers, once the procedures above have been completed, try moving the TUNE control a small amount higher or lower and re-peaking the LOAD control. Also known as "rocking" the TUNE control, this small variation can find settings with a few percent more output power or better efficiency.

Once tuning has been completed, it is a good idea to mark the settings of the TUNE and LOAD controls for each band. This reduces the amount of time for on-the-air or dummy-load tuning, reducing stress to the tube and interference to other stations. Usually, a quick "fine-tune" adjustment is all that is required for maximum output. The set of markings also serves as a diagnostic tool, should the settings for maximum power suddenly shift. This indicates a change in the antenna system, such as a failing connector or antenna. — *Roger Halstead, K8RI*

series resistors in the 500 Ω range, either carbon film or the older carbon composition type will work, but *not* wire wound. The tube must remain in its socket and all the normal connections to it should be in place. Covers should be installed, at least for the final tests, since they may affect tuning.

Connect a test instrument to the 50 Ω output. This can be an antenna bridge or other 50 Ω measuring device. Examples of suitable test equipment would be a vector network analyzer, preferably with an impedance step up transformer, a vector impedance meter or an RX meter, such as the Boonton 250A. If the wattage of the resistor across the plate can stand it, it can even be a low power transmitter.

Select the correct band and tune the plate and load capacitors so that the instrument at the output connector shows 50 Ω or a low SWR at the 50 Ω point. Since this type of circuit is bilateral, you now have settings that will be the same ones you need to transform the 50 Ω load to look like the resistive load you used at the tube plate for the test. If you have an instrument capable of measuring relatively high impedances at RF frequencies, you can terminate the output with 50 Ω and measure the impedance on the plate. It will look something like **Figure 17.20**.

A similar test will work for the input, although it is sometimes more difficult to know what the input impedance at the tube will be. In fact, it will change somewhat with drive level so a low power cold test may not give a full picture. However, just like the case of the plate circuit, you can put your best estimate of the input impedance at the grid using a non-inductive resistor. Then, tune the input circuits for a match.

An old timer's method for tuning these circuits, especially the plate circuit, is to use a dip meter. These are getting pretty hard to find these days and, in any case, only show resonance. You won't know if the transformation ratio between plate and output is correct, but it is better than nothing. At least, if you can't get a dip at the proper frequency, you will know that something is definitely wrong.

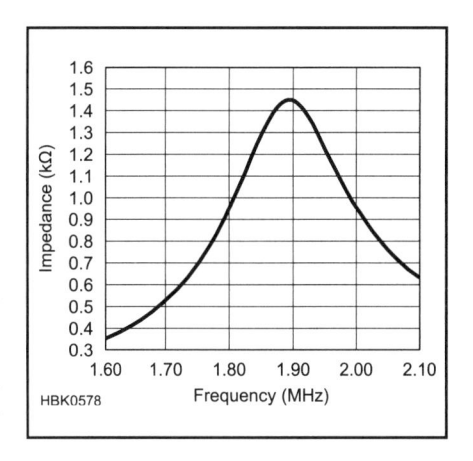

Figure 17.20 — Impedance as would be measured at the plate of an amplifier tube with the output network tuned to 1.9 MHz and the output terminated in its proper load.

17.5 Transmitting Tube Ratings

17.5.1 Plate, Screen and Grid Dissipation

The ultimate factor limiting the power-handling capability of a tube is often (but not always) its maximum plate dissipation rating. This is the measure of how many watts of heat the tube can safely dissipate, if it is cooled properly, without exceeding critical temperatures. Excessive temperature can damage or destroy internal tube components or vacuum seals — resulting in tube failure. The same tube may have different voltage, current and power ratings depending on the conditions under which it is operated, but its safe temperature ratings must not be exceeded in any case! Important cooling considerations are discussed in more detail later in this chapter.

The efficiency of a power amplifier may range from approximately 25% to 85%, depending on its operating class, adjustment and circuit losses. The efficiency indicates how much of the dc power supplied to the stage is converted to useful RF output power; the rest is dissipated as heat, mostly by the plate. The *TubeCalculator* program will calculate the dissipation of the plate as one of its outputs. Otherwise, it can be determined by multiplying the plate voltage (V) times the plate current (A) and subtracting the output power (W).

For a class AB amplifier, the resting dissipation should also be noted, since with no RF input, *all* of the dc power is dissipated in the plate. Multiply plate voltage times the resting plate current to find this resting dissipation value. Screen dissipation is simply screen voltage times screen current. Grid dissipation is a bit more complicated since some of the power into the grid goes into the bias supply, some is passed through to the output (when grounded grid is used) and some is dissipated in the grid. Some tubes have very fragile grids and cannot be run with any grid current at all.

Almost all vacuum-tube power amplifiers in amateur service today operate as linear amplifiers (Class AB or B) with efficiencies of approximately 50% to 65%. That means that a useful power output of approximately 1 to 2 times the plate dissipation generally can be achieved. This requires, of course, that the tube is cooled enough to realize its maximum plate dissipation rating and that no other tube rating, such as maximum plate current or grid dissipation, is exceeded.

Type of modulation and duty cycle also influence how much output power can be achieved for a given tube dissipation. Some types of operation are less efficient than others, meaning that the tube must dissipate more heat. Some forms of modulation, such as CW or SSB, are intermittent in nature, causing less average heating than modulation formats in which there is continuous transmission (RTTY or FM, for example).

Power-tube manufacturers use two different rating systems to allow for the variations in service. CCS (Continuous Commercial Service) is the more conservative rating and is used for specifying tubes that are in constant use at full power. The second rating system is based on intermittent, low-duty-cycle operation, and is known as ICAS (Intermittent Commercial and Amateur Service). ICAS ratings are normally used by commercial manufacturers and individual amateurs who wish to obtain maximum power output consistent with reasonable tube life in CW and SSB service. CCS ratings should be used for FM, RTTY and SSTV applications. (Plate power transformers for amateur service are also rated in CCS and ICAS terms.).

MAXIMUM RATINGS

Tube manufacturers publish sets of maximum values for the tubes they produce. No maximum rated value should ever be exceeded. As an example, a tube might have a maximum plate-voltage rating of 2500 V, a maximum plate-current rating of 500 mA, and a maximum plate dissipation rating of

350 W. Although the plate voltage and current ratings might seem to imply a safe power input of 2500 V × 500 mA = 1250 W, this is true only if the dissipation rating will not be exceeded. If the tube is used in class AB2 with an expected efficiency of 60%, the maximum safe dc power input is

$$P_{IN} = \frac{100 P_D}{100 - N_D} = \frac{100 \times 350}{100 - 60} = 875 \text{ W}$$

Table 17.2
Typical Tank-Capacitor Plate Spacings

Spacing Inches	Peak Voltage	Spacing Inches	Peak Voltage	Spacing Inches	Peak Voltage
0.015	1000	0.07	3000	0.175	7000
0.02	1200	0.08	3500	0.25	9000
0.03	1500	0.125	4500	0.35	11000
0.05	2000	0.15	6000	0.5	13000

17.5.2 Tank Circuit Components

CAPACITOR RATINGS

The tank capacitor in a high-power amplifier should be chosen with sufficient spacing between plates to preclude high-voltage breakdown. The peak RF voltage present across a properly loaded tank circuit, without modulation, may be taken conservatively as being equal to the dc plate voltage. If the dc supply voltage also appears across the tank capacitor, this must be added to the peak RF voltage, making the total peak voltage twice the dc supply voltage. At the higher voltages, it is usually desirable to design the tank circuit so that the dc supply voltages do not appear across the tank capacitor, thereby allowing the use of a smaller capacitor with less plate spacing. Capacitor manufacturers usually rate their products in terms of the peak voltage between plates. Typical plate spacings are given in **Table 17.2**.

Output tank capacitors should be mounted as close to the tube as possible to allow short low inductance leads to the plate. Especially at the higher frequencies, where minimum circuit capacitance becomes important, the capacitor should be mounted with its stator plates well spaced from the chassis or other shielding. In circuits in which the rotor must be insulated from ground, the capacitor should be mounted on ceramic insulators of a size commensurate with the plate voltage involved and — most important of all, from the viewpoint of safety to the operator — a well-insulated coupling should be used between the capacitor shaft and the knob. The section of the shaft attached to the control knob should be well grounded. This can be done conveniently by means of a metal shaft bushing at the panel.

COIL RATINGS

Tank coils should be mounted at least half their diameter away from shielding or other large metal surfaces, such as blower housings, to prevent a marked loss in Q. Except perhaps at 24 and 28 MHz, it is not essential that the coil be mounted extremely close to the tank capacitor. Leads up to 6 or 8 inches are permissible. It is more important to keep the tank capacitor, as well as other components, out of the immediate field of the coil.

The principal practical considerations in designing a tank coil usually are to select a conductor size and coil shape that will fit into available space and handle the required power without excessive heating. Excessive power loss as such is not necessarily the worst hazard in using too-small a conductor. It is not uncommon for the heat generated to actually unsolder joints in the tank circuit and lead to physical damage or failure. For this reason it's extremely important, especially at power levels above a few hundred watts, to ensure that all electrical joints in the tank circuit are secured mechanically as well as soldered.

Table 17.3 shows recommended conductor sizes for amplifier tank coils, assuming loaded tank circuit Q of 15 or less on the 24 and 30 MHz bands and 8 to 12 on the lower frequency bands. In the case of input circuits for screen-grid tubes where driving power is quite small, loss is relatively unimportant and almost any physically convenient wire size and coil shape is adequate.

The conductor sizes in Table 17.3 are based on experience in continuous-duty amateur CW, SSB and RTTY service and assume that the coils are located in a reasonably well ventilated enclosure. If the tank area is not well ventilated and/or if significant tube heat is transferred to the coils, it is good practice to increase AWG wire sizes by two (for example, change from #12 to #10) and tubing sizes by 1/16 inch.

Larger conductors than required for current handling are often used to maximize unloaded Q, particularly at higher frequencies. Where skin depth effects increase losses, the greater surface area of large diameter conductors can be beneficial. Small-diameter copper tubing, up to 3/8 inch outer diameter, can be used successfully for tank coils up through the lower VHF range. Copper tubing in sizes suitable for constructing high-power coils is generally available in 50 foot rolls from plumbing and refrigeration equipment suppliers. Silver-plating the tubing may further reduce losses. This is especially true as the tubing ages and oxidizes. Silver oxide is a much better conductor than copper oxide, so silver-plated tank coils maintain their low-loss characteristics even after years of use.

Table 17.3
Copper Conductor Sizes for Transmitting Coils for Tube Transmitters

Power Output (W)	Band (MHz)	Minimum Conductor Size
1500	1.8-3.5	10
	7-14	8 or 1/8"
	18-28	6 or 3/16"
500	1.8-3.5	12
	7-14	10
	18-28	8 or 1/8"
150	1.8-3.5	16
	7-14	12
	18-28	10

*Whole numbers are AWG; fractions of inches are tubing ODs.

(There is some debate in amateur circles about the benefits of silver plating.).

At VHF and above, tank circuit inductances do not necessarily resemble the familiar coil. The inductances required to resonate tank circuits of reasonable Q at these higher frequencies are small enough that only strip lines or sections of transmission line are practical. Since these are constructed from sheet metal or large diameter tubing, current-handling capabilities normally are not a relevant factor.

17.5.3 Other Components

RF CHOKES

The characteristics of any RF choke vary with frequency. At low frequencies the choke presents a nearly pure inductance. At some higher frequency it takes on high impedance characteristics resembling those of a parallel-resonant circuit. At a still higher frequency it goes through a series-resonant condition, where the impedance is lowest — generally much too low to perform satisfactorily as a shunt-feed plate choke. As frequency increases further, the pattern of alternating parallel and series resonances repeats. Between resonances, the choke will show widely varying amounts of inductive or capacitive reactance.

In most high-power amplifiers, the choke

is directly in parallel with the tank circuit, and is subject to the full tank RF voltage. See **Figure 17.21A**. If the choke does not present a sufficiently high impedance, enough power will be absorbed by the choke to burn it out. To avoid this, the choke must have a sufficiently high reactance to be effective at the lowest frequency (at least equal to the plate load resistance) and yet have no series resonances near any of the higher frequency bands. A resonant-choke failure in a high-power amplifier can be very dramatic and damaging!

Thus, any choke intended for shunt-feed use should be carefully investigated. The best way would be to measure its reactance to ground with an impedance measuring instrument. If the dip meter is used, the choke must be shorted end-to-end with a direct, heavy braid or strap. Because nearby metallic objects affect the resonances, it should be mounted in its intended position, but disconnected from the rest of the circuit. A dip meter coupled an inch or two away from one end of the choke nearly always will show a deep, sharp dip at the lowest series-resonant frequency and shallower dips at higher series resonances.

Any choke to be used in an amplifier for the 1.8 to 28 MHz bands requires careful (or at least lucky!) design to perform well on all amateur bands within that range. Most simply put, the challenge is to achieve sufficient inductance that the choke doesn't "cancel" a large part of tuning capacitance at 1.8 MHz. At the same time, try to position all its series resonances where they can do no harm. In general, close wind enough #20 to #24 magnet wire to provide about 135 µH inductance on a ¾ to 1-inch diameter cylindrical form of ceramic, Teflon or fiberglass. This gives a reactance of 1500 Ω at 1.8 MHz and yet yields a first series resonance in the vicinity of 25 MHz. Before the advent of the 24 MHz band this worked fine. But trying to "squeeze" the resonance into the narrow gaps between the 21, 24 and/or 28 MHz bands is quite risky unless sophisticated instrumentation is available. If the number of turns on the choke is selected to place its first series resonance at 23.2 MHz, midway between 21.45 and 24.89 MHz, the choke impedance will typically be high enough for satisfactory operation on the 21, 24 and 28 MHz bands. The choke's first series resonance should be measured very carefully as described above using a dip meter and calibrated receiver or RF impedance bridge, with the choke mounted in place on the chassis.

Investigations with a vector impedance meter have shown that "trick" designs, such as using several shorter windings spaced along the form, show little if any improvement in choke resonance characteristics.

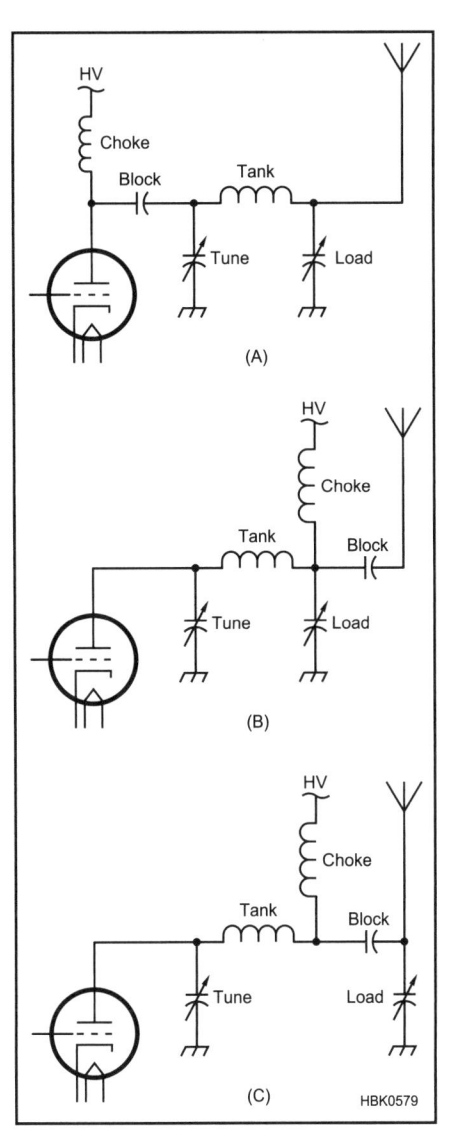

Figure 17.21 — Three ways of feeding dc to a tube via an RF choke. See text for a discussion of the tradeoffs.

Some commercial amplifiers circumvent the problem by band switching the RF choke. Using a larger diameter (1 to 1.5 inches) form does move the first series resonance somewhat higher for a given value of basic inductance. Beyond that, it is probably easiest for an all-band amplifier to add or subtract enough turns to move the first resonance to about 35 MHz and settle for a little less than optimum reactance on 1.8 MHz.

However, there are other alternatives. If one is willing to switch the choke when changing bands, it is possible to have enough inductance for 1.8 to 10 MHz, with series resonances well above 15 MHz. Then for 14 MHz and above, a smaller choke is used which has its resonances well above 30 MHz. Providing an extra pole on the band switch is, of course, the trade-off. This switch must withstand the full plate voltage. Switches suitable for changing bands for the pi network would handle this fine.

Another approach is to feed the high-voltage dc through the main tank inductor, putting the RF choke at the loading capacitor, instead of at the tube. (See Figure 17.21B) This puts a much lower RF voltage on the choke and, thus, not as much reactance is required for satisfactory rejection of the RF voltage. However, this puts both dc and RF voltages on the plate and loading capacitors which may be beyond their ratings. The blocking capacitor can be put before the loading capacitor, as in Figure 17.21C. This removes the dc from the loading capacitor, which typically has a lower voltage rating than the plate capacitor, but puts high current in the blocker.

Yet another method involves using hollow tubing for the plate tank and passing the dc lead through it. This lowers the RF voltage on the choke without putting dc voltage on the tuning components. This method works best for higher power transmitters where the tuning inductor can be made of ⅛ inch or larger copper tubing.

BLOCKING CAPACITORS

A series capacitor is usually used at the input of the amplifier output circuit. Its purpose is to block dc from appearing on matching circuit components of the antenna. As mentioned in the section on tank capacitors, output-circuit voltage requirements are considerably reduced when only RF voltage is present.

To provide a margin of safety, the voltage rating for a blocking capacitor should be at least 25% to 50% greater than the dc voltage applied. A large safety margin is desirable, since blocking capacitor failure can bring catastrophic results. The worse case is when dc is applied to the output of the transmitter and even to the antenna, with potentially fatal results. Often an RF choke is placed from the RF output jack to ground as a safety backup. A shorted blocker will blow the power supply fuse.

To avoid affecting the amplifier's tuning and matching characteristics, the blocking capacitor should have a low impedance at all operating frequencies. If it presents more than 5% of the plate load resistance, the pi components should be adjusted to compensate. Use of a *SPICE* analysis provides a useful way to see what adjustments might be required to maintain the desired match.

The capacitor also must be capable of handling, without overheating or significantly changing value, the substantial RF current that flows through it. This current usually is greatest at the highest frequency of operation where tube output capacitance constitutes a significant part of the total tank capacitance. A significant portion of circulating tank current, therefore, flows through the blocking capacitor. When using the connection of the RF choke shown in Figure 17.21C, the entire circulating current must be accommodated.

Transmitting capacitors are rated by their manufacturers in terms of their RF current-carrying capacity at various frequencies. Below a couple hundred watts at the high frequencies, ordinary disc ceramic capacitors of suitable voltage rating work well in high-impedance tube amplifier output circuits. Some larger disk capacitors rated at 5 to 8 kV also work well for higher power levels at HF. For example, two inexpensive Centralab type DD-602 discs (0.002 µF, 6 kV) in parallel have proved to be a reliable blocking capacitor for 1.5-kW amplifiers operating at plate voltages to about 2.5 kV. At very high power and voltage levels and at VHF, ceramic "doorknob" transmitting capacitors are needed for their low losses and high current handling capabilities. When in doubt, adding additional capacitors in parallel is cheap insurance against blocking capacitor failure and also reduces the impedance. So-called "TV doorknobs" may break down at high RF current levels and should be avoided.

The very high values of Q_L found in many VHF and UHF tube-type amplifier tank circuits often require custom fabrication of the blocking capacitor. This can usually be accommodated through the use of a Teflon "sandwich" capacitor. Here, the blocking capacitor is formed from two parallel plates separated by a thin layer of Teflon. This capacitor often is part of the tank circuit itself, forming a very low-loss blocking capacitor. Teflon is rated for a minimum breakdown voltage of 2000 V per mil of thickness, so voltage breakdown should not be a factor in any practically realized circuit. The capacitance formed from such a Teflon sandwich can be calculated from the information presented elsewhere in this *Handbook* (use a dielectric constant of 2.1 for Teflon). In order to prevent any potential irregularities caused by dielectric thickness variations (including air gaps), Dow-Corning DC-4 silicone grease should be evenly applied to both sides of the Teflon dielectric. This grease has properties similar to Teflon, and will fill in any surface irregularities that might cause problems.

17.6 Sources of Operating Voltages

17.6.1 Tube Filament or Heater Voltage

A power vacuum tube can use either a directly heated filament or an indirectly heated cathode. The filament voltage for either type should be held within 5% of rated voltage. Because of internal tube heating at UHF and higher, the manufacturers' filament voltage rating often is reduced at these higher frequencies. The de-rated filament voltages should be followed carefully to maximize tube life.

Series dropping resistors may be required in the filament circuit to attain the correct voltage. Adding resistance in series will also reduce the inrush current when the tube is turned on. Cold tungsten has much lower resistance than when hot. Circuits are available that both limit the inrush current at turn on and also regulate the voltage against changes in line voltage.

The voltage should be measured with a true RMS meter at the filament pins of the tube socket while the amplifier is running. The filament choke and interconnecting wiring all have voltage drops associated with them. The high current drawn by a power-tube heater circuit causes substantial voltage drops to occur across even small resistances. Also, make sure that the plate power drawn from the power line does not cause the filament voltage to drop below the proper value when plate power is applied.

Thoriated filaments lose emission when the tube is overloaded appreciably. If the overload has not been too prolonged, emission, sometimes, may be restored by operating the filament at rated voltage, with all other voltages removed, for a period of 30 to 60 minutes. Alternatively, you might try operating the tube at 20% above rated filament voltage for five to ten minutes.

17.6.2 Vacuum-Tube Plate Voltage

DC plate voltage for the operation of RF amplifiers is most often obtained from a transformer-rectifier-filter system (see the **Power Sources** chapter) designed to deliver the required plate voltage at the required current. It is not unusual for a power tube to arc over internally (generally from the plate to the screen or control grid) once or twice, especially soon after it is first placed into service. The flashover by itself is not normally dangerous to the tube, provided that instantaneous maximum plate current to the tube is held to a safe value and the high-voltage plate supply is shut off very quickly.

A good protective measure against this is the inclusion of a high-wattage power resistor in series with the plate high-voltage circuit. The value of the resistor, in ohms, should be approximately 10 to 15 times the no-load plate voltage in KV. This will limit peak fault current to 67 to 100 A. The series resistor should be rated for 25 or 50 W power dissipation; vitreous enamel coated wire-wound resistors have been found to be capable of handling repeated momentary fault-current surges without damage. Aluminum-cased resistors (Dale) are not recommended for this application. Each resistor also must be large enough to safely handle the maximum value of normal plate current; the wattage rating required may be calculated from $P = I^2R$. If the total filter capacitance exceeds 25 µF, it is a good idea to use 50 W resistors in any case. Even at high plate-current levels, the addition of the resistors does little to affect the dynamic regulation of the plate supply.

Since tube (or other high-voltage circuit) arcs are not necessarily self-extinguishing, a fast-acting plate overcurrent relay or primary circuit breaker is also recommended to quickly shut off ac power to the HV supply when an arc begins. Using this protective system, a mild HV flashover may go undetected, while a more severe one will remove ac power from the HV supply. (The cooling blower should remain energized, however, since the tube may be hot when the HV is removed due to an arc.) If effective protection is not provided, however, a "normal" flashover, even in a new tube, is likely to damage or destroy the tube, and also frequently destroys the rectifiers in the power supply as well as the plate RF choke. A power tube that flashes over more than about 3 to 5 times in a period of several months likely is defective and will have to be replaced before long.

17.6.3 Grid Bias

The grid bias for a linear amplifier should be highly filtered and well regulated. Any ripple or other voltage change in the bias circuit modulates the amplifier. This causes hum and/or distortion to appear on the signal. Since most linear amplifiers draw only small amounts of grid current, these bias-supply requirements are not difficult to achieve.

Fixed bias for class AB1 tetrode and pentode amplifiers is usually obtained from a variable-voltage regulated supply. Voltage adjustment allows setting bias level to give the desired resting plate current. **Figure 17.22A** shows a simple Zener-diode-regulated bias supply. The dropping resistor is chosen to allow approximately 10 mA of Zener current. Bias is then reasonably well regulated for all drive conditions up to 2 or 3 mA of grid current. The potentiometer allows bias to be adjusted between Zener and approximately 10 V higher. This range is usually adequate to allow for variations in the characteristics of different tubes. Under standby conditions, when it is desirable to cut off the tube entirely, the Zener ground return is interrupted so the full bias supply voltage is applied to the grid.

In Figure 17.22B and C, bias is obtained from the voltage drop across a Zener diode in the cathode (or filament center-tap) lead. Operating bias is obtained by the voltage drop across D1 as a result of plate (and screen) current flow. The diode voltage drop effectively raises the cathode potential relative to the grid. The grid is, therefore, negative with respect to the cathode by the Zener voltage of the diode. The Zener-diode wattage rating should be twice the product of the maximum cathode current times the rated Zener voltage. Therefore, a tube requiring 15 V of bias with a maximum cathode current of 100 mA would dissipate 1.5 W in the Zener diode. To allow a suitable safety factor, the diode rating should be 3 W or more. The circuit of Figure 17.22C illustrates how D1 would be used with a cathode driven (grounded grid) amplifier as opposed to the grid driven example at B.

In all cases, the Zener diode should be bypassed by a 0.01-µF capacitor of suitable voltage. Current flow through any type of diode generates shot noise. If not bypassed, this noise would modulate the amplified signal, causing distortion in the amplifier output.

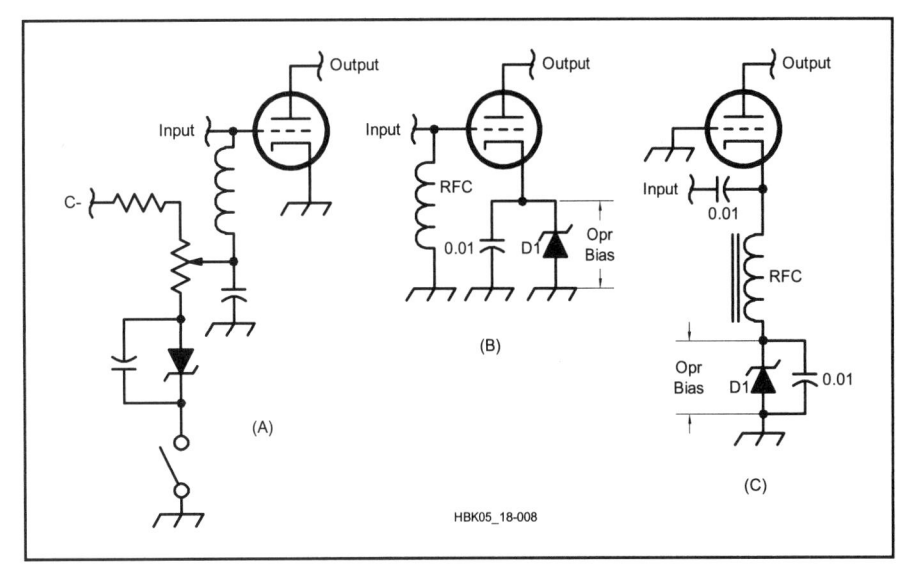

Figure 17.22 — Various techniques for providing operating bias with tube amplifiers.

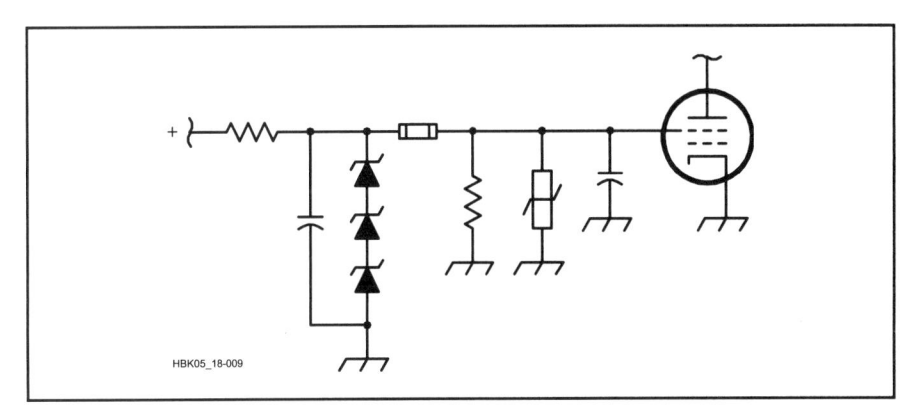

Figure 17.23 — A Zener-regulated screen supply for use with a tetrode. Protection is provided by a fuse and a varistor.

17.6.4 Screen Voltage For Tubes

Power tetrode screen current varies widely with both excitation and loading. The current may be either positive or negative, depending on tube characteristics and amplifier operating conditions. In a linear amplifier, the screen voltage should be well regulated for all values of screen current. The power output from a tetrode is very sensitive to screen voltage, and any dynamic change in the screen potential can cause distorted output. Zener diodes are commonly used for screen regulation.

Figure 17.23 shows a typical example of a regulated screen supply for a power tetrode amplifier. The voltage from a fixed dc supply is dropped to the Zener stack voltage by the current-limiting resistor. A screen bleeder resistor is connected in parallel with the Zener stack to allow for the negative screen current developed under certain tube operating conditions. Bleeder current is chosen to be roughly 10 to 20 mA greater than the expected maximum negative screen current, so that screen voltage is regulated for all values of current between maximum negative screen current and maximum positive screen current. For external-anode tubes in the 4CX250 family, a typical screen bleeder current value would be 20 mA. For the 4CX1000 family, a screen-bleeder current of 70 mA is required.

Screen voltage should never be applied to a tetrode unless plate voltage and load also are applied; otherwise, the screen will act like an anode and will draw excessive current. Perhaps the best way to insure this is to include logic circuits that will not allow the

RF Power Amplifiers 17.19

screen supply to turn on until it senses plate voltage. Supplying the screen through a series-dropping resistor from the plate supply affords a measure of protection, since the screen voltage only appears when there is plate voltage. Alternatively, a fuse can be placed between the regulator and the bleeder resistor. The fuse should not be installed between the bleeder resistor and the tube because the tube should never be operated without a load on the screen. Without a load, the screen potential tends to rise to the anode voltage. Any screen bypass capacitors or other associated circuits are likely be damaged by this high voltage.

In Figure 17.23, a varistor is connected from screen to ground. If, because of some circuit failure, the screen voltage should rise substantially above its nominal level, the varistor will conduct and clamp the screen voltage to a low level. If necessary to protect the varistor or screen dropping resistors, a fuse or overcurrent relay may be used to shut off the screen supply so that power is interrupted before any damage occurs. The varistor voltage should be approximately 30% to 50% higher than normal screen voltage.

17.7 Tube Amplifier Cooling

Vacuum tubes must be operated within the temperature range specified by the manufacturer if long tube life is to be achieved. Tubes having glass envelopes and rated at up to 25 W plate dissipation may be used without forced-air cooling if the design allows a reasonable amount of convection cooling. If a perforated metal enclosure is used, and a ring of ¼ to ⅜-inch-diameter holes is placed around the tube socket, normal convective airflow can be relied on to remove excess heat at room temperatures.

For tubes with greater plate dissipation ratings, and even for very small tubes operated close to maximum rated dissipation, forced-air cooling with a fan or blower is needed. Most manufacturers rate tube-cooling requirements for continuous-duty operation. Their literature will indicate the required volume of airflow, in cubic feet per minute (CFM), at some particular back pressure. Often, this data is given for several different values of plate dissipation, ambient air temperature and even altitude above sea level.

One extremely important consideration is often overlooked by power-amplifier designers and users alike: a tube's plate dissipation rating is only its maximum potential capability. The power that it can actually dissipate safely depends directly on the cooling provided. The actual power capability of virtually all tubes used in high-power amplifiers for amateur service depends on the volume of air forced through the tube's cooling structure.

17.7.1 Blower Specifications

This requirement usually is given in terms of cubic feet of air per minute (CFM), delivered into a back pressure, representing the resistance of the tube cooler to air flow, stated in inches of water. Both the CFM of airflow required and the pressure needed to force it through the cooling system are determined by ambient air temperature and altitude (air density), as well as by the amount of heat to be dissipated. The cooling fan or blower must be capable of delivering the specified airflow into the corresponding back pressure. As a result of basic air flow and heat transfer principles, the volume of airflow required through the tube cooler increases considerably faster than the plate dissipation, and back pressure increases even faster than airflow. In addition, blower air output decreases with increasing back pressure until, at the blower's so-called "cutoff pressure," actual air delivery is zero. Larger and/or faster-rotating blowers are required to deliver larger volumes of air at higher back pressure.

Values of CFM and back pressure required to realize maximum rated plate dissipation for some of the more popular tubes, sockets and chimneys (with 25 °C ambient air and at sea level) are given in **Table 17.4**. Back pressure is specified in inches of water and can be measured easily in an operational air system as indicated in **Figures 17.24** and **17.25**. The pressure differential between the air passage and atmospheric pressure is measured with a device called a *manometer*. A manometer is nothing more than a piece of clear tubing, open at both ends and fashioned in the shape of a "U." The manometer is temporarily connected to the chassis and is removed after the measurements are completed. As shown in the diagrams, a small amount of water is placed in the tube. At Figure 17.25A, the blower is "off" and the water seeks its own level, because the air pressure (ordinary atmospheric pressure) is the same at both ends of the manometer tube. At B, the blower is "on" (socket, tube and chimney in place) and the pressure difference, in terms

Table 17.4
Specifications of Some Popular Tubes, Sockets and Chimneys

Tube	CFM	Back Pressure (inches)	Socket	Chimney
3-500Z	13	0.13	SK-400, SK-410	SK-416
3CX800A7	19	0.50	SK-1900	SK-1906
3CX1200A7	31	0.45	SK-410	SK-436
3CX1200Z7	42	0.30	SK-410	—
3CX1500/8877	35	0.41	SK-2200, SK-2210	SK-2216
4-400A/8438	14	0.25	SK-400, SK-410	SK-406
4-1000A/8166	20	0.60	SK-500, SK-510	SK-506
4CX250R/7850	6.4	0.59	SK602A, SK-610, SK-610A SK-611, SK-612, SK-620, SK-620A, SK-621, SK-630	
4CX400/8874	8.6	0.37	SK1900	SK606
4CX400A	8	0.20	SK2A	—
4CX800A	20	0.50	SK1A	—
4CX1000A/8168	25	0.20	SK-800B, SK-810B, SK-890B	SK-806
4CX1500B/8660	34	0.60	SK-800B, SK-1900	SK-806
4CX1600B	36	0.40	SK3A	CH-1600B

These values are for sea-level elevation. For locations well above sea level (5000 ft/1500 m, for example), add an additional 20% to the figure listed.

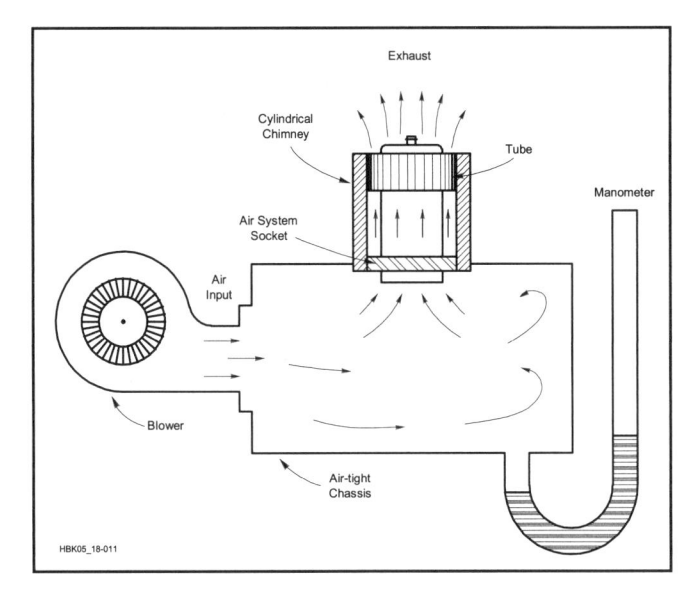

Figure 17.24 — Air is forced into the chassis by the blower and exits through the tube socket. The manometer is used to measure system back pressure, which is an important factor in determining the proper size blower.

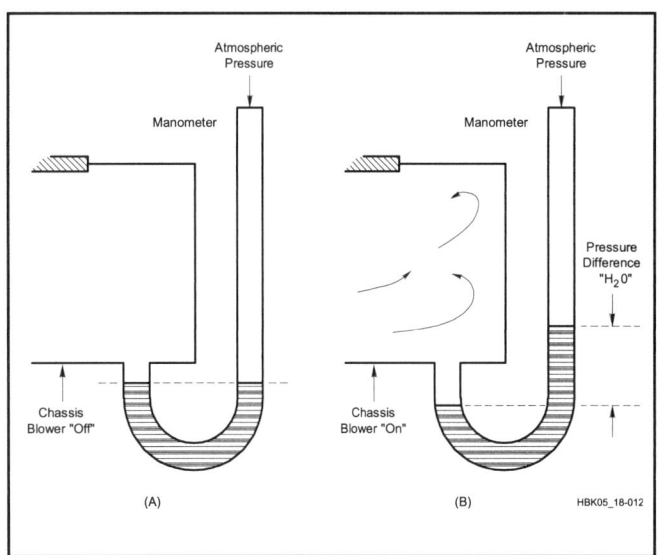

Figure 17.25 — At A the blower is "off" and the water will seek its own level in the manometer. At B the blower is "on" and the amount of back pressure in terms of inches of water can be measured as indicated.

Table 17.5
Blower Performance Specifications

Wheel Dia	Wheel Width	RPM	Free Air CFM	\-\-\-\-\-\-\-CFM for Back Pressure (inches)\-\-\-\-\-\-\-					Stock No.
				0.1	0.2	0.3	0.4	0.5	
2"	1"	3340	12	9	6	—	—	—	1TDN2
2¹⁵⁄₁₆"	1½"	3388	53	52	50	47	41	23	1TDN5
3"	1⅞"	3036	50	48	44	39	32	18	1TDN7
3"	1⅞"	3010	89	85	78	74	66	58	1TDP1
3¹⁵⁄₁₆"	1¹⁵⁄₁₆"	3016	75	71	68	66	61	56	1TDP3
3¾"	1⅞"	2860	131	127	119	118	112	105	1TDP5

Representative sample of Dayton squirrel cage blowers. More information and other models available from Grainger Industrial Supply (**www.grainger.com**).

of inches of water, is measured. For most applications, a standard ruler used for measurement will yield sufficiently accurate results.

Table 17.5 gives the performance specifications for a few of the many Dayton blowers, which are available through Grainger Industrial Supply (**www.grainger.com**). Other blowers having wheel diameters, widths and rotational speeds similar to any in Table 17.5 likely will have similar flow and back pressure characteristics. If in doubt about specifications, consult the manufacturer. Tube temperature under actual operating conditions is the ultimate criterion for cooling adequacy and may be determined using special crayons or lacquers that melt and change appearance at specific temperatures. The setup of Figure 17.25, however, nearly always gives sufficiently accurate information.

17.7.2 Cooling Design Example

As an example, consider the cooling design of a linear amplifier to use one 3CX800A7 tube to operate near sea level with the air temperature not above 25 °C. The tube, running 1150 W dc input, easily delivers 750 W continuous output, resulting in 400 W plate dissipation ($P_{DIS} = P_{IN} - P_{OUT}$). According to the manufacturer's data, adequate tube cooling at 400 W P_D requires at least 6 CFM of air at 0.09 inches of water back pressure. In Table 17.5, a Dayton no. 1TDN2 will do the job with a good margin of safety.

If the same single tube were to be operated at 2.3 kW dc input to deliver 1.5 kW output (substantially exceeding its maximum electrical ratings!), P_{IN} would be about 2300 W and $P_D \approx 800$ W. The minimum cooling air required would be about 19 CFM at 0.5 inches of water pressure — doubling P_{DIS}, more than tripling the CFM of air flow required and increasing back pressure requirements on the blower by a factor of 5.5!

However, two 3CX800A7 tubes are needed to deliver 1.5 kW of continuous maximum legal output power in any case. Each tube will operate under the same conditions as in the single-tube example above, dissipating 400 W. The total cooling air requirement for the two tubes is, therefore, 12 CFM at about 0.09 inches of water, only two-thirds as much air volume and one-fifth the back pressure required by a single tube. While this may seem surprising, the reason lies in the previously mentioned fact that both the airflow required by a tube and the resultant back pressure increase much more rapidly than P_D of the tube. Blower air delivery capability, conversely, decreases as back pressure is increased. Thus, a Dayton 1TDN2 blower can cool two 3CX800A7 tubes dissipating

800 W total, but a much larger (and probably noisier) no. 1TDN7 would be required to handle the same power with a single tube.

In summary, three very important considerations to remember are these:

• A tube's actual safe plate dissipation capability is totally dependent on the amount of cooling air forced through its cooling system. Any air-cooled power tube's maximum plate dissipation rating is meaningless unless the specified amount of cooling air is supplied.

• Two tubes will always safely dissipate a given power with a significantly smaller (and quieter) blower than is required to dissipate the same power with a single tube of the same type. A corollary is that a given blower can virtually always dissipate more power when cooling two tubes than when cooling a single tube of the same type.

• Blowers vary greatly in their ability to deliver air against back pressure so blower selection should not be taken lightly.

17.7.3 Other Considerations

A common method for directing the flow of air around a tube involves the use of a pressurized chassis. This system is shown in Figure 17.24. A blower attached to the chassis forces air around the tube base, often through holes in its socket. A chimney is used to guide air leaving the base area around the tube envelope or anode cooler, preventing it from dispersing and concentrating the flow for maximum cooling.

A less conventional approach that offers a significant advantage in certain situations is shown in **Figure 17.26**. Here the anode compartment is pressurized by the blower. A special chimney is installed between the anode heat exchanger and an exhaust hole in the compartment cover. When the blower pressurizes the anode compartment, there are two parallel paths for airflow: through the anode and its chimney, and through the air

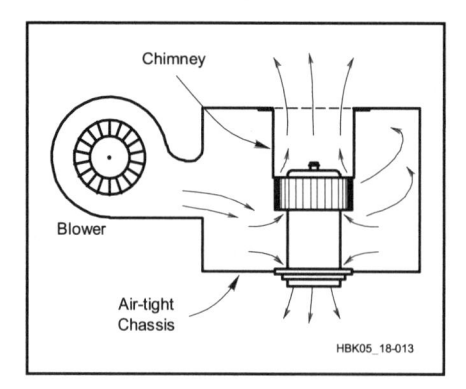

Figure 17.26 — Anode compartment pressurization may be more efficient than grid compartment pressurization. Hot air exits upwards through the tube anode and through the chimney. Cool air also goes down through the tube socket to cool tube's pins and the socket itself.

system socket. Dissipation, and hence cooling air required, generally is much greater for the anode than for the tube base. Because high-volume anode airflow need not be forced through restrictive air channels in the base area, back pressure may be very significantly reduced with certain tubes and sockets. Only airflow actually needed is bled through the base area. Blower back pressure requirements may sometimes be reduced by nearly half through this approach.

Table 17.4 also contains the part numbers for air-system sockets and chimneys available for use with the tubes that are listed. The builder should investigate which of the sockets listed for the 4CX250R, 4CX300A, 4CX1000A and 4CX1600A best fit the circuit needs. Some of the sockets have certain tube elements grounded internally through the socket. Others have elements bypassed to ground through capacitors that are integral parts of the sockets.

Depending on your design philosophy and tube sources, some compromises in the cooling system may be appropriate. For example, if glass tubes are available inexpensively as broadcast pulls, a shorter life span may be acceptable. In such a case, an increase of convenience and a reduction in cost, noise, and complexity can be had by using a pair of "muffin" fans. One fan may be used for the filament seals and one for the anode seal, dispensing with a blower and air-system socket and chimney. The airflow with this scheme is not as uniform as with the use of a chimney. The tube envelope mounted in a cross flow has flow stagnation points and low heat transfer in certain regions of the envelope. These points become hotter than the rest of the envelope. The use of multiple fans to disturb the cross airflow can significantly reduce this problem. Many amateurs have used this cooling method successfully in low-duty-cycle CW and SSB operation but it is not recommended for AM, SSTV or RTTY service.

The true test of the effectiveness of a forced air cooling system is the amount of heat carried away from the tube by the air stream. The power dissipated can be calculated from the airflow temperatures. The dissipated power is

$$P_D = 0.543 \, Q_A \, (T_2 - T_1) \qquad (7)$$

where

P_D = the dissipated power, in W
Q_A = the air flow, in CFM (cubic feet per minute).
T_1 = the inlet air temperature, °C (normally quite close to room temperature).
T_2 = the amplifier exhaust temperature, °C.

The exhaust temperature can be measured with a cooking thermometer at the air outlet. The thermometer should not be placed inside the anode compartment because of the high voltage present.

17.8 Vacuum Tube Amplifier Stabilization

Purity of emissions and the useful life (or even survival) of a tube depend heavily on stability during operation. Oscillations can occur at the operating frequency, or far from it, because of undesired positive feedback in the amplifier. Unchecked, these oscillations pollute the RF spectrum and can lead to overdissipation and subsequent failure. Each type of oscillation has its own cause and its own cure.

17.8.1 Amplifier Neutralization

An RF amplifier, especially a linear amplifier, can easily become an oscillator at various frequencies. When the amplifier is operating, the power at the output side is large. If a fraction of that power finds its way back to the input and is in the proper phase, it can be re-amplified, repeatedly, leading to oscillation. An understanding of this process can be had by studying the sections on feedback and oscillation in the **Radio Fundamentals** chapter. Feedback that is self-reinforcing is called "positive" feedback, even though its effects are undesirable. Even when the positive feedback is insufficient to cause actual oscillation, its presence can lead to excessive distortion and strange effects on the tuning of the amplifier and it, therefore, should be eliminated or at least reduced. The deliberate use of "negative" feedback in amplifiers to increase linearity is discussed briefly elsewhere in this chapter.

The power at the output of an amplifier will couple back to the input of the amplifier through any path it can find. It is a good practice to isolate the input and output circuits of an amplifier in separate shielded compartments. Wires passing between the two compartments should be bypassed to ground if possible. This prevents feedback via paths external to the tube.

However, energy can also pass back through the tube itself. To prevent this, a process called neutralization can be used. Neutralization seeks to prevent or to cancel out any transfer of energy from the plate of the tube back to its input, which will be either the grid or the cathode. An effective way to neutralize a tube is to provide a grounded shield between the input and the output. In the grounded grid connection, the grid itself serves this purpose. For best neutralization, the grid should be connected through a low inductance conductor to a point that is at RF ground. Ceramic external tube types may have multiple low inductance leads to ground to enhance the shielding effect. Older glass type tubes may have significant inductance inside the tube and in the socket, and this will limit the effectiveness of the shielding effect of the grid. Thus, using a grounded grid circuit with those tube types does not rule out the need for further efforts at neutralization, especially at the higher HF frequencies.

When tetrodes are used in a grounded cathode configuration, the screen grid acts as an RF shield between the grid and plate. Special tube sockets are provided that provide a very low inductance connection to RF ground. These reduce the feed through from plate to grid to a very small amount, making the effective grid-to-plate capacitance a tiny fraction of one picofarad. If in doubt about amplifiers that will work over a large frequency range, use a network analyzer or impedance measuring instrument to verify how well grounded a "grounded" grid or screen really is. If at some frequencies the impedance is more than an ohm or two, a different grounding configuration may be needed.

For amplifiers to be used at only a single frequency, a series resonant circuit can be used at either the screen or grid to provide nearly perfect bypassing to ground. Typical values for a 50 MHz amplifier are shown in **Figure 17.27**.

For some tubes, at a certain frequency, the lead inductance to ground can just cancel the grid-to-plate capacitance. Due to this effect, some tube and socket combinations have a naturally self-neutralizing frequency based on the values of screen inductance and grid-to-plate capacitance. For example, the "self-neutralizing frequency" of a 4-1000 is about 30 MHz. This effect has been utilized in some VHF amplifiers.

BRIDGE NEUTRALIZATION

When the shielding effect of a grid or screen bypassed to ground proves insufficient, other circuits must be devised to cancel out the remaining effect of the grid-to-plate or grid-to-cathode capacitance. These, in effect, add an additional path for negative feedback that will combine with the undesired positive feedback and cancel it. The most commonly used circuit is the "bridge neutralization" circuit shown in **Figure 17.28**. This method gets its name from the fact that the four important capacitance values can be redrawn as a bridge circuit, as shown in **Figure 17.29**. Clearly when the bridge is properly balanced, there is no transfer of energy from the plate to the grid tanks. Note that four different capacitors are part of the bridge. C_{gp} is characteristic of the chosen tube, somewhat affected by the screen or grid bypass mentioned earlier. The other components must be chosen properly so that bridge balance is achieved. C1 is the neutralizing capacitor. Its value should be adjustable to the point where

$$\frac{C1}{C3} = \frac{C_{gp}}{C_{IN}} \qquad (8)$$

where

C_{gp} = tube grid-plate capacitance
C_{IN} = tube input capacitance

The tube input capacitance must include all strays directly across the tube. C3 is not simply a bypass capacitor on the ground side of the grid tank, but rather a critical part of the bridge. Hence, it must provide a stable value of capacitance. Sometimes, simple bypass capacitors are of a type which change their value drastically with temperature. These are not suitable in this application.

Neutralization adjustment is accomplished

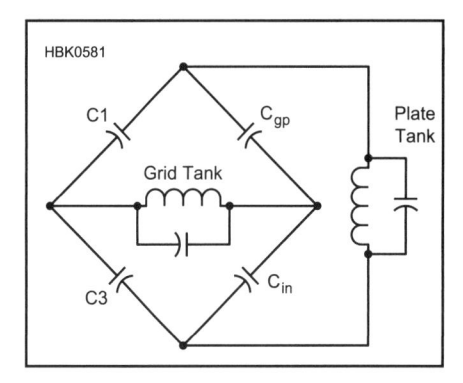

Figure 17.29 — The "bridge neutralization" circuit of Figure 17.28 redrawn to show the capacitance values.

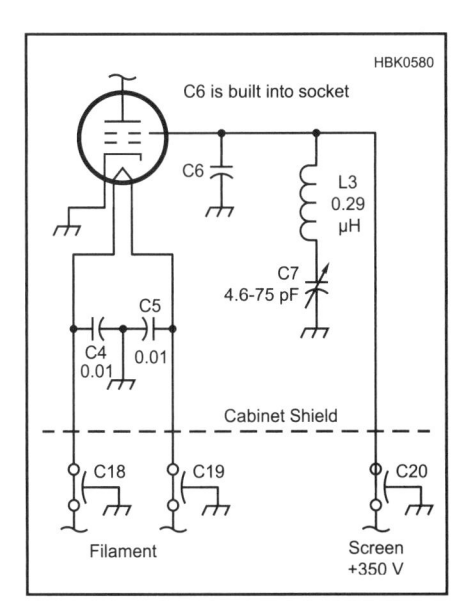

Figure 17.27 — A series-resonant circuit can be used to provide nearly perfect screen or grid bypassing to ground. This example is from a single-band 50 MHz

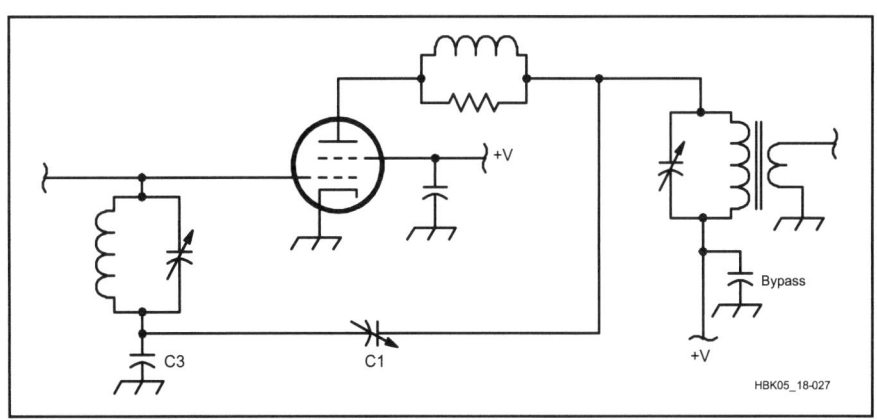

Figure 17.28 — A neutralization circuit uses C1 to cancel the effect of the tube internal capacitance.

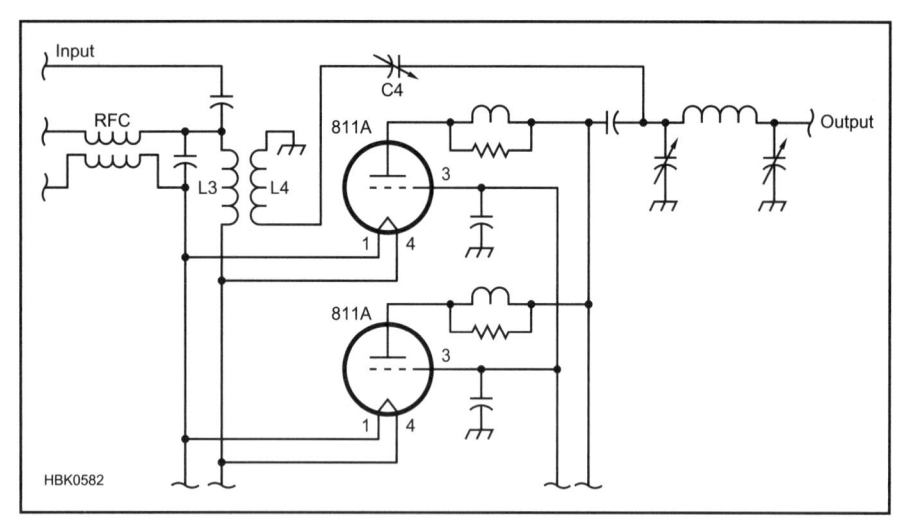

Figure 17.30 — In this neutralizing method, a broadband transformer (L3, L4) provides the needed out-of-phase signal. L3 is 6 turns of #14 wire close wound, ½ inch diameter. L4 is 5 turns of insulated wire over L3. C4 is 6 pF with 0.06-inch spacing. This circuit was originally featured in June 1961 *QST* and is still found in modern amplifiers using 811A tubes.

by applying energy to the output of the amplifier, and measuring the power fed through the input. Conversely, the power may be fed to the input and the output power measured. *with the power off*, the neutralization capacitor C1 is adjusted for minimum feed through, while keeping the output tuning circuit and the input tuning (if used) at the point of maximum response. Since the bridge neutralization circuit is essentially broad band, it will work over a range of frequencies. Usually, it is adjusted at the highest anticipated frequency of operation, where the adjustment is most critical.

BROADBAND TRANSFORMER

Another neutralizing method is shown in **Figure 17.30**, where a broadband transformer provides the needed out of phase signal. C4 is adjusted so that the proper amount of negative feedback is applied to the input to just cancel the feedback via the cathode to plate capacitance. Though many 811A amplifiers have been built without this neutralization, its use makes tuning smoother on the higher bands. This circuit was featured in June 1961 *QST* and then appeared in the *RCA Transmitting Tube Handbook*. Amplifiers featuring this basic circuit are still being manufactured in 2009 and are a popular seller. Many thousands of hams have built such amplifiers as well.

An alternate method of achieving stable operation is to load the grid of a grounded cathode circuit with a low value of resistance. A convenient value is 50 Ω as it provides a match for the driver. This approach reduces the power being fed back to the grid from the output to a low enough level that good stability is achieved. However, the amplifier gain will be much less than without the grid load. Also, unlike the grounded grid circuit, where much of the power applied to the input feeds through to the output, with this "loaded grid" approach, the input power is lost in the load, which must be able to dissipate such power. Distortion may be low in that the driver stage sees a very constant load. In addition, no tuning of the input is required.

17.8.2 VHF and UHF Parasitic Oscillations

RF power amplifier circuits contain parasitic reactances that have the potential to cause so-called parasitic oscillations at frequencies far above the normal operating frequency. Nearly all vacuum-tube amplifiers designed for operation in the 1.8 to 29.7 MHz frequency range exhibit tendencies to oscillate somewhere in the VHF-UHF range — generally between about 75 and 250 MHz depending on the type and size of tube. A typical parasitic resonant circuit is shown in **Figure 17.31**. Stray inductance between the tube plate and the output tuning capacitor forms a high-Q resonant circuit with the tube's C_{OUT}. C_{OUT} normally is much smaller (higher X_C) than

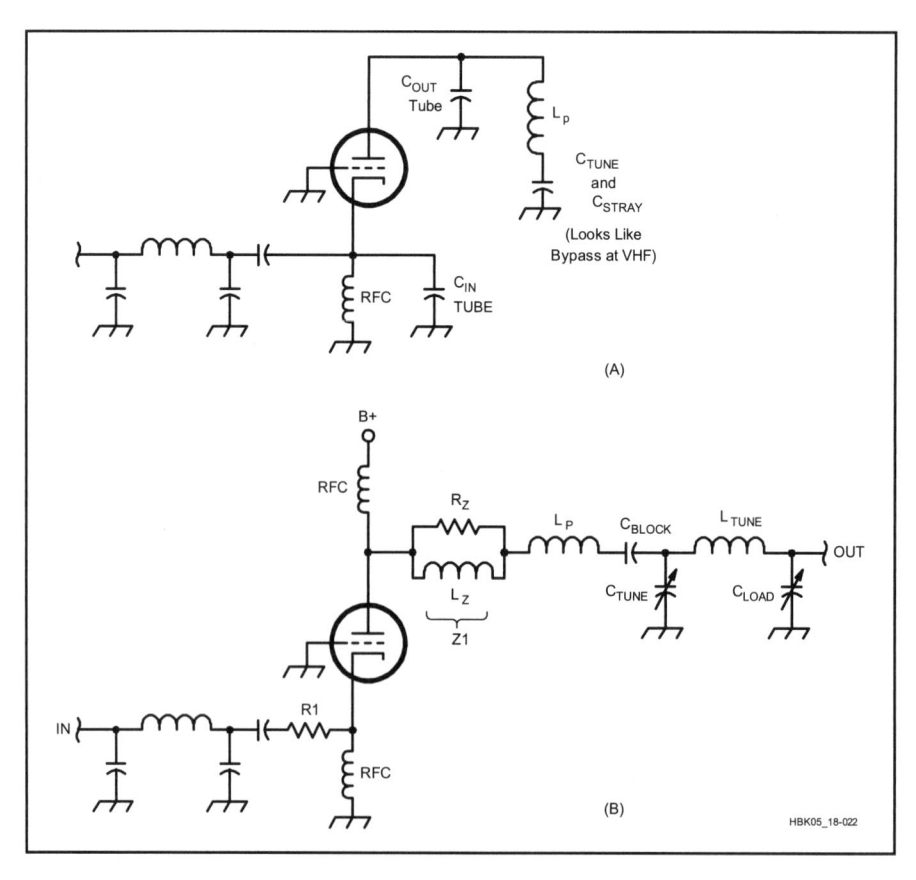

Figure 17.31 — At A, typical VHF/UHF parasitic resonance in plate circuit. The HF tuning inductor in the pi network looks like an RF choke at VHF/UHF. The tube's output capacitance and series stray inductance combine with the pi-network tuning capacitance and stray circuit capacitance to create a VHF/UHF pi network, presenting a very high impedance to the plate, increasing its gain at VHF/UHF. At B, Z1 lowers the Q and therefore gain at parasitic frequency.

any of the other circuit capacitances shown. The tube's C_{IN} and the tuning capacitor C_{TUNE} essentially act as bypass capacitors, while the various chokes and tank inductances shown have high reactances at VHF. Thus, the values of these components have little influence on the parasitic resonant frequency.

Oscillation is possible because the VHF resonant circuit is an inherently high-Q parallel-resonant tank that is not coupled to the external load. The load resistance at the plate is very high and thus, the voltage gain at the parasitic frequency can be quite high, leading to oscillation. The parasitic frequency, f_r, is approximately:

$$f_r = \frac{1000}{2\pi\sqrt{L_P C_{OUT}}} \quad (9)$$

where

f_r = parasitic resonant frequency in MHz
L_P = total stray inductance between tube plate and ground via the plate tuning capacitor (including tube internal plate lead) in µH.
C_{OUT} = tube output capacitance in pF.

In a well-designed HF amplifier, L_P might be in the area of 0.2 µH and C_{OUT} for an 8877 is about 10 pF. Using these figures, the equation above yields a potential parasitic resonant frequency of

$$f_r = \frac{1000}{2\pi\sqrt{0.2\times 10}} = 112.5 \text{ MHz}$$

For a smaller tube, such as the 3CX800A7 with C_{OUT} of 6 pF, f_r = 145 MHz. Circuit details affect f_r somewhat, but these results do, in fact, correspond closely to actual parasitic oscillations experienced with these tube types. VHF-UHF parasitic oscillations can be prevented (*not* just minimized!) by reducing the loaded Q of the parasitic resonant circuit so that gain at its resonant frequency is insufficient to support oscillation. This is possible with any common tube, and it is especially easy with modern external-anode tubes like the 8877, 3CX800A7 and 4CX800A.

PARASITIC SUPPRESSORS

Z1 of Figure 17.31B is a parasitic suppressor. Its purpose is to add loss to the parasitic circuit and reduce its Q enough to prevent oscillation. This must be accomplished without significantly affecting normal operation. L_z should be just large enough to constitute a significant part of the total parasitic tank inductance (originally represented by L_P), and located right at the tube plate terminal(s). If L_z is made quite lossy, it will reduce the Q of the parasitic circuit as desired.

The inductance and construction of L_z depend substantially on the type of tube used. Popular glass tubes like the 3-500Z and 4-1000A have internal plate leads made of wire. This significantly increases L_P when compared to external-anode tubes. Consequently, L_z for these large glass tubes usually must be larger in order to constitute an adequate portion of the total value of L_P. Typically a coil of 3 to 5 turns of #10 wire, 0.25 to 0.5 inches in diameter and about 0.5 to 1 inches long is sufficient. For the 8877 and similar tubes it usually is convenient to form a "horseshoe" in the strap used to make the plate connection. A "U" about 1-inch wide and 0.75 to 1 inch deep usually is sufficient. In either case, L_z carries the full operating-frequency plate current; at the higher frequencies this often includes a substantial amount of circulating tank current, and L_z must be husky enough to handle it without overheating even at 29 MHz. **Figure 17.32** shows a typical parasitic suppressor.

Regardless of the form of L_z, loss may be introduced as required by shunting L_z with one or more suitable non-inductive resistors. In high-power amplifiers, two composition or metal film resistors, each 100 Ω, 2 W, connected in parallel across L_z usually are adequate. For amplifiers up to perhaps 500 W a single 47 Ω, 2 W resistor may suffice. The resistance and power capability required to prevent VHF/UHF parasitic oscillations, while not overheating as a result of normal plate circuit current flow, depend on circuit parameters. Operating-frequency voltage drop across L_z is greatest at higher frequencies, so it is important to use the minimum necessary value of L_z in order to minimize power dissipation in R_z.

The parasitic suppressors described above very often will work without modification, but in some cases it will be necessary to experiment with both L_z and R_z to find a suitable combination. Some designers use nichrome or other resistance wire for L_z.

In exceptionally difficult cases, particularly when using glass tetrodes or pentodes, additional parasitic suppression may be attained by connecting a low value resistor (about 10 to 15 Ω) in series with the tube input, near the tube socket. This is illustrated by R1 of Figure 17.31B. If the tube has a relatively low input impedance, as is typical of grounded-grid amplifiers and some grounded-cathode tubes with large C_{IN}, R1 may dissipate a significant portion of the total drive power.

TESTING TUBE AMPLIFIERS FOR VHF-UHF PARASITIC OSCILLATIONS

Every high-power amplifier should be tested, before being placed in service, to insure that it is free of parasitic oscillations. For this test, nothing is connected to either the RF input or output terminals, and the band switch is first set to the lowest-frequency range. If the input is tuned and can be band switched separately, it should be set to the highest-frequency band. The amplifier control system should provide monitoring for both grid current and plate current, as well as a relay, circuit breaker or fast-acting fuse to quickly shut off high voltage in the event of excessive plate current. To further protect the tube grid, it is a good idea to temporarily insert in series with the grid current return line a resistor of approximately 1000 Ω to prevent grid current from soaring in the event a vigorous parasitic oscillation breaks out during initial testing.

Apply filament and bias voltages to the amplifier, leaving plate voltage off and/or cutoff bias applied until any specified tube warm-up time has elapsed. Then apply the lowest available plate voltage and switch the amplifier to transmit. Some idling plate current should flow. If it does not, it may be necessary to increase plate voltage to normal or to reduce bias so that at least 100 mA or so does flow. Grid current should be zero. Vary the plate tuning capacitor slowly from maximum capacitance to minimum, watching closely for any grid current or change in plate current, either of which would indicate a parasitic oscillation. If a tunable input net-

Figure 17.32 — Typical parasitic suppressor.

work is used, its capacitor (the one closest to the tube if a pi circuit) should be varied from one extreme to the other in small increments, tuning the output plate capacitor at each step to search for signs of oscillation. If at any time either the grid or plate current increases to a large value, shut off plate voltage immediately to avoid damage! If moderate grid current or changes in plate current are observed, the frequency of oscillation can be determined by loosely coupling an RF absorption meter or a spectrum analyzer to the plate area. It will then be necessary to experiment with parasitic suppression measures until no signs of oscillation can be detected under any conditions. This process should be repeated using each band switch position.

When no sign of oscillation can be found, increase the plate voltage to its normal operating value and calculate plate dissipation (idling plate current times plate voltage). If dissipation is at least half of, but not more than its maximum safe value, repeat the previous tests. If plate dissipation is much less than half of maximum safe value, it is desirable (but not absolutely essential) to reduce bias until it is. If no sign of oscillation is detected, the temporary grid resistor should be removed and the amplifier is ready for normal operation.

LOW-FREQUENCY PARASITIC OSCILLATIONS

The possibility of self-oscillations at frequencies lower than VHF is significantly lower than in solid state amplifiers. Tube amplifiers will usually operate stably as long as the input-to-output isolation is greater than the stage gain. Proper shielding and dc-power-lead bypassing essentially eliminate feedback paths, except for those through the tube itself.

On rare occasions, tube-type amplifiers will oscillate at frequencies in the range of about 50 to 500 kHz. This is most likely with high-gain tetrodes using shunt feed of dc voltages to both grid and plate through RF chokes. If the resonant frequency of the grid RF choke and its associated coupling capacitor occurs close to that of the plate choke and its blocking capacitor, conditions may support a tuned-plate tuned-grid oscillation. For example, using typical values of 1 mH and 1000 pF, the expected parasitic frequency would be around 160 kHz.

Make sure that there is no low-impedance, low-frequency return path to ground through inductors in the input matching networks in series with the low impedances reflected by a transceiver output transformer. Usually, oscillation can be prevented by changing choke or capacitor values to insure that the input resonant frequency is much lower than that of the output.

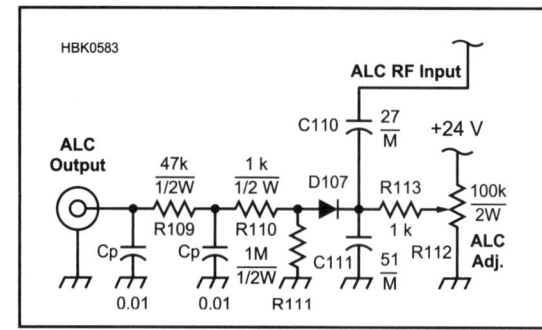

Figure 17.33 — An amplifier ALC circuit can be used to automatically limit the drive power from the transceiver to a safe level.

Overshoot and Overdrive Protection

The ALC and power control circuits of numerous transceivers allow short excess power transients at the beginning of transmission. While tube amplifiers are fairly tolerant of short overloads, solid-state amplifiers are not. To avoid damaging your amplifier input, some kind of protection is necessary. The article "Amplifier Overshoot — Drive Protection" by Phil Salas, AD5X, shows how to use a gas-discharge tube to limit short over-power pulses. It is available as part of the downloadable supplemental information for this book.

17.8.3 Reduction of Distortion

As mentioned previously, a common cause of distortion in amplifiers is over drive (flat topping). The use of automatic level control (ALC) is a practical way of reducing the ill effects of flat topping while still being assured of having a strong signal. This circuit detects the voltage applied to the input of the amplifier. Other circuits are based on detecting the onset of grid current flow. In either case, when the threshold is reached, the ALC circuit applies a negative voltage to the ALC input of the transceiver and forces it to cut back on the driving power, thus keeping the output power within set limits. Most transceivers also apply an ALC signal from their own output stage, so the ALC signal from the amplifier will add to or work in parallel with that. See **Figure 17.33** for a representative circuit.

Some tube types have inherently lower distortion than others. Selection of a tube specifically designed for linear amplifier service, and operating it within the recommended voltage and current ranges is a good start. In addition, the use of tuned circuits in the input circuits when running class AB2 will help by maintaining a proper load on the driver stages over the entire 360° cycle, rather than letting the load change as the tube begins to draw grid current. Another way to accomplish this is with the "loaded grid," the use of a rather low value of resistance from the grid to cathode. Thus, when grid current flows, the change in impedance is less drastic, having been swamped by the resistive load.

For applications where the highest linearity is desired, operating class A will greatly reduce distortion but at a high cost in efficiency. Some solid state amateur transceivers have provision for such operation. The use of negative feedback is another way of greatly reducing distortion. High efficiency is maintained, but there is a loss of overall gain. Often, two stages of gain are used and the feedback applied around both stages. In this way, gain can be as high as desired, and both stages are compensated for any inherent non-linearities. Amplifiers using RF negative feedback can achieve values of intermodulation distortion (IMD) as much as 20 dB lower than amplifiers without feedback.

It must be remembered that distortion tends to be a cumulative problem, with each nonlinear part of the transmission chain adding its part. It is not worthwhile to have a super clean transceiver if it is followed by an amplifier with poor linearity. In the same way, a very good linear will look bad if the transceiver driving it is poor. It is even possible to have a clean signal out of your amplifier, but have it spoiled by a ferrite core tuner inductor or balun that is saturated.

Distortion in a linear amplifier is usually measured with a spectrum analyzer while transmitting a two tone test. If the spectrum analyzer input is overloaded, this can also produce apparent distortion in the amplifier. Reducing the level so that the analyzer is not clipping the input signal is necessary to see the true distortion in the amplifier chain. Use of test equipment for various types of measurements is covered in the **Test Equipment and Measurements** chapter.

17.9 MOSFET Design for RF Amplifiers

There are two general classes of MOSFETs: high and low frequency designs. (See the **Circuits and Components** chapter for MOSFET basics.) The low frequency types are generally optimized for high volume commercial switching applications: computer power supplies, motor controllers, inverters, and so on. They have molded plastic packages, the die are made with aluminum top side metallization, they have maximum junction temperature ratings of 150 to 175°C. Most have polysilicon gate conductors. Polysilicon is easy to manufacture consistently and it's cheap. This works very well for applications up to 200 kHz, but the gate losses start to increase dramatically when they are used at higher frequencies.

A MOSFET gate is essentially a capacitor, but its folded structure is long and skinny. The gate in a 500 W device may be more than a meter long! ("Meter" is not a misprint.) If its conductor material is a lossy material like polysilicon, the gate becomes a long distributed RC network. If an RF signal does make it all the way to the end it will be attenuated and no longer be in phase with the start. This effectively reduces the useful area of the device as frequency increases. It takes a lot of RF current to feed the gate capacitance: I = CVf, where C is the gate capacitance, V is the peak gate voltage, and f is the operating frequency. If the gate capacitance is 500 pF and is being driven to 10 V at 30 MHz, the gate current is 150 mA RMS. While the current is directly proportional to the frequency, the power loss is I^2R. If the gate's top conductor is not low loss, it will fail due to I^2R losses at the gate bond pad (the metallization melts) when used at frequencies much higher than it was designed for.

There are two MOSFET manufacturers that use a metal gate instead of polysilicon for their switchmode devices, IXYS and Microsemi. While the die of these devices are quite capable of HF operation, their packaging (usually TO-247 or TO-264) does not provide an optimum HF layout. Because these are aimed at the switchmode market, their drain terminal is on the mounting surface and the source bond-wire length adds gain-killing degeneration at higher frequencies. But on the other hand, they are cheap in terms of cost per watt of dissipation and are acceptable for single-band designs through 20 meters.

When these same metal-gate MOSFET die are placed in packages that are specifically for RF use, the source is often connected to the mounting surface of the package. The source bond wires are thus short, which improves the available gain at all frequencies. This is very convenient because the source is grounded in most RF power amplifier circuits. It also eliminates the need for a mounting insulator, which in turn improves the power dissipation capability.

In MOSFETs specifically designed for RF, the main distinguishing feature is the gate structure. The channels are "shorter" (there is less distance between the gate and source) which reduces the transit time for electrons. As the active area of a device is increased by making the channel "wider," its power dissipation capability is increased. At the same time, the intrinsic (inter-electrode) capacitances also get bigger. A larger device is more difficult to use at higher frequencies because the input impedance (mostly gate capacitance) becomes ever smaller, which makes it harder to drive. In order to solve the gate loss problem mentioned earlier, the long skinny gate is folded into a comb shape. (See **Figure 17.34**.) The gate signal now only has to travel to the end of each finger. The highest frequency designs use multiple combs

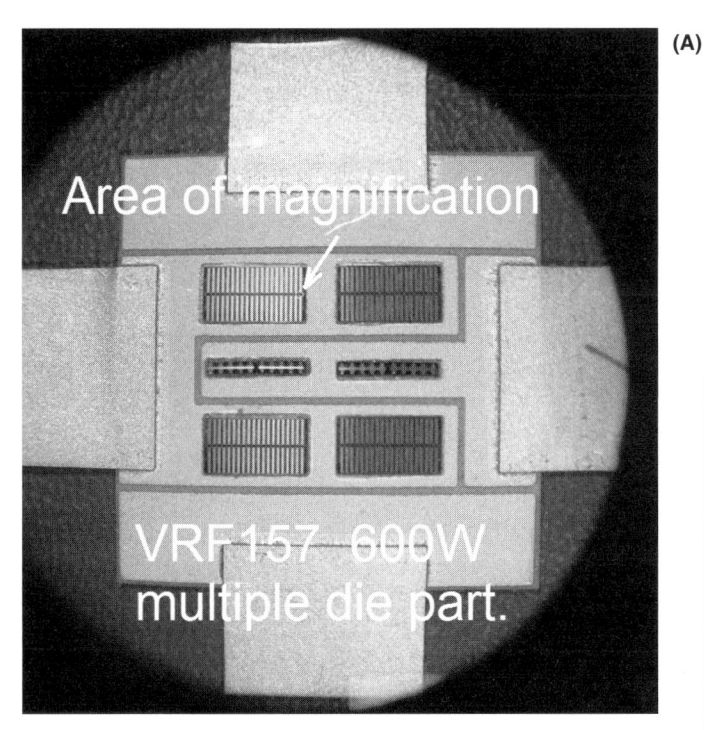

Figure 17.34 — A shows the layout of a multiple-die RF MOSFET (VRF157). B illustrates the comb structure of the gate. C is a closeup of the gate showing the interleaved source and gate finger structure. [Dick Frey, K4XU, photos]

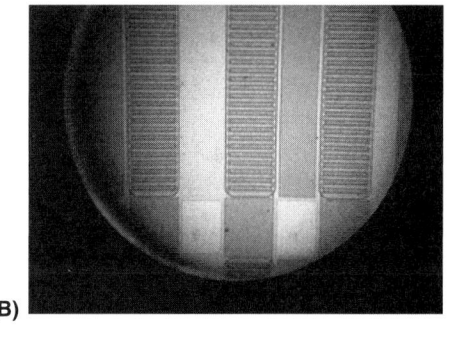

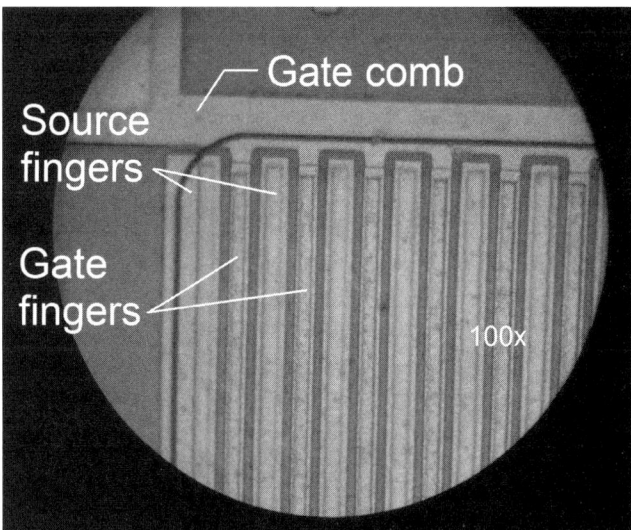

with shorter fingers. Several of these comb structures are arrayed on the die and are connected in parallel when the die is wire-bonded in the package.

The top metallization for RF parts is either aluminum or gold. Aluminum is cheaper but gold is best because it has a higher operating temperature rating, up to 225 °C, and it is immune to power cycling failures due to its excellent ductility. The downside is that it is more expensive and the devices are much harder to manufacture because gold likes to dissolve into silicon. Its higher temperature rating means you can get more power from a small device, which offsets their higher cost somewhat.

17.9.1 LDMOS versus VDMOS

So far all the devices discussed are vertical MOSFETs, or VDMOS. Their gate and source electrodes are on the top surface of the die and the drain is on the bottom. For RF applications there is another type, LDMOS. This is a lateral device. Here the MOS structure is laid on edge and all the electrodes are on the top side of the die. Vertical p+ source connections are made through the die to make the bottom side of the die a source contact in order to get the optimum "common source" configuration. The channel area is low so the capacitances are smaller, especially the feedback capacitance, C_{GD}. However, the operating voltage capability is also low. There are none rated for more than 50 V operation. The gates are particularly sensitive to ESD and overdrive. However, they have spectacular high frequency capability and gain, and reasonable ruggedness. Your mobile phone would not work without LDMOS technology.

New RF amplifier designs are using LDMOS to replace bipolar transistors, which manufacturers are no longer making. The ability of LDMOS to operate at lower voltages is well suited for 12 V operation and, with its high gain and frequency response, providing 6 meter capability is simple. The downside is that these devices are not as linear as the bipolar transistor they replace.

Bipolar transistors need emitter ballasting resistors in each tiny bipolar cell so they can be paralleled in the die. The resistors also provide negative feedback, which improves linearity. MOSFETs do not require source resistors: paralleled cells will naturally share the load because their ON resistance has a positive temperature coefficient that prevents thermal runaway. As a result, LDMOS amplifiers require more negative feedback to provide comparable IMD performance, which offsets their higher gain advantage.

Regardless of the device type, the packaging is particularly important to an RF device. It must have low parasitics (see the **RF Techniques** chapter) and superior thermal qualities. The package insulator is made of ceramics, beryllia BeO (which is toxic), and/or alumina Al_2O_3, for high temperature capability. The conductors are gold-plated copper or Kovar, and the base flanges are often copper-tungsten or copper-molybdenum. The package is the major determining factor in the cost of an RF part. Parasitic inductance introduced by gate and source bond wires limits the ultimate frequency capability of a VDMOS part. LDMOS parts have gate and drain bond wires. LDMOS devices have an advantage in terms of frequency and package cost because they are free of the gain degeneration caused by source wire inductance and their die may be soldered directly to a metal mounting flange.

17.9.2 Designing Amplifiers with MOSFETs

Designing an amplifier requires a systems approach. You will need to consider how much power supply is required, as well as the cooling and control systems needed to keep it happy. If you have the transistors and want to build them into an amplifier, the design procedure is a little different. The place to start in any case is with its transistor's data sheet. This will show the voltage and power capabilities, and from these the circuit requirements can be calculated and the cooling system defined.

VOLTAGE RATINGS

Designing an amplifier with MOSFETs requires knowledge of the part being used. Generally, the cheap plastic-packaged switchmode parts will be best for single-band operation. Switchmode parts are rated by their drain breakdown voltage (BV_{DSS}), ON resistance (R_{DS}), and power dissipation. They are available in voltage ratings from as little as 5 V to over 1200 V. RF parts are sold by operating voltage, V_{DD}, power dissipation and frequency capability.

Select the part to suit your power supply requirements. A 500 V MOSFET will not work on a 12 V supply and will barely work at 50 V. This is because the MOSFET's intrinsic capacitances are higher at low voltage. Between the drain and source of every MOSFET is a parasitic "body diode" as shown in **Figure 17.35**. It's too slow to rectify RF, but like any diode, its capacitance changes with reverse bias voltage. This relationship is always given in the device's C-V curves on its data sheet. (See **Figure 17.36**.) Data sheets can be found on manufacturer or distributor websites or perform an Internet search for the part number and "data sheet."

In class AB operation, a MOSFET works best when operated at a little less than one-half of its rated breakdown voltage, BV_{DSS}. The drain voltage will swing up to 2 or even 3.562 times (for class E) the supply voltage. Under high VSWR, the drain voltage can be somewhat higher still. The RF voltage breakdown of a MOSFET is typically 20% higher than its data sheet value but is hard to specify

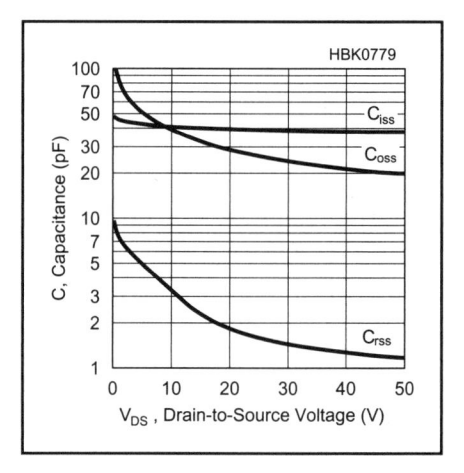

Figure 17.36 — The capacitance versus voltage (C-V) curves for the Microsemi VRF151 RF MOSFET. (Illustration courtesy Microsemi Corp.)

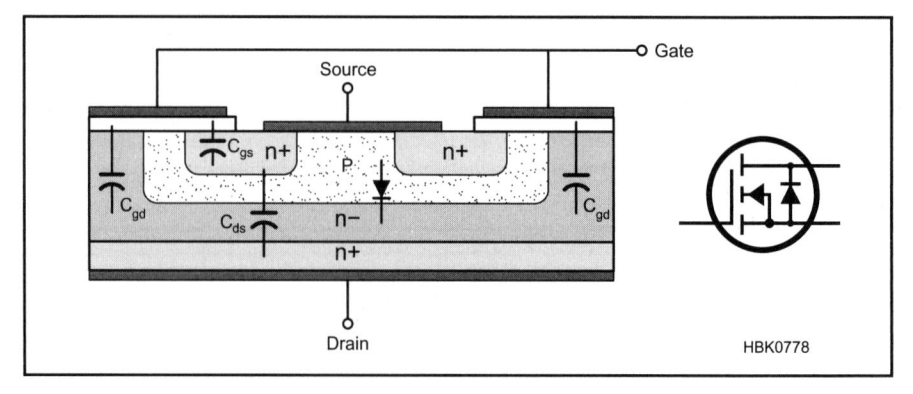

Figure 17.35 — All MOSFETs have parasitic capacitances as shown and a body diode between the drain and source in the cross-section and schematic symbol. The diode is shown for an N-channel device. It is reversed for P-channel devices.

reliability, so RF devices are rated by their dc operating voltages rather than BV_{DSS}. This takes into account the requirement for operating overhead.

RF parts are usually rated at a specific operating voltage such as 13.5 V, 28 V or 50 V. Originally these were common battery voltages for civilian and military vehicles and the tradition persists. The devices are optimized for their operating voltage. Choosing the operating voltage is a matter of considering many different parameters, not just the breakdown voltage.

THERMAL DESIGN

Suffice it to say that the thermal design of a high power transistor PA is often as challenging as the electrical design. It can be done "by the numbers" but the tricky part is making it fit into the available space. A thermal design example and an Advanced Power Technology application note by the author are provided with this book's downloadable supplemental content.

A word of caution is in order: tubes used in power amplifiers have a great deal of "headroom" in their specifications and are quite forgiving of momentary operator errors. RF power transistors, because they are more expensive in terms of cost per watt, are specified much closer to their limits. These limits must be observed at all times. Even though the data sheet says the device can do X watts, the designer must observe the requirements for proper cooling in order to reach this level in practice. In addition, manufacturers rate the power dissipation in theoretical terms. You will be lucky to achieve half of it.

As with tubes, there are CW ratings and SSB ratings. For transistors, the ratings are based on average power. The difference is simply the size of the heat sink required, as the peak power is the same for each. Each transistor has a thermal rating expressed as $R_{\theta JC}$, the thermal resistance from the transistor junction to the bottom of its case. Since the device has an upper junction temperature limit, somewhere between 150 and 200 °C, the power dissipation is determined by the difference between the junction and the case temperature:

$$P_d = (T_J - T_C) / R_{\theta JC}$$

where P_d is the available power dissipation, T_J is junction and T_C is case temperature. What this says is that without any cooling, the transistor's case will be almost the same as the junction temperature so its power dissipation capability is nearly zero. When placed on a heat sink, the case will be cooler and it then has power dissipation capability. It follows that the better the heat sink, the more power can be dissipated by the transistor.

There is another thermal consideration: the thermal resistance between the case of the transistor and the heat sink, $R_{\theta CS}$. Even if the base of the transistor and the heat sink are flat and smooth, microscopic air gaps still exist. These do not conduct heat and so reduce the net effectiveness of the heat sink. The solution is to use a thermal interface compound or *thermal grease*. The simplest and best is silicone oil loaded with zinc oxide powder. The oil does most of the work: the powder thickens it to a paste so it doesn't run out of the joint. It is applied as a very thin coat between the heat sink and device. When using thermal grease, always wiggle the transistor around on the sink to insure a minimum of grease between the part and the sink. Remember, thermal grease is not a good thermal conductor, it's just much better than air. Use it sparingly!

Most commercial high power broadcast amplifiers are cooled with circulated water, or a water-glycol mix if the minimum ambient temperature will be below 0 °C. While it has yet to be introduced to the amateur market, liquid cooling has great potential. The advances in plastic fittings, small pumps and heat exchangers driven by the high-performance computer market have great potential benefits to the amateur high power amplifier. Water is more than four times better than air for absorbing and moving heat. **Figure 17.37** illustrates both open- and closed-loop cooling systems. But regardless of where it is moved to, the heat must still be dissipated. It can warm the air in the shack, heat the rest of the house, or warm the septic tank.

17.9.3 The Transistor Data Sheet

Regardless of manufacturer, all data sheets contain the same basic information. The following should help make sense of what can be very confusing to a first time user. Transistor specifications rely heavily on several ideal conditions that cannot happen in practice but since it is a common practice by all manufacturers, the numbers are very useful for comparing different devices. As long as you have the part number (and it is not a custom part), the corresponding data sheet can be found easily by searching for the part number and "data sheet."

The Microsemi VRF151 N-channel enhancement-mode VDMOS transistor will be used as an example. It is used in the 250 W broadband amplifier project presented in this chapter. The following discussion assumes the reader has obtained a data sheet for this part (see the company website at **www.microsemi.com**) and can refer to it.

MINIMUM, TYPICAL AND MAXIMUM

All of the specification parameters which the manufacturer guarantees are subject to either a minimum value or a maximum value. This is the worst case. As in an automobile, there is a maximum safe stopping distance and a minimum gas tank capacity. Most parameters also have a *typical* value that is generally representative of typical performance than the specified minimum or maximum. Some quantities have both upper and lower limits. Every parameter has specific test conditions under which it is measured.

ABSOLUTE MAXIMUM RATINGS

These are all dc ratings, easily verified with a variable power supply and a multimeter. If the manufacturer finds that any of these have been exceeded, any warranty claims are voided.

V_{DSS} is the maximum drain to source voltage rating, with the gate is shorted to the source. Think of the device as a high voltage Zener diode. As soon as it draws any current,

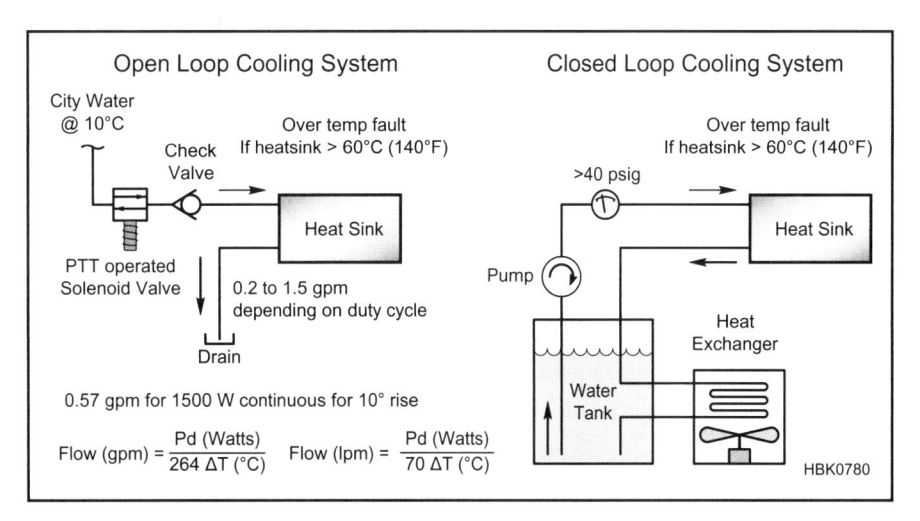

Figure 17.37 — Open- and closed-loop water cooling systems for solid-state amplifiers.

power is dissipated, and temperature rises very quickly. Damage occurs either from puncturing through the junction or by arcing over the edge of the die.

Maximum drain current, I_D, is the current that will cause the device to dissipate its maximum rated power when fully turned on. Every device has an ON resistance called $R_{DS(ON)}$. The power dissipated is due to $I_D^2 \times 2.5\ R_{DS(ON)}$. The factor of 2.5 accounts for $R_{DS(ON)}$ having a positive temperature coefficient which causes it to roughly double by the point at which the junction temperature is 200 °C.

V_{GS} is the maximum gate to source voltage. The gate is essentially a capacitor, with a SiO_2 dielectric perhaps 400 to 1000 Angstroms (10^{-10} m) thick. The limit is lower on LDMOS than VDMOS, and cannot be exceeded without destroying the device. Because LDMOS devices have much lower V_{GS} ratings and thinner dielectrics, some LDMOS manufacturers build in diode protection to make them less susceptible to electrostatic discharge, ESD.

P_D is the maximum power dissipation of the device under theoretical conditions: The bottom of the case at 25 °C and the junction at its maximum temperature, T_{jmax}. If not stated directly, the thermal resistance $R_{\theta JC}$ is equal to $P_D / (T_{jmax} - 25°C)$.

Storage temperature is straightforward. Maximum T_J is the junction temperature above which things start to come unsoldered, or the reliability seriously impaired, or smoke emitted.

STATIC ELECTRICAL CHARACTERISTICS

V_{DSS} is specified again, this time showing the measurement conditions, the guaranteed minimum, and the typical production values. $V_{DS(ON)}$ or sometimes $R_{DS(ON)}$ is the minimum resistance between drain and source that is obtained when the device is fully ON and carrying half the rated current. It is more commonly specified on switchmode parts, but it is of particular importance in high-efficiency saturated modes like class D and E because it limits the maximum obtainable efficiency.

I_{DSS} is the maximum drain current flowing with the gate shorted to the source. In an N-channel enhancement device one must apply a positive voltage to the gate to turn it on. The VRF151 will not conduct more than 1 mA at 100 V by itself without gate bias. This is a leakage current. In a perfect device it is zero.

Similarly, I_{GSS} is gate leakage current with the $V_{DS} = 0$. It represents a resistor in parallel with the gate capacitor. In this case, 1 µA at 20 V is 20 MΩ. This does not sound like much but if the drain has voltage on it and there is no resistor across the gate, this leakage current will cause the gate to charge from the drain, eventually turning the device fully ON with bad consequences.

Forward transconductance, g_{fs}, is the dc gain of the device expressed in terms of change in drain current per change in gate volts measured at a particular drain current. It has only a mild relationship with RF gain and too high a g_{fs} can cause bias instability and/or parasitics.

V_{TH} is the gate threshold specification. When V_{DS} is 10 V, V_{GS} of no less than 2.9 V and no more than 4.4 V will cause 100 mA of drain current to flow. A typical Class AB quiescent bias condition is 100 mA. Of all the parameters, this one has the widest window. Enough variation exists so that manufacturers sort parts into "bins" of values across the range, and assign letter codes to each which are marked on the package. This allows one to make matched pairs within a device type.

THERMAL CHARACTERISTICS

$R_{\Theta JC}$ is equal to $P_{Dmax} / (T_{j\ max} - 25°C)$. Specifying the first two parameters ($R_{\Theta JC}$ and P_{Dmax}) generates the third ($T_{j\ max}$). In this sense specifying $T_{j\ max}$ is redundant but it is often reiterated for those who are looking for the particular parameter.

Because thermal performance is just as important as RF performance, much of the information in the data sheet is concerned with it. In addition to the static thermal impedance, $R_{\Theta JC}$, there is a dynamic thermal impedance $Z_{\Theta JC}$. Transistor packages have thermal mass so the die temperature does not change instantaneously. For pulsed operation, the effective $R_{\Theta JC}$, can be much lower than it is for steady-state operation.

The dynamic thermal impedance is shown in **Figure 17.38** (Figure 5 of the VRF151 data sheet). It shows how the device can be used for pulse operation at higher power than it can on CW because the effective thermal impedance is lower for short pulses. This has some application to SSB, but there are other constraints on peak power that boil down to just allowing a smaller heat sink when used only for intermittent service — a bad practice for amateur amplifiers!

DYNAMIC CHARACTERISTICS

Somewhat of a misnomer, these are the parasitic capacitances between the gate, drain and gate. Except for the gate capacitance which is a fixed value based on device dimen-

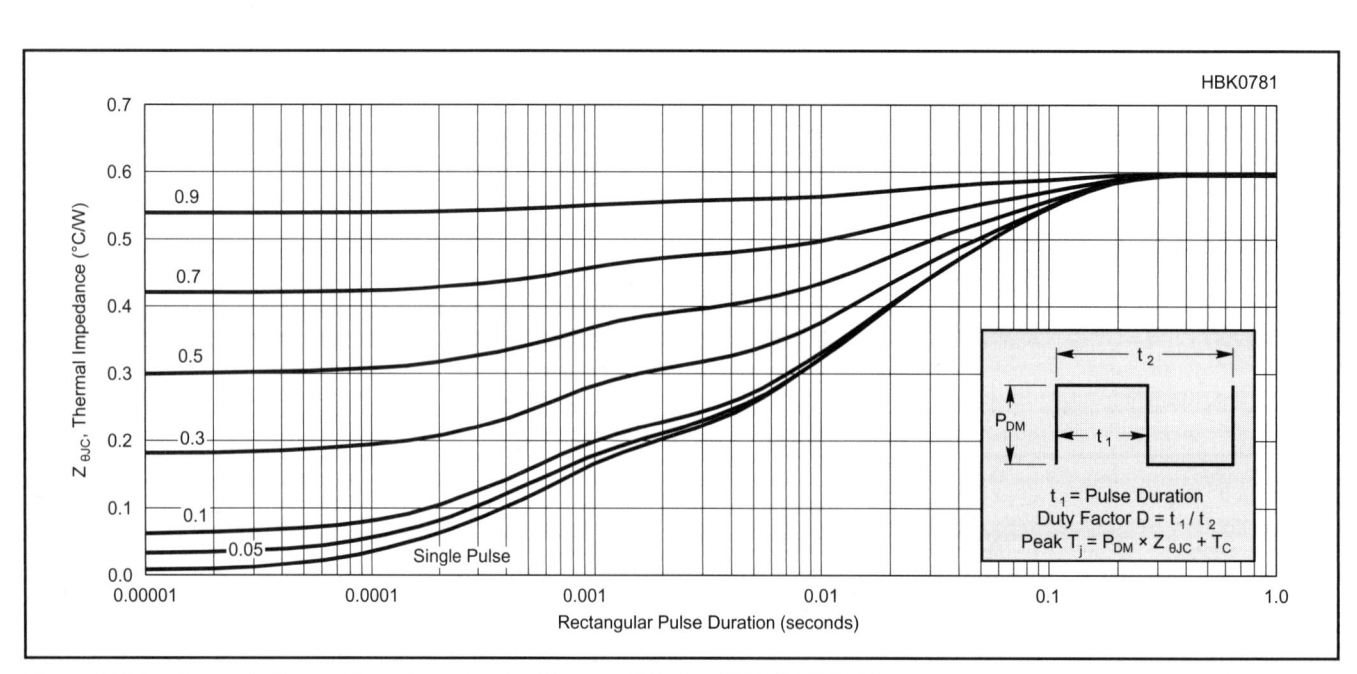

Figure 17.38 — Dynamic thermal impedance for the Microsemi VRF151 RF MOSFET. (Illustration courtesy Microsemi Corp.)

sions, the other two are a function of the drain voltage, just like varactors (voltage-variable capacitors). Because it is rather difficult to measure these parameters, the parameters are defined in a common-source configuration. C_{ISS} is the gate-to-source capacitance with the drain ac-shorted to the source. It is actually C_{GS} in parallel with C_{GD}. The three parameters are usually measured at the specified drain supply voltage with V_{GS} at zero. They are also usually displayed as in Figure 17.36 (Figure 3 of the data sheet), a graph of C vs drain voltage.

This voltage-varying capacitance is one of the causes of IMD in a transistor. Its effect is to impart some phase modulation (PM) on the signal. PM can be observed as unequal IMD products on each side of the carrier pair in a two-tone test. PM distortion generates pairs of odd-order carriers like AM distortion but the high side carriers are −180° out of phase with the AM products. This causes them to reduce the level of amplitude products on the high side of the carrier pair and increases them on the lower side. (See the reference list entry for Sabin and Schoenike, *Single Sideband Systems and Circuits*.)

TRANSFER CHARACTERISTICS

As discussed above, g_{fs} describes the gain of a MOSFET as the change in drain current per change in gate voltage: $\Delta I_D / \Delta V_{GS}$. This means that g_{fs} is the slope of the transfer curve. The transfer curve for the VRF151 is shown in **Figure 17.39** (the data sheet's Figure 2). There are three curves in this graph, depicting the transfer characteristic at three different temperatures.

The three curves cross each other at the "thermal neutral point." This is where the temperature coefficient of V_{TH} changes from negative to positive and it is usually at a current much higher than the part normally operates. This explains why MOSFETs must have thermally compensated gate bias. Below the crossover point, where the part would be biased for class AB, the temperature coefficient of V_{TH} is negative. This means the gate voltage required for a given current goes down as the part heats up. Without thermal bias compensation we can have thermal runaway. The part will usually melt before it reaches the crossover point.

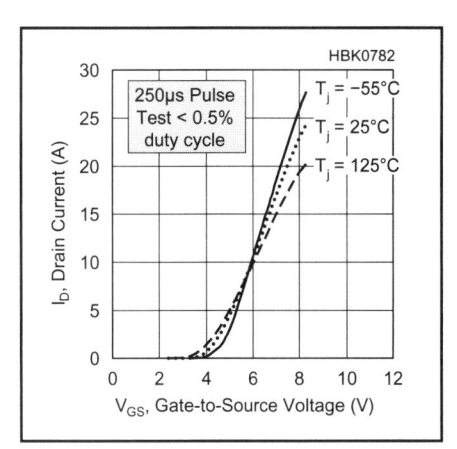

Figure 17.39 — Transfer characteristics for the Microsemi VRF151 RF MOSFET. (Illustration courtesy Microsemi Corp.)

The transfer curve also shows that the gain of the device is not constant. It is quite low at low current and increases to a nominal value over its linear range and then the curves flatten out at higher current as the part saturates. This demonstrates why very low distortion amplifiers are usually operated in class A.

FUNCTIONAL CHARACTERISTICS

This section is where the RF performance is specified — how much gain at what frequency, IMD performance, and ruggedness. While gain and IMD are easily understood, ruggedness is more difficult and it is very poorly defined by most manufacturers. The VRF151 has a ruggedness specification at all phase angles of a 30:1 VSWR when putting out 150 W PEP at 30 MHz. The test circuit is shown on page 4 in the data sheet. Nothing is said about how long the test takes or how well the device is cooled. If the test time and cooling conditions are not given, the specification is inadequate to guarantee that a design will remain within the device power limits. In the author's experience, 90% of all VSWR-related failures are due to over-dissipation. This says that limiting the amplifier's drain current is a simple and effective means for VSWR protection.

DATA SHEET EXTRAS

Test circuits are usually provided so customers can duplicate the test conditions for gain, IMD and output power. Sometimes circuit layouts and complete part lists are also provided. Note however, that while most high power parts are usually used in push-pull circuits, parts in data sheets are always tested one at a time in single-ended circuits. The last page of the data sheet gives the mechanical outline and sometimes mounting information. The VRF151 is "binned" (sorted into similarly performing groups) for V_{TH} as it exits the final testing and the bin letter code is marked on the package. This allows very close matching of gate threshold which is important when used in a push-pull circuit with a common bias supply for both parts. Most designers use separate bias adjustments regardless of matching, but it insures a measure of gain matching also, especially if the parts are from the same lot date code.

17.9.4 Summary Observations

MOSFETs are not perfect devices. g_{fs}, V_{TH}, BV and R_{DS} are all affected by die temperature. g_{fs} goes down with increasing die temperature. While this might cause the output power to sag a bit as the amplifier gets hotter, it is generally a benefit. MOSFETs can be paralleled without requiring source resistors because as the one carrying more current heats up, it loses gain and its resistance goes up, allowing the others to share the load. R_{DS} rises with temperature, a useful trait in hard-switching applications using paralleled devices. Breakdown voltage, BV_{DSS}, increases with temperature and so is usually not a concern in a part that heats up as it is being used. It has implications in cases of extreme cold, as in satellites.

One caveat when paralleling MOSFETs: always be mindful that they will easily oscillate at UHF. The device's inter-electrode capacitances and bonding wire inductances conspire to form a cross-coupled multivibrator. The solution is to place a small resistor in series with the gate leads, 3.3 Ω will usually suffice. This lowers the circuit Q enough to prevent oscillation from starting. [ref: Motorola *Engineering Bulletin 104*, et al]

17.10 Solid State RF Amplifiers

17.10.1 Solid State vs Vacuum Tubes

Solid state amplifiers have become the norm in transceivers, but their use in external high power amplifiers has not. The primary reason is economic. It is more expensive to generate a kilowatt or more with transistors because they are smaller and have less dissipation capability. This is changing as the broadcast and industrial RF industry converts to solid state, making RF power transistors available for amateur use at lower prices. A number of legal-limit solid state Amateur Radio amplifiers are available.

17.10.2 Classes of Operation

This topic applies to transistors as well as tubes, and it was covered earlier in this chapter and also in the **RF Techniques** chapter. In communications amplifiers, Class A is used mainly for driver stages where linearity is desired and efficiency is not a concern.

Class B is usually passed over in favor of the more linear Class AB. Class AB offers RF amplifiers increased linearity, mainly in less crossover distortion, for a very small (perhaps 1% or 2%) reduction in efficiency. It is the most commonly used class of operation for linear power amplifiers that must cover a wide range of frequencies. Broadband solid state Class AB amplifiers typically achieve 50 to 60% efficiency.

Class C is used where efficiency is important and linearity and bandwidth or harmonics are not. FM transmitters are the most common application in communications. Single-band tuned amplifiers can be as much as 80% efficient. However, in a single-ended amplifier they require a tank circuit. Class C amplifiers are *not* suitable for on-off keyed modes like CW without extensive pre-distortion of the driving signal in order to prevent key clicks.

Class D and E are most efficient, up to 95% in practical circuit applications. But both of these both require a narrow band tuned tank circuit to achieve this efficiency. They are not linear; their output is essentially either on or off. They can be used quite effectively for linear amplification by the process of EER (envelope elimination and restoration) but it is always in a single-band circuit. On-off keying can be employed if the power supply is keyed with a properly shaped envelope. EER is difficult to do well and requires very complex circuitry. Without careful system design, EER results in poor SSB performance.

17.10.3 Modeling Transistors

The design method using performance curves that was detailed earlier in this chapter is more applicable to vacuum tube amplifier design than solid state. The most common method used with solid state is electronic design analysis (EDA, also called computer-aided design, or CAD) using electronic models. *SPICE* or S-parameter models are available for some high power transistors, and simple amplifiers can be readily designed with the aid of an appropriate analysis program. (See the **Computer-Aided Circuit Design** chapter for more information on *SPICE* and related modeling techniques.)

Full-featured circuit design and analysis programs are expensive, and the resulting designs are only as good as the accuracy of the transistor models they use. A complicating factor is that any design relies heavily on models for all the passive components in the circuit. While passive part models can be obtained for some commercial components, many others — such as ferrite-loaded transformers — must also be designed before the circuit can be modeled. It is not unusual for the electronic design to take much longer and cost more than the benefits are worth.

As detailed in the **Computer-Aided Circuit Design** chapter, many of the EDA vendors offer free or inexpensive "student versions" of their products. These are fully capable up to a certain level of circuit complexity. Although they usually are not big enough to analyze a whole amplifier, student versions are still particularly useful for looking at parts of the whole.

Electronic design is very useful for getting the circuit design "in the ballpark." The design will be close enough that it will work when built, and any necessary fine tuning can be done easily once it is constructed. Computer modeling is very useful for evaluating the stresses on the circuit's passive components so they can be properly sized. Another very helpful use of CAD is in the development of the output filters. *SVC Filter Designer* by Jim Tonne, W4ENE, available with this book's downloadable supplemental content, is exceptional in this regard.

17.10.4 Impedance Transformation — "Matching Networks"

Aside from the supply voltage, there is little difference between the operation of a tube amplifier and a transistor amplifier. Each amplifies the input signal, and each will only work into a specific load impedance. In a tube amplifier, the proper plate load impedance is provided by an adjustable pi or pi-L plate tuning network, which also transforms the impedance down to 50 Ω.

A single-transistor amplifier can be made in the same way, and in fact most single-band VHF amplifier "bricks" are. A tuned matching network provides the proper load impedance for the transistor and transforms it up to 50 Ω. The major difference is that the proper load impedance for a transistor, at any reasonable amount of power, is much *lower* than 50 Ω. For vacuum tubes it is much *higher* than 50 Ω.

BROADBAND TRANSFORMERS

Broadband transformers are often used in matching to the input impedance or optimum load impedance in a power amplifier. Unlike the tuned matching circuits, transformers can provide constant impedance transformation over a wide range of frequency without tuning. Multi-octave power amplifier performance can be achieved by appropriate application of these transformers. The input and output transformers are two of the most critical components in a broadband amplifier. Amplifier efficiency, gain flatness, input SWR, and even linearity all are affected by transformer design and application.

There are two basic RF transformer types, as described in the **RF Techniques** and **Transmission Lines** chapters: the conventional transformer and the transmission line transformer. More information on RF transformers is included with this book's downloadable supplemental content.

The conventional transformer is wound much the same way as a power transformer. Primary and secondary windings are wound around a high-permeability core, usually made from a ferrite or powdered-iron material. Coupling between the secondary and primary is made as tight as possible to minimize leakage inductance. At low frequencies, the coupling between windings is predominantly magnetic. As the frequency rises, core permeability decreases and leakage inductance increases; transformer losses increase as well.

Typical examples of conventional transformers are shown in **Figure 17.40**. In Figure 17.40A, the primary winding consists of brass or copper tubes inserted into ferrite sleeves. The tubes are shorted together at one end by a piece of copper-clad circuit board material, forming a single turn loop. The secondary winding is threaded through the tubes. Since the low-impedance winding is only a single turn, the impedance transformation ratio is limited to the squares of integers — 1, 4, 9, 16 and so on.

The lowest effective transformer frequency is determined by the inductance of the one-turn winding. It should have a reactance, at the lowest frequency of intended operation, at least four times greater than the impedance

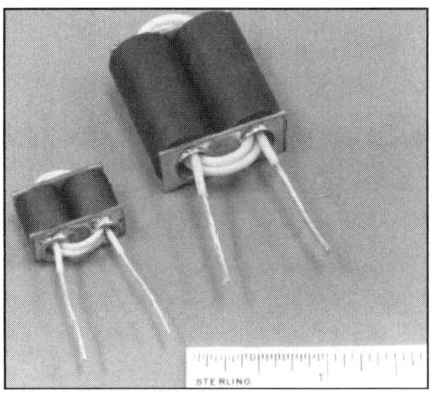

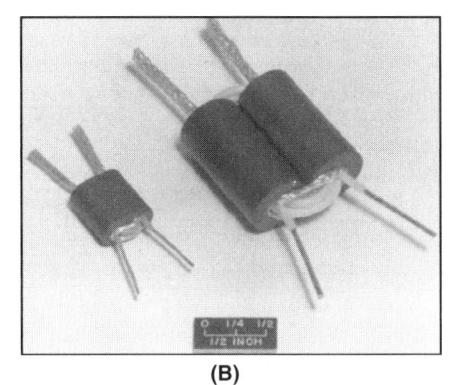

Figure 17.40 — The two methods of constructing the transformers outlined in the text. At A, the one-turn loop is made from brass tubing; at B, a piece of coaxial cable braid is used for the loop.

it is connected to. The coupling coefficient between the two windings is a function of the primary tube diameter and its length, and the diameter and insulation thickness of the wire used in the high-impedance winding. High impedance ratios, greater than 36:1, should use large-diameter secondary windings. Miniature coaxial cable (using only the braid as the conductor) works well. Another use for coaxial cable braid is illustrated in Figure 17.40B. Instead of using tubing for the primary winding, the secondary winding is threaded through copper braid. Because of the increased coupling between the primary and secondary of the transformer made with multiple pieces of coax, leakage reactance is reduced and bandwidth performance is increased.

The cores used must be large enough so the core material will not saturate at the power level applied to the transformer. Core saturation can cause permanent changes to the core permeability, as well as overheating. Transformer nonlinearity also develops at core saturation. Harmonics and other distortion products are produced — clearly an undesirable situation. Multiple cores can be used to increase the power capabilities of the transformer.

Transmission line transformers are similar to conventional transformers, but can be used over wider frequency ranges. In a conventional transformer, high-frequency performance deterioration is caused primarily by leakage inductance, the reactance of which rises with frequency. In a transmission line transformer, the windings are arranged so there is tight capacitive coupling between the two. A high coupling coefficient is maintained up to considerably higher frequencies than with conventional transformers.

The upper frequency limit of the transmission line transformer is limited by the length of the lines. As the lines approach ¼ wavelength, they start to exhibit resonant line effects and the transformer action becomes erratic.

MATCHING NETWORKS AND TRANSFORMERS

The typical tube amplifier tank circuit is an impedance transforming network in a pi or pi-L configuration. With reasonable loaded Q, it also functions as a low-pass filter to reduce the output signal harmonic levels below FCC minimums.

If a transistor amplifier uses a broadband transformer, it must be followed by a separate low-pass filter to achieve FCC harmonic suppression compliance. This is one reason broadband transistor amplifiers are operated in push-pull pairs. The balance between the circuit halves naturally discriminates against even harmonics, making the filtering job easier, especially for the second harmonic. The push-pull configuration provides double the power output when using two transistors, with very little increase in circuit complexity or component count. Push-pull pairs are also easier to match. The input and output impedance of a push-pull stage is twice that of a single-ended stage. The impedance is low, and raising it usually makes the matching task easier.

The transistor's low-impedance operation provides the opportunity to use a simple broadband transformer to provide the transformation needed from the transistor's load impedance up to 50 Ω. This low impedance also swamps out the effects of the device's output capacitance and, with some ferrite loading on the transformer, the amplifier can be made to operate over a very wide bandwidth without adjustment. This is not possible with tubes.

On the other hand, a tube amplifier with its variable output network can be adjusted for the actual output load impedance. The transistor amplifier with its fixed output network cannot be adjusted and is therefore much less forgiving of load variations away from 50 Ω. Circuits are needed to protect the transistor from damage caused by mismatched loads. These protection circuits generally operate "behind the scenes" without any operator intervention. They are essential for the survival of any transistor amplifier operating in the real world.

CALCULATING PROPER LOAD IMPEDANCE

The proper load impedance for a single transistor (or a tube for that matter) is defined by $R = E^2/P$. Converting this from RMS to peak voltage, the formula changes to $R = E^2/2P$. If two devices are used in push-pull (with twice the power and twice the impedance) the formula becomes $R = 2E^2/P$.

There is a constraint. Transformer impedance ratios are the square of their turns ratios. Those with single turn primaries are limited to integer values of 1, 4, 9, 16 and so on. Real-world transformers quickly lose their bandwidth at ratios larger than 25:1 due to stray capacitance and leakage inductance. A design solution must be found which uses one of these ratios. We will use the ubiquitous 100 W, 12 V transceiver power amplifier as an example. Using the push-pull formula, the required load impedance is $2 \times 12.5^2/100 = 3.125$ Ω. The required transformer impedance ratio is $50/3.125 = 16$, which is provided by a turns ratio of 4:1.

Transistor manufacturers, recognizing the broadband transformer constraint, have developed devices that operate effectively using automotive and military battery voltages and practical transformer ratios: 65 W devices for 12 V operation and 150 W devices for 48 V. Bigger 50 V devices have been designed (for example, the MRF154) that will put out 600 W, but practical transformer constraints limit 50 V push-pull output power to 900 W. There are higher voltage devices developed for the industrial markets and they are gradually finding their way into amateur designs. Being able to adjust the impedance to a convenient value for a common transformer turns ratio by adjusting the operating voltage is a powerful design option. These device and transformer limitations on output power can also be overcome by combining the outputs of several PA modules.

17.10.5 Combiners and Splitters

With some exceptions, practical solid state amplifiers have an upper power limit of about 500 W. This is a constraint imposed by the available devices and, to some extent, the ability to cool them. As devices are made more powerful by increasing the area of silicon die, the power density can become so high that only water cooling can provide adequate heat removal. Large devices also have large parasitic capacitances that make securing a broadband match over several octaves very difficult. By building a basic amplifier cell or "brick" and then combining several cells together, transmitter output powers are only limited by the complexity. Combiners and splitters have losses and add cost, so there are practical limits.

Broadband combiners usually take the form of an N-way 0° hybrid followed by an N:1 impedance transformer. The square ratio rule applies here too because the output impedance of a broadband combiner with N input ports is 50/N Ω — so combiners are usually 2, 4, 9 and 16-way. The higher the ratio, the lower the bandwidth will be.

Many types of combiners have been developed. The most common is the 4-way. It is easy to construct and has very good bandwidth. Most of the commercial "1 kW" broadband amplifiers use a 4-way combiner to sum the output of four 300 W push-pull modules operating on 48 V. Every combiner has loss. It may only be a few percent, but this represents a considerable amount of heat and loss of efficiency for a kilowatt output. This is a case where 4 × 300 does not make 1200.

The combiner approach to make a 1 kW solid state amplifier uses a large number of individual parts. A comparable 1 kW tube amplifier requires relatively few. This makes the high-powered solid state unit more expensive and potentially less reliable.

There is an alternative. If we had higher voltage transistors, we could use the same output transformer network configuration to get more output because power rises with the square of the operating voltage. There are high voltage transistors that can operate on 200 V or more. The problem is that these transistors must be capable of handling the corresponding higher power dissipation. The downside of making bigger, more powerful devices is an increase in parasitic capacitance. These bigger transistors become harder to drive and to match over broad bandwidths. However, the circuit simplicity and elimination of the combiner and its losses makes the higher voltage approach quite attractive.

TRANSMISSION LINE TRANSFORMERS AND COMBINERS

Figure 17.41 illustrates, in skeleton form, how transmission-line transformers can be used in a push-pull solid state power amplifier. The idea is to maintain highly balanced stages so that each transistor shares equally in the amplification in each stage. The balance also minimizes even-order harmonics so that low-pass filtering of the output is made much easier. In the diagram, T1 and T5 are current (choke) baluns that convert a grounded connection at one end to a balanced (floating) connection at the other end, with a high impedance to ground at both wires. T2 transforms the 50 Ω generator to the 12.5 Ω (4:1 impedance) input impedance of the first stage. T3 performs a similar step-down transformation from the collectors of the first stage to the gates of the second stage. The MOSFETs require a low impedance from gate to ground. The drains of the output stage require an impedance step up from 12.5 Ω to 50 Ω, performed by T4. Note how the choke baluns and the transformers collaborate to maintain a high degree of balance throughout the amplifier. Note also the various feedback and loading networks that help keep the amplifier frequency response flat.

Three methods are commonly used to combine modules: parallel (0°), push-pull (180°) and quadrature (90°). In RF circuit design, the combining is often done with special types of "hybrid" transformers called splitters and combiners. These are both the same type of transformer that can perform either function. The splitter is at the input, the combiner at the output.

Figure 17.42 illustrates one example of each of the three basic types of combiners. In a 0° hybrid splitter at the input the tight coupling between the two windings forces the voltages at A and B to be equal in amplitude and also equal in phase if the two modules are identical. The 2R resistor between points A and B greatly reduces the transfer of power between A and B via the transformer, but only if the generator resistance is closely equal to R. The output combiner

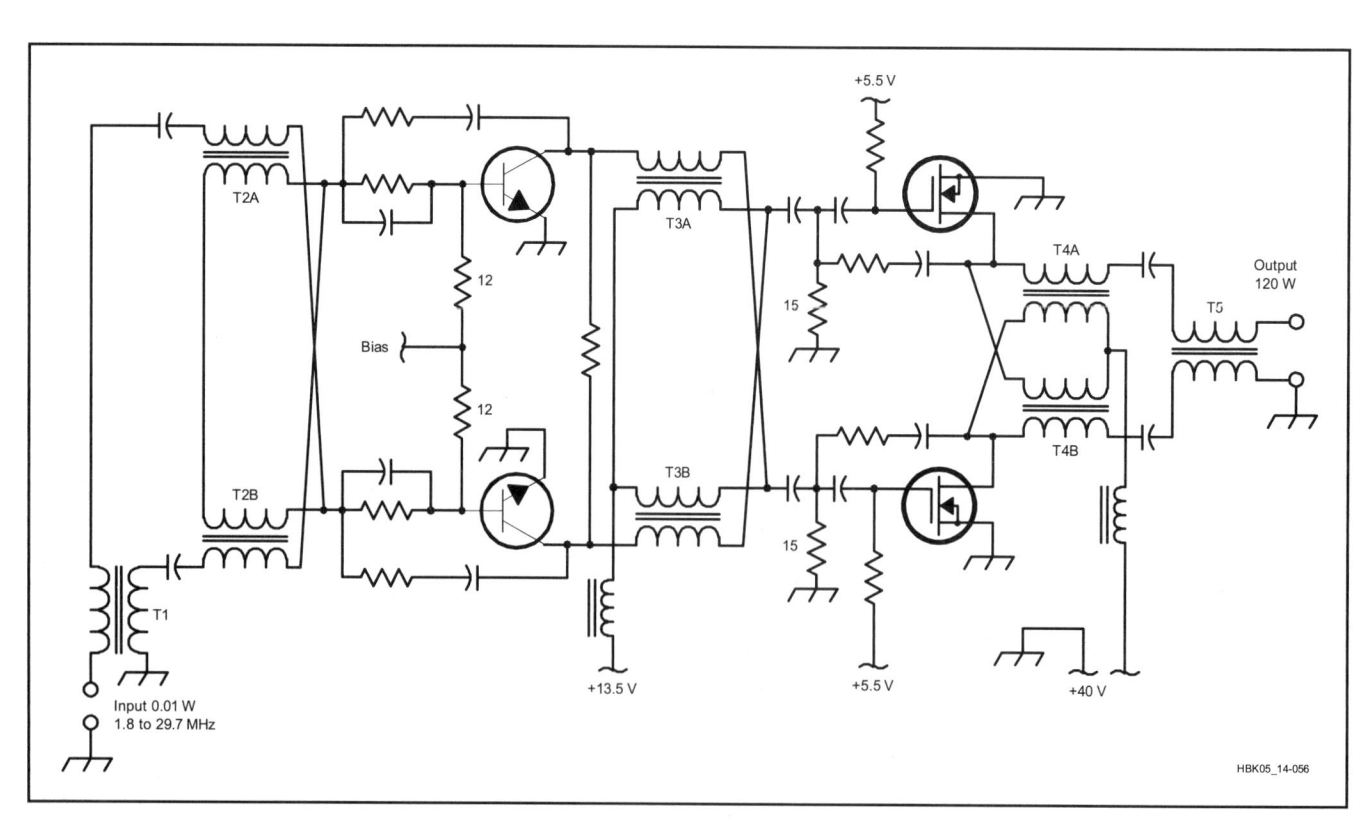

Figure 17.41 — Typical use of transmission line transformers as baluns and combiners in solid state power amplifiers.

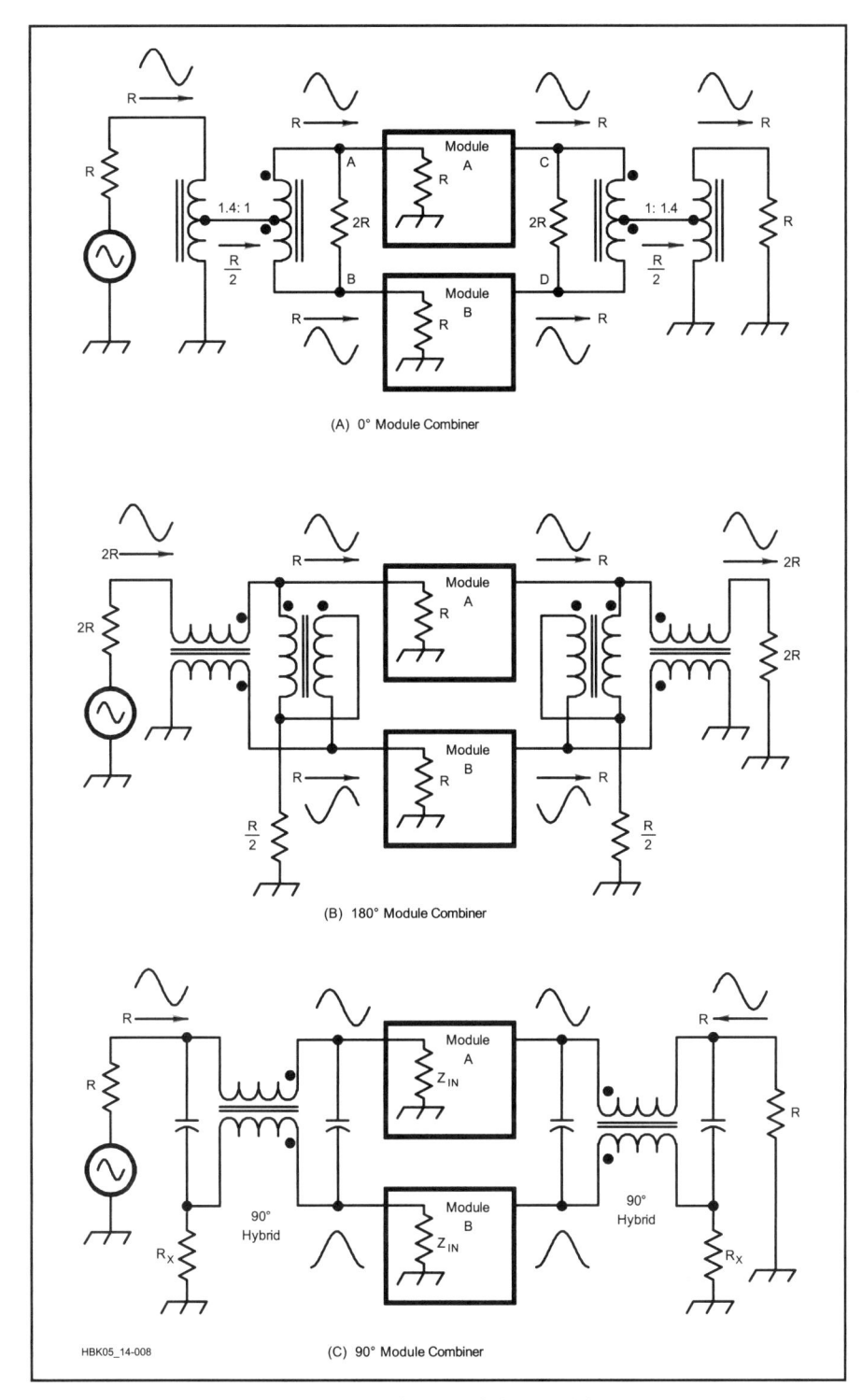

Figure 17.42 — Three basic techniques for combining modules.

separates the two outputs C and D from each other in the same manner, if the output load is equal to R, as shown. No power is lost in the 2R resistor if the module output levels are identical. This section covers the subject of combiners very lightly. We suggest that the reader consult the considerable literature for a deeper understanding and for techniques used at different frequency ranges.

17.10.6 Amplifier Stabilization

Purity of emissions and the useful life (or even survival) of the active devices in a tube or transistor circuit depend heavily on stability during operation. Oscillations can occur at or away from the operating frequency because of undesired positive feedback in the amplifier. Unchecked, these oscillations pollute the RF spectrum and can lead to tube or transistor over-dissipation and subsequent failure. Each type of oscillation has its own cause and its own cure.

In a linear amplifier, the input and output circuits operate on the same frequency. Unless the coupling between these two circuits is kept to a small enough value, sufficient energy from the output may be coupled in phase back to the input to cause the amplifier to oscillate. Care should be used in arranging components and wiring of the two circuits so that there will be negligible opportunity for coupling external to the tube or transistor itself. A high degree of shielding between input and output circuits usually is required. All RF leads should be kept as short as possible and particular attention should be paid to the RF return paths from input and output tank circuits to emitter or cathode.

In general, the best arrangement using a tube is one in which the input and output circuits are on opposite sides of the chassis. Individual shielded compartments for the input and output circuitry add to the isolation. Transistor circuits are somewhat more forgiving, since all the impedances are relatively low. However, the high currents found on most amplifier circuit boards can easily couple into unintended circuits. Proper layout, the use of double-sided circuit boards (with one side used as a ground plane and low-inductance ground return), and heavy doses of bypassing on the dc supply lines often are sufficient to prevent many solid state amplifiers from oscillating.

PARASITIC OSCILLATIONS

In low-power solid state amplifiers, parasitic oscillations can be prevented by using a small amount of resistance in series with the base or collector lead, as shown in **Figure 17.43A**. The value of R1 or R2 typically should be between 10 and 22 Ω. The use of both resistors is seldom necessary, but an empirical determination must be made. R1 or R2 should be located as close to the transistor as practical.

At power levels in excess of approximately 0.5 W, the technique of parasitic suppression shown in Figure 17.43B is effective. The voltage drop across a resistor would be prohibitive at the higher power levels, so one or more ferrite beads placed over connecting leads can be substituted (Z1 and Z2). A bead permeability of 125 presents a high impedance at VHF and above without affecting HF performance. The beads need not be used at both circuit locations. Generally, the terminal carrying the least current is the best place for these suppression devices. This suggests that the resistor or ferrite beads should be connected in the base lead of the transistor.

C3 of Figure 17.43C can be added to some

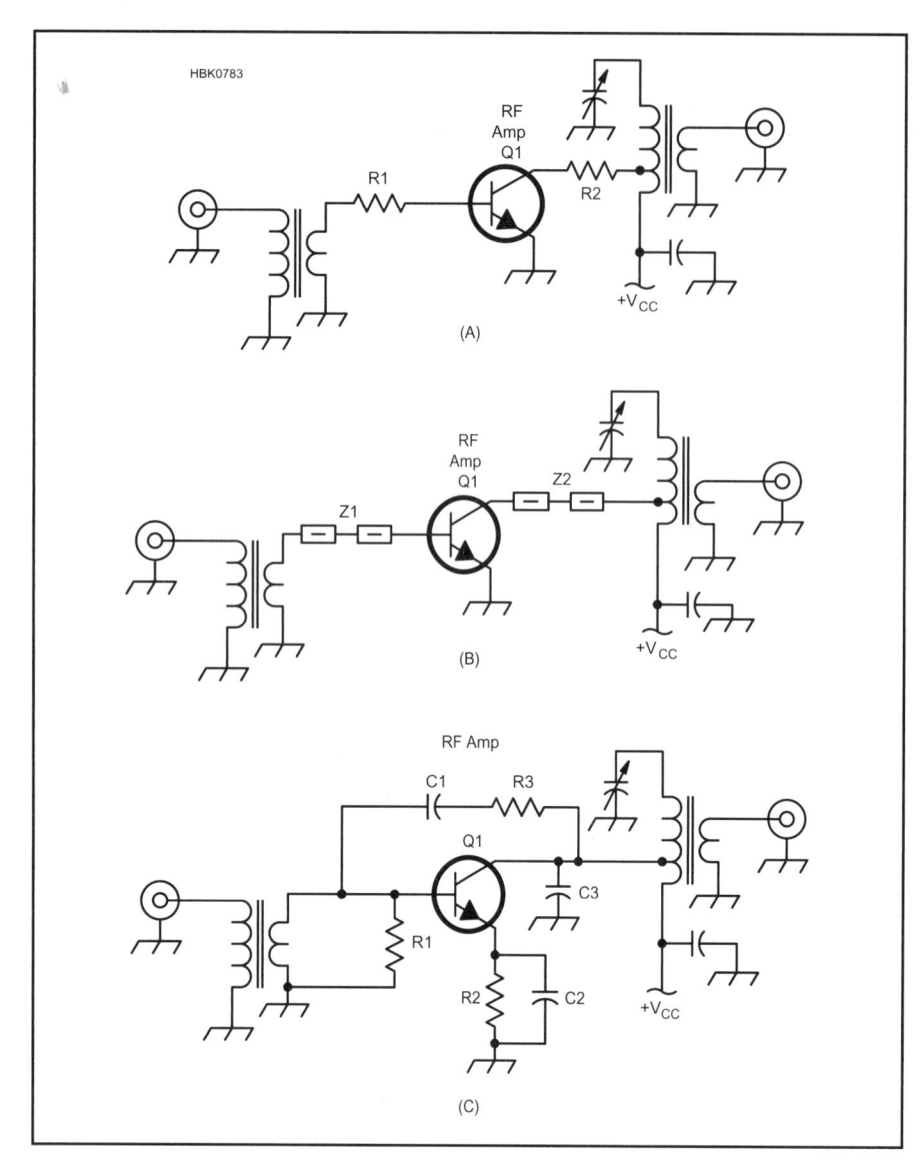

Figure 17.43 — Suppression methods for VHF and UHF parasitics in solid state amplifiers. At A, small base and collector resistors are used to reduce circuit Q. B shows the use of ferrite beads to increase circuit impedance. In circuit C, C1 and R3 make up a high-pass network to apply negative feedback.

power amplifiers to dampen VHF/UHF parasitic oscillations. The capacitor should be low in reactance at VHF and UHF, but must present a high reactance at the operating frequency. The exact value selected will depend upon the collector impedance. A reasonable estimate is to use an X_C of 10 times the collector impedance at the operating frequency. Silver-mica or ceramic chip capacitors are suggested for this application. An additional advantage is the resultant bypassing action for VHF and UHF harmonic energy in the collector circuit. C3 should be placed as close to the collector terminal as possible, using short leads.

The effects of C3 in a broadband amplifier are relatively insignificant at the operating frequency. However, when a narrow-band collector network is used, the added capacitance of C3 must be absorbed into the network design in the same manner as the C_{OUT} of the transistor.

LOW-FREQUENCY PARASITIC OSCILLATIONS

Bipolar transistors and MOSFETs exhibit a rising gain characteristic as the operating frequency is lowered. To preclude low-frequency instabilities because of the high gain, shunt and degenerative feedback are often used. In the regions where low-frequency self-oscillations are most likely to occur, the feedback increases by nature of the feedback network, reducing the amplifier gain. In the circuit of Figure 17.43C, C1 and R3 provide negative feedback, which increases progressively as the frequency is lowered. The network has a small effect at the desired operating frequency but has a pronounced effect at the lower frequencies. The values for C1 and R3 are usually chosen experimentally. C1 will usually be between 220 pF and 0.0015 µF for HF-band amplifiers while R3 may be a value from 51 to 5600 Ω.

R2 of Figure 17.43C develops emitter degeneration at low frequencies. The bypass capacitor, C2, is chosen for adequate RF bypassing at the intended operating frequency. The impedance of C2 rises progressively as the frequency is lowered, thereby increasing the degenerative feedback caused by R2. This lowers the amplifier gain. R2 in a power stage is seldom greater than 10 Ω, and may be as low as 1 Ω. It is important to consider that under some operating and layout conditions R2 can cause instability. This form of feedback should be used only in those circuits in which unconditional stability can be achieved.

R1 of Figure 17.43C is useful in swamping the input of an amplifier. This reduces the chance for low-frequency self-oscillations, but has an effect on amplifier performance in the desired operating range. Values from 3 to 27 Ω are typical. When connected in shunt with the normally low base impedance of a power amplifier, the resistors lower the effective device input impedance slightly. R1 should be located as close to the transistor base terminal as possible, and the connecting leads must be kept short to minimize stray reactances. The use of two resistors in parallel reduces the amount of inductive reactance introduced compared to a single resistor.

17.10.7 Amplifier "Pallet" Modules

Since the early RF amplifier transistors were introduced by Motorola, TRW, and RCA, marketing of these devices was done by having applications engineers design them into functional amplifier modules. The schematic and parts list was provided in the devices' data sheet or in a separate published Application Note. The first and most famous applications engineer was Motorola's Helge Granberg, K7ES. He was inventive and had a very clear and engaging writing style. As more companies entered the RF transistor market, they adopted the same strategy. Even as the technology has evolved from bipolars to VDMOS and LDMOS devices, this is still a valid strategy.

The manufacturers want these applications circuits to demonstrate the capabilities of their products but are understandably reluctant about building, selling, and warranting them. This has provided a business opportunity for other companies to bundle the difficult-to-source components and devices and sell them as semi-kits. Some entrepreneurs go further and build up amplifier modules or "pallets," either from the manufacturer's application notes or of their own design. This has resulted in a wide variety of available kits and pallets. The oldest of these is Communications Concepts in Ohio, but there are many others. Some are listed at the end of this section.

Modules are available in a wide range of power levels, operating voltage, and frequency ranges. They come in two forms: single-band amplifiers using a single-ended topology typically used at VHF or UHF, and broadband amplifiers using balanced "push-pull" topology for HF and even up to 2 meters. **Figure 17.44** shows a 1 kW output pallet designed for HF use.

It is not difficult to read some of these application notes and become excited about having one of them to use on the air. It seems so easy — buy a module, hook up a power supply, your exciter, an antenna and you are on the air! Well, in your dreams. Buying an RF amplifier "brick" and thinking it will be a complete system is more like buying a car engine without the rest of the car. The pallet in Figure 17.44 can be made into a complete amplifier at significant extra cost for supporting electronics. There are many things that are crucially important to comprehend and address before you can put it on the air and have it survive in the typical amateur station.

USING PALLETS IN AN AMPLIFIER

The first concern is stability. Pallets are rated for a 50 Ω load and are seldom characterized for output harmonics. The pallet in Figure 17.44 requires a low-pass filter to operate legally, for example. Some are wildly unstable when operated with real-world VSWR, or when terminated with a low-pass filter that reflects all the harmonic energy back into the module. Oscillation of any sort is a device killer.

The amplifier must meet FCC regulations for harmonic output. This necessitates a low-pass filter. Filters are designed for a specific input and load impedance, usually 50 Ω. The filter may become less effective as the load impedance deviates from 50 Ω but more importantly, a bad load at full power can damage the filter due to high current or voltage stress on the capacitors. The amplifier's efficiency changes as the load changes. While certain non-50 Ω loads may actually cause the amplifier to be more efficient than at 50 Ω, they can still overstress the filter and need to be avoided. Well-designed protection will start to act when the load VSWR exceeds 1.5:1 and absolutely trip at 2:1.

The amplifier needs a power supply with a regulated output that keeps the voltage within 3% of nominal. Voltage sag under load causes flat-topping. It must also have an absolute limit at 125% of normal current. This alone is insufficient to protect an amplifier but will go a long way to prevent "collateral damage" in the event of a circuit failure. There are several reputable manufacturers of small lightweight switchmode supplies available through electronic supply houses and online. Some of these have built-in cooling fans, good regulation and current limiting. Be sure to check that any switchmode supply is RF-quiet when running without a load. Some can generate RF hash in your receiver. Some designs can be keyed, remaining in standby when not powering the amplifier. For such designs, check the wake-up time to ensure it responds quickly enough not to degrade CW keying waveforms.

Many of the currently available commercial amplifiers use a microprocessor-based protection and control system. This provides lots of flexibility, communications capability with the transceiver, and even remote control. If this route is chosen, care must be taken to ensure it is fast enough. VSWR trips must be enabled within 15 ms to be safe. (See the following discussion on transient thermal protection.) Some multi-channel A-to-D circuits take far longer and are not suitable. The controller designed for the 250 W solid-state amplifier in this chapter represents a suitable means of total analog protection. Its fast and simple circuitry can be adapted easily to fit just about any amplifier.

Figure 17.44 — Typical HF amplifier "pallet" designed by Jim Klitzing, W6PQL (www.w6pql.com/index.htm). This design is capable of 1 kW output power and uses the NXP BLF188XR LDMOS amplifier transistor module. [Jim Klitzing, W6PQL, photo]

COOLING A PALLET MODULE

Cooling must be provided and at these power levels is not trivial. Most often the amplifiers are tested on a water-cooled heatsink for which a description and specification are not supplied. However, Granberg did write several expanded application notes describing complete amplifiers that were subsequently published in *QST*. (See the References and Bibliography section at the end of this chapter for articles by Granberg.) Even so, these are lacking by today's standards for ruggedness, operability, safety, and "ham-proofing."

By far the most common cause (> 95%) of expensive RF device failure is thermal overstress when the transistors got too hot and melted before something could be done to relieve the stress — regardless of the cause. There is very little silicon inside an RF transistor (see Figure 17.34). A typical transistor die is less than 0.2-inch square and perhaps 4 mils thick. Thinner is better because all of the heat is produced in the top 0.3 mils and all the heat has to travel through the silicon and through the base of the package header before it reaches the heat sink. Heat transfer takes time, so even if there is a thermal sensor on the heat sink, it will indicate a problem far too late to save the device. Recall that the available device dissipation is related to the difference between the maximum allowed junction temperature and the device's mounting flange. Heat sink temperature sensing is required to limit the long-term accumulated heat in high duty cycle operation, not protect transistor junctions.

Proper thermal protection recognizes all of the possible causes of sudden thermal stress: overdrive, high VSWR (possibly causing poor efficiency), over-current, incorrect low-pass filter selection, and others. The thermal protection system needs to quickly determine when the input power (RF + dc) minus the RF output power exceeds the allowable power dissipation, then disable the amplifier. Disabling can be as simple as opening the PTT line, removing the RF drive, or as enlightened as switching in a 3 dB pad on the input. (Reducing input power might possibly allow you to stay on the air at half power until the transistor cools down.) In any case, disabling the amplifier must be accomplished quickly and in proper sequence — the drive must be removed before the output is disconnected — without "hot switching" of the output.

Thermal protection for transient loads is one thing. Thermal design of the cooling system is another. As covered in the section on MOSFET Design for Amplifiers, the amplifier needs a heat sink with enough cooling capacity to continuously dissipate a power equal to the output power. Above 100 W a fan is needed to ensure adequate airflow over the heat sink. A proportional speed control is recommended. It can be off when the sink is below 100 °F and full speed when the sink reaches 140 °F. This will reduce the harmful dust buildup on the fins in standby and low duty cycle operation. Design of proportional fan controls is covered in articles such as "Why and How to Control Fan Speed for Cooling Electronic Equipment" by Mary Burke from Analog Devices (**www.analog.com/en/analog-dialogue/articles/how-to-control-fan-speed.html**).

Some of the available amplifier modules have adequate heat spreaders, others have none. This is very important. Considering that all of the power dissipation comes from a very small device footprint, a good layer of copper the same size as the heat sink fin extrusion area ensures the sink is adequately "illuminated."

CURRENT SUPPLIERS OF RF PALLET MODULES

These are not the only manufacturers providing pallet modules and more vendors are entering the market. This list is intended to provide a sample of current sources for RF pallet modules.

RF Source: **www.rfsource.gr/phv305-hf-pallet.html**

R3KBO: **eb104.ru/**

Italab: **www.italab.it/prodotti_uk.php?cat=3&scat=10**

Broadcast Concepts, Inc.: **broadcastconcepts.com/ISM-Pallets/**

Brounley RF, Inc.: **www.rfpowerdesign.com/Products.html**

RF Parts Company: **www.rfparts.com/module.html**

Mouser Electronics (typical part): **www.mouser.com/ds/2/161/MRFE6VP61K25H-67773.pdf**

17.11 Solid State Amplifier Projects

This section presents three solid state amplifier designs that operate on a very wide range of frequencies. The first is an HF+6 meter design by Dick Frey, K4XU that will amplify the output of QRP radios in the 10-15 W range to 250 W. It provides an excellent design example of current solid state amplifier design practices described in the previous sections, especially the control and protection circuitry. A second amplifier by James Klitzing, W6PQL, covers 2 meters. It is a linear design suitable for both SSB/CW and FM and has an output power of around 80 W. The final design by Steve Lampereur, KB9MWR, operates on the microwave band of 10 GHz. While the 2 W output may not sound like a lot of power, at X band it is considered QRO especially when combined with a dish antenna that provides tens of dB of gain!

Complete design and construction information for all of these amplifier designs is included with this book's downloadable supplemental content. In addition, several other amplifier designs are presented for both HF and VHF/UHF operation.

17.11.1 Project: A 250 W Broadband Linear Amplifier

The amplifier described here and shown in **Figure 17.45** is neither revolutionary nor daring. It uses commonly available parts — no special parts and no "flea market specials." It is based on well-proven commercial designs and "best design practices" acquired over the past 30 years as solid state technology has matured. This design project was undertaken for the 2010 edition of the *ARRL Handbook* as a detailed design example as well as a practical solid state amplifier you can build. It is a continuing project. The full description of the amplifier including construction and operating details is provided with this book's downloadable supplemental content.

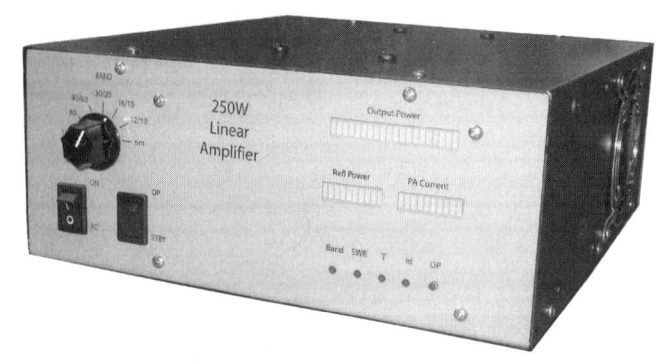

Figure 17.45 — This 250 W amplifier for 160 through 6 meters provides a detailed design example as well as a practical project. Additional photos and information about the interior layout may be found with this book's downloadable supplemental content.

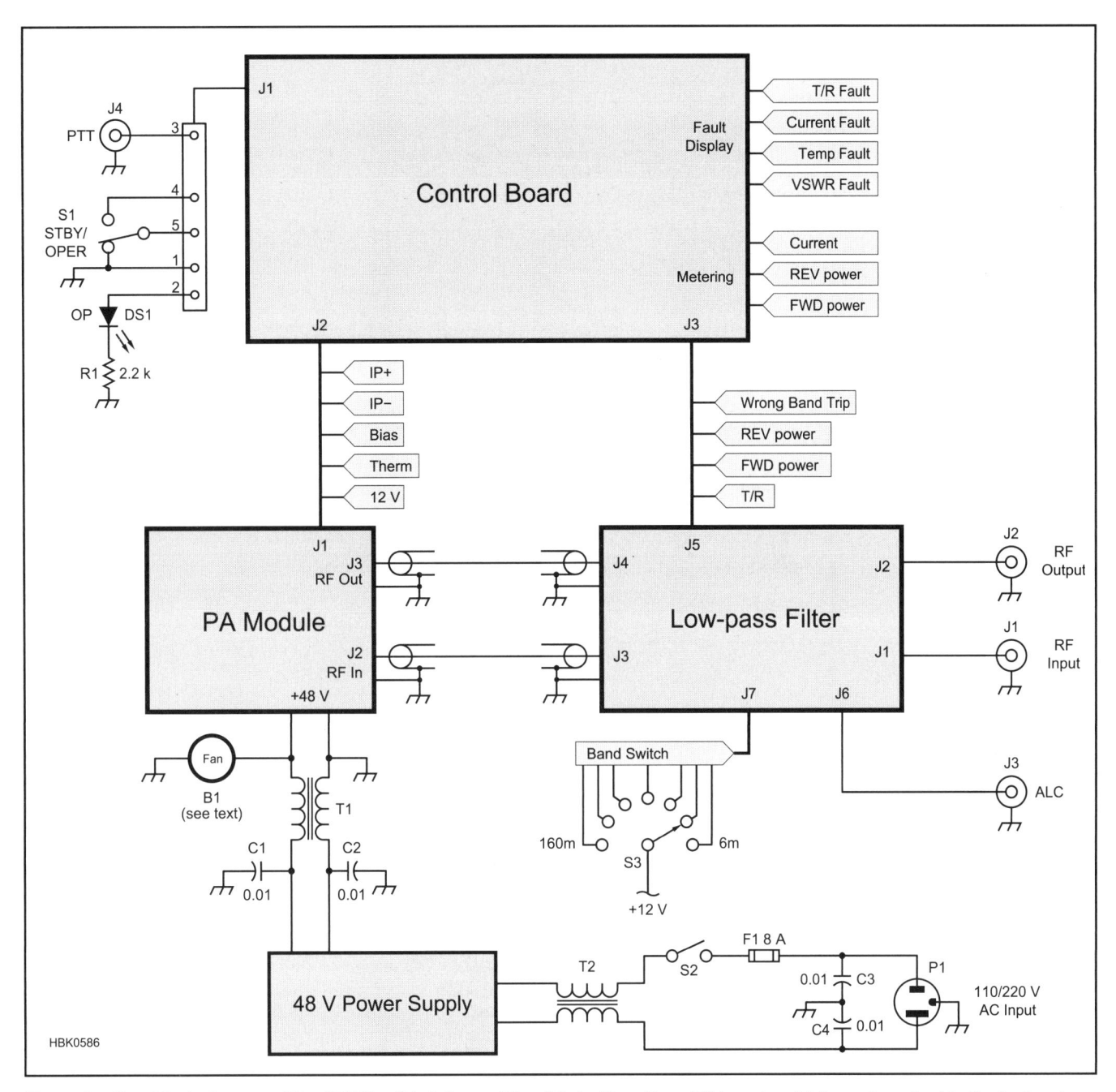

Figure 17.46 — Block diagram of the 250 W solid state amplifier. It is built on three PC boards, which are described in the text and accompanying diagrams. T1 and T2 are 2 turns through a Fair-Rite 2643540002 ferrite bead if needed to suppress RFI from the switching power supply.

A block diagram for the project is given in **Figure 17.46**. The amplifier is built on three PC boards — a PA module, a low-pass filter assembly, and a board for control, protection and metering circuitry. This book's downloadable supplemental content includes *ExpressPCB* files for these boards, and the artwork can be used to have boards made in small quantities (see **www.expresspcb.com** for details).

The basic PA configuration has been in the *Handbook* since the 2010 edition. It is intended to be a "ham-proof" external amplifier for QRP transceivers that put out 15 W or less. It is designed for a gain of 30×, or 15 dB. Drive power of less than 10 W will provide 250 W output from 1.8 through 51 MHz. The amplifier provides exceptionally linear performance, necessary for high quality SSB and PSK modes, and is rugged enough to withstand the most rigorous contest environment.

Amplifier design tends to focus on the RF section, but a successful stand-alone solid state amplifier is equally dependent on its control system. The control requirements for a tube amplifier are well known, while those for solid state amplifiers are not. This is mostly because the functions of a solid state amplifier's control system are generally transparent to the user. Parameters are monitored and protection is applied without any operator intervention. This must be. While tubes are fairly forgiving of abuse, semiconductors can heat so quickly that intervention *must* be automatic or they can be destroyed.

Transistors are sensitive to heat, so cooling and temperature compensation are critical to a successful design. Transistors require a heat

RF Power Amplifiers 17.39

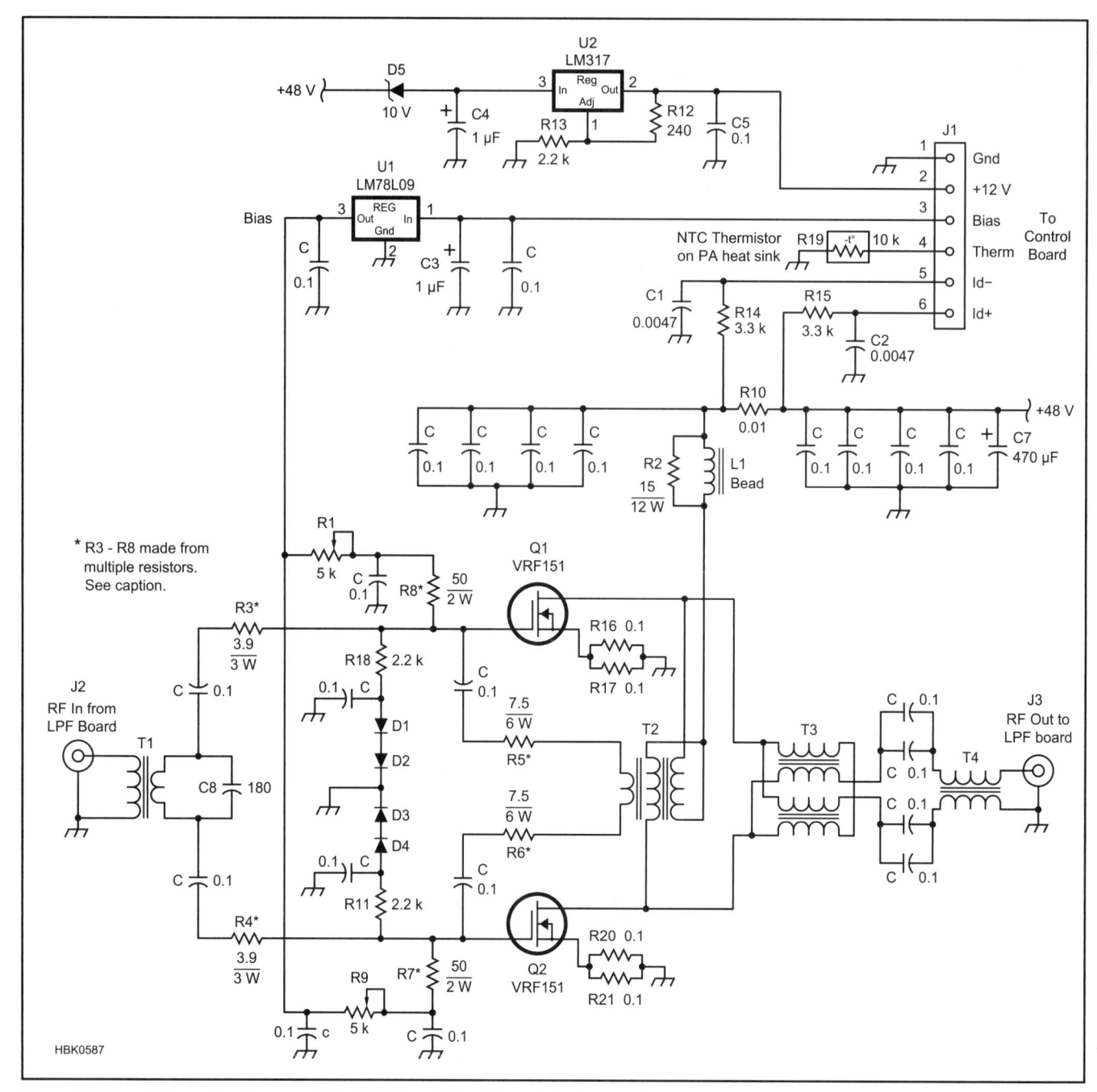

Figure 17.47 — Schematic diagram of the 250 W amplifier PA module. A complete parts list may be found with this book's downloadable supplemental content.

sink. Power amplifier tubes have large surface areas and are cooled by air blown on or through them. Transistors are small. Mounting them on a heat sink increases their thermal mass and provides a much larger surface area so the heat dissipated in the devices can be removed either by convection or forced air. The thermal design of an amplifier is just as important as the electrical design. More information on thermal design may be found in the **Circuits and Components** chapter.

Silicon's thermal coefficient causes the bias current to increase as the device heats up if the bias source is fixed. The increased current causes even more heating and can lead to thermal runaway. For stable Class AB linear operation, the gate bias for a MOSFET or bipolar transistor must track the temperature of the device. The control circuit typically uses another silicon device such as a diode thermally coupled to the amplifier heat sink near the transistor to sense the temperature and adjust the bias to maintain a constant bias current.

Transistor power amplifiers are designed to operate into 50 Ω. Operation into a VSWR other than 1:1 will cause an increase in device dissipation and other stress. The success of the solid state transceiver is due to its integrated PA protection system. The temperature of the heatsink, the load VSWR, the output power and the supply current are all monitored by the control system. If any of these exceed their threshold limits, the RF drive is reduced by the transceiver's ALC system.

An external solid state PA protection system must perform the same functions, but the driver's ALC circuit is not always available so other means must be used to protect the PA. This is usually accomplished simply by taking the amplifier out of the circuit. An indicator then tells the operator which condition caused the fault so appropriate action can be taken. Access to the driver's ALC system would make this protection task more automatic, smoother and less troublesome, but no two transceiver models have the same ALC characteristic. This makes the design of a universal ALC interface more difficult.

THE 1.8 TO 55 MHz PA

Figure 17.47 shows the power amplifier (PA) schematic. Two Microsemi VRF151 MOSFETs are used in this amplifier. The circuit topology is a 4:1 transmission line transformer type, rather than a "tube and sleeve" type common in many PA designs and discussed earlier. This style offers more bandwidth, necessary to provide performance on 6 meters. Typical gain is 15 dB; 10 W drive will easily provide 250 W output with a 48 V supply. There is a lot of latitude in this design. It can even be operated on an unregulated supply. As long as the maximum unloaded voltage does not exceed 65 V, the transistors will not be overstressed. Other devices such as the MRF151, SD2931 or BLF177 would probably also work but have not been tested. They will require a regulated power supply, however.

FEEDBACK — TWO KINDS

The amplifier's gain is controlled by two kinds of feedback. Shunt feedback (from drain to gate) is provided by the link on T2 through resistors R5 and R6. It tends to lower the input impedance, but it also helps to keep the gain constant over frequency and improve the linearity. Series feedback is provided by the 0.05 Ω of resistance in each source. This increases the input impedance, cuts the gain by 3 dB, and most importantly, it has a huge effect on the linearity.

Without any feedback at all, the amplifier would have more than about 30 dB of gain (×1000) at some frequencies, tending to make it unstable — prone to parasitic oscillation. And the linearity would be terrible, –25 dBc or so IMD products. It would also be very sensitive to load changes. The input SWR is 1.2:1 on 160 meters and rises to 1.5:1 on 6 meters. The amplifier's gain is 15 dB ±0.5 dB over the same frequency range.

CONTROL AND PROTECTION

The control board appears far more complicated than the PA but in reality, it is just a few analog and logic ICs. This circuitry monitors several parameters, displays them, and if necessary, puts the amplifier into standby if one of them goes out of range. This control system could be used on any amplifier. All solid state amplifiers need similar protection. The amplifier is protected for:

1. Over temperature, by a thermistor on the heatsink and setting a limit.

2. Over current, by measuring the PA current and setting a maximum limit.

3. High SWR, by monitoring the reflected power and setting a maximum limit.

4. Selection of a low-pass filter lower than the frequency in use.

Each of these fault trips results in forcing the amplifier into the standby position and out of the RF path, and lighting an error LED. There is also an ALC level detector that generates a negative-going feedback voltage for the driver when the RF drive goes above the level corresponding to maximum power. If this PA were part of a transceiver, the several faults described above would generate inputs into the ALC system and turn back the drive rather than taking it off the air. We do not always have that luxury so the best course is to take it off line until the cause can be fixed.

PERFORMANCE

The maximum for the PA design itself is 300 W. Increasing its output past 300 W to make up for filter loss quickly degrades the IMD performance. It needs some headroom. So, in very un-amateur fashion, this amplifier is conservatively rated at 250 W output. This provides a clean signal and plenty of margin for wrong antenna selection, disconnected feed lines, and all the other things that can kill amplifiers that are run too close to their limit.

The PA will provide 250 W PEP for sideband or PSK and 250 W CW. The design goal for this PA was to make it reliable and at least as good as any competitive transceiver. The harmonics are –60 dB on HF and –70 dB on 6 meters. Transmit IMD is >38 dB down from either tone.

Parasitics are not usually a problem in broadband amplifiers because of the feedback used. The prototype was tested into a 3:1 SWR load at all phase angles without breaking into parasitic oscillation anywhere.

17.11.2 *Project:* All-Mode, 2 Meter, 80 W Linear Amp

This solid state amplifier by James Klitzing, W6PQL, is designed for the many low-power 2 meter rigs, ranging from handheld transceivers for FM to older multimode transceivers and even the newer all purpose types such as the Yaesu FT-817 or the Elecraft 2 meter transverters.

The project was featured in the May 2013 issue of *QST* and that article is available with this book's downloadable supplemental content. The article explains more about the amplifier design and supplies additional construction details. Artwork for the PC board is provided on the *QST* in Depth web page (**www.arrl.org/qst-in-depth**), along with fabrication drawings for sheet metal parts.

The amplifier shown in **Figure 17.48** is low in cost and simple (no preamp or power meters), yet capable of fixed station or mobile operation in any mode and operation from the usual nominal 12 V dc power supply. The same supply that powers a 100 W HF transceiver can likely power the amplifier. The amplifier includes:

• An output low-pass filter to comply with FCC regulations for harmonic and spurious suppression.

• A low-loss antenna relay.

• An RF-sensing TR switch for remote operation, as well as a hard key option.

• TR sequencing to protect the S-AV36 module and prevent hot switching of the antenna relay.

Figure 17.48 — The 80 W 2 meter linear amplifier is suitable for operation with any mode.

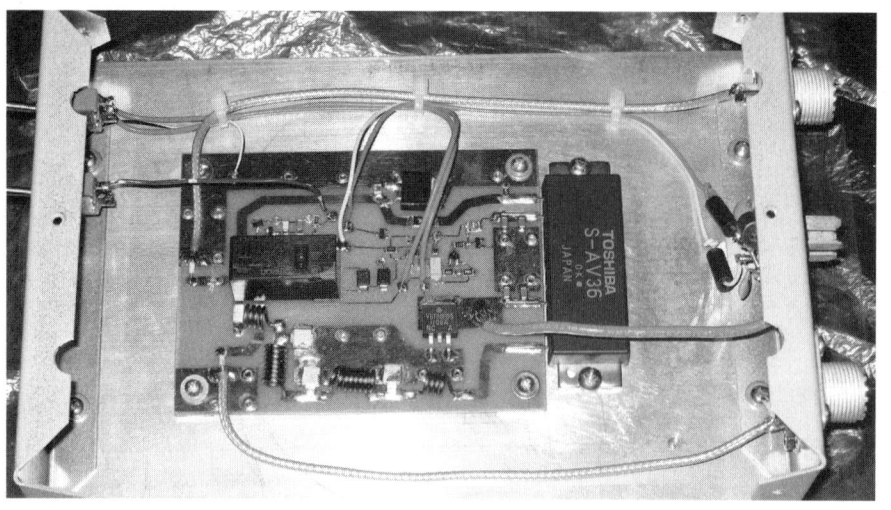

Figure 17.49 — Inside of the compact amplifier showing the simplicity of the final design. The amplifier module is the black rectangle connected to the right edge of the PC board.

Table 17.6
2 Meter Amplifier Operating Parameters

Output power and current required with resting current at 8 A

Drive Power (W)	Output Power (W)	Current (A) at 13.5 V
1	12	8.2
2	29	9.0
3	44	9.5
4	53	10.0
5	66	11.0
6	74	11.5
7	80	12.0
8	85	12.5
9	89	12.8
10	92	13.0

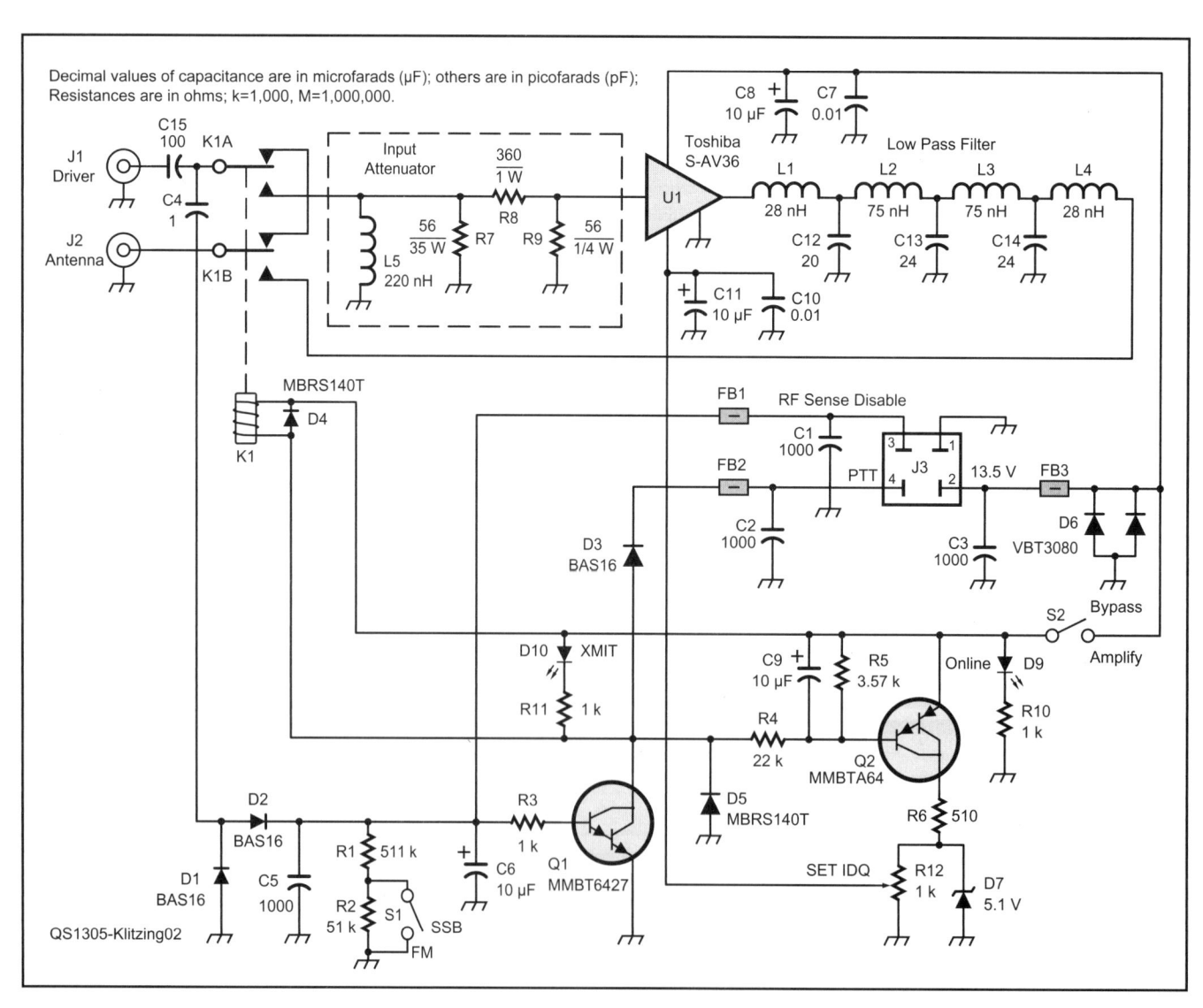

Figure 17.50 — Schematic of the 80 W, 2 meter linear amplifier. A complete parts list is included with this book's downloadable supplemental content.

17.42   Chapter 17

- Indicator LEDs and control switches.
- Reverse polarity protection.

The inside construction is shown in **Figure 17.49**. The small PC board can be made at home (see the **Construction Techniques** chapter) or ordered from the author (see **www.arrl.org/qst-in-depth**). The schematic is provided in **Figure 17.50** and a complete parts list is included in the full article with this book's downloadable supplemental content. The input and output power of the amplifier with the built in attenuator for a 10 W exciter is provided in **Table 17.6**. This also shows the current required at 13.8 V dc.

The amplifier is designed around the Toshiba S-AV36 module. The module provides 50 Ω input and output impedances and supplies enough gain that less than 50 mW can drive it to full output in any mode. This design will work with any exciter providing 1 to 10 W of drive, through the use of a built-in attenuator (R7, R8, and R9 in the schematic — see the full article for a table of resistor values that create different levels of attenuation.)

The low-pass filter (L1-L4, C12-C14) is a standard pi network, seven-pole Chebyshev filter. The design provides the required additional harmonic suppression to meet the FCC requirements with very little insertion loss at the operating frequency.

A PCB-mount DPDT general purpose relay was chosen for TR and bypass switching. The contacts are rated at 8 A. At 2 meters, a bit of reactance is introduced by this part, but compensated for by a small capacitor (C15) in series with its input.

The amplifier can be switched ON and OFF by using a control line back to the driving radio (PTT) or an RF sensing circuit is includes that samples the drive from the input connector to provide the transmit trigger.

TR switching is sequenced to prevent the module from attempting to transmit until the relay contacts have switched and settled completely. Hot-switching damages the relay contacts and stressed the amplifier module. The circuitry associated with the base of Q1 does the sampling and controls the sequence timing. Less than ½ W of drive will trigger TR operation.

17.11.3 Project: 10 GHz 2 W Amplifier

Generating RF power above a few milliwatts in the 10 GHz band used to be very difficult. Thankfully, Hittite Microwave Corp (**www.hittite.com**) has the HMC487 (the version currently available is the HMC487LP5), which is an easy-to-use X-band amplifier chip that requires no complicated external RF circuitry or special voltage biasing. The HMC487 costs around $60 in single quantities and the evaluation board — which is highly recommended — is a couple hundred dollars. This amplifier project by Steve Lampereur, KB9MWR, is based on the HMC487 evaluation board to help make construction of the final amplifier very easy, even for a beginner microwave experimenter.

The complete article is available with this book's downloadable supplemental content, including construction details and adjustment instructions. The HMC487 data sheet is available from the manufacturer's website.

The HMC487 has around 20 dB of gain from 9 to 12 GHz and is internally matched to 50 Ω on both the RF input and output. It will easily generate 1 W (+30 dBm) of RF output with a 10 mW (+10 dBm) RF input over most of the X-band. It saturates at around 2 W (+33 dBm). The only real drawback to the HMC487 is the large amount of heat it needs to dissipate. Its RF efficiency is only around 20% and the rest of this energy will need to be dissipated as heat.

There are two components to the project — the power supply shown in **Figure 17.51** and the evaluation board. The power supply must generate +7 V at high current to supply the amplifier and –0.3 V for biasing the amplifier gate.

The evaluation board is shown in **Figure 17.52**, where it is mounted on an aluminum plate that acts as a heat sink. A 10 GHz isolator is added to the output to prevent any power reflected from the load from reaching the amplifier IC. Short cables with SMA connectors are used to connect the evaluation board to the chassis-mounted receptacles.

Figure 17.51 — Power supply board that generates the +7 V dc operating and -0.3 V dc bias voltages for the amplifier evaluation board.

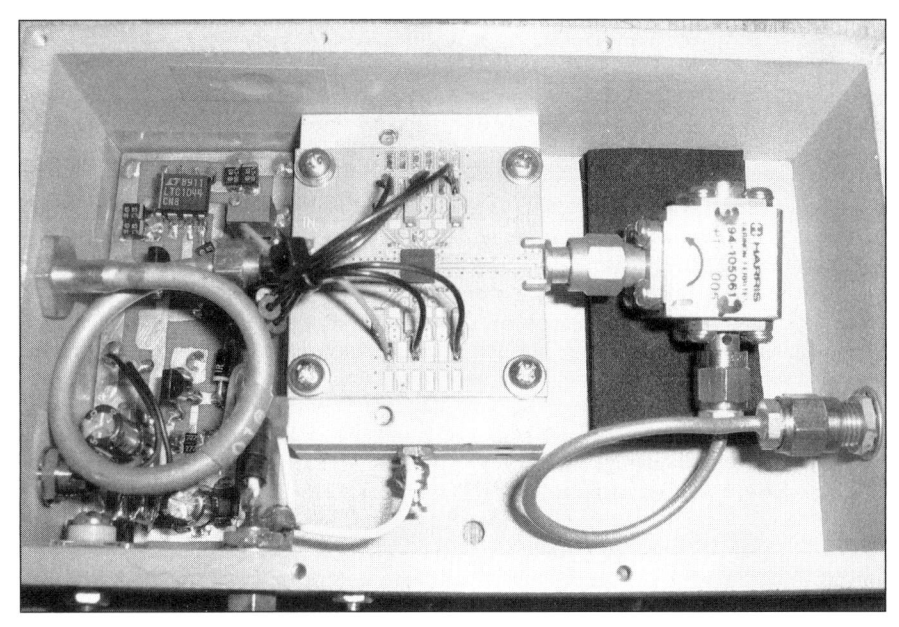

Figure 17.52 — Assembled 10 GHz amplifier. The power supply board is at the left of the enclosure. The evaluation board at center is mounted on an aluminum block to dissipate heat. An isolator at right protects the amplifier output from high SWR.

17.12 Tube Amplifier Projects

Vacuum tube amplifier projects involve several aspects that the builder, particularly beginning amplifier builders, should be aware of and respect. First and foremost are the high voltages associated with these projects — even at the low end of the output power scale. Read the section on High Voltage Techniques in the **Power Sources** chapter and the cautions on measuring high voltages in the **Test Equipment and Measurements** chapter — comply with those recommendations and cautions. Make sure your antenna system and test equipment are suitable for the power and voltages level you will encounter. Consider RF exposure, particularly at 10 meters and higher frequencies at which the Maximum Permissible Exposure limits can be easily reached with a high-power amplifier. (See the **Safety** chapter for more information on RF exposure.) Respect the capabilities of high-power RF!

This section contains overviews of three tube amplifier projects.

- The "Everyham's Amp" is a simple, entry level amplifier design that can develop an output of several hundred watts. The amplifier can be built around several combinations of inexpensive tubes currently available new or surplus. It is intended for the first-time amp builder or for someone who needs a utility amplifier, perhaps for a single band.
- The 3CX1500D7 amplifier is a sophisticated legal-limit design competitive with top-of-the-line commercial models. This model is intended for intermediate builders who have experience with basic metalworking skills and high-power amplifiers.
- A 6 meter kilowatt amplifier design is also suitable for intermediate builders and uses a single 4CX1600 ceramic tube to reach power outputs of about 1 kW, depending on drive level.

Complete design and construction information for all of these amplifier designs is included with this book's downloadable supplemental content. In addition, several other amplifier designs are presented for both HF and VHF/UHF operation.

17.12.1 *Project:* The Everyham's Amplifier

Recent editions of the *Handbook* have featured amplifiers that are true works of art, nearly as capable and as elegant as any on the market. Amplifiers such as the HF legal limit amplifier design by Jerry Pittenger, K8RA, in this and recent editions clearly show what advanced amateurs can do.

Many hams who would like to build a basic linear amplifier for their station may not feel ready for advanced amplifier designs — either technically or financially. Contributed by John Stanley, K4ERO, the amplifier project in **Figure 17.53** is a very basic design that will satisfy the need for more power and encourage the reader to experience amplifier building, while providing only the bands and features desired. Once a simple amplifier has been constructed successfully, more advanced designs will be easier to tackle.

The following is an overview and summary of the amplifier's design. A complete description of this amplifier, including additional photographs and drawings, construction details, and additional features is available with this book's downloadable supplemental content. An additional three-band design by Leigh Tregellas, VK5TR, is also included with this book's downloadable supplemental content.

AMPLIFIER CONFIGURATION

The design presented here is based on a modular approach. Each of the three major sections (tubes, tuning network, power supply) is somewhat independent and can be changed out separately. In addition, the starting design is "bare bones," containing nothing that is not absolutely essential for the amplifier to work and provide a minimum level of safety against overloads, abuse, or accidents. TR switching is included in the most basic design because it gives significant advantages at low cost. For the basic design, each part will be described and its purpose explained.

Several options for the major components are presented with the builder being able to choose what best meets his or her needs and best uses the components available in junk boxes, online, or at hamfests. Many small parts such as resistors and diodes are cheap enough that one need not buy them used. Control transformers and tubes are easy to find through online auction sites. Be sure to check shipping costs on heavy items such as transformers.

By shopping carefully, you can avoid the budget being busted by that one essential component costing lots more than expected. Don't overlook acquiring a damaged commercial amplifier or a "basket case" homebrew project — the parts and enclosure hardware available from these are often worth many times the asking price! Refer to the sidebar in this chapter, "Using 'Surplus' Parts for Your Amplifier" for more information about purchasing used and surplus amplifier parts.

Additions and modifications that will improve performance are described in the expanded article with this book's downloadable supplemental content and can be added after the initial amplifier is built and tested. Most can be installed in a day, so you need not discontinue using the amp in order to upgrade.

DESIGN OVERVIEW

The basic circuit is shown in **Figure 17.54**. The tubes used in this design are triodes, connected in a grounded-grid configuration. The amplifier can be constructed to use a single 3-500Z or a pair of 811A, 572B, GI-6B or GI-7B tubes. All of these are currently available new or surplus at reasonable cost. The input grid circuit input is driven directly. Tuned input circuits are discussed later as an option.

C3, L1 and C4 form an impedance-matching pi network that transforms the 50 Ω load at the output to the several thousand ohm load that the tube requires. In addition, this "tank" filters out the harmonics from the tube while passing the desired fundamental signal. An optional band switch, S3, is shown. In its simplest form it shorts out sections of L1 as the operating frequency increases. A single-band design doesn't need S3.

Figure 17.53 — The front panel of the Everyham's Amplifier. This version is designed to cover three bands (80, 40, and 20 meters). A window is included at left to allow viewing of the tube.

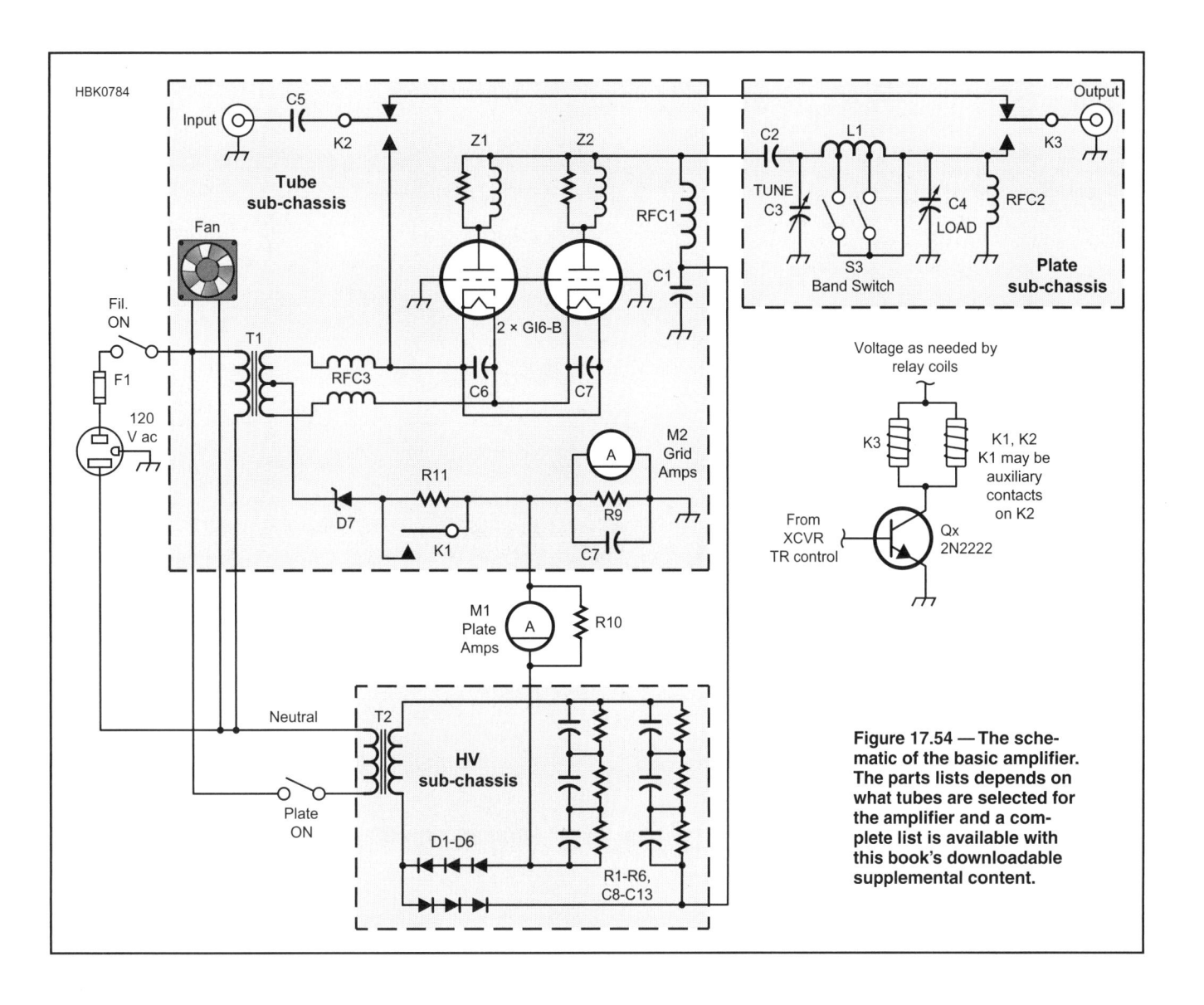

Figure 17.54 — The schematic of the basic amplifier. The parts lists depends on what tubes are selected for the amplifier and a complete list is available with this book's downloadable supplemental content.

When the amplifier is OFF or the transceiver is in receive, the antenna connects directly to the transceiver antenna jack via the two relays as shown in **Figure 17.55**. (K2 and K3 in the main schematic.) When the transceiver is in transmit *and* the amplifier turned on, the transceiver output is routed through the amplifier and amplified.

As part of the TR process, we will want to bias the amplifier off during receive. This saves energy, cools the tube(s) and also removes any RF noise the tube(s) might produce that could get into the receiver. When opened during receive, K1 in Figure 17.54 lifts the center tap of the filament transformer (tube cathode) from ground. K1 can be a separate relay or an additional set of contacts on the TR relays K2 and K3 if they are internal to the amplifier. Usually a resistor (R11), perhaps 47 kΩ or so, is left between the center tap and ground to provide a dc current path.

The power supply shown is a basic voltage doubler. (See the **Power Sources** chapter for information on rectifier and voltage multiplier circuits, as well as an alternative power supply design.) If a high-voltage secondary transformer is available, a rating of 500 VA is required for intermittent service up to 1 kW output. A 250 VA rating is sufficient for intermittent service to 500 W with a voltage quadrupler. At one time, TV transformers were commonly used for amplifiers of this size. However, they are becoming hard to find and their age leads to insulation breakdown, thus they are not recommended for this project.

For T2, the main power transformer, the circuit uses two 480/240 to 120 V "control" transformers with the two 480 V windings in series as a secondary. Control transformers are used in industry to reduce the plant's 480 or 240 V equipment wiring to 120 V for the purpose of operating instrumentation and control electronics. These typically have two 240 V windings that can be connected in series for 480 V or run in parallel for higher current. These transformers are commonly

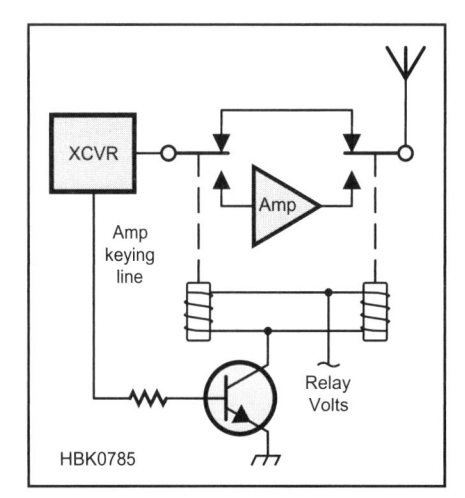

Figure 17.55 — The TR switching of transmit and receive signals for the basic amplifier is controlled by the transceiver's amplifier keying output signal, assumed here to be a positive voltage to key the amplifier with a suitable current-limiting resistor and relay drive transistor installed in the amplifier.

RF Power Amplifiers   17.45

Using "Surplus" Parts for Your Amplifier

First-time builders of power amplifiers soon discover that buying all new electronic components from a parts list is costly. Manufacturers realize significant savings by purchasing components in bulk, but the builder of a single unit will pay top dollar for each new part thus negating any savings in the labor costs. While some impressive equipment has been built using all new parts, pride of design and workmanship are usually the goals, not cost savings.

The way to break this economic barrier is to use surplus parts. These are items left over when a project is finished, a design changes, or a war ends. Sometimes, costly parts can be recovered from relatively new but obsolete equipment. Alert dealers locate sources of surplus parts, buy them at auction, often for pennies on the dollar, and make them available in stores, on-line or at hamfests.

Parts can become available when a project is abandoned for which parts have been gathered. Many hams maintain a "junk box" of parts against future needs, only to find it has grown beyond a manageable size. This may contain a mixture of new, used and NOS parts (new old stock, meaning unused but stored for many years).

When buying electronic parts from other than a trusted supplier of new stock, some precautions are in order. Before shopping the surplus shelves or making an on-line purchase, do some research. You are leaving behind the security of buying a specific part that the designer of the amplifier has tested in actual operation. One has to be sure not only that the part is sound, but that it is suited for the intended purpose. This effort is justified by the anticipated savings of up to 80%. Using "odd" parts may make your amplifier a "one of a kind" project, since the next builder won't be able to obtain the same items. Your amplifier may not be reproducible, but it can still be an object of pride and usefulness.

Surplus vacuum tubes may be of military origin. In the 50s and 60s WWII tubes powered many ham amplifiers. Tubes made in Russia in past decades are now available.[1] Many hams have used these tubes for new designs and even as replacements for hard-to-find or more expensive tube types in existing amplifiers. Since tubes have a limited life, one may wish to buy a spare or two before committing to using a surplus type, since future availability is always a concern. Broadcast or medical "pulls" or "pull-outs" provide a source of good used

Figure 17.A4 — A hamfest is often a good source of used, surplus, and even new parts for building amplifiers and other high-power RF equipment, such as impedance matching units or full-power filters. Follow the cautions in this sidebar when evaluating parts and pieces.

---

available at online auction sites.

The rectifier diodes D1-D6 are rated at 3 A and 1 kV PIV. The filter capacitors C8-C13 are 100 µF, 450 V electrolytics. Modern rectifiers do not need equalizing resistors and capacitors as seen in older articles and designs. Today, it is cheaper to overrate the diode stack instead. C8-C13 do need equalizing resistors, which also serve as bleeder resistors to discharge the capacitors when the supply is turned off.

A meter in the negative lead of the supply monitors the plate current. Several inexpensive options are included in the parts list. Some way to indicate RF output voltage or current is needed, but if you have an external SWR or forward/reflected power meter already, it need not be included in the amp.

CONSTRUCTION NOTES

The type of construction chosen will depend on the enclosure (chassis) which is required for good RF performance and for safety reasons. Having a spacious enclosure and an oversized chassis will make construction easier and upgrades simple. If your situation dictates, you can certainly build everything on a single chassis.

The power supply should be included in the enclosure and not built as a separate piece of equipment. Constructing safe high voltage connections between pieces of equipment requires experience and strict attention to safety-related details that may not be obvious to the beginning amplifier builder. For that reason, this basic design assumes an internal

tubes. For highest equipment reliability, these tubes are replaced on a scheduled basis rather than at failure. They will have less life than a new tube, but can be so cheap that they are still a good deal.

When buying used tubes at a hamfest, a quick ohmmeter check is important. Between the filament pins there should be only a few ohms, with high resistance between all other connections. Signs of obvious overheating, such as discoloration or warping, are a concern and call at the least for a reduced price. There is no 100% guarantee that a tube is good apart from trying it in a circuit, since tube testers usually will not test large power tubes. Experience with on-line suppliers of NOS tubes indicates that a small percentage will be duds. If your supplier guarantees them you should be willing to pay a bit more. Some dealers will test or even match the tubes for parallel operation.

Finding sockets for odd tubes may be a challenge. Several enterprising hams supply sockets for popular types, such as the Russian GI7B, or you can sometimes bolt the tubes into place with straps and screws.[2]

Using vacuum capacitors really adds class and value to an amplifier. Check the vacuum by setting the capacitor to minimum capacitance and watching to see if the vacuum is sufficiently strong to pull the plates all the way in when the screw or hand pressure is released. Weak vacuum means the capacitor will not withstand its rated voltage. With the plates fully meshed, check for a short circuit, which indicates damaged plates. Be sure that the adjusting screw moves freely. Lubrication won't always free up a sticky screw. Check that the voltage and current ratings are suitable for your application. The voltage rating is usually printed on the capacitor. The current rating will be on a factory data sheet or use physical size as an indication.

Vacuum TR (transmit-receive) relays work well in an amplifier and often switch quickly enough to be used for full-QSK (full break-in) operation. If you shop carefully, a surplus relay can cost little more than a much-inferior open-frame type. Visual inspection of the contacts and an ohmmeter check on the coil will generally insure that the relay is good. If the relay's coil voltage is 24 V or some value other than what you wanted, remember that a small power supply can be added cheaply. Be aware that the amplifier keying circuits of most transceivers are not rated to switch the large coil currents of surplus relays, particularly those that operate at 24 V or higher. An outboard switching interface will be needed for these relays. Older non-vacuum relays also have long switching times that, if not accounted for in the amplifier design, may cause "hot-switching" and contact damage.

Inductors can usually be evaluated by inspection since hidden faults are rare. The current rating is determined by conductor size. With formulas found in the **Electrical Fundamentals** chapter, you can determine the inductance. Carry a hand calculator when shopping.

Choose RF switches based on physical size and inspection. Avoid badly arced-over or pitted contacts or insulators.

For power transformers, finding the exact required voltage may be difficult. You can use extra low-voltage windings to buck or boost the primary voltage. External transformers can also be used in an autotransformer connection for adjustment. Use of a variable autotransformer (Variac or similar) can adapt a transformer to your needs, but the extra winding and core losses may cause voltage sag under load. Amplifiers normally use a separate transformer for supplying the tube filaments as filaments are often turned on before the high-voltage supply. Therefore, filament windings on a plate transformer are not needed. Also, with either center-tapped, full bridge or voltage doubler circuits, you have three options for ac secondary voltage.

Transformers should be rated for 50 or 60 Hz operation, not 400 Hz as used in aircraft. Check that the current and overall VA (volt-amp) ratings are adequate. Use an ohmmeter to detect shorts or open windings, and to be sure that you understand the terminal connections. Check each winding to ground and to each other. Reject transformers with charred insulation. Use your nose to detect burned smells from internal overloads. A rusty core can be wire brushed and spray painted, but might indicate moisture has gotten to the windings. Test the primary with 120 or 240 V ac, if possible. High current or loud buzzing can indicate shorted turns. Be very careful when measuring the secondary windings as the high voltage can easily destroy your multimeter, not to mention endanger your life! (See the **Power Sources** chapter for a method of testing transformers safely.)

Blowers can be found on otherwise worthless equipment, such as a rack of old tube gear. It may be worth buying the whole rack just to get a nice blower. The pressure and volume ratings of a blower may not be known, but apart from noise, there is no disadvantage in over-sizing your blower. An over-sized blower can be slowed down by reducing the voltage or throttled back with baffles. Remember that if the voltage rating is strange, providing an odd voltage may be cheaper than buying a more expensive blower. Avoid 400 Hz aircraft blowers. For blowers needing an external capacitor, try to obtain the capacitor with the blower.

Racks and chassis components can often be refurbished for an amplifier. Standard 19-inch rack-type cabinets are widely available surplus and at hamfests. Even new, they are available at modest cost and have good fit and finish. Filling the many panel holes and painting or adding a new front panel can make them look like new, while saving a lot of expensive and time consuming metal work.[3]
— *Roger Halstead, K8RI*

[1] www.nd2x.net/base-1.html
[2] http://gi7b.com
[3] W. Yoshida, KH6WZ, "Recycling Old Cabinets and Chassis Boxes," *QST*, Jul 2008, p 30.

power supply. Rectifiers and filter caps can be mounted on an insulated board (plexiglass or other plastic), or an etched PC board. Install that board on top of the transformer for a neat and compact installation. Board layouts are included with this book's downloadable supplemental content for both the doubler and quadrupler circuits.

If you find an old piece of equipment you can reclaim, that may dictate the layout. Hamfests usually provide a choice of obsolete tube-type lab or medical instrumentation with high quality cabinets at low cost. They may include desirable items such as a blower or meter in addition to the enclosure. The author chose to use a cabinet from an old piece of Heathkit gear, which had no chassis, and so built a front panel and several sub-chassis sections for the various parts of the amplifier. This allows changing out various parts of the circuit easily and even to maintain several different sub-sections to allow experiments with different tubes, frequency ranges or power supply types.

The tube circuit layout will depend on which tube type is chosen. The 811A/572B option is a great place to start. There is just no other option that can compete in price, counting the tubes and sockets. A pair is recommended for this design although up to four tubes in parallel are common in ham-built amplifiers. A single 3-500Z is another popular choice and, for higher power, a pair of them if the power supply is adequately rated. Ceramic sockets are available for the 3-500Z. Surplus Russian triodes such as the GI-6B and GI-7B are becoming popular and one or a pair is commonly used. The sockets will have to be built as described in the construction details or purchased from ham sources.

External anode tubes such as the Russian GI-6B or GI-7B will need a blower. With the 811A or 3-500Z options, a muffin fan blowing on the tubes will allow them to work much harder. This fan also keeps the other components cooler for extended operation.

Finding suitable capacitors and coils and the band switch will be a significant part of the total procurement process. This is where you can save a lot by using surplus parts. The parts list will specify certain types, mainly so you will know what to look for, but if you simply buy new parts from the list, you will spend your entire budget on these items alone. You don't need exact values for the circuit to work. Limiting the bands to be covered can greatly relax the coil, capacitor and switch requirements.

17.12.2 *Project:* 3CX1500D7 RF Linear Amplifier

This project is a 160 through 10 meter RF linear amplifier that uses the compact Eimac 3CX1500D7 metal ceramic triode. It was designed and constructed by Jerry Pittenger, K8RA. The complete description of this amplifier including construction and operating details is provided with this book's downloadable supplemental content. The 3CX1200D7 tube may be more affordable, and the design can be adapted to use it with somewhat less plate dissipation.

The amplifier features instant-on operation and provides a solid 1500 W RF output with less than 100 W drive. Specifications for this rugged tube include 1500 W anode dissipation, 50 W grid dissipation and plate voltages up to 6000 V. A matching 4000 V power supply is included. The amplifier can be easily duplicated and provides full output in key-down service with no time constraints in any mode. **Figure 17.56** shows the RF deck and power supply cabinets.

DESIGN OVERVIEW

The Eimac 3CX1500D7 was designed as a compact, but heavy duty, alternative to the popular lineup of a pair of 3-500Z tubes. It has a 5 V/30 A filament and a maximum plate dissipation of 1500 W, compared to the 1000 W dissipation for a pair of 3-500Zs. The 3CX1500D7 uses the popular Eimac SK410 socket and requires forced air through the anode for cooling. The amplifier uses a conventional grounded-grid design with an adjustable grid-trip protection circuit. See the RF Deck schematic in **Figure 17.57**.

Output impedance matching is accomplished using a pi-L tank circuit for good harmonic suppression. The 10 to 40 meter coils are hand wound from copper tubing, and they are silver plated for efficiency. Toroids are used for the 80 and 160 meter coils for compactness. The amplifier incorporates a heavy-duty shorting-type bandswitch. Vacuum variable capacitors are used for pi-L tuning and loading.

A unique feature of this amplifier is the use of a commercial computer-controlled impedance-matching module at the input. This greatly simplifies the amplifier design by eliminating the need for complex ganged switches and sometimes frustrating setup adjustments. Unfortunately, the LDG AT-100AMP module kit the author used is no longer available.

An adjustable ALC circuit is also included to control excess drive power. The amplifier metering circuits allow simultaneous monitoring of plate current, grid current, and a choice of RF output, plate voltage or filament voltage.

The blower was sized to allow full 1500 W plate dissipation (65 cfm at 0.45 inches H_2O hydrostatic backpressure). The design provides for blower mounting on the rear of the RF deck or optionally in a remote location to reduce ambient blower noise in the shack. The flange on the socket for connecting an air hose was ground off for better air flow. (This is not necessary.).

The power supply is built in a separate cabinet with casters and is connected to the RF deck using a 6-conductor control cable, with a separate high voltage (HV) cable. The power transformer has multiple primary taps (220/230/240 V ac) and multiple secondary taps (2300/2700/3100 V ac). No-load HV ranges can be selected from 3200 to 4600 V dc using different primary-secondary combinations. The amplifier is designed to run at 4000 V dc under load to maintain a reasonable plate resistance and component size. A step-start circuit is included to protect against current surge at turn on that can damage the diode bank. The power supply schematic is shown in **Figure 17.58** and a photo of the inside of the power supply is shown in **Figure 17.59**.

Since this project was first published, Peter W. Dahl has discontinued business and transformers built to the Dahl specifications are now available from Hammond Manufacturing Company, Inc. of Cheektowaga, NY (**www.hammfg.com**). Contact Hammond to cross-reference the Peter Dahl part numbers in the parts list for T1, T2 and RFC103 with current stock or equivalent designs.

Both +12 V and +24 V regulated power supplies are included in the power supply. The +12 V is required for the computer-controlled input network and +24 V is needed for the output vacuum relay. The input and output relays are time sequenced to avoid amplifier drive without a 50 Ω load. Relay actuation from the exciter uses a low-voltage/low-current circuit to accommodate the amplifier switching constraints imposed by many new solid state radios.

GENERAL CONSTRUCTION NOTES

Much thought was put into the physical appearance of the amplifier. The goal was to obtain a unit that looks commercial and that would look good sitting on the operating table. To accomplish the desired look, commercial cabinets were used. Not only does this help obtain a professional look but it eliminates a large amount of the metal work required in construction. Careful attention was taken making custom meter scales and cabinet labeling. The results are evident in the pictures provided.

The amplifier was constructed using basic shop tools and does not require access to a

Figure 17.56 — At the top, front panel view of RF Deck and Power Supply for 3CX1500D7 amplifier. At bottom, rear view of RF Deck and Power Supply.

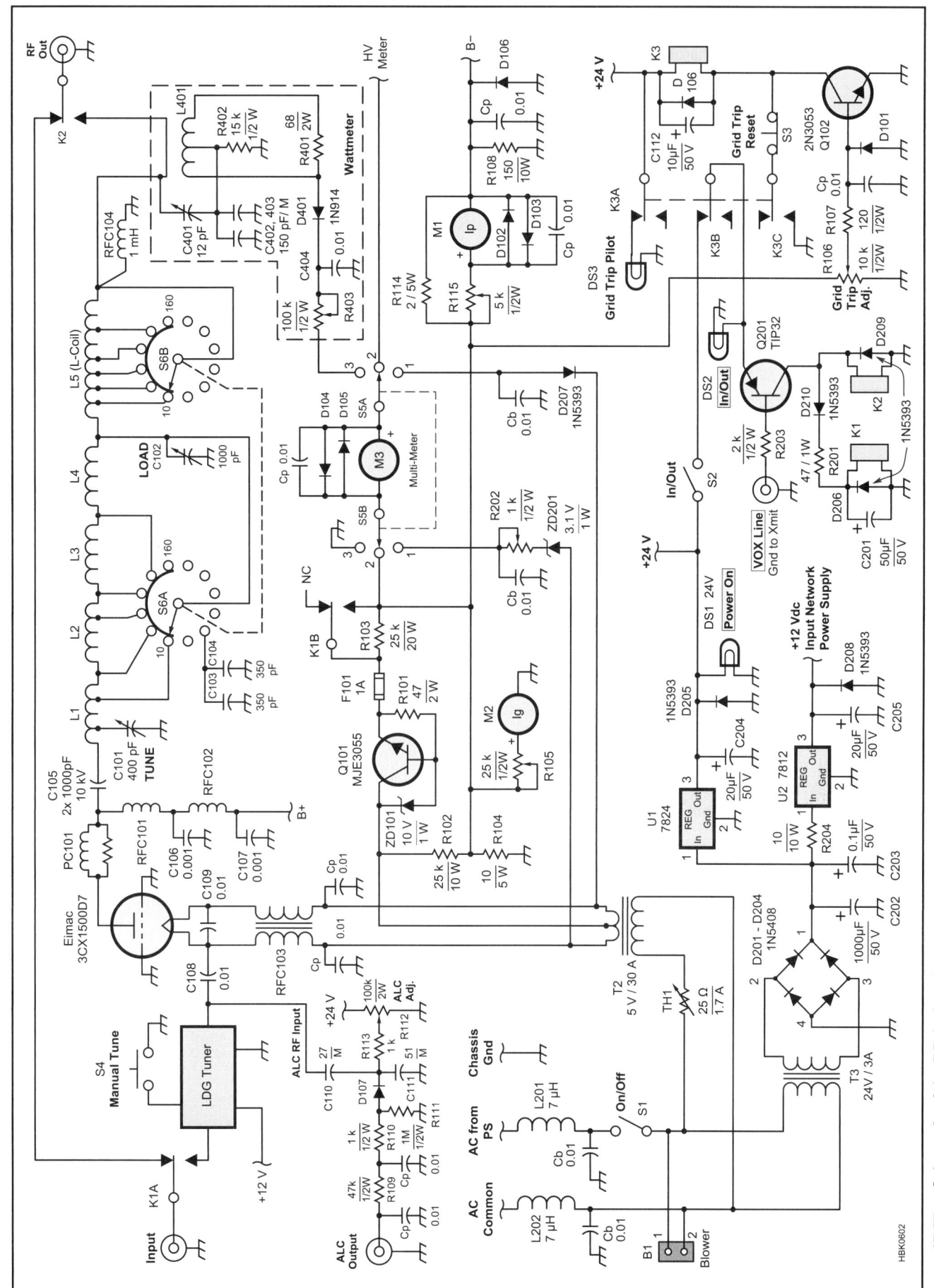

Figure 17.57 — Schematic of the RF deck and control circuitry. A complete parts list is available with this book's downloadable supplemental con-

RF Power Amplifiers 17.49

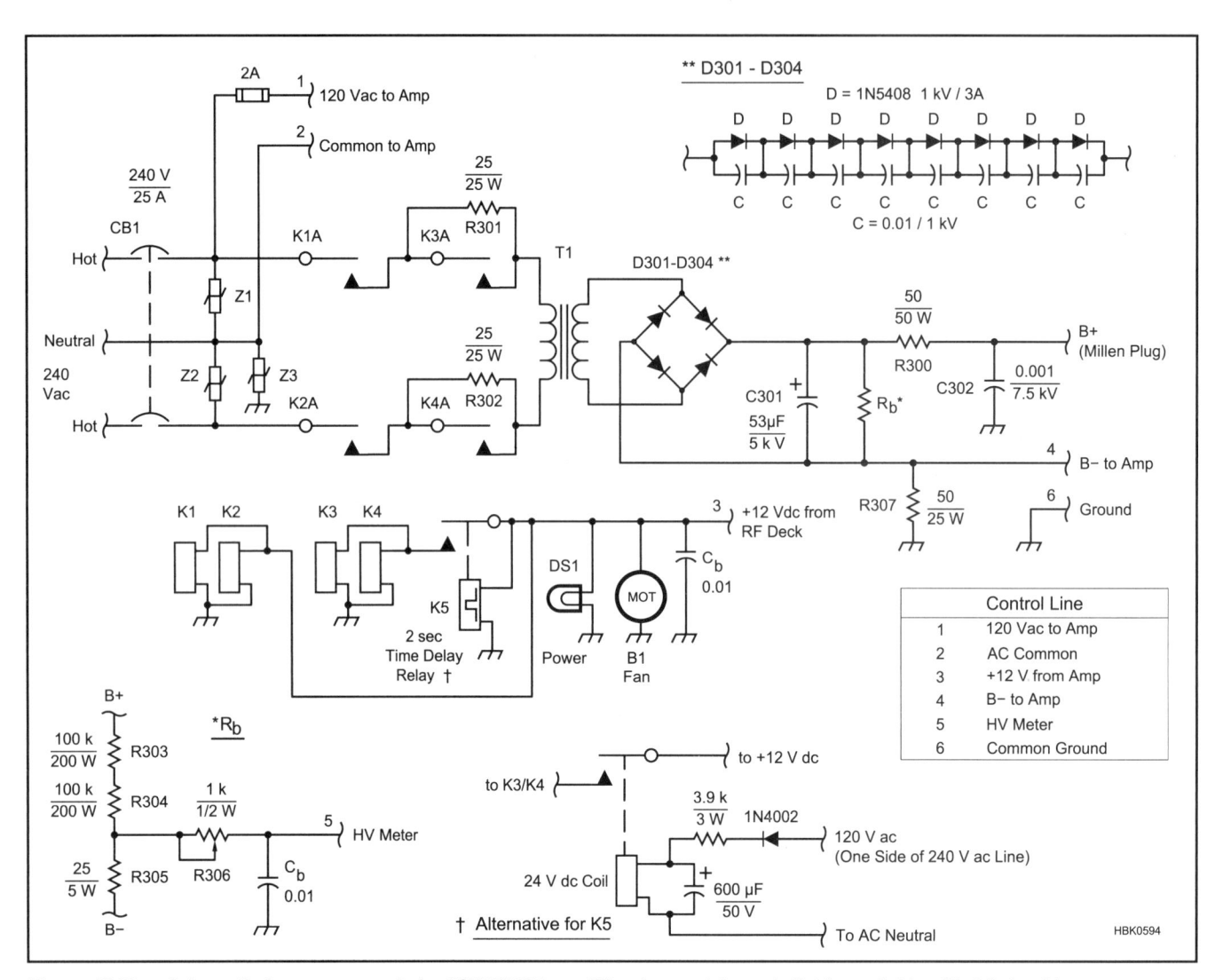

Figure 17.58 — Schematic for power supply for 3CX1500D7 amplifier. A complete parts list is available with this book's downloadable supplemental content.

Figure 17.59 — Inside view of the power supply, showing rectifier stack, control relays and HV filter capacitor with bleeder resistors. The heavy-duty high voltage transformer is at the upper left in this photo.

17.50　Chapter 17

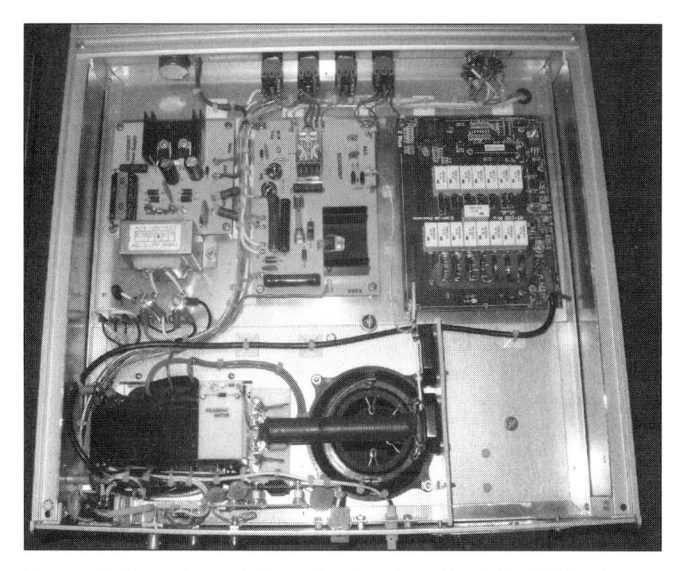

Figure 17.60 — At the left, under the chassis of the RF Deck. The autotuner used as the input network for this amplifier is at the upper right. At right, view of the Pi-L output network in the RF Deck.

sophisticated metal shop or electronics test bench. Basic tools included a band saw, a jig saw capable of cutting thin aluminum sheet, a drill press and common hand tools. Some skill in using tools is needed to obtain good results and ensure safety, but most people can accomplish this project with careful planning and diligence.

The amplifier is built in modules. This breaks the project into logical steps and facilitates testing the circuits along the way. For example, modules include the HV power supply, LV power supply, input network, control circuits, tank circuit and wattmeter. Each module can be tested prior to being integrated into the amplifier.

The project also made extensive use of computer tools in the design stage. The basic layout of all major components was done using the *Visio* diagramming software package. The printed-circuit boards were designed using a free layout program called *ExpressPCB* (**www. expresspcb. com,** see also the **Computer-Aided Circuit Design** chapter). Masks were developed and the iron-on transfer technique was used to transfer the traces to copper-clad board. The boards were then etched with excellent results. The layout underneath the RF Deck is shown in **Figure 17.60A** and the top side of the RF Deck is shown in Figure 17.60B.

Meter scales were made using an excellent piece of software called *Meter* by Jim Tonne, W4ENE (**www.tonnesoftware.com**). Also, K8RA wrote an *Excel* spread-sheet to calculate the pi-L tank parameters. A copy of the spreadsheet and ExpressPCB files for the PC boards are all included on with this book's downloadable supplemental content. Meter Basic software is also available with this book's downloadable supplemental content.

17.13 References and Bibliography

VACUUM TUBE AMPLIFIERS

ARRL members can download many *QST* articles on amplifiers from: **www.arrl. org/arrl-periodicals-archive-search**. Enter the keyword "amplifiers" in the "Title/Keywords:" search window.

Badger, G., W6TC, "The 811A: Grandfather of the Zero Bias Revolution," *QST*, Apr 1996, pp 51-53.

Care and Feeding of Power Grid Tubes, **www.cpii.com/library.cfm/9**

EIMAC tube performance computer, **www.cpii.com/library.cfm/9**

Grammer, G., "How to Run Your Linear," *QST*, Nov 1962, pp 11-14.

LTSPICE, download from Linear Technology, **www.linear.com/design-tools/software/ltspice.jsp**

Measures, R., AG6K, "Improved Parasitic Suppression for Modern Amplifier Tubes," *QST*, Oct 1988, pp 36-38, 66, 89.

Orr, W., W6SAI, *Radio Handbook*, 22nd Ed (Howard W. Sams & Co, Inc, 1981).

Pappenfus, Bruene and Schoenike, *Single Sideband Principles and Circuits* (McGraw-Hill, 1964).

Potter and Fich, *Theory of Networks and Lines* (Prentice-Hall, 1963).

RCA Transmitting Tubes Technical Manual TT-5, Radio Corporation of America, 1962.

Rauch, T., W8JI, "Filament Voltage life," **www.w8ji/filament_voltage_life.htm**.

Rauch, T., W8JI, "Neutralizing Amplifiers," **www.w8ji.com/ neutralizing_amplifier.htm**

Reference Data for Radio Engineers, ITT, Howard W. Sams Co, Inc.

Simpson, *Introductory Electronics for Scientists and Engineers* (Allyn and Bacon, 1975).

Terman, *Electronic and Radio Engineering* (McGraw-Hill).

Wilson, R., K4POZ, "All About the GI-7B," **http://gi7b.com**

Wingfield, E., "New and Improved Formulas for the Design of Pi and Pi-L Networks," *QST*, Aug 1983, pp 23-29. (Feedback, *QST*, Jan 1984, p 49.).

Wingfield, E., "A Note on Pi-L Networks," *QEX*, Dec 1983, pp 5-9.

ADDITIONAL VACUUM TUBE AMPLIFIER PROJECTS

Heck, S. LAØBY/DF9PY, "Description of a 144 MHz high power amplifier for 2 x 4CX250B," sm2yer.dyndns.org/projects/pa2x_4cx250b/2m_pa_4cx250.pdf.

Knadle, R., K2RIW, "A Strip-line Kilowatt Amplifier 432 MHz," *QST*, Apr 1972, pp 49-55.

Meade, E., K1AGB, "A High-Performance 50-MHz Amplifier," *QST*, Sep 1975, pp 34-38.

Meade, E., K1AGB, "A 2-KW PEP Amplifier for 144 MHz," *QST*, Dec 1973, pp 34-38.

Peck, F., K6SNO, "A Compact High-Power Linear," *QST*, Jun 1961, pp 11-14.

Additional projects are available with this book's downloadable supplemental content.

SOLID STATE AMPLIFIERS

References for RF Power Amplifiers and Power Combining

Classic Works in RF Engineering: Combiners, Couplers, Transformers and Magnetic Materials, Edited by Myer, Walker, Raab, Trask. (Artech House, June 2005. ISBN: 9781580530569).

Abulet, Mihai, *RF Power Amplifiers* (Noble Publishing, 2001. ISBN: 1-884932-12-6).

Blinchikoff, Zverev, *Filtering in the Time and Frequency Domains* (Noble Publishing, 2001, ISBN: 1884932177).

Bowick, *RF Circuit Design*, 2nd Ed. (Newnes imprint of Butterworth-Heinemann, 1982. ISBN: 0750685182).

Cripps, Steve C. *Advanced Techniques in RF Power Amplifier Design* (Artech House, 2002. ISBN: 1-58053-282-9).

Dye, Norman. and Helge Granberg, *Radio Frequency Transistors — Principles and Practical Applications* (Butterworth-Heinemann, 1993. ISBN: 0750690593; 2nd Ed, 2001. ISBN: 0750672811).

Egan, William F., *Practical RF System Design,* (Wiley, 2003. ISBN: 0471200239).

Kraus, Bostian and Raab, *Solid State Radio Engineering,* (Wiley, 1980. ISBN: 0-471-03018-x).

Ludwig and Bogdanov, *RF Circuit Design: Theory and Applications* (Prentice Hall, 2009. ISBN: 0-13-147137-6).

Oxner, Edwin, *Power FETS and Their Applications* (Prentice-Hall, 1982. ISBN: 0-13-686923-8).

Pozar, *Microwave Engineering,* 3rd Ed. (Wiley, 2004. ISBN: 0471448788).

Rutledge, David B., *The Electronics of Radio* (Cambridge University Press, August 1999. ISBN: 9780521646451).

Sabin, Schoenike, et al, *Single Sideband Systems and Circuits* (McGraw-Hill, 1993. ISBN: 0-07-912038-5).

Sevick, J., *Transmission Line Transformers,* 4th Ed., (Noble Publishing, 2001. ISBN: 1884932185).

Vizmuller, *RF Design Guide: Systems, Circuits, and Equations* (Artech House, 1995. ISBN: 0890067546).

White, Joseph F., *High Frequency Techniques: An Introduction to RF and Microwave Engineering* (Wiley, 2004. ISBN: 0471455911).

Zverev, A. I., *Handbook of Filter Synthesis* (Wiley, 1970. ISBN: 0471986801).

Articles

Davis and Rutledge, "Industrial Class-E Power Amplifiers With Low-cost Power MOSFETs and Sine-wave Drive" Conf. Papers for RF Design '97, Santa Clara, CA, Sep 1997, pp. 283-297.

Franke and Noorani, "Lumped-Constant Line Stretcher For Testing Power Amplifier Stability," *rf Design*, Mar/Apr 1983.

Frey, R., "A 50 MHz, 250 W Amplifier using Push-Pull ARF448A/B," APT Application Note APT9702.

Frey, R., "Low Cost 1000 Watt 300 V RF Power Amplifier for 27.12 MHz," APT Application Note APT9701.

Frey, R., "A push-pull 300 watt amplifier for 81.36 MHz," *Applied Microwave and Wireless*, vol 10 no 3, pp 36-45, Apr 1998.

Frey, R., "Push-Pull ARF449A/B Amplifier for 81.36 MHz," APT Application Note APT9801.

Gonzalez, Martin, Lopez "Effects of Matching on RF Power Amplifier Efficiency and Output Power," *Microwave Journal*, Apr 1998.

Granberg, H., "Broadband Transformers and Power Combining Techniques for RF," AN-749, Motorola Semiconductor Products Inc.

Granberg, H. O., WB2BHX, "One KW — -Solid-State Style, Part 1," Apr 1976, *QST*, p 11.

Granberg, H. O., WB2BHX, "One KW — Solid-State Style, Part 2," May 1976, *QST*, p 28.

Granberg, Helge, K7ES/OH2ZE, "Build This Solid-State Titan, Part 1," Jun 1977, *QST*, p 27.

Granberg, Helge, K7ES/OH2ZE, "Build This Solid-State Titan, Part 2," Jul 1977, *QST*, p 11.

Granberg, Helge, K7ES/OH2ZE, "Printed Line Techniques Applied to VHF Amplifier Design," Sep 1979, *QST*, p 11.

Granberg, Helge, K7ES/OH2ZE, "MOSFET RF Power: An Update - Part 1," Dec 1982, *QST*, p 13.

Granberg, Helge, K7ES/OH2ZE, "MOSFET RF Power: An Update - Part 2," Jan 1983, *QST*, p 30.

Hejhall, R. "Systemizing RF Power Amplifier Design," Motorola Semiconductor Products, Inc., Phoenix, AZ, Application note AN282A.

Hilbers, A.H., "Design of HF wideband power transformers," Philips Semiconductors, ECO 6907, Mar 1998.

Hilbers, A.H., "Design of HF wideband power transformers Part II," Philips Semiconductors, ECO 7213, Mar 1998.

Hilbers, A.H., "Power Amplifier Design," Philips Semiconductors, Application Note, March 1998.

Klitzing, J, W6PQL, "Build a Linear 2 Meter 80 W All Mode Amplifier," *QST*, May 2013, pp 30-34. Feedback, Jul 2013 *QST*, p 40.

Trask, C., N7ZWY, "Designing Wide-band Transformers for HF and VHF Power Amplifiers," *QEX,* Mar/Apr 2005, pp 3-15.

Microwave — Cellular Applications

Cripps, *RF Power Amplifiers for Wireless Communication* (Artech House, 1999. ISBN: 1596930187).

Groe and L. E. Larson, *CDMA Mobile Radio Design* (Artech House, 2000. ISBN: 1580530591).

Pozar, *Microwave Engineering,* 3rd Ed. (Wiley, 2004. ISBN: 0471448788).

Raghavan, Srirattana, Laskar *Modeling and Design Techniques for RF Power Amplifiers,* (Wiley-IEEE Press, 2008. ISBN: 0471717460).

van Nee and Prasad, *OFDM for Wireless Multimedia Communications*, (Artech House, 2000. ISBN: 0890065306).

York and Popovic, *Active and Quasi-Optical Arrays for Solid-State Power Combining*, (Wiley, 1997. ISBN: 0471146145).

Contents

18.1 A Brief History
18.2 Repeater Overview
   18.2.1 Types of Repeaters
   18.2.2 Advantages of Using a Repeater
   18.2.3 Digital Voice Repeaters on VHF/UHF
   18.2.4 Non-Voice Repeater Uses
   18.2.5 Repeaters and FCC Regulations
18.3 FM Voice Repeaters
   18.3.1 FM Repeater Operation
   18.3.2 Home, Mobile and Handheld Equipment
   18.3.3 Coded Squelch and Tones
   18.3.4 Narrowbanding
   18.3.5 Linked Repeaters
18.4 D-STAR Repeater Systems
   18.4.1 D-STAR Station IDs
   18.4.2 Station Routing
   18.4.3 Enhancing D-STAR Operation with *DPlus*
   18.4.4 D-STAR Repeater Hardware
18.5 Digital Mobile Radio (DMR)
   18.5.1 DMR Standards
   18.5.2 DMR Structure
   18.5.3 DMR Channels
   18.5.4 DMR Equipment
   18.5.5 DMR Operation
18.6 System Fusion
   18.6.1 System Fusion Versions
   18.6.2 System Fusion Modes
   18.6.3 System Fusion Network
   18.6.4 Third-Party Enhancements and Options
18.7 Other Digital Voice Repeater Technologies
18.8 Glossary of FM and Repeater Terminology
18.9 References and Bibliography

Chapter 18

Repeaters

For decades, FM has been a mainstay of Amateur Radio operation. FM and repeaters fill the VHF and UHF bands, and most hams have at least one handheld or mobile FM radio. Thousands of repeaters throughout the country provide reliable communication for amateurs operating from portable, mobile and home stations. Digital voice systems are now beginning to dominate new installations. Along with the well-established D-STAR (now offered by Kenwood as well as Icom), Yaesu's System Fusion, and Digital Mobile Radio (DMR) are two popular new systems. DMR makes extensive use of the Internet to build hybrid systems similar to the trunking systems used by public service agencies. A whole new era of repeater-based communications is at hand.

The first part of this chapter, by Paul M. Danzer, N1II, describes FM voice repeaters. Later sections, contributed by Jim McClellan, N5MIJ, and Pete Loveall, AE5PL, of the Texas Interconnect Team, cover more recent developments in D-STAR digital voice and data repeaters. Gary Pearce, KN4AQ, maintains the chapter's basic material. John Burningham, W2XAB, contributed the section on DMR and Cory Sickles, WA3UVV, updated the System Fusion section for this edition.

18.1 A Brief History

Few hams today don't operate at least some VHF/UHF FM, and for many hams, FM *is* Amateur Radio. That wasn't always the case.

Until the late 1960s, the VHF and UHF Amateur Radio bands were home to a relatively small number of highly skilled operators who used CW and SSB for long distance communication and propagation experiments. This operation used just a small fraction of the spectrum available at 50 MHz and above. A somewhat larger number of hams enjoyed low power, local operation with AM transceivers on 6 and 2 meters. Our spectrum was underutilized, while public safety and commercial VHF/UHF two-way operation, using FM and repeaters, was expanding rapidly.

The business and public-safety bands grew so rapidly in the early 1960s that the FCC had to create new channels by cutting the existing channels in half. Almost overnight, a generation of tube-type, crystal-controlled FM equipment had to be replaced with radios that met the new channel requirements. Surplus radios fell into the hands of hams for pennies on the original dollar. This equipment was designed to operate around 150 MHz and 450 MHz, just above the 2 meter and 70 cm amateur bands. It was fairly easy to order new crystals and retune them to operate inside the ham bands. Hams who worked in the two-way radio industry led the way, retuning radios and building repeaters that extended coverage. Other hams quickly followed, attracted by the noise-free clarity of FM audio, the inexpensive equipment, and the chance to do something different.

That initial era didn't last long. The surplus commercial equipment was cheap, but it was physically large, ran hot and consumed lots of power. By the early 1970s, manufacturers recognized an untapped market and began building solid-state equipment specifically for the Amateur Radio FM market. The frequency synthesizer, perfected in the mid-1970s, eliminated the need for crystals. The stage was set for an explosion that changed the face of Amateur Radio. Manufacturers have added plenty of new features to equipment over the years, but the basic FM operating mode remains the same.

In the 1980s, hams experimenting with data communications began modulating their FM radios with tones. *Packet radio* spawned a new system of *digipeaters* (digital repeaters).

Digitized audio has been popular since audio compact discs (CDs) were introduced in the 1980s. In the 1990s, technology advanced enough to reduce the bandwidth needed for digital audio, especially voice, to be carried over the Internet and narrowband radio circuits. The first digital-voice public safety radio systems (called APCO-Project 25) appeared and a variety of Internet voice systems for conferencing and telephone-like use were developed.

Hams are using VHF/UHF digital voice technology, too. The Japan Amateur Radio League (JARL) developed a true ham radio standard called D-STAR, a networked VHF/UHF repeater system for digital voice and data that is beginning to make inroads around the world. Yaesu has developed a hybrid analog/digital system called System Fusion. Another digital voice system, generically known as DMR (Digital Mobile Radio) and by the Motorola trade name MOTOTRBO, is being adapted from commercial service to the ham bands. Hams are also using surplus Project 25 (or just P25) radios.

18.2 Repeater Overview

Amateurs learned long ago that they could get much better use from their mobile and portable radios by using an automated relay station called a *repeater*. Home stations benefit as well — not all hams are located near the highest point in town or have access to a tall tower. A repeater, whose basic idea is shown in **Figure 18.1**, can be more readily located where the antenna system is as high as possible and can therefore cover a much greater area.

18.2.1 Types of Repeaters

The most popular and well-known type of amateur repeater is an FM voice system on the 144 or 440 MHz bands. Amateurs operate many repeaters on the 29, 50, 222, 902, and 1240 MHz bands as well, but 2 meters and 70 cm are the most popular. Tens of thousands of hams use mobile and handheld radios for casual ragchewing, emergency communications, public service activities or just staying in touch with their regular group of friends during the daily commute.

While the digital voice modes are gaining ground, FM is still the most popular mode for voice repeaters. Operations are *channelized* — all stations operate on specific, planned frequencies, rather than the more or less random frequency selection employed in CW and SSB operation. In addition, since the repeater receives signals from mobile or fixed stations and retransmits these signals simultaneously, the transmit and receive frequencies are different, or *split*. Direct contact between two or more stations that listen and transmit on the same frequency is called operating *simplex*.

Individuals, clubs, emergency communications groups and other organizations all sponsor repeaters. Anyone with a valid amateur license for the band can establish a repeater in conformance with the FCC rules. No one owns specific repeater frequencies, but nearly all repeaters are *coordinated* to minimize repeater-to-repeater interference. Frequency coordination and interference are discussed later in this chapter. Operational aspects are covered in more detail in *The ARRL Operating Manual*. Special operating notes for the digital repeaters are included in the sections on each mode.

18.2.2 Advantages of Using a Repeater

When we use the term *repeater* we are almost always talking about transmitters and receivers on VHF or higher bands, where radio-wave propagation is normally line of sight. Don't take "line of sight" too literally. VHF/UHF radio signals do refract beyond what you can actually see on the horizon, but the phrase is a useful description. (See the **Propagation of Radio Signals** chapter for more information on these terms.)

We know that the effective range of VHF and UHF signals is related to the height of each antenna. Since repeaters can usually be located at high points, one great advantage of repeaters is the extension of coverage area from low-powered mobile and portable transceivers.

Figure 18.2 illustrates the effect of using a repeater in areas with hills or mountains. The same effect is found in metropolitan areas, where buildings provide the primary blocking structures.

Siting repeaters at high points can also have disadvantages. Since most repeaters have co-channel neighbors (other repeaters operating on the same channel) less than 150 miles away, there may be times when your transceiver can receive both. But since it operates FM, the *capture effect* usually ensures that the stronger signal will capture your receiver and the weaker signal will not be heard — at least as long as the stronger repeater is in use.

It is also simpler to provide a very sensitive receiver, a good antenna system, and a slightly higher power transmitter at just one location — the repeater — than at each mobile, portable or home location. A superior repeater system compensates for the low power (5 W or less), and small, inefficient antennas that many hams use to operate through them. The repeater maintains the range or coverage we want, despite our equipment deficiencies. If both the handheld

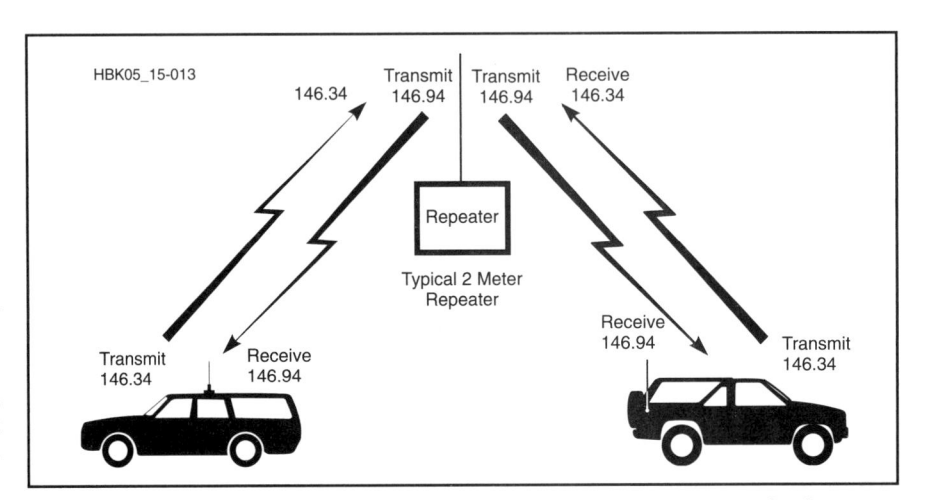

Figure 18.1 — Typical 2 meter repeater, showing mobile-to-mobile communication through a repeater station. Usually located on a hill or tall building, the repeater amplifies and retransmits the received signal on a different frequency.

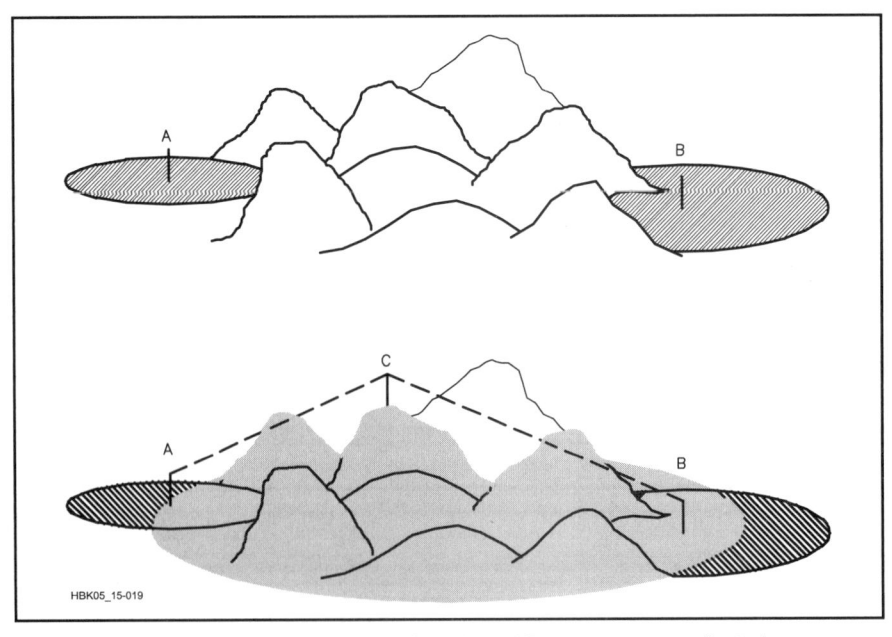

Figure 18.2 — In the upper diagram, stations A and B cannot communicate because their mutual coverage is limited by the mountains between them. In the lower diagram, stations A and B can communicate because the coverage of each station falls within the coverage of repeater C, which is on a mountaintop.

transceiver and the repeater are at high elevations, for example, communication is possible over great distances, despite the low output power and inefficient antenna of the transceiver (see **Figure 18.3**).

Repeaters also provide a convenient meeting place for hams with a common interest. It's usually geographic — your town, or your club. A few repeaters are dedicated to a particular interest such as DX or passing traffic. Operation is channelized, and usually in any area you can find out which channel — or repeater — to pick to ragchew, get highway information or whatever your need or interest is. The conventional wisdom is that you don't have to tune around and call CQ to make a contact, as on the HF bands. Simply call on a repeater frequency — if someone is there and they want to talk, they will answer you. But with a few dozen repeaters covering almost any medium size town, you probably use the scan function in your radio to seek activity.

EMERGENCY OPERATIONS

When there is a weather-related emergency or a disaster (or one is threatening), most repeaters in the affected area immediately spring to life. Emergency operation and traffic always take priority over other ham activities, and many repeaters are equipped with emergency power sources just for these occasions. See **Figure 18.4**.

Almost all Amateur Radio emergency organizations use repeaters to take advantage of their extended range, uniformly good coverage and visibility. Most repeaters are well known — everyone active in an area with suitable equipment knows the local repeater frequencies.

18.2.3 Digital Voice Repeaters on VHF/UHF

Digital voice transmits digitized audio speech as a digital data stream over the RF or wired media. The process of converting between analog voice and the digital data stream utilizes a vocoder (voice encoder). A package of software or firmware that performs the encoding and decoding of the speech is called a codec (coder-decoder).

The transmitted digital voice data stream is encapsulated inside a protocol which handles the addressing and communication management. For a sender and receiver to communicate both must be using the same vocoder and protocol. Additional information on the digital voice modes is available in the **Digital Protocols and Modes** chapter and at the websites listed in the References and Bibliography section of this chapter.

The primary digital voice technologies utilized in the amateur VHF/UHF bands are D-STAR (Digital Smart Technologies for Amateur Radio), DMR (Digital Mobile Radio), System Fusion and P25. Both D-STAR and System Fusion were designed specifically for the amateur radio market. Developed by the European Telecommunications Standards Institute (ETSI) for government and commercial users, DMR has been adapted for Amateur Radio use.

D-STAR is supported by Icom and Kenwood according to the standard originally developed for the Japanese Amateur

Figure 18.3 — In the Rocky Mountain west, handheld transceivers can often cover great distances, thanks to repeaters located atop high mountains. [Photo courtesy Rachel Witte, KC0ETU, and Bob Witte, K0NR]

Radio League (JARL). Yaesu is the only manufacturer for System Fusion. There are over a dozen manufacturers producing DMR compatible equipment including Motorola Solutions, Hytera, Vertex Standard, TYT, Connect Systems, BFDX, Kirisun, and Kenwood.

D-STAR and System Fusion protocols both include the amateur's call sign in the transmitted digital data, DMR utilizes a Radio ID number for users and repeaters which amateurs must obtain from DMR-MARC (Motorola Amateur Radio Club) which serves as a central registry for worldwide amateur users.

DIGITAL VS ANALOG

If you are used to operating on analog FM repeaters, you will have noticed that the audio quality degrades gradually. As a station's signal into the repeater gets weaker; there is an increase in noise bursts mixed with the audio until the signal gets so weak that the station can no long access the repeater or you cannot understand the audio because of noise. Similarly, as you move further from the repeater you will start hearing the same noise as the repeater's transmitted signal gets weaker. A combination of a station's weak signal into a repeater and a repeater's weak signal to the listener degrades usability faster.

For digital repeaters the audio quality remains the same for both input and output to the edge of the coverage range. At that point,

Figure 18.4 — Repeaters provide communication over a wide area to support disaster relief, emergency communication, and public service. They allow portable and mobile stations to communicate effectively with each other and with served agencies and event management. The operators shown here (F-B AE5MT, KE5YBC, and KE5NCR) are supporting an Oklahoma City marathon, getting valuable training while providing a service to the community. (Photo by Frank Tassone, KE5KQL)

the audio becomes broken (missing portions of the speech) caused by lost packets in the digital protocol. Further signal degradation causes complete signal loss. (The same effect is seen on digital television (DTV) as the image becomes pixilated and finally is dropped completely.) The Internet can also drop packets used for transferring the audio data stream between repeaters and bridges, causing the same broken audio affect.

All of major digital voice technologies include Forward Error Correction (FEC) which can correct limited errors, slightly extending the usable range and improving communication quality. Better quality receivers can operate at a lower noise floor, higher power transmitters, and higher gain antenna systems will also extend coverage of both analog and digital systems.

18.2.4 Non-Voice Repeater Uses

In addition to FM voice, there are several other types of ham radio repeaters.

ATV (amateur TV) — ATV repeaters are used to relay wideband television signals in the 70 cm and higher bands. They are used to extend coverage areas, just like voice repeaters. ATV repeaters are often set up for *crossband* operation, with the input on one band (say, 23 cm) and the output on another (say, 70 cm). More information on ATV repeaters may be found in the **Image Communications** chapter in the downloadable supplement.

Digipeaters — Digital repeaters are used primarily for packet communications, including APRS (the Amateur Packet/position Reporting System). They can use a single channel (single port) or several channels (multi-port) on one or more VHF and UHF bands. See the **Digital Protocols and Modes** chapter and the **Digital Communications** chapter in the *Handbook's* downloadable supplemental information for details of these systems.

Multi-channel (wideband) — Amateur satellites are the best-known examples. Wide bandwidth (perhaps 50 to 200 kHz) is selected to be received and transmitted so all signals in bandwidth are heard by the satellite (repeater) and retransmitted, usually on a different VHF or UHF band. See the **Space Communications** chapter in the *Handbook's* downloadable supplemental information for details.

18.2.5 Repeaters and FCC Regulations

Repeaters are specifically authorized by the FCC rules. For a brief period when the repeater concept was new in the amateur service, the FCC required special repeater licenses identified by a "WR" call sign prefix and a fairly complex application process. While that complexity is gone, repeaters are still restricted to certain band segments and have lower maximum power limits. But most of the "rules" that make our repeater systems work are self-imposed and voluntary. Hams have established frequency coordination, band plans, calling frequencies, digital protocols and rules that promote efficient communication and interchange of information.

FCC rules on prohibited communication have also been somewhat relaxed, allowing hams to communicate with businesses, and allowing employees of emergency-related agencies and private companies to participate in training and drills while "on the clock." There are significant restrictions to this operation, so for the latest rules and how to interpret them, see *QST* and the ARRL website, www.arrl.org.

FREQUENCY COORDINATION AND BAND PLANS

Since repeater operation is channelized, with many stations sharing the same frequency pairs, the amateur community has formed coordinating groups to help minimize conflicts between repeaters and among repeaters and other modes. Over the years, the VHF and UHF bands have been divided into repeater and non-repeater sub-bands. These frequency-coordination groups maintain lists of available frequency pairs in their areas (although in most urban areas,

Table 18.1
Standard Frequency Offsets for Repeaters

Band	Offset
29 MHz	–100 kHz
52 MHz	Varies by region –500 kHz, –1 MHz, –1.7 MHz
144 MHz	+ or –600 kHz
222 MHz	–1.6 MHz
440 MHz	+ or –5 MHz
902 MHz	12 MHz
1240 MHz	12 MHz

there are no "available" pairs on 2 meters, and 70 cm pairs are becoming scarce). A complete list of frequency coordinators, band plans and repeater pairs is included in the *ARRL Repeater Directory*.

Each VHF and UHF repeater band has been subdivided into repeater and nonrepeater channels. In addition, each band has a specific *offset* — the difference between the transmit frequency and the receive frequency for the repeater. While most repeaters use these standard offsets, others use "oddball splits." These nonstandard repeaters are generally also coordinated through the local frequency coordinator. **Table 18.1** shows the standard frequency offsets for each repeater band.

FM repeater action isn't confined to the VHF and UHF bands. There are a large handful of repeaters on 10 meters around the US and the world. "Wideband" FM is permitted only above 29.0 MHz, and there are four band-plan repeater channels (outputs are 29.62, 29.64, 29.66 and 29.68 MHz), plus the simplex channel 29.60 MHz. Repeaters on 10 meters use a 100 kHz offset, so the corresponding inputs are 29.52, 29.54, 29.56 and 29.58 MHz. During band openings, you can key up a repeater thousands of miles away, but that also creates the potential for interference generated when multiple repeaters are keyed up at the same time. CTCSS would help reduce the problem, but not many 10 meter repeater owners use it and too many leave their machines on "carrier access."

18.3 FM Voice Repeaters

Repeaters normally contain at least the sections shown in **Figure 18.5**. Repeaters consist of a receiver and transmitter plus a couple more special devices. One is a *controller* that routes the audio between the receiver and transmitter, keys the transmitter and provides remote control for the repeater licensee or designated control operators.

The second device is the *duplexer* that lets the repeater transmit and receive on the same antenna. A high power transmitter and a sensitive receiver, operating in close proximity within the same band, using the same antenna, present a serious technical challenge. You might think the transmitter would just blow the receiver away. But the duplexer keeps the transmit energy out of the receiver with a series of tuned circuits. Without a duplexer, the receiver and transmitter would need separate antennas, and those antennas would need to be 100 or more feet apart on a tower. Some repeaters do just that, but most use duplexers. A 2 meter duplexer is about the size of a two-drawer filing cabinet. See **Figure 18.6**.

Receiver, transmitter, controller, and duplexer: the basic components of most repeaters. After this, the sky is the limit on imagination. As an example, a remote receiver site can be used to extend coverage (**Figure 18.7**).

The two sites can be linked either by telephone ("hard wire") or a VHF or UHF link. Once you have one remote receiver site, it is natural to consider a second site to better hear those "weak mobiles" on the other side of town (**Figure 18.8**). Some of the stations using the repeater are on 2 meters while others are on 70 cm? Just link the two repeaters! (See **Figure 18.9**).

For even greater flexibility, you can add an auxiliary receiver, perhaps for a NOAA weather channel (**Figure 18.10**).

The list goes on and on. Perhaps that is why so many hams have put up repeaters.

18.3.1 FM Repeater Operation

There are almost as many operating procedures in use on repeaters as there are repeaters. Only by listening can you determine the customary procedures on a particular machine. A number of common operating techniques are found on many repeaters, however.

One such common technique is the transmission of *courtesy tones*. Suppose several stations are talking in rotation — one following another. The repeater detects the end of a transmission of one user, waits a few seconds, and then transmits a short tone or beep. The next station in the rotation waits until the beep before transmitting, thus giving any other station wanting to join in a brief period to transmit their call sign. Thus the term *courtesy tone* — you are politely pausing to allow other stations to join in the conversation.

Another common repeater feature that encourages polite operation is the *repeater timer*. A 3-minute timer is actually designed to comply with an FCC rule for remotely controlled stations, but in practice the timer serves a more social function. Since repeater

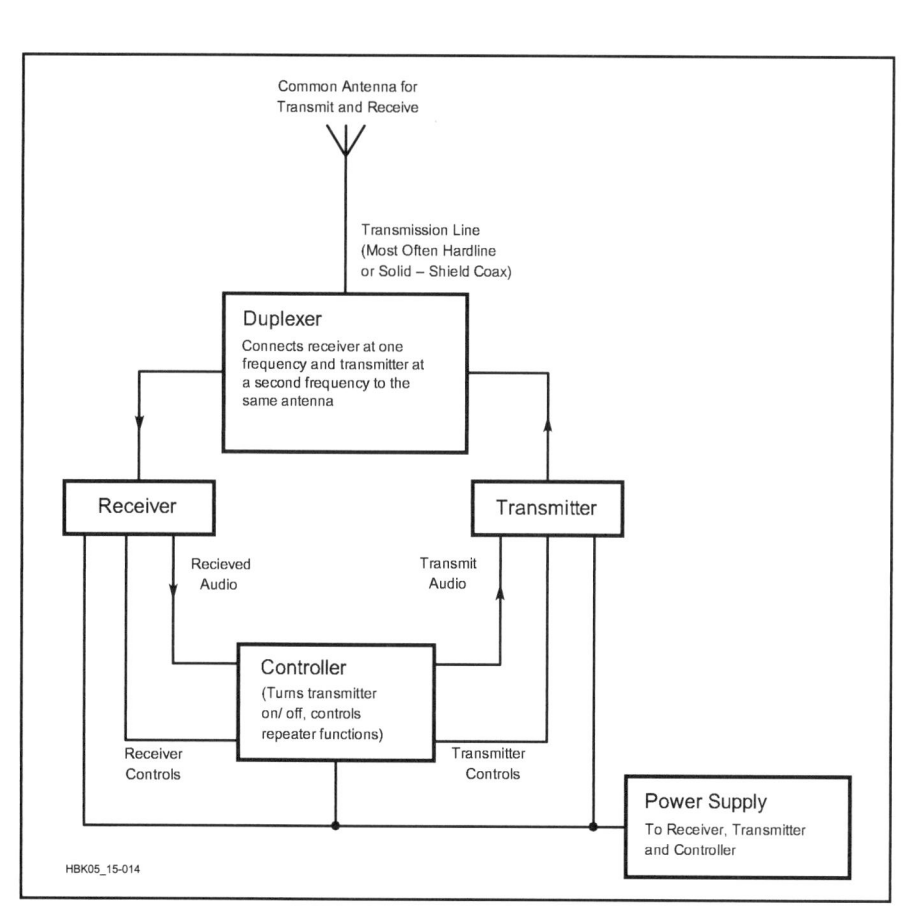

Figure 18.5 — The basic components of a repeater station. In the early days of repeaters, many were home-built. Today, most are commercial, and are far more complex than this diagram suggests.

Figure 18.6 — The W4RNC 2 meter repeater includes the repeater receiver, transmitter and controller in the rack. The large object underneath is the duplexer. [Photo courtesy Gary Pearce, KN4AQ]

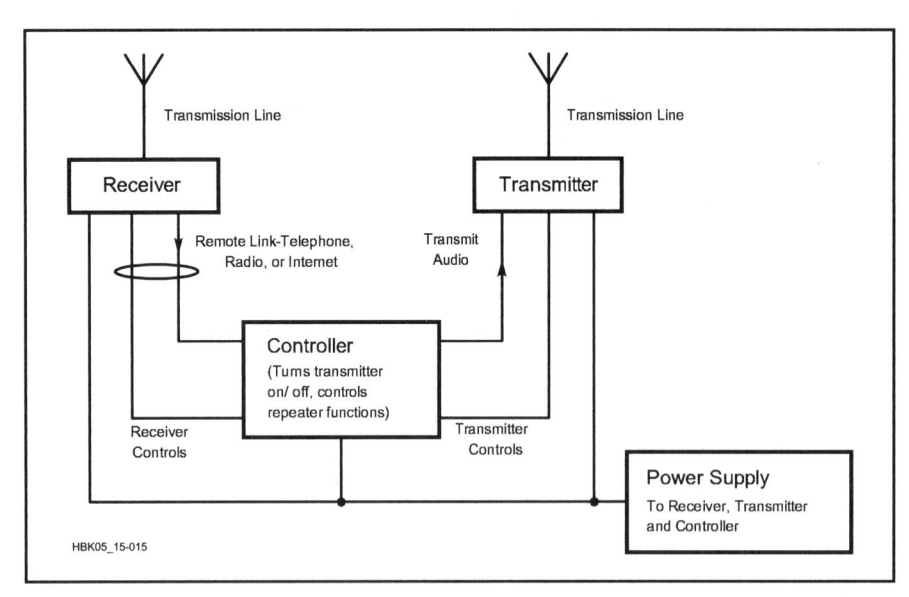

Figure 18.7 — Separating the transmitter from the receiver can extend the repeater's coverage area. The remote receiver can be located on a different building or hill, or consist of a second antenna at a different height on the tower.

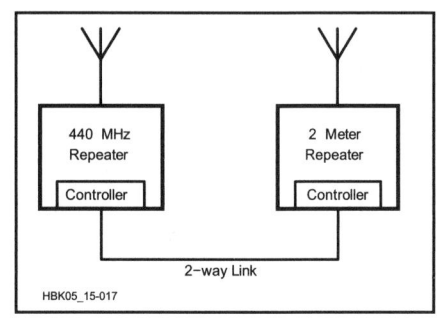

Figure 18.9 — Two repeaters using different bands can be linked for added convenience.

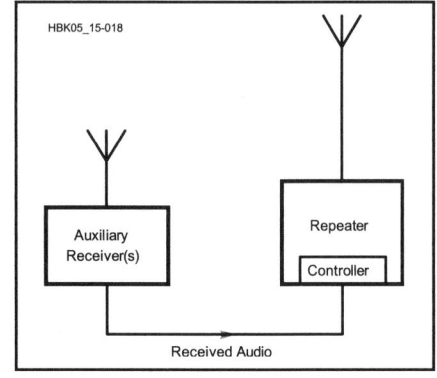

Figure 18.10 — For even greater flexibility, you can add an auxiliary receiver.

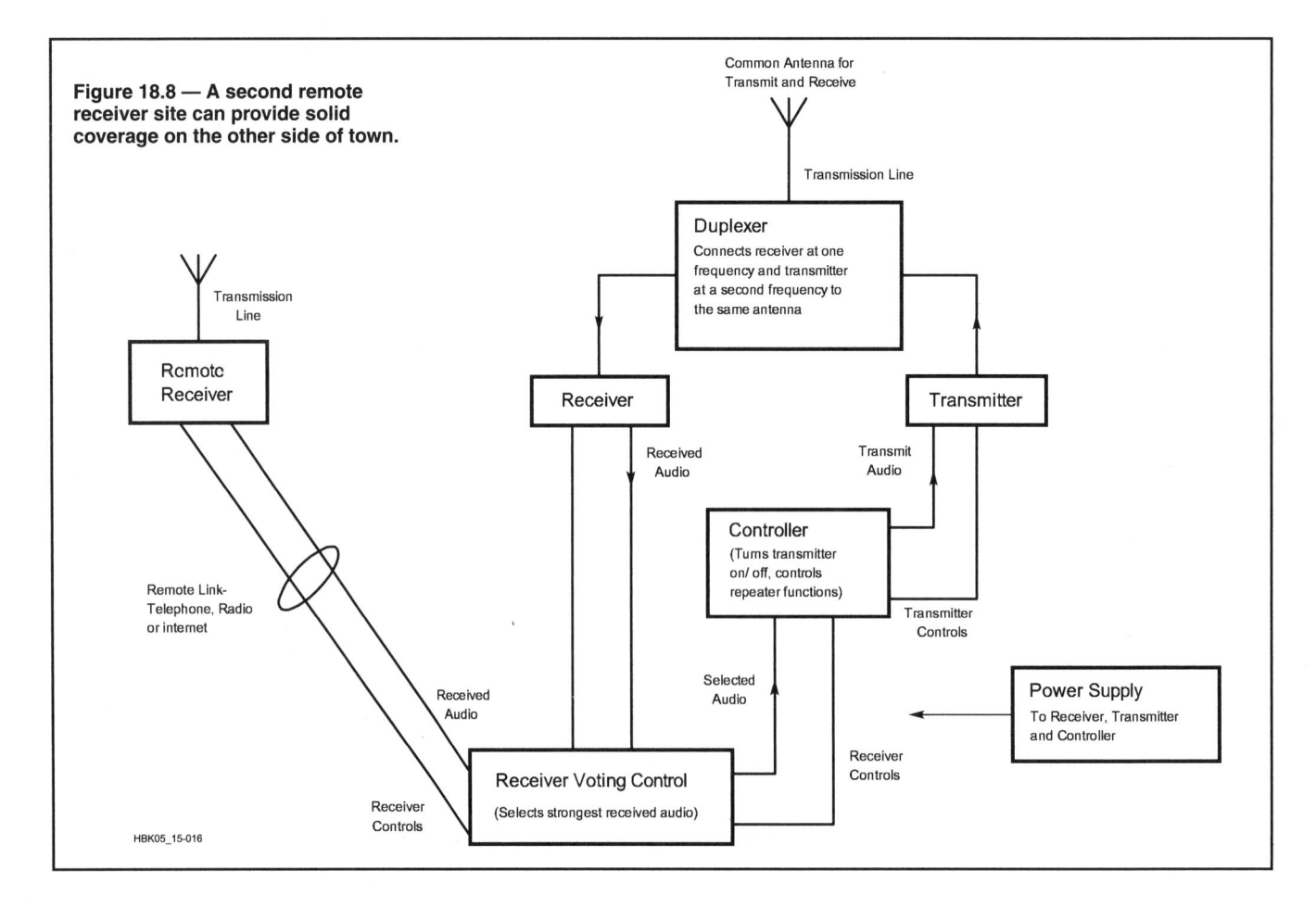

Figure 18.8 — A second remote receiver site can provide solid coverage on the other side of town.

18.6   Chapter 18

operation is channelized — allowing many stations to use the same frequency — it is polite to keep your transmissions short. If you forget this little politeness many repeaters simply cut off your transmission after 2 or 3 minutes of continuous talking. If the repeater "times out," it remains off the air until the station on the input frequency stops transmitting.

A general rule, in fact law — both internationally and in areas regulated by the FCC — is that emergency transmissions always have priority. These are defined as relating to life, safety and property damage. Many repeaters are voluntarily set up to give mobile stations priority, at least in checking into the repeater. If there is going to be a problem requiring help, the request will usually come from a mobile station. This is particularly true during rush hours; some repeater owners request that fixed stations limit their use of the repeater during these hours.

Some parts of the country have one or more *closed repeaters*. These are repeaters whose owners wish, for any number of reasons, to not make them available for general use. Often they require transmission of a *subaudible* or *CTCSS* tone (discussed later). Not all repeaters requiring a CTCSS tone are closed — many open repeaters use tones to minimize interference among machines in adjacent areas using the same frequency pair. Other closed repeaters require the transmission of a special tone sequence to turn on. It is desirable that all repeaters, including generally closed repeaters, be made available at least long enough for the presence of emergency information to be made known.

Repeaters have many uses. In some areas they are commonly used for formal traffic nets, replacing or supplementing HF nets. In other areas they are used with tone alerting for severe weather nets. Even when a particular repeater is generally used for ragchewing it can be linked for a special purpose. As an example, an ARRL volunteer official may hold a periodic section meeting across her state, with linked repeaters allowing both announcements and questions directed back to her.

One of the most common and important uses of a repeater is to aid visiting hams. Since repeaters are listed in the *ARRL Repeater Directory* and other directories, hams traveling across the country with mobile or handheld radios often check into local repeaters asking for travel route, restaurant or lodging information. Others just come on the repeater to say hello to the local group. In most areas courtesy prevails — the visitor is given priority to say hello or get the needed help.

Detailed information on repeater operating techniques is included in a full chapter of the *ARRL Operating Manual*.

18.3.2 Home, Mobile and Handheld Equipment

There are many options available in equipment used on repeaters. A number of these options are shown in **Figure 18.11**.

HANDHELD TRANSCEIVERS

A basic handheld radio with an output power of 500 mW to 5 W can be used almost anywhere — in a building, walking down a street, or in a car.

Several types of antennas can be used in the handheld mode. The smallest and most convenient is a rubber flex antenna, known as a "rubber duck," a helically wound antenna encased in a flexible tube. Unfortunately, to obtain the small size the use of a wire helix or coil produces a very low efficiency.

A quarter-wave whip, which is about 19 inches long for the 2 meter band, is a good choice for enhanced performance. The rig and your hand act as a ground plane and a reasonably efficient result is obtained. A longer antenna, consisting of several electrical quarter-wave sections in series, is also commercially available. Although this antenna usually produces extended coverage, the mechanical strain of 30 or more inches of antenna mounted on the radio's antenna connector can cause problems. After several months, the strain may require replacement of the connector.

Most newer handheld radios are supplied with lithium-ion (Li-ion) batteries. These high-capacity batteries are lightweight and allow operation for much longer periods than the classic NiCd battery pack. Charging is accomplished either with a "quick" charger in an hour or less or with a trickle charger overnight. See the **Power Sources** chapter for more information on batteries.

Power levels higher than 7 W may cause a safety problem on handheld units, since the antenna is usually close to the operator's head and eyes. See the **Safety** chapter for more information.

For mobile operation, an external antenna provides much greater range than the "rubber duck" as discussed in the following Mobile Equipment section. A power cord plugs into the vehicle cigarette lighter so that the battery remains charged, and a speaker-microphone adds convenience. In addition, commercially available "brick" amplifiers can be used to raise the output power level of the handheld radio to 50 W or more. Many hams initially go this route, but soon grow tired of frequently connecting and disconnecting all the accessories from the handheld and install a permanent mobile radio.

MOBILE EQUIPMENT

Compact mobile transceivers operate from 11-15 V dc and generally offer several transmit power levels up to about 50 W. They can operate on one or more bands. Most common are the single band and dual-band transceivers. "Dual-band" usually means 2 meters and 70 cm, but other combinations are available, as are radios that cover three or more bands.

Mobile antennas range from the quick and easy magnetic mount to "drill through the car roof" assemblies. The four general classes of mobile antennas shown in the center section of Figure 18.11 are the most popular choices. Before experimenting with antennas for your vehicle, there are some precautions to be taken.

Through-the-glass antennas: Rather than trying to get the information from your dealer or car manufacturer, test any such antenna first using masking tape or some other temporary technique to hold the antenna in place. Some windshields are metalicized for defrosting, tinting and car radio reception. Having this metal in the way of your through-the-glass antenna will seriously decrease its efficiency.

Magnet-mount or "mag-mount" antennas are convenient if your car has a metal roof or trunk. The metal also serves as the ground plane. They work well, but are not a good long-term solution. Eventually they'll scratch the car's paint, and the coax run through a door can be subject to flexing or crimping and can eventually fail.

Through-the-roof antenna mounting: Most hams are reluctant to drill a hole in their car roof, unless they intend to keep the car for a long time. This mounting method provides the best efficiency, however, since the (metal) roof serves as a ground plane. Before you drill, carefully plan and measure how you intend to get the antenna cable down under the interior car headliner to the radio. Be especially careful of side-curtain air bags. Commercial two-way shops can install antennas and power cables, usually for a reasonable price.

Trunk lip and clip-on antennas: These antennas are good compromises. They are usually easy to mount and they perform acceptably. Cable routing must be planned. If you are going to run more than a few watts, do not mount the antenna close to one of the car windows — a significant portion of the radiated power may enter the car interior.

More information on mobile equipment may be found in the **Assembling a Station** and **Antennas** chapters.

HOME STATION EQUIPMENT

Most "base station" FM radios are actually mobile rigs, powered either from rechargeable batteries or ac-operated power

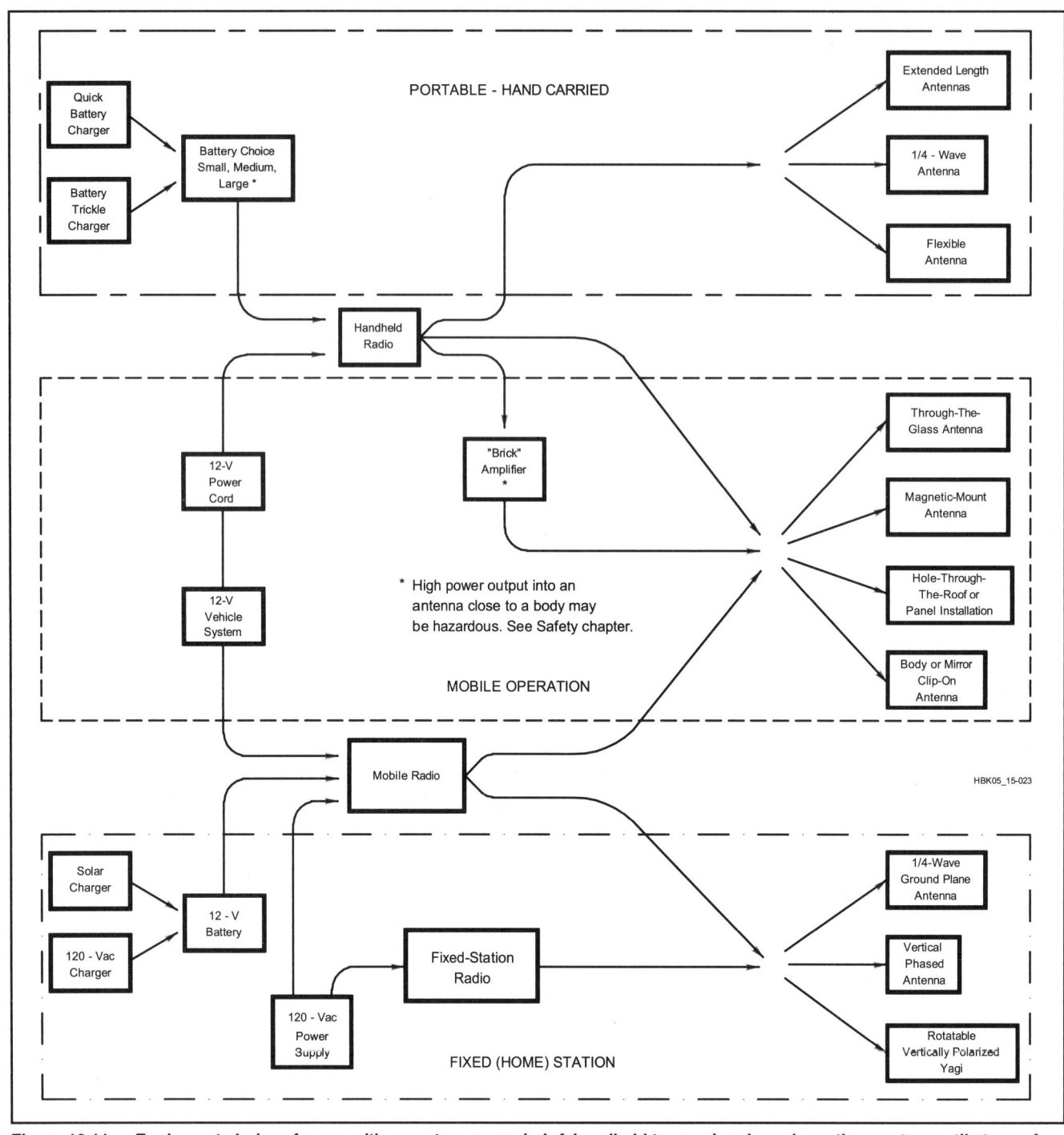

Figure 18.11 — Equipment choices for use with repeaters are varied. A handheld transceiver is perhaps the most versatile type of radio, as it can be operated from home, from a vehicle and from a mountaintop.

supplies. Use of batteries has the advantage of providing back-up communications ability in the event of a power interruption. Some HF transceivers designed for fixed-station use also offer operation on the VHF or VHF/UHF bands, using SSB and CW in addition to FM. Using them means that you will not be able to monitor a local FM frequency while operating HF.

The general choice of fixed-location antennas is also shown in Figure 18.11. Most hams use an omnidirectional vertical, but if you are in an area between two repeaters on the same channel, a rotatable Yagi may let you pick which repeater you will use without interfering with the other repeater. Vertical polarization is the universal custom, since it is easiest to accomplish in a mobile installation. VHF/UHF SSB operation is customarily horizontally polarized. An operator with a radio that does both has a tough choice, as there can be a serious performance hit between stations using cross-polarized antennas.

Both commercial and homemade ¼-λ and larger antennas are popular for home use. A number of these are shown in the **Antennas** chapter. Generally speaking, ¼-λ sections may be stacked up to provide more gain on any band. As you do so, however, more

18.8 Chapter 18

and more power is concentrated toward the horizon. This may be desirable if you live in a flat area. See **Figure 18.12**.

18.3.3 Coded Squelch and Tones

Squelch is the circuit in FM radios that turns off the loud rush of noise with no signal present. Most of the time, hams use *noise squelch*, also called *carrier squelch*, a squelch circuit that lets any signal at all come through. But there are ways to be more selective about what signal gets to your speaker or keys up your repeater. That's generically known as *coded squelch*, and more than half of the repeaters on the air require you to send coded squelch to be able to use the repeater.

CTCSS

The most common form of coded squelch has the generic name *CTCSS* (Continuous Tone Coded Squelch System), but is better known by the nickname "tone." Taken from the commercial services, subaudible tones are generally not used to keep others from using a repeater but rather are a method of minimizing interference from users of the same repeater frequency. CTCSS tones are sine-wave audio tones between 67 and 250 Hz, that are added to the transmit audio at a fairly low level. They are *sub*audible only because your receiver's audio circuit is supposed to filter them out. A receiver with CTCSS will remain silent to all traffic on a channel unless the transmitting station is sending the correct tone. Then the receiver sends the transmitted audio to its speaker.

For example, in **Figure 18.13** a mobile station on hill A is nominally within the normal coverage area of the Jonestown repeater (146.16/76). The Smithtown repeater, also on the same frequency pair, usually cannot hear stations 150 miles away. The mobile is on a hill and so he is in the coverage area of both Jonestown and Smithtown. Whenever the mobile transmits both repeaters hear him.

The common solution to this problem, assuming it happens often enough, is to equip the Smithtown repeater with a CTCSS decoder and require all users of the repeater to transmit a CTCSS tone to access the repeater. Thus, the mobile station on the hill does not come through the Smithtown repeater, since he is not transmitting the required CTCSS tone.

Table 18.2 shows the available CTCSS tones. Most radios built since the early 1980s have a CTCSS encoder built in, and most radios built since the early 1990s also have a CTCSS *decoder* built in. Newer radios have a "tone scan" feature that will hunt the tone, *if* the repeater output includes a tone. Most repeaters that require tone also transmit their tone, but they don't have to. Listings in the *ARRL Repeater Directory* include the CTCSS tone required, if any.

If your local repeater sends a CTCSS tone, you can use your decoder to monitor just that repeater, and avoid hearing the co-channel neighbor, intermod or the annoying fizzes of nearby consumer electronics. Radios typically store CTCSS frequency and mode in their memory channels.

DIGITAL-CODED SQUELCH (DCS)

A newer form of coded squelch is called *DCS* (Digital-Coded Squelch). DCS appeared in commercial service because CTCSS didn't

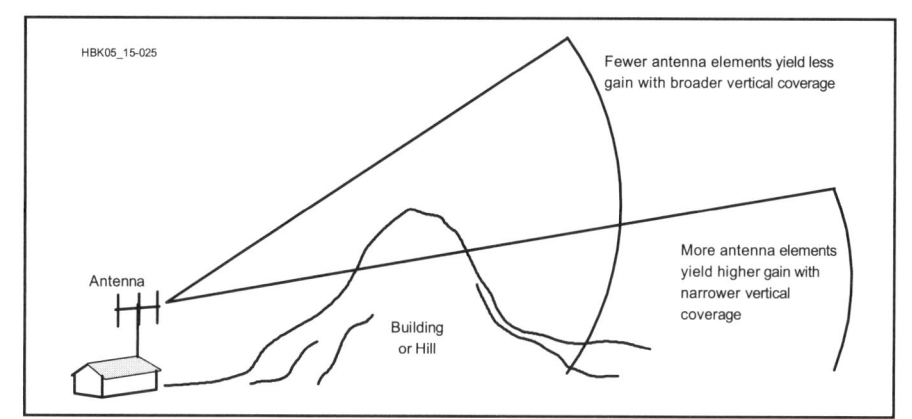

Figure 18.12 — As with all line-of-sight communications, terrain plays an important role in how your signal gets out.

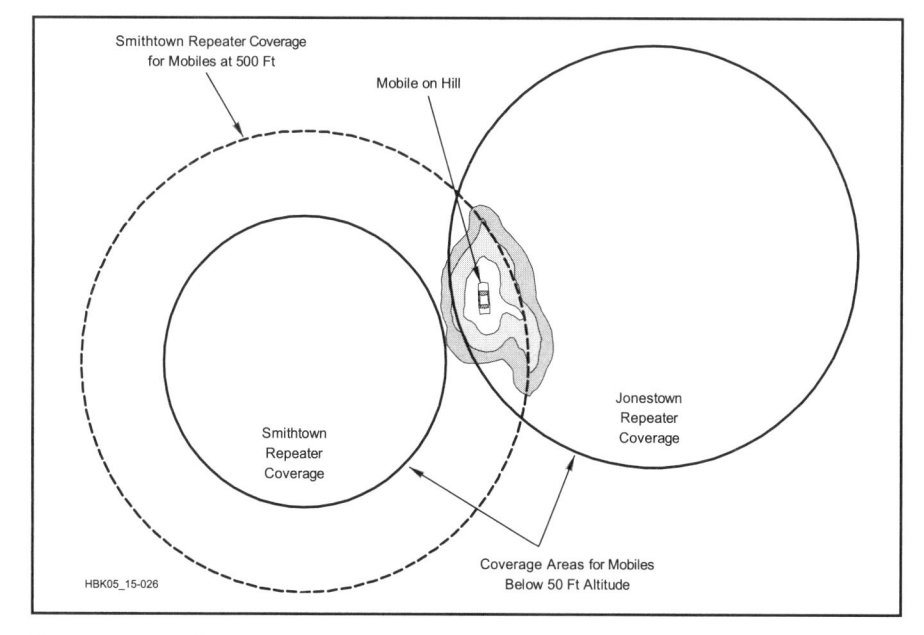

Figure 18.13 — When two repeaters operate on the same frequencies, a well-situated operator can key up both repeaters simultaneously. A directional antenna may help.

Table 18.2
CTCSS Tone Frequencies

The purpose of CTCSS is to reduce cochannel interference during band openings. CTCSS equipped repeaters would respond only to signals having the CTCSS tone required for that repeater. These repeaters would not respond to weak distant signals on their inputs and correspondingly not transmit and repeat to add to the congestion. The standard ANSI/EIA frequency codes, in hertz, are as follows:

67.0	118.8	179.9
69.3	123.0	183.5
71.9	127.3	186.2
74.4	131.8	189.9
77.0	136.5	192.8
79.7	141.3	199.5
82.5	146.2	203.5
85.4	151.4	206.5
88.5	156.7	210.7
91.5	159.8	218.1
94.8	162.2	225.7
97.4	165.5	229.1
100.0	167.9	233.6
103.5	171.3	241.8
107.2	173.8	250.3
110.9	177.3	254.1
114.8		

provide enough tones for the many users. DCS adds another 100 or so code options. DCS started showing up in Amateur Radio transceivers several years ago and is now a standard feature in most new radios. Open repeaters generally still use CTCSS rather than DCS, since many older radios still in use don't have DCS.

DTMF

In the days before widespread use of cell phones, one of the most attractive features of repeaters was the availability of autopatch services that allowed a mobile or portable station to use a standard telephone DTMF (dual-tone multi-frequency, or Touch-Tone) key pad to connect the repeater to the local telephone line and make outgoing calls.

Although autopatches see less use today, DTMF key pads are still used for sending control signals. DTMF can also be used as a form of squelch, to turn a receiver on, though it's more often used to control various functions such as autopatch and talking S meters. Some repeaters that require CTCSS have a DTMF "override" that puts the repeater into carrier-squelch mode for a few minutes if you send the proper digits. Other applications for DTMF tones include controlling linked repeaters, described in a later section.

Table 18.3 shows the DTMF tones. Some keyboards provide the standard 12 sets of tones corresponding to the digits 0 through 9 and the special signs # and *. Others include the full set of 16 pairs, providing special keys A through D. The tones are arranged in two groups, usually called the low tones and high tones. Two tones, one from each group, are required to define a key or digit. For example, pressing 5 will generate a 770-Hz tone and a 1336-Hz tone simultaneously.

The standards used by the telephone company require the amplitudes of these two tones to have a certain relationship.

18.3.4 Narrowbanding

We noted in the previous section that in most urban areas, there are no "available" frequencies for new repeaters. And you might recall from our short history section at the beginning of this chapter that the Amateur Radio FM boom began when the business and public-safety services ran out of room and had to buy all new radios. Their solution to overcrowding, mandated by the FCC, was to reduce the spectrum used for each channel. In the 1960s, that meant reducing the modulation ("deviation") of FM signals from 15 kHz to 5 kHz, and splitting each channel in two. Hams inherited the 15 kHz deviation radios (called "wideband" at the time), but soon adopted the 5 kHz "narrowband" standard.

History is repeating itself. Our spectrum neighbors are again out of room, and the FCC is again requiring them to reduce deviation, from 5 kHz (now called "wideband"), to 2.5 kHz (the new "narrowband"). It's been postponed for several years, but is finally happening.

Will hams follow suit and create space for more repeaters in our own crowded bands? So far, the answer is "no." While most Amateur Radio FM equipment built in the past decade has a "narrow" option that reduces the deviation and incorporates tighter receive filters, we still have a lot of legacy equipment in the field, and no corporate or municipal budget to draw on to replace it. Most of our repeaters are still made of old hardware converted from commercial service. Few repeater councils have seriously considered adjusting frequency coordination to accommodate narrowbanding. No one expects the FCC to require hams to adopt narrowbanding.

What *is* happening is the placement of D-STAR digital repeaters, which are especially "narrow" already, in between the channels occupied by analog FM repeaters. Since there is still some spectrum overlap, the D-STAR repeaters must also be a good distance away from their new adjacent-channel neighbors — 30 to 50 miles — to reduce the field strength of all the signals involved.

To help you understand how this all works, we'll explain that the terminology "5 kHz" and "2.5 kHz" deviation for analog FM signals is misleading. It refers to the peak frequency shift a modulated signal takes *in one direction* from the center frequency. But the FM signal moves both up and down from that center, and has some sidebands as well. The actual spectrum used by a "5 kHz" FM signal peaks at 16 kHz and the "narrow" 2.5 kHz signal hits 11 kHz on peaks — not much of a savings. The digital D-STAR signal is about 6.25 kHz wide. The digital signals fill their spectrum completely, all the time, and don't vary with modulation.

Narrowbanding may become a voluntary practice in Amateur Radio, though *your* use would be "mandated" by remaining compatible with narrowbanded repeaters. It's not on the horizon as of this edition of the *Handbook*.

18.3.5 Linked Repeaters

Most repeaters are standalone devices, providing their individual pool of coverage and that's it. But a significant number of repeaters are linked — connected to one or more other repeaters. Those other repeaters can be on other bands at the same location, or they can be in other locations, or both. Linked repeaters let users communicate between different bands and across wider geographic areas than they can on a single repeater. **Figure 18.14** shows an example.

There are many ways to link repeaters. Repeaters on the same tower can just be wired together, or they may even share the same controller. Repeaters within a hundred miles or so of each other can use a radio link — separate link transmitters and receivers at each repeater, with antennas pointed at each other. Multiple repeaters, each still about 100 miles apart, can "daisy-chain" their links to cover even wider territory. There are a few linked repeater systems in the country that cover several states with dozens of repeaters, but most radio-linked repeater systems have more modest ambitions, covering just part of one or two states.

Repeater linking via the Internet has created the ability to tie repeaters together around the world and in nearly unlimited number. We'll talk more about Internet linking in the next section.

There are several ways linked repeaters can be operated, coming under the categories of *full-time* and *on demand*. Full-time linked repeaters operate just as the name implies — all the repeaters in a linked network are connected all the time. If you key up one of them, you're heard on all of them, and you can talk to anyone on any of the other repeaters on the network at any time. You don't have to do anything special to activate the network, since it's always there.

In an on-demand system, the linked repeaters remain isolated unless you take some action, usually by sending a code by DTMF digits, to connect them. Your DTMF sequence may activate all the repeaters on the network, or the system may let you address just one specific repeater, somewhat like dialing a telephone. When you're finished, another DTMF code drops the link, or a timer

Table 18.3
Standard Telephone (DTMF) Tones

	Low Tone Group		High Tone Group	
	1209 Hz	1336 Hz	1477 Hz	1633 Hz
697 Hz	1	2	3	A
770 Hz	4	5	6	B
852 Hz	7	8	9	C
941 Hz	*	0	#	D

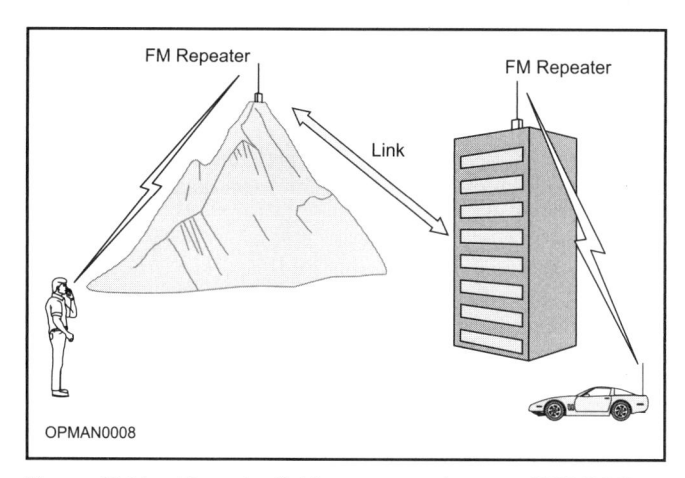

Figure 18.14 — Repeater linking can greatly expand VHF/UHF communication distances. Repeater links are commonly made via dedicated radio hardware or via the Internet.

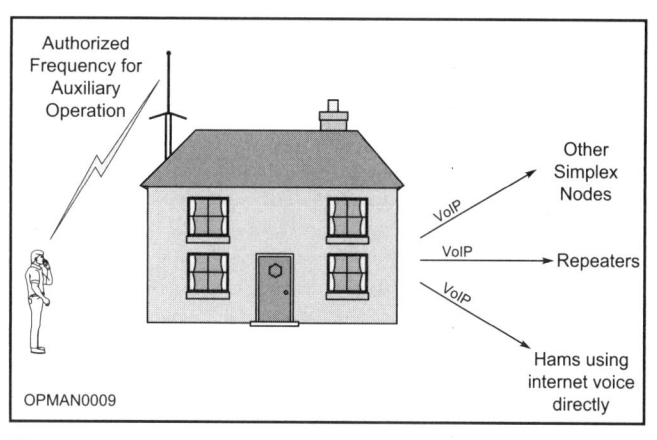

Figure 18.15 — A diagram of a VoIP simplex node. If a control operator is not physically present at the station location and the node is functioning with wireless remote control, the control link must follow the rules for *auxiliary* operation.

may handle that chore when the repeaters are no longer in use.

INTERNET LINKING

The Internet and *Voice over Internet Protocol* (VoIP) has expanded repeater linking exponentially, making worldwide communication through a local repeater commonplace. Two Internet linking systems, IRLP and EchoLink, have reached critical mass in the US and are available almost everywhere. The D-STAR and DMR digital systems also have a significant Internet linking component. A brief overview is included here; more information may be found in the **Digital Communications** downloadable supplement.

IRLP

The Internet Radio Linking Project (IRLP) is the most "radio" based linking system. User access is only via radio, using either simplex or repeater stations, while linking is done using VoIP on the Internet. An IRLP system operator establishes a *node* by interfacing his radio equipment to a computer with an Internet connection, and then running IRLP software. Once that's set up, repeater users send DTMF tones to make connections, either directly to other individual repeater or simplex nodes (**Figure 18.15**), or to *reflectors* — servers that tie multiple nodes together as one big party line.

The direct connections work like on-demand linked repeaters. You dial in the node number you want to connect to and access code (if required), and you are connected to the distant repeater. Once connected, everyone on both ends can communicate. When finished, another DTMF sequence takes the link down. Someone from a distant repeater can make a connection to you as well.

Reflectors work like a hybrid between on-demand and full-time linked repeaters. You can connect your local repeater to a reflector and leave it there all day, or you can connect for a special purpose (like a net), and drop it when the event is over.

EchoLink

EchoLink requires a PC with sound card and appropriate software. It allows repeater connections like IRLP, and it has Conference Servers, similar to IRLP reflectors that permit multiple connections. The big difference is that EchoLink allows individuals to connect to the network from their computers, without using a radio.

The EchoLink conference servers all have more or less specific functions. Some are just regional gathering places, while some are region, topic or activity based (SKYWARN and National Hurricane Center Nets, Jamboree on the Air, and so on).

You can connect your EchoLink-enabled computer to your base station radio fairly easily through a sound card, and create an on-air node. Don't pipe EchoLink to a local repeater without permission from the repeater owner, though.

If you decide to create a full-time link from a computer to a repeater, consider using a dedicated UHF link frequency rather than just a base station on the repeater input. This applies to IRLP connections as well. Of course, the Internet is infrastructure dependent, and both power and Internet access can be interrupted during storms or other disasters.

18.4 D-STAR Repeater Systems

D-STAR is a digital protocol developed by the Japan Amateur Radio League (JARL) that takes Amateur Radio into the 21st century. D-STAR is a bit-streaming protocol able to encapsulate voice and low speed data (DV) or higher speed Ethernet data (DD). Because the protocol is entirely digital (GMSK modulation is used for amateur station transceivers and the respective repeaters), signaling is carried entirely out-of-band (ie, control codes are a separate part of the data stream from the voice or Ethernet information). When looking at the D-STAR repeater systems, it is important to keep that aspect in mind. Amateurs are more familiar with in-band signaling (DTMF tones, for example) in the analog world. Additional information on D-STAR may be found in the **Digital Communications** downloadable supplement.

18.4.1 D-STAR Station IDs

The D-STAR specification defines a protocol that can be used for simplex communication or repeater operations. When used simplex, the D-STAR radios function similarly to analog radios with the additional capability to enable selective listening based on station ID (call sign and a character or space). To operate through a repeater, you must know the repeater's station ID as well as the frequency the repeater is on. In this case, consider the repeater's station ID equivalent to a unique CTCSS tone in the analog world.

The D-STAR specification defines all station IDs as seven upper-case alphanumeric characters (space padded) and one upper-case alphanumeric station identifier (which may also be a space). In other words, W1AW can operate multiple D-STAR stations where the first seven characters of the station ID are "W1AW<space><space><space>" (three space characters follow W1AW) and the eighth character may be a space or upper-case alphanumeral. The G2 gateway software restricts the eighth character to a space or upper-case alphanumeral. For instance, two stations could operate at the same time using "W1AW<space><space><space>" and "W1AW<space><space><space>P".

To talk to someone via D-STAR, you need to set your radio with four station IDs:
• your station ID (MYCALL)
• their station ID (URCALL)
• your local repeater station ID (RPT1)
• your local gateway station ID (RPT2).

MYCALL is always set to your call sign, followed by a character or space. RPT1 is set to your local repeater's station ID (the repeater call sign, followed by a character or space).

If you want to talk locally through the repeater:
• Set URCALL to CQCQCQ.
• Set RPT2 to your local gateway station ID (this isn't needed for local communication, but allows some new network functions to operate, and has become the default recommendation).

The power of the D-STAR protocol becomes evident when D-STAR *gateways* are implemented, providing interconnectivity between repeater systems. This interconnectivity is the same whether you are using voice or Ethernet data.

To talk to someone elsewhere in the D-STAR world, beyond your local area:
• Set URCALL to the other station's ID.
• Set RPT2 to your local gateway station ID.

The RPT2 setting is very important. You don't need to know where the other station is. You simply tell your local repeater to send your bit stream (everything is digital) to the local gateway so that gateway can determine where to send it next. The local gateway looks at URCALL (remember, this is part of the bit stream) and determines where that station was heard last. It then sends the bit stream on to that remote gateway, which looks at URCALL again to determine which repeater at the far end should transmit the bit stream.

Sounds complex? Yes, the implementation can be complex but the user is shielded from all of this by simply setting the four station IDs. **Figure 18.16** shows an example.

18.4.2 Station Routing

There are several different ways to set the destination station ID using URCALL:
• If URCALL is set to CQCQCQ, this means "don't go any farther."
• If URCALL is set to the remote station's ID and RPT2 is set to the local gateway, this means "gateway, send my bit stream to be transmitted out the repeater that the remote station was last heard on."
• If URCALL is set to/followed by a remote *repeater* station ID, and RPT2 is set to the local gateway, this means "gateway, send my bit stream to be transmitted out the repeater designated."

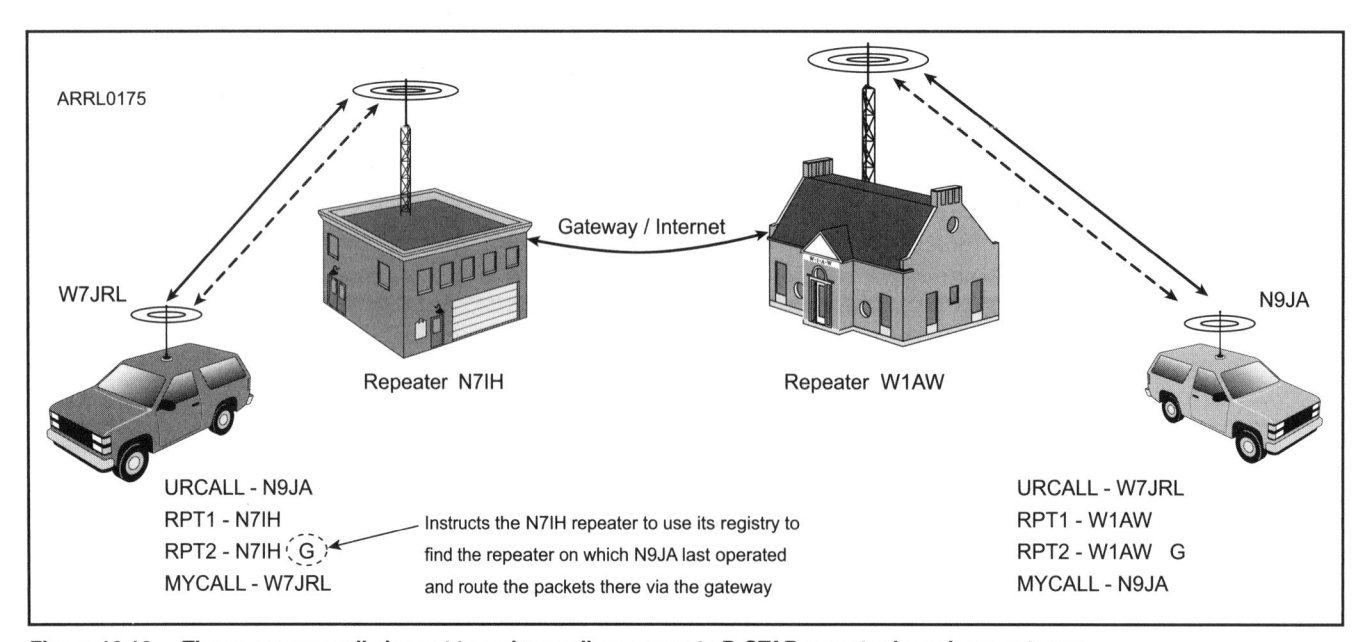

ARRL0175

W7JRL

Repeater N7IH — Gateway / Internet — Repeater W1AW

N9JA

URCALL - N9JA
RPT1 - N7IH
RPT2 - N7IH G — Instructs the N7IH repeater to use its registry to find the repeater on which N9JA last operated and route the packets there via the gateway
MYCALL - W7JRL

URCALL - W7JRL
RPT1 - W1AW
RPT2 - W1AW G
MYCALL - N9JA

Figure 18.16 — The necessary call sign set to make a call on a remote D-STAR repeater by using a gateway.

D-STAR Network Overview

The D-STAR specification defines the repeater controller/gateway communications and defines the general D-STAR network architecture. The diagram shown here as Figure 18.A1 is taken from the English translation of the D-STAR specification:

The Comp. IP and Own IP are shown for reference if this were a DD communications. As they do not change and are not passed as part of the D-STAR protocol, they can safely be ignored for the purposes of the following explanation.

Headers 1 through 4 are W$1QQQ calling W$1WWW. Headers 5 through 8 are W$1WWW calling W$1QQQ. Note that "Own Callsign" and "Companion Callsign" are never altered in either sequence. The "Destination Repeater Callsign" and the "Departure Repeater Callsign" are changed between the gateways. This is so the receiving gateway and repeater controller know which repeater to send the bit stream to. It also makes it easy to create a "One Touch" response as ICOM has done by simply placing the received "Own Callsign" in the transmitted "Companion Callsign", the received "Destination Repeater Callsign" in the transmitted "Departure Repeater Callsign", and the received "Departure Repeater Callsign" in the transmitted "Destination Repeater Callsign".

Use of the "special" character "/" at the beginning of a call sign indicates that the transmission is to be routed to the repeater specified immediately following the slash. For instance, entering "/K5TIT B" in the "Companion Callsign" would cause the transmission to be routed to the "K5TIT B" repeater for broadcast. Using the above example, W$1QQQ would put "/W$1SSS" in the "Companion Callsign" for the same sequence 1 through 4 to occur. At the W$1VVV gateway, however, the "/W$1SSS" in the "Companion Callsign" would be changed to "CQCQCQ". All stations within range of W$1SSS would see the transmission as originating from W$1QQQ and going to CQCQCQ just like that station was local (but the "Departure Repeater Callsign" would be "W$1VVV G" and the "Destination Repeater Callsign" would be "W$1SSS"). Replying would still be done the same way as before since the received "Companion Callsign" is ignored when programming the radio to reply.

Every "terminal" (station) has an IP address assigned to it for DD purposes. The address is assigned from the 10.0.0.0/8 address range. The D-STAR gateway is always 10.0.0.2. The router to the Internet is always 10.0.0.1. The addresses 10.0.0.3-31 are reserved for local-to-the-gateway (not routable) use. What this makes possible is the ability to send Ethernet packets to another station by only knowing that terminal's IP address and the remote station can directly respond based solely on IP address. This is because the gateway software can correlate IP address with call sign and ID. This makes it possible to route DD Ethernet packets based on the "Companion Callsign" or based on IP address with "Companion Callsign" set to "CQCQCQ". — *Pete Loveall, AE5PL*

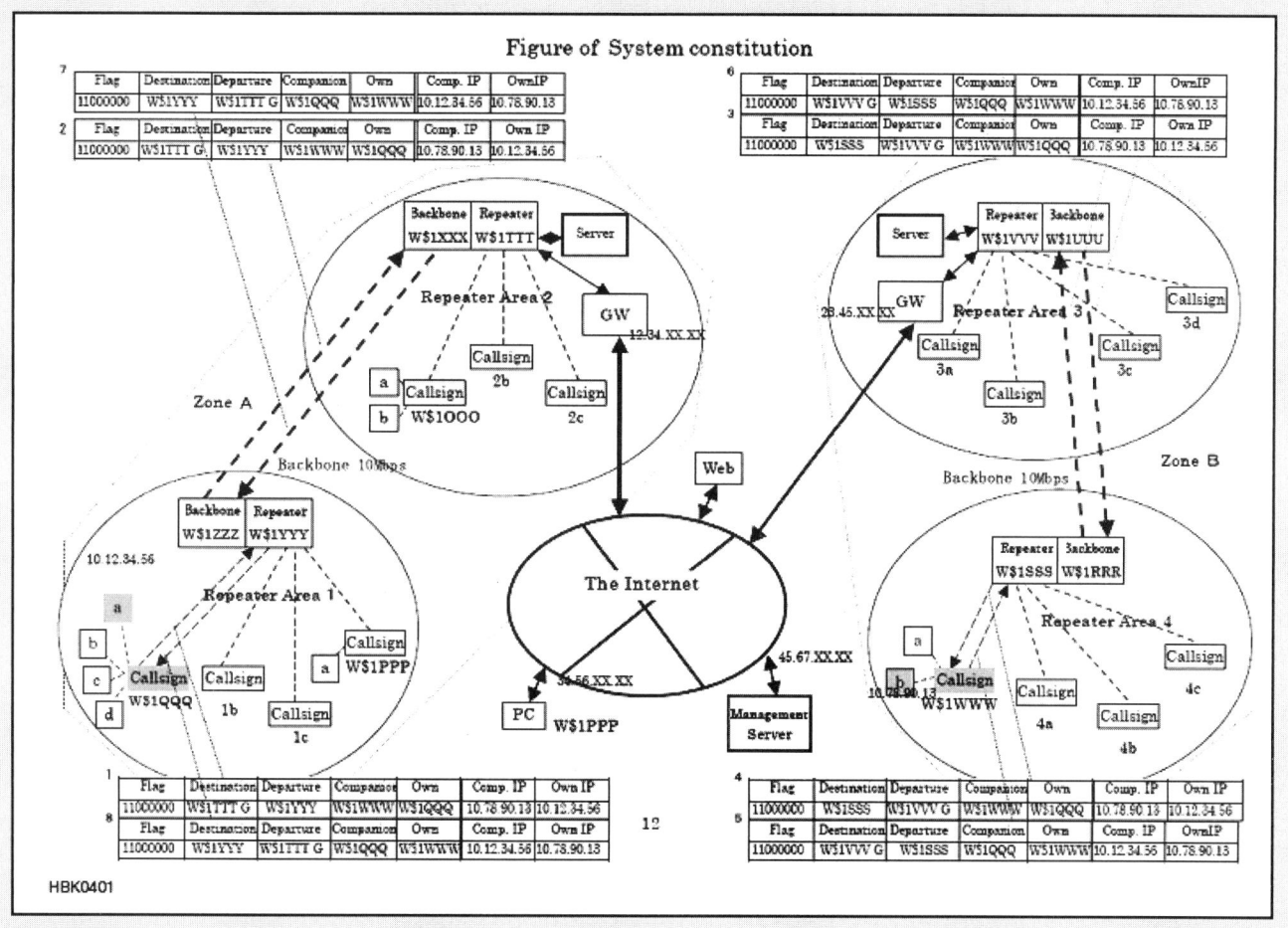

Figure 18.A1 — A D-STAR system overview.

Some people mistakenly call this "call sign routing." In fact, this is "station routing" because you are specifying the station you want to hear your bit stream (voice or Ethernet data). This is not source routing because the source station is only defining what station they want to talk to; it is up to the gateways to determine routing (very similar to Internet routers).

You can specify a destination but you have no guarantee that:

1) The designated station is on the air to receive your transmission.

2) The repeater that the designated station is using is not busy.

3) Other factors will not prevent your bit stream from reaching the designated station.

Station routing is similar to your address book. In your address book you may have a work number, home number, cell number, fax number and email address for a person. How do you know which one to contact them at? Maybe the email address is best if you want to send them data (equivalent to the station ID for their Ethernet data radio). Maybe the cell phone number if that is what they normally have with them (equivalent to their hand-held transceiver station ID).

How do I know if they heard me? When they talk (or send Ethernet data) back to you. D-STAR is connectionless. Therefore, there is no equivalence in D-STAR to repeater linking as we think of it in the analog world. However, there have been independent implementations of linking of repeaters similar to the linking we see with IRLP (see the section on *DPlus*).

In all cases of D-STAR repeater use, all digital voice (DV) signals with a proper RPT1 are always repeated so everyone hears your transmission through the repeater, regardless of the other settings. Ethernet data (DD) signals are not repeated on frequency because the "repeater" is actually a half-duplex Ethernet bridge operating on a single frequency.

For more details, see the sidebar, "D-STAR Network Overview."

18.4.3 Enhancing D-STAR Operation with *DPlus*

Because D-STAR is a true digital protocol, repeaters have no need for decoding the audio transmitted as bits from each radio. As mentioned previously, this requires all signaling to be out-of-band (with regard to the voice or Ethernet data).

Applications can be built to work with this out-of-band signaling to implement enhancements to the base product without modifying those products. One of these applications is *DPlus*, software that runs on the D-STAR Gateway computer at the repeater site. It provides many capabilities and more are being added as the software develops.

A key concept is the capability to link repeaters either *directly* (everything heard on one repeater is heard on another) or *indirectly* through a *reflector* (everything sent to a reflector is reflected back out to all linked repeaters). A reflector is a special version of *DPlus* that runs on a standalone computer that is not part of a repeater system. Linking and unlinking a repeater is done by altering the contents of URCALL according to the *DPlus* documentation. (These features continue to evolve, so specific operating commands are not covered here.)

There is no way to directly link two DD "repeaters." Because DD is Ethernet bridging, however, full TCP support is available, allowing each individual station to make connections as needed to fit their requirements.

For a station to make use of a linked repeater, the station must have URCALL set to CQCQCQ and RPT2 set to the local gateway. If RPT2 is not set to the local gateway, *DPlus* running on the local gateway computer will never see the bit stream and therefore not be able to forward the bit stream to the linked repeater or reflector. This is why setting RPT2 for your local gateway should be your default setting.

If your radio is set for automatic low-speed data transmission, remember that low-speed data is carried as part of the digital voice bit stream and is not multiplexed. Therefore, any low-speed data transmission will block the frequency for the time the transmission is occurring. Caution: if you are using a linked repeater or if you have set URCALL to something other than CQCQCQ, your bit stream will be seen by all stations that are on the other end of that transmission. A reflector could have over 100 other repeaters listening to your transmission.

18.4.4 D-STAR Repeater Hardware

D-STAR repeaters are a bit different from the FM repeaters with which we're all familiar. A quick comparison will help to illustrate.

A complete FM repeater such as in **Figure 18.17** consists of at least three identifiable components. A receiver receives the original signal and demodulates it. The demodulated audio is routed to a controller, where it is mixed with other audio. The resulting combined audio signal is routed back to one or more transmitters. At least one additional source of audio is present in the controller, as it is a legal requirement to ID the repeater transmitter correctly. A well-constructed system includes validation that the levels and frequency response of the processed audio are consistent and true to the originally transmitted signals.

A D-STAR repeater's block diagram (**Figure 18.18**) looks very similar, but functions very differently. A receiver receives the original signal and demodulates it. That signal is passed to a controller, which then drives one or more transmitters. The most significant difference is that there is no audio involved! D-STAR is a digital protocol. All required manipulation of information is performed in the digital domain, including the necessary ID functions. Most existing D-STAR repeaters do not contain the vocoders necessary to recover audio information, so there exists no local speaker or microphone. There is also no level-setting to consider with D-STAR.

D-STAR REPEATER OPTIONS

There is much discussion about "homebrew" D-STAR repeaters. The two most common approaches are to modify an existing FM repeater to pass the digital signal, or to wire two radios back-to-back. Both approaches provide the desired extended RF coverage, but fail to accurately process the digital signal. Thus both approaches fall short in either functional capability or in legality of the transmitted signal.

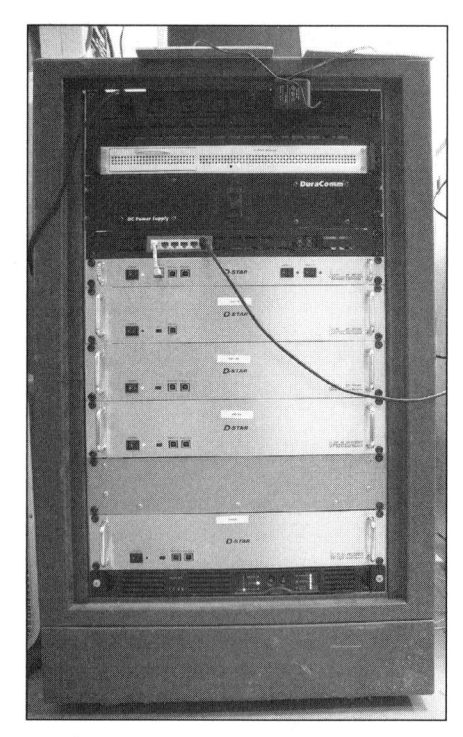

Figure 18.17 — A full rack of D-STAR equipment on the bench of Jim McClellan, N5MIJ. Top to bottom: ICOM IP-RPC2 controller, ID-RP2V 1.2-GHz voice repeater, ID-RP4000 440 MHz voice and data repeater, a blank panel and an ID-RP2000 146 MHz voice and data repeater.

It is relatively simple to modify an existing FM repeater to pass the digital signal. The limitations of this approach are that there can be no additional capability added (for example, a D-STAR Gateway), since the digital signal is never decoded. Additionally, this method lacks the ability to encapsulate the ID for the repeater transmitter into the transmitted data.

It is also very simple to wire two D-STAR radios back-to-back, such that the incoming signals are retransmitted. Again, the functionality is limited by the inability to process the entire data stream. This approach presents an additional consideration, as the radio used as a transmitter does not process the data stream as is done in the D-STAR repeater system, and the ID of the originating transmitter is lost, replaced by the ID of the "repeater" transmitter.

Current commercially produced D-STAR repeaters are designed to be used across a broad frequency range. They do not have some of the tight front-end filtering provided by our familiar FM repeaters, so repeater builders must provide that front-end filtering externally. Installing additional band-pass filters between the antenna and the repeater will significantly improve the performance of the system. This is true for both digital voice (DV) repeaters and digital data (DD) access points.

Following good engineering practices will ensure good performance of the system. A properly constructed and installed D-STAR repeater can exhibit performance improvements of 15% or more in range, as compared to a comparably constructed FM repeater. This performance gain comes from the combination of the forward error correction (FEC) contained in the transmitted signal, and the fact that the radiated power is contained within a narrower bandwidth.

D-STAR is an exciting new system for the amateur community, providing significant opportunities for us to develop applications and implementations using capabilities we've never had before. We truly are limited only by our imaginations. The growth of the world-wide D-STAR network illustrates the level of interest in the technology by both amateurs and our served agencies. Amateurs are once again developing at the leading edge of technology. What we do with the new tools is up to us. How will you use D-STAR?

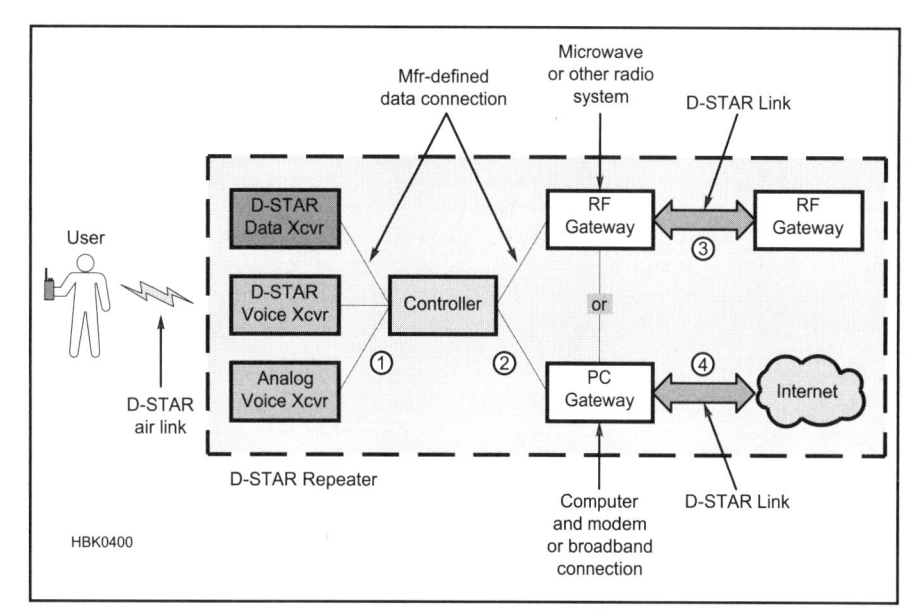

Figure 18.18 — Internal and external connections of a D-STAR repeater stack.

18.5 Digital Mobile Radio (DMR)

The following sections are contributed by John Burningham, W2XAB, from "Amateur Radio Guide to Digital Mobile Radio" (see Reference section).

Digital Mobile Radio (DMR) was developed by the European Telecommunications Standards Institute (ETSI) and is used worldwide by professional mobile radio users. It supports both fully-digital and dual-mode (analog/digital) operation.

Amateurs have implemented DMR with over 3,400 repeaters and 49,000 users registered worldwide as of March 2017. Majority of the repeaters are interconnected via the Internet. There are a number of US amateur international, regional and state networks. Most are interconnected with the DMR-MARC (Motorola Amateur Radio Club) DMRX core servers, Brandmeister, and DMR-Plus.

In the early era of amateur analog repeaters, most amateurs used modified ("retuned") surplus commercial equipment. Over time, equipment designed for Amateur Radio reached the marketplace. Today you can find used commercial DMR gear, but new DMR radios are now available with street prices within the range of a typical ham budget ($100 to $800). DMR mobile and handheld radios are referred to as "user radios" to distinguish them from repeaters.

18.5.1 DMR Standards

DMR is divided into three tiers. Tier I is a single channel specification originally for the European unlicensed dPMR446 service. It is a single-channel FDMA 6.25 kHz bandwidth; the standard supports peer-to-peer (mode 1), repeater (mode 2) and linked repeater (mode 3) configurations. The use of the Tier I standard has been expanded into radios for use in other than the unlicensed dPMR446 service.

Tier II is a 2-slot TDMA 4FSK 12.5 kHz wide peer-to-peer and repeater mode specification, resulting in a spectrum efficiency of 6.25 kHz per channel. Each time slot can be either voice and/or data depending upon system needs. Most Amateur Radio implementations of DMR are using voice on both time slots.

Tier III builds upon Tier II, adding trunking operation involving multiple repeaters at a single site. Not all manufacturers' trunking implementation is compatible with Tier III. Vendor-specific protocols have expanded trunking to multiple-site operations. Any Tier III-capable radio will also work on Tier II systems but neither will work on Tier I.

DMR Tier II is being implemented in amateur MOTOTRBO and Hytera infrastructure networks along with homebrew repeaters. The IP-based protocols used by the different repeater manufacturers are not compatible. It is doubtful the equipment manufacturers will ever standardize for business reasons but conversion (a "bridge") between the two vendor protocols is possible. Any DMR (Tier II) user (mobile or handheld) radio will work on any Tier II system, although some manufacturers offer proprietary features for their infrastructure.

DMR VOCODER

The current implementation of DMR utilizes the DSVI AMBE+2 vocoder by agreement of the manufacturers; it is not specified in the ESTI standard. Many of the radio manufacturers have implemented the vocoder in licensed software, while others use a DSVI IC. The AMBE+2 vocoder is more recent technology than the AMBE vocoder used by D-STAR.

DMR NETWORKS

Amateur MOTOTRBO and Hytera DMR networks operate the same from the end user perspective. Amateur MOTOTRBO networks are much larger, cover many more areas, and most are interconnected. Not all the amateur DMR repeaters are connected to the wide area networks; some are standalone either because they have yet to obtain an ISP connection at their repeater site or because the repeater is only intended for local communications. Some standalone systems are operating in dual-mode (analog/digital) which allows the repeater to support both digital and legacy analog users. MOTOTRBO repeaters operating in dual-mode do not support interconnection via the Internet using the IPSC proprietary protocol.

Some hams have installed DMR repeaters in a vehicle, using 3G/4G cellular wireless services for Internet access. Others have implemented remote bases to interconnect to other networks or radios; it is important to remember that the wide area networks typically have policies prohibiting interconnected traffic, but what is implemented locally and stays local is acceptable. FCC regulations regarding commercial and business traffic must be followed when transferring content to and from the Internet.

TWO-SLOT TDMA

DMR Tier II/Tier III occupies a 12.5 kHz bandwidth shared between two channels using Time-Division Multiple Access (TDMA), resulting in a spectrum efficiency of 6.25 kHz per channel. Each time slot can carry either voice and/or data depending on system design. The time slots are called Time Slot 1 (TS1) and Time Slot 2 (TS2). You can think of the two time slots as separate channels.

For the amateur, this means one repeater allows two separate channels at the same time. Currently most amateur DMR repeater system implementations utilize both channels for voice and some limited text messaging. Normally one time slot is used for wide-area and the second is local and regional.

For repeater operators, a single two-slot TDMA repeater offers a significant savings over two standalone repeaters to obtain two separate communication channels as only one repeater and one antenna system is required.

The two-slot TDMA implemented in DMR uplinks (portable/mobile to repeater) uses a 30-ms window for each time slot, the 30-ms is further divided into a 27.5-ms frame and a 2.5-ms gap. This means when transmitting, your transmitter is only turned on for 27.5 ms every 60 ms, resulting in about a 40% battery savings on transmit.

The DMR repeater transmits a continuous data stream even if only one timeslot is being used; the 2.5-ms uplink gap is replaced with a CACH burst (Common Announcement Channel) that is used for channel management and low-speed signaling.

The 27.5-ms frame consists of a total of 264 bits; a 108-bit payload, 48-bit SYNC or embedded signaling, and a second 108-bit payload for a total of 216-bits of payload per frame. The vocoder must compress 60 ms of audio with FEC (forward error correction) into 216 bits of data for transmission. The 2.5 ms gap is used as guard time to allow for PA ramping (turn-on time) and propagation delay.

IPSC AND BRIDGES

IP Site Connect (IPSC) is a vendor-specific repeater feature offered by some manufacturers. Note that MOTOTRBO repeaters will only interconnect over the Internet with other MOTOTRBO repeaters because it is not part of the ETSI specifications and the manufacturers don't want to interconnect their infrastructures. IP Site Connect (IPSC) is not part of the current ETSI standards.

The Motorola Solutions MOTOTRBO IPSC implementation allows up to 15 MOTOTRBO repeaters operating in DMR mode to be connected on a fully meshed IPv4 network, with one of the repeaters or a bridge serving as a Master and the others are Peers. Any traffic originating on one of the interconnected repeaters is relayed over the IP network to each of the other repeaters. The Peers will first establish a connection with the Master and obtain the database of the other Peers along with their IPv4 and port addresses.

The more repeaters in this fully-meshed IPSC network, the more IP network bandwidth is required for each repeater. To expand beyond the limits of basic IPSC network requires the utilization of a bridge to interconnect the different IPSC networks. Rayfield Communications (*c-Bridge*) and BridgeCom Systems (*TL-Net*) are the current commercial preference in North America. In the European market, *SmartPTT* is common. These bridges require static IPv4 addresses and larger network bandwidths than individual repeaters. Besides the commercial bridging products, Brandmeister and DMR Plus are available.

18.5.2 DMR Structure

TALK GROUPS (TG)

Talk Groups (TG) are a way for groups of users to share a time slot without distracting and disrupting other users of the time slot. It should be noted that only one TG can be using a time slot at one time on a repeater. If your radio is not programmed to listen to a TG, you will not hear that TG's traffic. In this regard it is similar to coded squelch, discussed earlier in this chapter. Talk Groups can be considered as conference bridges that are used to interconnect multiple users together, other technologies use the term *reflectors*, or *rooms*.

The DMR-MARC MOTOTRBO network supports many Talk Groups on TS1 including World Wide (TG1), North America (TG3), World Wide English (TG13), and DMR-Plus USA (TG133). TS2 is for local, state, and regional traffic. Check with your local repeater operator to find out what Talk Groups/Time Slots are available on a repeater. Other networks such as Brandmeister and DMR Plus have their own assignment of TGs.

There are TGs implemented for individual states and regional on many networks. Some TGs are available all the time, while others only at preprogrammed times or require a local user to PTT on the TG to activate it for a programmed time. Since only one TG can be transmitting at a time on a time slot, many systems will disable other TGs when a local user is active on a different TG on the time slot. Be courteous and try to use TGs that tie up the fewest number of repeaters if you are going to have a long QSO. Further information about specific Talk Groups can be found on the DMR-MARC, DMRX, Brandmeister, DMR-PLUS and regional group websites.

ZONES

User DMR radios support *zones*. Zones are a way to organize channels, much like file folders or directories on your computer. A zone is just a grouping of individual channels. Some model radios may limit the number of channels per zone and the number of zones allowed.

You could program zones for local channels (DMR or analog), another zone for a neighboring state, and a zone for business and government channels. For example, you could program a zone to include all of the NWS Weather Channels. If you do program non-amateur channels in your radio, make sure they are receiver-only unless you are licensed to use them as required by FCC 90.427(b) to avoid committing a violation.

ENCRYPTION AND DMR

The DMR standard also supports private calls (one-to-one), encryption, and data. Private calls are not allowed by most of the amateur networks and many consider private calls inappropriate for Amateur Radio. Private calls can tie up large number of repeaters across the network and can't be heard by other users. Encryption is not legal for Amateur Radio in the US and in most other parts of the world. Data and text messaging is supported on some networks.

18.5.3 DMR Channels

On a DMR radio, a channel is a combination of frequency, CC, TS, and TG. A single repeater may occupy six or more programmed channels depending on the number of TGs available.

COLOR CODES

DMR repeaters use Color Codes (CC) much like analog repeaters use CTCSS or DCS. To access a repeater, you must program your radio to use the same CC as the repeater. There are 16 different CCs (CC0-CC15). The use of Color Codes is not optional on DMR systems. If your Color Code is not set correctly, you will not be able to access the repeater. Many repeater councils are assigning CCs with frequency assignments.

ADMIT CRITERIA

The Admit Criteria determines when your radio can transmit. The recommended setting for repeater channels is COLOR CODE FREE; this configures your radio to be polite to your own digital system. You should configure the radio in Call Criteria to FOLLOW ADMIT CRITERIA. Simplex channels should be configured as ALWAYS for both Admit Criteria and ALWAYS or FOLLOW TX for in Call Criteria.

18.5.4 DMR Equipment

USER RADIOS

There are many sources of new and used DMR radios. Presently all DMR radios are professional (commercial) radios marketed primarily to commercial radio users. If you want to purchase a new DMR radio for ham use, you can easily find a dealer. Some dealers are "ham friendly" and will offer reasonable discounts to hams. Check with other DMR users or on DMR related websites for further information.

You can also search on eBay and other online flea markets for both new and used radios. Larger hamfests may also have DMR dealers or sellers in their flea markets or vendor areas. Here are a few things you need to know before buying a DMR radio:

New or Used — For used DMR radios, it is buyer beware! Just remember that you will not be able to repair a non-working DMR radio unless you have the technical skills and necessary test equipment, and that test equipment can cost hundreds of times the cost of the radio. The street price for new DMR radios is $100 to $800. Arguably higher quality, name brand radios, such as those bearing the name Motorola or Hytera, typically sell for more used than brand new radios cost from newer entrants into the DMR market. Higher priced radios usually have more features, are better constructed and can handle more abuse than less expensive radios. For the average amateur, one of the new lower-cost radios is a good initial radio.

VHF, UHF, or 900 MHz — UHF is the most commonly used band for DMR, but because of military radar in some US areas, VHF repeaters may be the local choice. There are only few amateur 902-928 MHz DMR repeaters in the US. If you are purchasing UHF equipment, make sure it covers the amateur band (420-450 MHz) from the factory.

Programming Software — Some manufactures supply programming software free. Motorola Solutions charges ~$175 for a three-year subscription (which covers all their models within a region) to their software and updates. Many DMR radios typically do not allow keyboard programming because they are sold in the professional market. If a vendor charges for the programming software, do not ask another ham to bootleg a copy for you. If you have a legal copy, you may program radios for others, but you cannot legally distribute the software.

Programming Cable — Some radios use standard USB cables for programming, while others use cables that can cost upward of $80.

Number of Channels — Some radios have as few as two channels while others have as more than 1,000 channels. You will need a channel for each combination of frequency, CC, TS, and TG. You can easily use six or more memory channels for each DMR repeater.

Display or Non-Display — Some radios have only a channel selector knob, while others have displays (monochrome or color) that will show TG and ID information. Some displays only show channel numbers.

Visually Impaired Operators — Consideration must be given to the channel selection knob on the radios. Most of the non-display models have channel selection knobs that have fixed stops instead of 360° continuous rotation to allow the operator to find channel one. Some LCD display models also have fixed stops on the channel selector knob; these include some Hytera and CSI radios. Many models offer programmable voice announcements.

DTMF Keypad — Some radios have a 12-button DTMF keypad. MOTOTRBO repeaters support an optional proprietary autopatch feature (Digital Telephone Interconnect) that only works with MOTOTRBO radios.

GPS — GPS is available on some models, but DMR does not natively support APRS (Amateur Packet Reporting System). On professional networks, one of the time slots is typically allocated for location reporting and is interconnected to server-based dispatch applications. GPS will shorten battery life if it is enabled.

Bluetooth and Wi-Fi — Some higher end radios have Bluetooth built in for wireless headsets and programming, Wi-Fi is also available on some models. This is a great feature at work and home to listen without bothering others. Some radios with Bluetooth support data and programming via the Bluetooth wireless connection to the radio. Some models have Bluetooth adapters available as options. Bluetooth and Wi-Fi will shorten battery life if enabled.

Analog — Most radio models support analog FM. Current FCC rules require narrowband for most commercial/government services. For DMR radios from some manufacturers, this requires a programming entitlement key or a different version of the programming software if you require wide-band FM that is still used on many amateur analog repeaters.

External Antenna on Portable — Not all portable radios support the connection of an external antenna, except for testing and alignment purposes. Using an adapter to connect an external antenna can place undue stress on the portable antenna connector which may result in premature equipment failure and expensive repair. If you are going to use an external antenna adapter, use an adapter cable that uses miniature coaxial cable to reduce stress on the radio's connector. Some MOTOTRBO models support an external microphone with an antenna mounted on the top.

Portable (Handheld) or Mobile — Portable models are available in the 2-5 W range. Mobiles are available with a maximum of 10-45 W. A portable is recommended as a first DMR radio unless you live beyond the handheld coverage of your local DMR repeater. If you spend significant time in your vehicle commuting, you will find a mobile a good investment. Mobiles can also be used as a base station with the addition of an external power supply.

External Amplifier — Many external amplifiers will not work with DMR radios unless they are specifically designed to meet the fast switching requirements of TDMA on DMR.

CODE PLUGS

A *code plug* is simply a radio's configuration file, the user programs their code plug from scratch or starts with one made available by a local group. This file is uploaded to the radio and typically should also be saved on your computer as a backup. You can also download the code plug from a radio to modify it. Building a code plug can take many hours, especially if you want to program hundreds of channels. The code plug can also contain a contact list of Radio IDs, call signs, and names to be displayed. You can find copies of configured code plugs online for different models of radio; check first with your local group. All DMR radios with an alpha/numeric display support a limited number of entries in the Contact List, radio without an alpha/numeric display do not support Contact Lists.

18.5.5 DMR Operation

SIMPLEX

On the professional side of DMR, *Talk-Around* refers to operating simplex on a repeater output channel. This allows a direct communication while still being able to hear the repeater. This allows users to directly contact other users listening on the repeater output frequency. Amateurs typically use dedicated simplex channels so as not to interfere with repeaters. The amateur DMR community has published a list of recommended simplex frequencies to be used instead of operating simplex on repeater outputs. **Table 18.4** shows recommended simplex DMR frequencies and configuration.

Avoid creating conflict with non-DMR analog users. Do not use 146.520 or 446.000; the national analog simplex channels. Avoid repeater inputs and outputs, locally-used non-DMR simplex channels, satellite sub-bands, and any other frequencies that could disrupt other amateur communications.

ACCESSING A DMR REPEATER

To access a DMR repeater, have the frequency, CC, TS, and TG set correctly. When a transmitted is keyed, an access-request signal is sent to the repeater and the repeater responds to permit transmitting. If a repeater's acknowledgement is not received, the radio will stop transmitting and a negative confirmation tone will be heard. This is one of the advantages of TDMA: allowing bidirectional communications between user radio and the repeater when transmitting. The repeater can also signal the radio to stop transmitting if there is contention on the network because more than one station is transmitting at a time.

Not all DMR repeaters are interconnected on the Internet. Internet connectivity may not be available at the repeater site, or not available at a reasonable cost. Some repeater operators may just prefer to keep their repeater for local usage only without connecting to the larger regional and worldwide networks.

Table 18.4
Recommended Simplex DMR Frequencies and Configuration
Frequency (MHz)
UHF   441.000, 446.500, 446.075, 433.450
VHF   145.790, 145.510
Channel configuration: TG99 / CC1 / TS1 / *Admit Criteria*: Always / *In Call Criteria*: TX or Always

OPERATING USING DMR

If you are unsure of "DMR etiquette," spend some time listening to other operate. Be considerate and learn the preferred operating style. This is good practice for learning any new mode, system, or protocol. Listen, listen, listen.

To place a call to another station, or to make a general call, announce your Talk Group because some users may be scanning or have radios without a display. Avoid calling CQ.

When you are talking on one of the wide area TGs, hundreds of repeaters will be tied up. If you are unable to move to a more localized TG, be considerate of the other users on the network. When one TG is active; other TGs on the same time slot will be blocked. Leave time between transmissions so others can break in. Remember that emergency traffic always has priority over all other traffic.

HOT SPOTS

A "hotspot" is an interface constructed with a very low power transceiver that interconnects to the Internet through an attached computer that is external or integrated to the hotspot. This is similar to a Wi-Fi access point. Some of the units currently available include the DV4mini, openSPOT, DVMEGA, and Micro Node Nano-DV. Beside supporting DMR most will also support D-STAR, System Fusion, NXDN, and P25 protocols. The hot spot allows a user outside the coverage of a repeater to access parts of the network using their radio. The hot spot then connects to the desired repeater via the Internet, similarly to EchoLink. Hot spots are supported by both the Brandmeister and DMR-Plus networks and offer connectivity to other networks.

18.6 System Fusion

Yaesu released the initial specification for System Fusion in 2013. System Fusion supports digital voice and data in a 12.5 kHz narrow-band channel at 9600 bps, using C4FM modulation over VHF (144~148 MHz) and UHF (440~450 MHz). System Fusion's low-level modulation and packet structure are discussed in the **Digital Modes and Protocols** chapter. Unless noted otherwise, references to "System Fusion" in this section apply to all versions of System Fusion equipment.

All System Fusion repeaters are configurable for VHF (144~148 MHz) or UHF (440~450 MHz) operation. VHF and UHF operation can be selected as required. All repeater models are configured through a touch-screen interface to set call sign, input frequency, output frequency, CTCSS or DCS setting, power level, mode selection, and so on. By using the lowest (5 W) power setting and a suitable attenuator, a variety of power amplifiers can be used.

Firmware upgrades are available for transceivers, including discontinued models, manufactured prior to the release of System Fusion II in 2017. Specific support levels of DG-ID memories (see below) and accessibility varies by transceiver. All updated transceivers can access and control unrestricted WIRES-X nodes.

CALL SIGN IDENTIFICATION

Call sign identification is embedded within the digital transmission packets. When powered up for the first time, a System Fusion transceiver prompts the user to enter their call sign. This establishes station identification. There is no requirement for advance call sign registration or a subscriber ID.

18.6.1 System Fusion Versions

SYSTEM FUSION I

The original DR-1 repeater was produced in 2014 for a beta testing program. The DR-1X repeater was then released as the production model. There is a significant difference between the internal controllers in the DR-1 and DR-1X. Note that while many DR-1 (beta) repeaters are installed and in daily use as standalone assets, they were not designed to be directly connected to external controller and networking interfaces, in the same manner as the DR-1X (production). The DR-1X is the appropriate choice for new installations and upgrades from the DR-1. System Fusion I is supported by DR-1 and DR-1X repeaters.

System Fusion II

System Fusion II adds new features and configuration options and is supported by DR-2X repeaters and enhanced controllers for DR-1X repeaters. Factory-upgraded or refurbished DR-1X models have been designated DR-1XFR and examination of the firmware version is necessary to determine the actual model. DR-2X repeaters were released in 2017, along with an upgraded internal controller for DR-1X repeaters. DR-2X repeaters also upgrade thermal control for higher duty-cycle operation at full-power. DR-2X repeaters feature a second receiver and additional over-the-air controls.

DSQ (Digital Squelch) has been renamed DG-ID (Digital Group IDentification) and provides a means of adding selective access

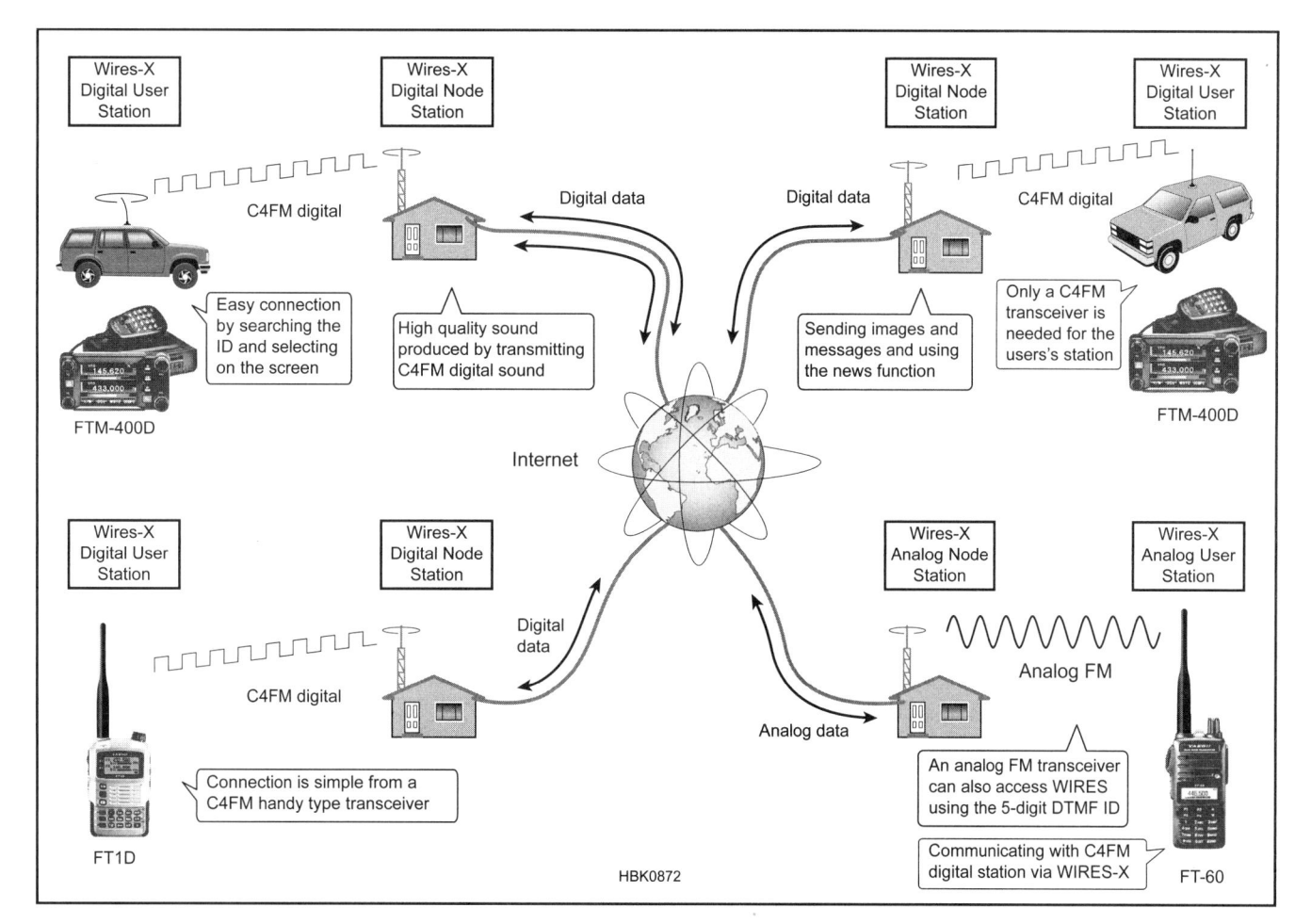

Figure 18.19 — System Fusion I configuration. (*graphic courtesy of Yaesu*)

for individual repeaters, repeater groups, and WIRES-X nodes. The DG-ID mantissa is 0 ~ 99, with 0 used as a "hear all" setting.

DP-ID (Digital Personal IDentification) is transceiver-specific and may be used to designate authorized control operators on a given DR-2X, by inclusion within that repeater's white list. DP-ID can also be used on an ad-hoc basis to aggregate sets of radios together, within a given DG-ID designation.

18.6.2 System Fusion Modes

System Fusion supports three modes of operation: voice full rate (Voice FR) mode, data full rate (Data FR) mode, or voice/data (V/D) mode. Voice FR mode is typically displayed on System Fusion transceivers as "VW" and Voice/Data as "DN." The two full-rate modes use the entire 9600 bps channel for their respective voice or data payloads, whereas the V/D mode splits the channel into two 4800 bps streams, with voice information on one and data on the other. Data is currently limited to image files and internally-generated data such as GPS, call sign, and routing elements. There is no external access to the data stream.

System Fusion repeaters can be configured in a combination of modes. While the older DR-1X repeaters are capable of operation in a purely analog mode, this prevents digitally-equipped users from accessing the repeater. The repeaters can also be configured to allow analog or digital reception, while forcing the output to analog only. While this configuration allows both analog and digital users to coexist, it does so in a constrained fashion. Analog-output mode strips away GPS, call sign and other information from a digital-mode input signal. Operating in purely digital mode is also possible, effectively locking out analog FM operation. This is typically implemented when there is more than one System Fusion repeater operating in a given area.

AMS CONFIGURATION

The hybrid Automatic Mode Select (AMS) operates in both FM analog and System Fusion digital modes. This supports both analog FM in to analog FM out and digital in to digital out. In this configuration, analog users are not suddenly "disconnected" from a repeater and other analog-only capable operators. Also, digital users are free to take full advantage of available features.

When configured in AMS, digital users can hear an analog call placed on the repeater in between transmission exchanges. The transceivers will switch to analog, automatically allowing them to communicate with the analog station. This allows both analog and digital users to share a repeater and does not require all users to switch to digital simultaneously.

Analog FM users can avoid hearing digital transmissions by enabling their transceiver's TONE SQUELCH feature to match the repeater's transmitted continuous tone coded subaudible squelch (CTCSS) or digital coded squelch (DCS) signal. Watching for a visual "channel busy" indicator on the analog users' transceivers or enabling a BUSY CHANNEL LOCKOUT feature will prevent accidental interference when digital communications are taking place.

Repeater networking options allow remote nodes or "points of presence" in cases where internet connectivity is not locally available. This enables systems without internet service to be integrated into a repeater network. Further, digital and analog signaling is supported throughout the WIRES-X (Wide-coverage Internet Repeater Enhancement System) networking protocols.

18.6.3 System Fusion Network

WIRES-X NETWORK OPERATION

WIRES-X nodes normally consist of a transceiver, a Windows-based computer executing the WIRES-X node software, and the WIRES-X interface. Alternately, a "local" configuration is possible, using the repeater as a replacement for the transceiver. With the acquisition of the HRI-200 WIRES-X interface, a node registration is required in order to enable secure communications to the network. A WIRES-X network map is presented in **Figure 18.19**.

WIRES-X presently supports nodes and "rooms." Each is assigned a number, although rooms can have alphanumeric identifiers ("America Link," "All Delaware," and so on). Compatible digital transceivers can select rooms and nodes with scrollable menus. Analog FM transceivers operating through analog WIRES-X nodes can access rooms and other nodes through use of the numeric identifiers, using the DTMF pad on a suitable microphone or portable radio. (See IMRS section below.)

Transceivers with enhanced feature sets allow for the ad-hoc selection of different rooms. In a digital setting, room lists may be scrolled through the display and selected, as desired. In an analog setting, rooms are not listed, but may be selected through a direct entry of the desired room's numeric identifier. Although not as popular, mixed rooms — supporting both analog and digital audio — are supported.

Internet-linked Multiple Repeater System (IMRS)

IMRS is a networking structure supported by System Fusion II DR-2X controllers. While WIRES-X is server-based, IMRS utilizes a peer-to-peer architecture using TCP/IP. IMRS allows a number of repeaters to be interconnected and accessed via DG-ID entries assigned to individual repeaters depending on how the overall repeater group's system administrator configures the repeater network. Some examples: A DG-ID of 01 may be used to access only a local DR-2X. A DG-ID of 11 may access a group of DR-2X repeaters within a county. A DG-ID 21 may access DR-2X repeaters across a region, state, province, and so on.

In System Fusion II, WIRES-X nodes, through the use of DG-ID, can be used to bridge normally non-connected IMRS groups together or to add the users of a room into an IMRS group. The DR-2X can support IMRS or direct connection of the HRI-200 for WIRES-X, but not both at the same time, due to shared signal lines. Use with a remote node avoids this limitation.

18.6.4 Third-Party Enhancements and Options

External repeater controllers can be attached via the repeater signal and control interface connections. Adapter cable sets are available that enable a microcontroller to read and assert the correct sequence of signals required for Automatic Mode Select configuration.

Following publication of the Common Air Interface (CAI) specification for System Fusion, a number of third-party additions have been offered for the repeaters. Protocol converters, typically operating in conjunction with Raspberry Pi3 and Arduino single-board computers, may allow the support of other DV functions with the DR-1X. DR-2X design enhancements may not support a given third-party protocol converter. Interfacing with analog repeater controllers is unaffected.

Other products in the "hot spot" category allow System Fusion repeaters and transceivers to connect through alternate networking schemes. As such, it is possible to use a System Fusion transceiver and network interface to communicate with other DV methodologies, while staying completely within the digital domain.

18.7 Other Digital Voice Repeater Technologies

P25 (or APCO Project 25) is a digital voice system designed for public safety (police, fire, EMS, and so on). It was developed in the 1990s to update the FM infrastructure. After about 10 years, the first P25 radios were retired and acquired by hams, who built P25 repeaters around the country. So far, though, they have not developed a digital P25 network.

Until recently there were no open-source vocoders that could generate a good-quality voice signal at the low bit-rates required for the narrowband digital voice technologies. As described in the **Digital Protocols and Modes** chapter, *CODEC2* is an open-source vocoder developed by VK5DGR that provides good performance without licensing fees. It has been implemented for both HF and VHF/UHF operation.

18.8 Glossary of FM and Repeater Terminology

Access code — One or more numbers and/or symbols that are keyed into the repeater with a DTMF tone pad to activate a repeater function, such as an autopatch.

Autopatch — A device that interfaces a repeater to the telephone system to permit repeater users to make telephone calls. Often just called a "patch."

Carrier-operated relay (COR) — A device that causes the repeater to transmit in response to a received signal. Solid state versions may be called COS (carrier-operated switch).

Channel — The pair of frequencies (input and output) used by a repeater, or a single frequency used for simplex.

Channel step — The difference (in kHz) between FM channels. The common steps are 15 and 20 kHz for 2 meter repeaters, 20 kHz for 222 MHz repeaters, and 25 kHz for 440 MHz repeaters. Closer spacing is beginning to be used in some congested areas.

Closed repeater — A repeater whose access is limited to a select group (see *open repeater*).

Control operator — The Amateur Radio operator who is designated to "control" the operation of the repeater, as required by FCC regulations.

Courtesy tone — An audible indication that a repeater user may go ahead and transmit.

Coverage — The geographic area within which the repeater provides communications.

Crossband — A repeater with its input on one band and output on another.

CTCSS — Abbreviation for continuous tone-controlled squelch system, a subaudible tone sent with an FM voice transmission to access a repeater.

DCS — Digital Coded Squelch. A newer version of CTCSS that uses a subaudible digital code instead of an analog tone to selectively open a receiver's squelch.

Digipeater — A packet radio (digital) repeater, usually using store-and-forward on a single frequency.

DTMF — Abbreviation for *dual-tone multifrequency,* commonly called Touch Tone, the series of tones generated from a keypad on a ham radio transceiver (or a regular telephone).

Duplex or full duplex — A mode of communication in which a user transmits on one frequency and receives on another frequency simultaneously (see *half duplex*).

Duplexer — A device that allows the repeater transmitter and receiver to use the same antenna simultaneously.

Frequency coordinator — An individual or group responsible for assigning frequencies to new repeaters without causing interference to existing repeaters.

Full quieting — A received signal that contains no noise.

Half duplex — A mode of communication in which a user transmits at one time and receives at another time.

Handheld — A small, lightweight portable transceiver small enough to be carried easily.

Hang time — A few seconds of repeater carrier following a user transmission that allows others who want to access the repeater a chance to do so; the *courtesy beep* sounds during the hang time.

Input frequency — The frequency of the repeater's receiver (and your transceiver's transmitter).

Intermod — Intermodulation distortion (IMD), the unwanted mixing of two strong RF signals that causes a signal to be received on an unintended frequency.

Key up — To turn on a repeater by transmitting on its input frequency.

Li-ion — Lithium-ion battery. Longer life, smaller and lighter than NiCd, Li-ion batteries are becoming more popular for use with handheld radios.

Machine — A repeater system.

Mag mount — Magnetic mount, an antenna with a magnetic base that permits quick installation and removal from a motor vehicle or other metal surface.

NiCd — A nickel-cadmium battery that may be recharged many times; often used to power portable transceivers. Pronounced *NYE-cad*.

NiMH — Nickel-metal-hydride battery; rechargeable, offers more capacity and lighter weight than an NiCd battery. Often used to power portable transceivers.

Offset — the spacing between a repeater's input and output frequencies.

Open repeater — a repeater whose access is not limited.

Output frequency — the frequency of the repeater's transmitter (and your transceiver's receiver).

Over — A word used to indicate the end of a voice transmission.

Repeater Directory — An annual ARRL publication that lists repeaters in the US, Canada and other areas.

Separation — The difference (in kHz) between a repeater's transmitter and receiver frequencies, also called the *offset*, or *split*. Repeaters that use unusual separations, such as 1 MHz on 2 meters, are sometimes said to have "oddball splits."

Simplex — A mode of communication in which users transmit and receive directly on the same frequency.

Squelch tail — The noise burst heard in a receiver that follows the end of an FM transmission, before the squelch circuit turns off the speaker.

Time-out — To cause the repeater or a repeater function to turn off because you have transmitted for too long.

Timer — A device that measures the length of each transmission and causes the repeater or a repeater function to turn off after a transmission has exceeded a certain length.

Tone pad — An array of 12 or 16 numbered keys that generate the standard telephone dual-tone multifrequency (*DTMF*) dialing signals. Resembles a standard telephone keypad. (see *autopatch*).

18.9 References and Bibliography

Burningham, J., W2XAB, *Amateur Radio Guide to Digital Mobile Radio (DMR)*, **w2xab@arrl.net**, downloadable copies available for amateur use only from DMR-MARC **www.dmr-marc.net/media/Amateur_Radio_Guide_to_DMR_Rev_I_20150510.pdf**

Digital Mobile Radio Association (Professional DMRA) — **www.dmrassociation.org**

DMR Core Talkgroup Server Project (NATS) — **dmr-na.com**

DMR Communications Interconnect Group (DCI) — **www.trbo.org**

DMR-MARC (Motorola Amateur Radio Club) — **www.dmr-marc.net**

DMR-MARC Canada — **www.va3xpr.net/dmr-marc-canada**

D-STAR Users website — **www.dstarusers.org**

Ford, S., WB8IMY, *ARRL's VHF Digital Handbook* (ARRL, 2008). Chapter 4 and Appendix B cover D-STAR.

Japan Amateur Radio League, *Translated D-STAR System Specification*, **www.jarl.com/d-star**

Loveall, P., AE5PL, "D-STAR Uncovered," *QEX*, Nov/Dec 2008, pp 50-56.

Moxon, L., K1KRC, "Discovering D-STAR," *QST*, Sep 2010, p 72.

Pearce, G., KN4AQ, "ICOM IC-92AD Dual-Band Hand Held Transceiver," Product Review, *QST*, Sep 2008, pp 39-43.

Pearce, G., KN4AQ, "Operating D-STAR," *QST*, Sep 2007, pp 30-33.

Pearce, G., KN4AQ, "From Analog to D-STAR," *QST*, May 2012, pp 36-39.

Texas Interconnect Team website — **www.k5tit.org**

The Repeater Builder's Technical Information Page — **www.repeaterbuilder.com**

Wilson, M., K1RO, ed., *The ARRL Operating Manual*, 10th ed. (ARRL: 2012). Chapter 2 covers FM, Repeaters, Digital Voice and Data.

Witte, B., KØNR, "TRBO Hits the Amateur Bands," *CQ VHF*, Spring 2012, pp 72-74.

Notes

Notes

Notes

Notes